Prentice Hall

2013
Edition

Accelerated Grade 7
MATHEMATICS
Common Core

Charles
Illingworth
McNemar
Mills
Ramirez
Reeves

PEARSON

Cover Art: Courtesy of Pearson Education, Inc.

Taken From:

Prentice Hall Mathematics Course 2 and *Course 3,* Global Edition
by Randall I. Charles, Mark Illingworth, Bonnie McNemar, Darwin Mills, Alma Ramirez, and Andy Reeves
Copyright © 2011 by Pearson Education, Inc.
Published by Prentice Hall
Upper Saddle River, New Jersey 07458

Prentice Hall Mathematics Course 2 and *Course 3,* Common Core Edition
by Randall I. Charles, Mark Illingworth, Bonnie McNemar, Darwin Mills, Alma Ramirez, and Andy Reeves
Copyrighty © 2012 by Pearson Education, Inc.
Published by Prentice Hall
Upper Saddle River, New Jersey 07458

Pearson Learning Solutions, 501 Boylston Street, Suite 900, Boston, MA 02116
A Pearson Education Company
www.pearsoned.com

Printed in the United States of America

1 2 3 4 5 6 7 8 9 10 V011 18 17 16 15 14 13

000200010271778952

CP

ISBN 10: 1-269-42685-0
ISBN 13: 978-1-269-42685-5

Authors

Series Author

Randall I. Charles, Ph.D., is Professor Emeritus in the Department of Mathematics and Computer Science at San Jose State University, San Jose, California. He began his career as a high school mathematics teacher, and he was a mathematics supervisor for five years. Dr. Charles has been a member of several NCTM committees and is the former Vice President of the National Council of Supervisors of Mathematics. Much of his writing and research has been in the area of problem solving. He has authored more than 75 mathematics textbooks for kindergarten through college. *Scott Foresman-Prentice Hall Mathematics Series Author Kindergarten through Algebra 2*

Program Authors

Mark Illingworth has taught in both elementary and high school math programs for more than twenty years. During this time, he received the Christa McAuliffe sabbatical to develop problem solving materials and projects for middle grades math students, and he was granted the Presidential Award for Excellence in Mathematics Teaching. Mr. Illingworth's specialty is in teaching mathematics through applications and problem solving. He has written two books on these subjects and has contributed to math and science textbooks at Prentice Hall.

Bonnie McNemar is a mathematics educator with more than 30 years' experience in Texas schools as a teacher, administrator, and consultant. She began her career as a middle school mathematics teacher and served as a supervisor at the district, county, and state levels. Ms. McNemar was the director of the Texas Mathematics Staff Development Program, now known as TEXTEAMS, for five years, and she was the first director of the Teachers Teaching with Technology (T³) Program. She remains active in both of these organizations as well as in several local, state, and national mathematics organizations, including NCTM.

Darwin Mills, an administrator for the public school system in Newport News, Virginia, has been involved in secondary level mathematics education for more than fourteen years. Mr. Mills has served as a high school teacher, a community college adjunct professor, a department chair, and a district level mathematics supervisor. He has received numerous teaching awards, including teacher of the year for 1999–2000, and an Excellence in Teaching award from the College of Wooster, Ohio, in 2002. He is a frequent presenter at workshops and conferences. He believes that all students can learn mathematics if given the proper instruction.

Alma Ramirez is co-director of the Mathematics Case Project at WestEd, a nonprofit educational institute in Oakland, California. A former bilingual elementary and middle school teacher, Ms. Ramirez has considerable expertise in mathematics teaching and learning, second language acquisition, and professional development. She has served as a consultant on a variety of projects and has extensive experience as an author for elementary and middle grades texts. In addition, her work has appeared in the 2004 NCTM Yearbook. Ms. Ramirez is a frequent presenter at professional meetings and conferences.

Andy Reeves, Ph.D., teaches at the University of South Florida in St. Petersburg. His career in education spans 30 years and includes seven years as a middle grades teacher. He subsequently served as Florida's K–12 mathematics supervisor, and more recently he supervised the publication of The Mathematics Teacher, Mathematics Teaching in the Middle School, and Teaching Children Mathematics for NCTM. Prior to entering education, he worked as an engineer for Douglas Aircraft.

Contributing Author

Denisse R. Thompson, Ph.D., is a Professor of Mathematics Education at the University of South Florida. She has particular interests in the connections between literature and mathematics and in the teaching and learning of mathematics in the middle grades. Dr. Thompson contributed to the Guided Problem Solving features.

Reviewers

Course 1 Reviewers

Donna Anderson
Math Supervisor, 7–12
West Hartford Public Schools
West Hartford, Connecticut

Nancy L. Borchers
West Clermont Local Schools
Cincinnati, Ohio

Kathleen Chandler
Walnut Creek Middle School
Erie, Pennsylvania

Jane E. Damaske
Lakeshore Public Schools
Stevensville, Michigan

Frank Greco
Parkway South Middle School
Manchester, Missouri

Rebecca L. Jones
Odyssey Middle School
Orlando, Florida

Marylee R. Liebowitz
H. C. Crittenden Middle School
Armonk, New York

Kathy Litz
K. O. Knudson Middle School
Las Vegas, Nevada

Don McGurrin
Wake County Public School System
Raleigh, North Carolina

Ron Mezzadri
K–12 Mathematics Supervisor
Fair Lawn School District
Fair Lawn, New Jersey

Sylvia O. Reeder-Tucker
Prince George's County Math
    Department
Upper Marlboro, Maryland

Julie A. White
Allison Traditional Magnet
    Middle School
Wichita, Kansas

Charles Yochim
Bronxville Middle School
Bronxville, New York

Course 2 Reviewers

Cami Craig
Prince William County Public Schools
Marsteller Middle School
Bristow, Virginia

Donald O. Cram
Lincoln Middle School
Rio Rancho, New Mexico

Pat A. Davidson
Jacksonville Junior High School
Jacksonville, Arkansas

Yvette Drew
DeKalb County School System
Open Campus High School
Atlanta, Georgia

Robert S. Fair
K–12 District Mathematics Coordinator
Cherry Creek School District
Greenwood Village, Colorado

Michael A. Landry
Glastonbury Public Schools
Glastonbury, Connecticut

Nancy Ochoa
Weeden Middle School
Florence, Alabama

Charlotte J. Phillips
Wichita USD 259
Wichita, Kansas

Mary Lynn Raith
Mathematics Curriculum Specialist
Pittsburgh Public Schools
Pittsburgh, Pennsylvania

Tammy Rush
Consultant, Middle School
    Mathematics
Hillsborough County Schools
Tampa, Florida

Judith R. Russ
Prince George's County Public Schools
Capitol Heights, Maryland

Tim Tate
Math/Science Supervisor
Lafayette Parish School System
Lafayette, Louisiana

Dondi J. Thompson
Alcott Middle School
Norman, Oklahoma

Candace Yamagata
Hyde Park Middle School
Las Vegas, Nevada

Course 3 Reviewers

Linda E. Addington
Andrew Lewis Middle School
Salem, Virginia

Jeanne Arnold
Mead Junior High School
Schaumburg, Illinois

Sheila S. Brookshire
A. C. Reynolds Middle School
Asheville, North Carolina

Jennifer Clark
Mayfield Middle School
Putnam City Public Schools
Oklahoma City, Oklahoma

Nicole Dial
Chase Middle School
Topeka, Kansas

Christine Ferrell
Lorin Andrews Middle School
Massillon, Ohio

Virginia G. Harrell
Education Consultant
Hillsborough County, Florida

Jonita P. Howard
Mathematics Curriculum Specialist
Lauderdale Lakes Middle School
Lauderdale Lakes, Florida

Patricia Lemons
Rio Rancho Middle School
Rio Rancho, New Mexico

Susan Noce
Robert Frost Junior High School
Schaumburg, Illinois

Carla A. Siler
South Bend Community School Corp.
South Bend, Indiana

Kathryn E. Smith-Lance
West Genesee Middle School
Camillus, New York

Kathleen D. Tuffy
South Middle School
Braintree, Massachusetts

Patricia R. Wilson
Central Middle School
Murfreesboro, Tennessee

Patricia Young
Northwood Middle School
Pulaski County Special School District
North Little Rock, Arkansas

Content Consultants

Ann Bell
Mathematics
Prentice Hall Consultant
Franklin, Tennessee

Blanche Brownley
Mathematics
Prentice Hall Consultant
Olney, Maryland

Joe Brumfield
Mathematics
Prentice Hall Consultant
Altadena, California

Linda Buckhalt
Mathematics
Prentice Hall Consultant
Derwood, Maryland

Andrea Gordon
Mathematics
Prentice Hall Consultant
Atlanta, Georgia

Eleanor Lopes
Mathematics
Prentice Hall Consultant
New Castle, Delaware

Sally Marsh
Mathematics
Prentice Hall Consultant
Baltimore, Maryland

Bob Pacyga
Mathematics
Prentice Hall Consultant
Darien, Illinois

Judy Porter
Mathematics
Prentice Hall Consultant
Raleigh, North Carolina

Rose Primiani
Mathematics
Prentice Hall Consultant
Harbor City, New Jersey

Jayne Radu
Mathematics
Prentice Hall Consultant
Scottsdale, Arizona

Pam Revels
Mathematics
Prentice Hall Consultant
Sarasota, Florida

Barbara Rogers
Mathematics
Prentice Hall Consultant
Raleigh, North Carolina

Michael Seals
Mathematics
Prentice Hall Consultant
Edmond, Oklahoma

Margaret Thomas
Mathematics
Prentice Hall Consultant
Indianapolis, Indiana

Dear Student,

We have designed this unique mathematics program with you in mind. We hope that Prentice Hall Mathematics will help you make sense of the mathematics you learn. We want to enable you to tap into the power of mathematics.

Examples in each lesson are broken into steps to help you understand how and why math works. Work the examples so that you understand the concepts and the methods presented. Then do your homework. Ask yourself how new concepts relate to old ones. Make connections! As you practice the concepts presented in this text, they will become part of your mathematical power.

The many real-world applications will let you see how you can use math in your daily life and give you the foundation for the math you will need in the future. The applications you will find in every lesson will help you see why it is important to learn mathematics. In addition, the Dorling Kindersley Real-World Snapshots will bring the world to your classroom.

This text will help you be successful on the tests you take in class and on high-stakes tests required by your state. The practice in each lesson will prepare you for the format as well as for the content of these tests.

Ask your teacher questions! Someone else in your class has the same question in mind and will be grateful that you decided to ask it.

We wish you the best as you use this text. The mathematics you learn this year will prepare you for your future as a student and your future in our technological society.

Sincerely,

Randy Charles.

Darwin E. Mills

Bonnie McNemar

Andy Reeves

Mark Illingworth

Alma Beatriz Ramirez

Contents in Brief

About the Common Core State Standards

In 2009, members of the National Governors Association agreed to work together to develop standards for mathematics and English language arts that many states would adopt. Having the same standards from one state to the next would make it much easier when students and their families move to a new school in a different state. The governors agreed to work with the National Governors' Association Center for Best Practices and the Council for Chief State School Officers to develop these standards.

The **Common Core State Standards for Mathematics** (CCSSM) were released in June 2010. Over 40 states have already adopted them. Schools and school districts are now working on plans to implement these standards. Teachers and administrators are developing curricula that teach the concepts and skills required at each grade level.

The CCSSM consist of two sets of standards, the Standards for Mathematical Practice and the Standards for Mathematical Content. The **Standards for Mathematical Practice** describe the processes, practices, and dispositions of mathematicians. These eight Standards for Mathematical Practice are the same across all grade levels, K–12 to emphasize that students are developing these processes, practices, and dispositions throughout their school career.

The **Standards for Mathematical Practice** are shown below.
1. Make sense of mathematics and persevere in solving them.
2. Reason abstractly and quantitatively.
3. Construct viable arguments and critique the reasoning of others.
4. Model with mathematics.
5. Use appropriate tools strategically.
6. Attend to precision.
7. Look for and make use of structure.
8. Look for and express regularity in repeated reasoning.

The **Standards for Mathematical Content** outline the concepts and skills that are important at each grade level. At Grade 6, these standards focus on these areas:
- Ratios and Proportional Relationships
- The Number System
- Expressions and Equations
- Geometry
- Statistics and Probability

These are many of the same topics that middle grade students have been studying for many years. One big difference, however, is that the Standards for Mathematical Content contain fewer standards and fewer topics to study at each grade level. With fewer topics, you can spend more time on concepts and achieve greater mastery of these concepts.

Assessing the Common Core State Standards

Partnership for Assessment of Readiness for College and Careers (PARCC)

The PARCC assessment system will be made up of Performance-Based Assessments and an End-of-Year or End-of-Course Assessment.

The **Performance-Based Assessment** will be an extended, multi-session performance-based assessment. It will focus on assessing students' proficiency with applying math content and skills learned throughout the school year. Students will be expected to complete two different tasks.

- They will be administered in the third quarter of the school year.
- Students will submit their responses on computers or other digital devices.
- The scoring will be a combination of computer-scored and human-scored.

The **End-of-Year Assessment** will assess all of the standards at the grade level. It will measure students' conceptual understanding, procedural fluency, and problem solving.
- It will be taken online during the last 4 to 6 weeks of the school year.
- It will have 40 to 65 items, with a range of item types (i.e., selected-response, constructed-response, performance tasks) and cognitive demand.
- It will be entirely computer-scored.

A student's score will be based on his or her scores on the Performance-Based Assessment and the End-of-Year Assessment. This score will be used for the purposes of accountability. PARCC will also make available aligned formative assessments that teachers can use in the classroom throughout the school year.

SMARTER Balanced Assessment Consortium (SBAC)

The SBAC summative assessment system consists of performance tasks and one End-of-Year Adaptive Assessment.
- Performance tasks: You will complete up to two performance tasks during the last 12 weeks of the school year. These tasks will measure your ability to integrate knowledge and skills from the CCSSM. You will take these assessments primarily on computers or other digital devices.
- The End-of-Year Assessment will also be administered during the last 12 weeks of the school year. It will be made up of 40 to 65 items, with a range of item types (i.e., selected-response, constructed-response, performance tasks). Some items will be computer-scored while others will be human-scored.

Your summative score will be based on your scores on the Performance Tasks and the End-of-Year Adaptive Assessment.

Integers and Rational Numbers

COMMON CORE STATE STANDARDS

In this chapter, you will apply and extend previous understandings of operations with fractions to add, subtract, multiply, and divide rational numbers. You will also solve multistep real-world and mathematical problems with positive and negative rational numbers. You will develop an understanding of irrational numbers and approximate them using rational numbers. You will also use square roots and cube roots to express solutions to equations.

The Number System

7.NS.1
7.NS.1.a
7.NS.1.b
7.NS.1.c
7.NS.1.d
7.NS.2
7.NS.2.a
7.NS.2.b
7.NS.2.c
7.NS.2.d
7.NS.3
8.NS.1
8.NS.2

Expressions & Equations

7.EE.3
8.EE.2

Exponents

COMMON CORE STATE STANDARDS

In this chapter, you will develop and apply properties of integer exponents, and use numbers expressed as a single digit times an integer power of 10 to estimate very large or very small quantities. You will also perform operations with numbers expressed in scientific notation.

Expressions & Equations
8.EE.1
8.EE.3
8.EE.4

3

Equations

COMMON CORE STATE STANDARDS

In this chapter, you will apply properties of operations as strategies to add, subtract, factor, and expand linear expressions with rational coefficients. You will also use variables to represent quantities and construct simple equations to solve problems. You will simplify equations to identify the different types of solutions of linear equations, such as having no solutions, one solution, or infinitely many solutions.

Expressions & Equations

7.EE.1
7.EE.3
7.EE.4
7.EE.4.a
8.EE.7
8.EE.7.a
8.EE.7.b

Assessment and Test Prep

CHAPTER 4

Inequalities

Assessment and Test Prep

COMMON CORE STATE STANDARDS

In this chapter, you will extend your understanding of the inverse relationship of operations to solve inequalities. You will use variables to write expressions and solve real-world and mathematical problems by graphing, writing, and solving inequalities. You will also develop a more complete understanding of variables and expressions as you begin to see patterns in the structure of inequalities.

Expressions & Equations
7.EE.4.b

CHAPTER 5

Ratios, Rates, and Proportions

COMMON CORE STATE STANDARDS

In this chapter, you will compute unit rates associated with ratios of fractions. You will also recognize and represent proportional relationships between quantities and solve problems involving scale drawings of geometric figures.

Ratios & Proportional Relationships
7.RP.1
7.RP.2
7.RP.2.a
7.RP.2.b
7.RP.2.c
7.RP.2.d

Geometry
7.G.1

Assessment and Test Prep

CHAPTER 6

Percents

COMMON CORE STATE STANDARDS

In this chapter, you will convert between forms of rational numbers and use proportional relationships to solve multistep ratio and percent problems (e.g., simple interest, tax, markups and markdowns, gratuities and commissions, fees, percent increase and decrease, percent error).

Ratios & Proportional Relationships
7.RP.3

Expressions & Equations
7.EE.2
7.EE.3

Assessment and Test Prep

CHAPTER 7

Introduction to Functions

COMMON CORE STATE STANDARDS

In this chapter, you will define and evaluate functions, and use functions to model relationships between quantities. You will also analyze linear graphs to express qualitative relationships between two quantities. In addition, you will understand and interpret linear functions. You will graph proportional relationships and interpret the unit rate as the slope of the graph. You will also write and graph functions to model linear relationships and compare two functions represented in different ways.

Expressions & Equations

8.EE.5
8.EE.6

Analyzing Data

COMMON CORE
STATE STANDARDS

In this chapter, you will use random sampling to draw inferences about a population. You will also draw informal comparative inferences about two populations and understand the effect sampling has on data collection.

Statistics & Probability

7.SP.1
7.SP.2
7.SP.3
7.SP.4

Assessment and Test Prep

Probability

COMMON CORE STATE STANDARDS

In this chapter, you will investigate chance processes and develop, use, and evaluate probability models. You will also compare theoretical probabilities of simple and compound events to observed frequencies.

Statistics & Probability

7.SP.5
7.SP.6
7.SP.7
7.SP.7.a
7.SP.7.b
7.SP.8
7.SP.8.a
7.SP.8.b
7.SP.8.c

Assessment and Test Prep

CHAPTER 10

Geometry and Area

COMMON CORE STATE STANDARDS

In this chapter, you will draw, construct, and describe geometrical figures and describe the relationships between them. You will also solve real-life and mathematical problems involving angle measure and area.

Geometry

7.G.2
7.G.4
7.G.5
7.G.6

Assessment and Test Prep

CHAPTER

11

Geometry Continued

COMMON CORE STATE STANDARDS

In this chapter, you will develop an understanding of the congruence and similarity of two-dimensional figures. You will also use informal arguments to establish facts about the sum of the angles of a triangle, the exterior angle of triangles, and the angles created when parallel lines are cut by a transversal.

Expressions & Equations
8.EE.6

Geometry
8.G.2
8.G.4
8.G.5

Assessment and Test Prep

Surface Area and Volume

Assessment and Test Prep

COMMON CORE STATE STANDARDS

In this chapter, you will solve real-world and mathematical problems involving volume and surface area of three-dimensional objects. You will also describe the two-dimensional figures that result from slicing three-dimensional figures.

Geometry
7.G.3
7.G.6
8.G.9

CHAPTER 13

Transformations

COMMON CORE STATE STANDARDS

In this chapter, you will explore the behavior of two-dimensional shapes under translations, rotations, reflections, and dilations. You will then apply the understandings to concepts of congruence and similarity and their relationship to transformations.

Geometry
8.G.1
8.G.1.a
8.G.1.b
8.G.1.c
8.G.3
8.G.4

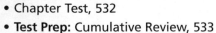
Assessment and Test Prep

Additional Features

Connect Your Learning
through problem solving, activities, and the Web

Applications: Real-World Applications

Applications: Math at Work and Careers

Applications: Interdisciplinary Applications

Activity Labs

Activity Labs: Hands On

Activity Labs: Technology

Go nline

Throughout this book you will find references to PearsonSuccessNet.com. Go to PearsonSuccessNet.com to gain direct access to online material.

Lesson Features

Lesson Quizzes: There is an online quiz for every lesson. Access these quizzes on PearsonSuccessNet.com.

Chapter Tests: For each chapter, a chapter test can be found online at PearsonSuccessNet.com.

Homework Video Tutor: For every lesson, there is additional support online to help students complete their homework. Access the Homework Video Tutors on PearsonSuccessNet.com.

Additional Features

Video Tutor Help:
Use PearsonSuccessNet.com to access engaging online instructional videos to help bring math concepts to life.

Data Updates:
Use PearsonSuccessNet.com to get up-to-date government data for use in examples and exercises.

Math at Work:
For information about each Math at Work feature, use PearsonSuccessNet.com

Using Your Book for Success

Welcome to *Prentice Hall Mathematics Accelerated Grade 7.* There are many features built into the daily lessons of this text that will help you learn the important skills and concepts you will need to be successful in this course. Look through the following pages for some study tips that you will find useful as you complete each lesson.

Getting Ready to Learn

Check Your Readiness

Complete the *Check Your Readiness* exercises to see what topics you may need to review before you begin the chapter.

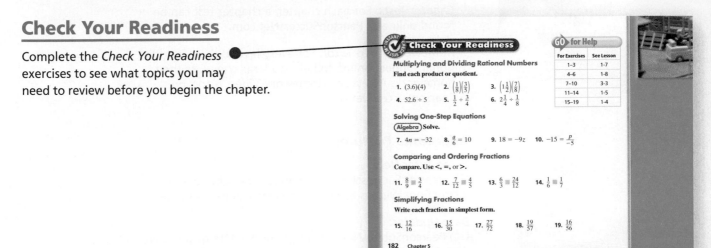

Check Skills You'll Need

Complete the *Check Skills You'll Need* exercises to make sure you have the skills needed to successfully learn the concepts in the lesson.

New Vocabulary

New Vocabulary is listed for each lesson, so you can pre-read the text. As each term is introduced, it is highlighted in yellow.

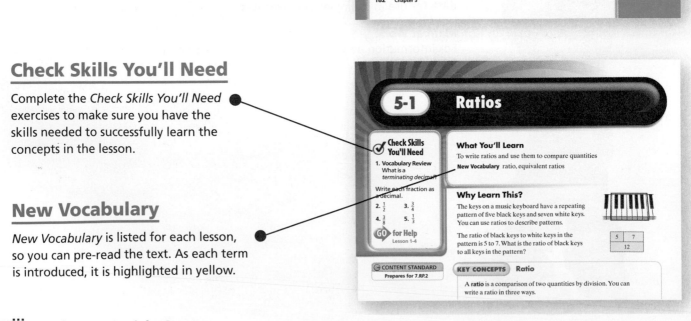

Built-In Help

Go for Help

Look for the green labels throughout your book that tell you where to "Go" for help. You'll see this built-in help in the lessons and in the homework exercises.

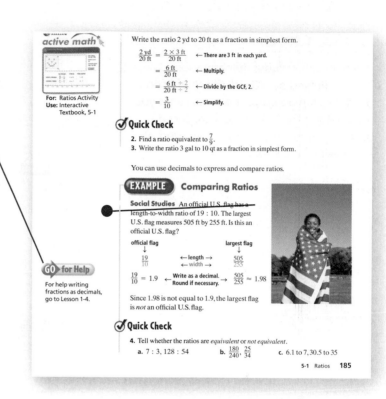

Video Tutor Help

Go online to see engaging videos to help you better understand important math concepts.

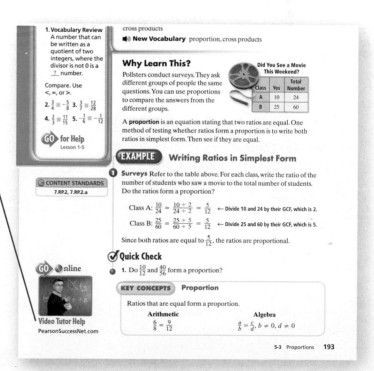

Understanding the Mathematics

Quick Check

Every lesson includes numerous examples, each followed by a *Quick Check* question that you can do on your own to see if you understand the skill being introduced. Check your progress with the answers at the back of the book.

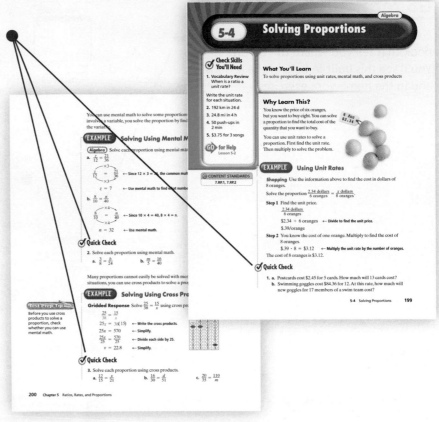

Understanding Key Concepts

Frequent *Key Concept* boxes summarize important definitions, formulas, and properties. Use these to review what you've learned.

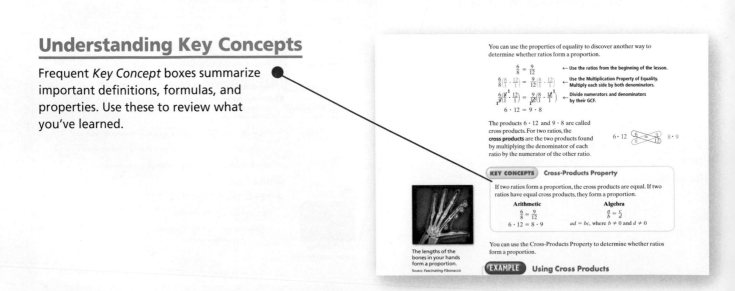

Online Active Math

Make math come alive with these online activities. Review and practice important math concepts with these engaging online tutorials.

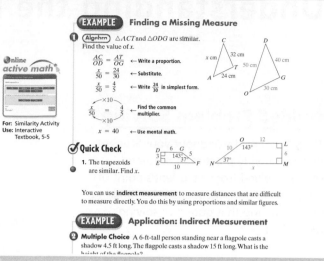

Online active math

For: Similarity Activity
Use: Interactive Textbook, 5-5

EXAMPLE Finding a Missing Measure

1 (Algebra) △ACT and △ODG are similar. Find the value of x.

$\frac{AC}{OD} = \frac{AT}{OG}$ ← Write a proportion.

$\frac{x}{50} = \frac{24}{30}$ ← Substitute.

$\frac{x}{50} = \frac{4}{5}$ ← Write $\frac{24}{30}$ in simplest form.

$\frac{x}{50} = \frac{4}{5}$ ← Find the common multiplier.

x = 40 ← Use mental math.

Quick Check

1. The trapezoids are similar. Find x.

You can use **indirect measurement** to measure distances that are difficult to measure directly. You do this by using proportions and similar figures.

EXAMPLE Application: Indirect Measurement

2 **Multiple Choice** A 6-ft-tall person standing near a flagpole casts a shadow 4.5 ft long. The flagpole casts a shadow 15 ft long. What is the height of the flagpole?

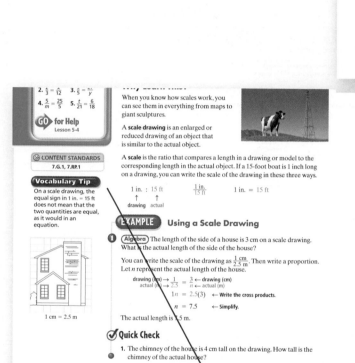

2. $\frac{6}{3} = \frac{x}{12}$ 3. $\frac{5}{c} = \frac{n}{y}$
4. $\frac{5}{m} = \frac{25}{5}$ 5. $\frac{t}{21} = \frac{6}{18}$

GO for Help
Lesson 5-4

CONTENT STANDARDS
7.G.1, 7.RP.1

Vocabulary Tip
On a scale drawing, the equal sign in 1 in. = 15 ft does not mean that the two quantities are equal, as it would in an equation.

1 cm = 2.5 m

Why Learn This?

When you know how scales work, you can see them in everything from maps to giant sculptures.

A **scale drawing** is an enlarged or reduced drawing of an object that is similar to the actual object.

A **scale** is the ratio that compares a length in a drawing or model to the corresponding length in the actual object. If a 15-foot boat is 1 inch long on a drawing, you can write the scale of the drawing in these three ways.

1 in. : 15 ft $\frac{1 \text{ in.}}{15 \text{ ft}}$ 1 in. = 15 ft
↑   ↑
drawing actual

EXAMPLE Using a Scale Drawing

1 (Algebra) The length of the side of a house is 3 cm on a scale drawing. What is the actual length of the side of the house?

You can write the scale of the drawing as $\frac{1 \text{ cm}}{2.5 \text{ m}}$. Then write a proportion. Let n represent the actual length of the house.

drawing (cm) → $\frac{1}{2.5} = \frac{3}{n}$ ← drawing (cm)
actual (m) →   ← actual (m)

1n = 2.5(3)   ← Write the cross products.

n = 7.5   ← Simplify.

The actual length is 7.5 m.

Quick Check

1. The chimney of the house is 4 cm tall on the drawing. How tall is the chimney of the actual house?

5-6 Maps and Scale Drawings   **213**

Vocabulary Support

Understanding mathematical vocabulary is an important part of studying mathematics. *Vocabulary Tips* and *Vocabulary Builders* throughout the book help focus on the language of math.

Vocabulary Builder

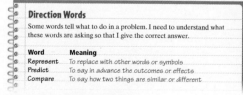

High-Use Academic Words

High-use academic words are words that you will see often in textbooks and on tests. These words are not math vocabulary terms, but knowing them will help you to succeed in mathematics.

Direction Words

Some words tell what to do in a problem. I need to understand what these words are asking so that I give the correct answer.

Word	Meaning
Represent	To replace with other words or symbols
Predict	To say in advance the outcomes or effects
Compare	To say how two things are similar or different

Exercises

1. Draw a picture to represent the weather outside today.

2. Predict the weather tomorrow.

Understanding the Mathematics

Guided Problem Solving

These features throughout your Student Edition provide practice in problem solving. Solved from a student's point of view, this feature focuses on the thinking and reasoning that goes into solving a problem.

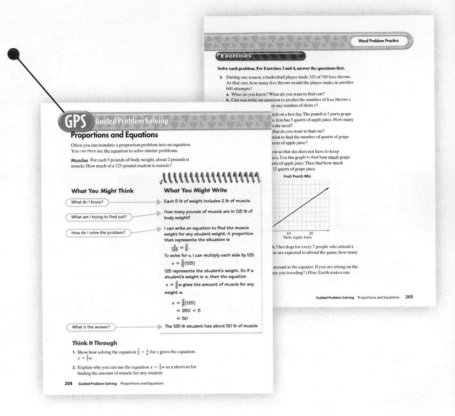

Activity Labs

Activity Labs throughout the book give you an opportunity to explore a concept. Apply the skills you've learned in these engaging activities.

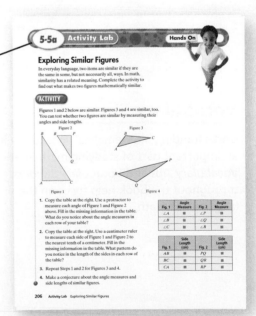

Practice What You've Learned

There are numerous exercises in each lesson that give you the practice you need to master the concepts in the lesson. The following exercises are included in each lesson.

Check Your Understanding

These exercises help you prepare for the Homework Exercises.

Practice by example

These exercises refer you back to the Examples in the lesson, in case you need help with completing these exercises.

Apply your skills

These exercises combine skills from earlier lessons to offer you richer skill exercises and multi-step application problems.

Homework Video Tutor

These interactive tutorials provide you with homework help for *every lesson*.

Challenge

This exercise gives you an opportunity to extend and stretch your thinking.

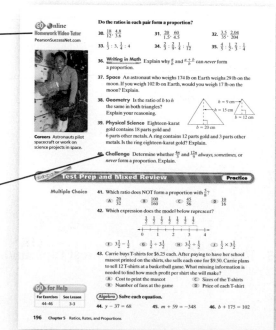

Beginning-of-Course Diagnostic Test

1. Write the value of the underlined digit in 523.6<u>5</u>4.

2. Write the value of the underlined digit in 402.<u>6</u>59.

3. Write a number for fifty-one and six thousandths.

4. Write 7.325 in words.

Use < or > to compare the whole numbers.

5. 2,648 ▦ 264

6. 625 ▦ 6,250

7. 42,509 ▦ 42,709

8. Round 75,845 to the nearest thousand.

9. Round 256.24 to the nearest whole number.

10. Round 546.256 to the nearest tenth.

11. Round 2.5879 to the nearest hundredth.

Multiply.

12.   4.6
    × 0.7

13.   0.421
    × 5.6

14. 3.08 × 12.4

15.   0.7
    × 0.02

16. 0.032 × 0.06

17. 0.28 × 0.07

18. 0.06 × 0.2

Divide.

19. $5\overline{)10.16}$

20. $13\overline{)34.918}$

21. $27.05 \div 2$

22. $0.036 \div 24$

Multiply.

23. $0.07 \times 1{,}000$

24. 478.24×0.01

25. 0.001×0.04

26. $0.9 \times 1{,}000$

27. 6.04×0.01

Divide.

28. $0.832 \div 0.26$

29. $0.5031 \div 0.039$

30. $0.42\overline{)0.273}$

31. $0.03\overline{)0.144}$

32. $0.00027 \div 0.18$

33. $0.018 \div 0.9$

Add or subtract. Write the answer in simplest form.

34. $\dfrac{5}{9} + \dfrac{2}{9}$ **35.** $\dfrac{7}{12} - \dfrac{3}{12}$

36. $5\dfrac{4}{8} + 4\dfrac{6}{8}$ **37.** $4\dfrac{8}{10} - 2\dfrac{6}{10}$

USING THE Problem Solving Plan

One of the most important skills you can have is the ability to solve problems. An integral part of learning mathematics is how adept you become at unraveling problems and looking back to see how you found the solution. Maybe you don't realize it, but you solve problems every day—some problems are easy to solve, and others are challenging and require a good plan of action. In this Problem Solving Handbook you will learn how to work though mathematical problems using a simple four-step plan:

THE 4-STEP PLAN

1. **Understand** **Understand the problem.**
   Read the problem. Ask yourself, "What information is given? What is missing? What am I being asked to find or to do?"

2. **Plan** **Make a plan to solve the problem.**
   Choose a strategy. As you use problem solving strategies throughout this book, you will decide which one is best for the problem you are trying to solve.

3. **Carry Out** **Carry out the plan.**
   Solve the problem using your plan. Organize your work.

4. **Check** **Check the answer to be sure it is reasonable.**
   Look back at your work and compare it against the information and question(s) in the problem. Ask yourself, "Is my answer reasonable? Did I check my work?"

Problem Solving Strategies

Creating a good plan to solve a problem means that you will need to choose a strategy. What is the best way to solve that challenging problem? Perhaps drawing a diagram or making a table will lead to a solution. A problem may seem to have too many steps. Maybe working a simpler problem is the key. There are a number of strategies to choose from. You will decide which strategy is most effective.

As you work through this book, you will encounter many opportunities to improve your problem solving and reasoning skills. Working through mathematical problems using this four-step process will help you to organize your thoughts, develop your reasoning skills, and explain how you arrived at a particular solution.

Putting this problem solving plan to use will allow you to work through mathematical problems with confidence. Getting in the habit of planning and strategizing for problem solving will result in success in future math courses and high scores on those really important tests!

Good Luck!

THE STRATEGIES

Here are some examples of problem solving strategies. Which one will work best for the problem you are trying to solve?

- **Draw a Picture**
- **Look for a Pattern**
- **Systematic Guess and Check**
- **Act It Out**
- **Make a Table**
- **Work a Simpler Problem**
- **Work Backward**
- **Write an Equation**

Draw a Picture

When to Use This Strategy You can *Draw a Picture* to show a problem visually. A picture often helps you understand a problem better.

A worm is trying to escape from a well 10 ft deep. The worm climbs up 2 ft per day, but each night it slides back 1 ft. How many days will the worm take to climb out of the well?

Understand

The total distance to travel is 10 ft. The worm gains 2 ft during the day, but loses 1 ft each night. The goal is to find out how many days the worm will take to get out of the well.

Plan

Draw a picture to track the worm's position from day to day.

Carry Out

The worm reaches 10 ft and climbs out of the well at the end of the ninth day.

Worm's Progress

Number of Feet Climbed vs *Days*

Check

You might think that the worm progresses 1 ft each day and so needs 10 days to escape. The worm does move a total of 1 ft each day, except on the ninth day. On the ninth day, it climbs 2 ft to the edge of the well.

● Practice

1. Suppose the worm in the example above climbs up 3 ft per day and slides back 2 ft per night. How many days will it take for the worm to climb out of the 10-ft well?

2. **Multiple Choice** You schedule the games for your basketball league's tournament. If a team loses a game, it is eliminated. There are 32 teams. How many games do you need to schedule to determine the league champion?
   A. 30 games
   B. 31 games
   C. 32 games
   D. 64 games

3. There are 10 girls and 8 boys in a club. The club advisor can send one boy and one girl to a conference. How many different pairs of students can go to the conference?

4. A bricklayer is removing a square section of a rectangular patio. The patio is 12 feet long by 20 feet wide. She needs to remove a section 5 ft long × 5 ft wide What is the area of the patio without the square section?

5. Use the pattern below:

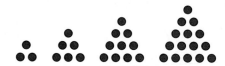

   How many dots will make up the 12th pattern?

6. A pizza party is having pizzas with pepperoni, pineapple chunks and green pepper slices. How many different pizzas can be made with these toppings? *Hint: A pizza with all the toppings is shown in the picture.*

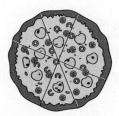

Look for a Pattern

When to Use This Strategy Certain problems allow you to look at similar cases. You can *Look for a Pattern* in the solutions of these cases to solve the original problem.

Geometry What is the sum of the measures of the angles of a 12-sided polygon?

Understand

The goal is to find the sum of the measures of the angles of a 12-sided polygon. The sum of the measures in a triangle is 180°

Plan

Draw polygons with 3, 4, 5, and 6 sides. Divide each polygon into triangles by drawing diagonals from one vertex.
Look for a pattern.

Carry Out

The diagrams below show polygons divided into triangles.

3 sides   4 sides   5 sides   6 sides

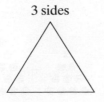 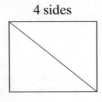 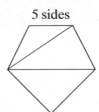 

The number of triangles formed is two less than the number of sides of the polygon. This means that the sum of the measures of the angles of each polygon is the number of triangles times 180° For a 12-sided polygon, the number of triangles is $12 - 2 = 10$. The sum of the measures of the angles is $10 \times 180° = 1{,}800°$.

Check

Draw a diagram to check that exactly ten triangles are formed when you draw diagonals from one vertex of a 12-sided polygon.

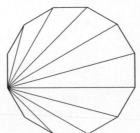

Practice

1. The figure below shows a pattern of black and white tiles. How many black tiles will you need for nine rows?

2. The figure below has four rows of small triangles. How many small triangles will you need for eight rows?

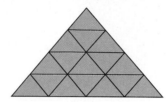

3. In a 3 × 3 grid, there are 14 squares of different sizes. There are nine 1 × 1 squares, four 2 × 2 squares, and one 3 × 3 square. How many squares of different sizes are in a 5 × 5 grid?

4. Your sister's new jobs pays $150 per week. After the first week, she decides to put $37.50 in a new savings account. After the second week, she puts $45.00 in the savings account. After the third week, she puts $52.50 in savings.

a. If the pattern continues, how much will she put in the account after the fourth and fifth weeks?

b. What will be the total amount in the savings account after the fifth week?

5.

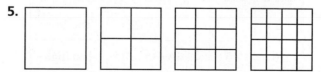

Which series of numbers best describe the next two shapes in the pattern?

Systematic Guess and Check

When to Use This Strategy The strategy *Systematic Guess and Check* works well when you can start by making a reasonable estimate of the answer.

Construction A group of students is building a sailboat. The students have 48 ft^2 of material to make a sail. They design the sail in the shape of a right triangle as shown below. Find the length of the base and the height.

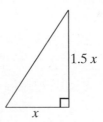

$1.5\,x$

x

Understand

The diagram shows that the height is 1.5 times the length of the base.

Plan

Test possible dimensions of the triangle formed by the boom (base), the mast (height), and the sail. Check to see if they produce the desired area. Organize your results in a table.

Carry Out

Boom	Mast	Area	Conclusion
6	9	$\frac{1}{2} \cdot 6 \cdot 9 = 27$	Too low
10	15	$\frac{1}{2} \cdot 10 \cdot 15 = 75$	Too high
8	12	$\frac{1}{2} \cdot 8 \cdot 12 = 48$	✔

Check

A triangle with a base length of 8 ft and a height of 12 ft has an area of 48 ft^2.

● Practice

1. The width of a rectangle is 4 cm less than its length. The area of the rectangle is 96 cm^2. Find the length and width of the rectangle.

2. **Multiple Choice** A dance floor is a square with an area of 1,444 ft^2. What are the dimensions of the dance floor?
   - **A.** 38 ft × 38 ft
   - **B.** 38 ft^2 × 38 ft^2
   - **C.** 361 ft × 361 ft
   - **D.** 361 ft^2 × 361 ft^2

3. You are building a rectangular tabletop for a workbench. The perimeter of the tabletop is 22 ft. The area of the tabletop is 24 ft^2. What are the dimensions of the tabletop?

4. You want to put up a fence around a rectangular garden. The length of the garden is twice its width. If the garden has an area of 2,450 ft^2, how much fencing material do you need?

5. The owner of the hot dog stand made $64.50 from selling 18 items from the menu. How many hot dogs did he sell?

Act It Out

When to Use This Strategy You can use the strategy *Act It Out* to simulate a problem.

A cat is expecting a litter of four kittens. The probabilities of having male and female kittens are equal. What is the probability that the litter contains three females and one male?

Understand

Your goal is to find the experimental probability that the litter of four kittens contains three females and 1 male.

Plan

Act out the problem by tossing a coin. Let heads represent a male and tails represent a female. Toss the coin 100 times. Separate the results into groups of 4 to represent the four kittens in a litter.

Carry Out

The table below shows 25 "litters" of 4.

T T H H	(H T T T)	H T H H	(H T T T)	T H T H
T T H H	H H H T	H H T T	(T H T T)	H H H H
H H T T	(T T T H)	T H T H	H T H H	H T H T
(T H T T)	H T H T	T H H T	H H H H	H H H H
T H H H	T T T T	T H H T	H T H H	(T T T H)

Six groups out of twenty-five contain three females and one male. So $P(3 \text{ females and 1 male}) = \frac{6}{25}$. The experimental probability is 0.24.

Check

Make a list of all 16 possible outcomes for having male and female kittens. Of these outcomes, only 4 have three females and one male. So the theoretical probability is $\frac{4}{16}$, or 0.25. This is close to the experimental value.

M M M M	F M M M	F M M F	M M F F
M M M F	F F M M	M F F M	(F M F F)
M M F M	(F F F M)	M F M F	(F F M F)
M F M M	F F F F	F M F M	(M F F F)

Practice

1. A sports jersey number has two digits. Even and odd digits are equally likely. Use a simulation to find the probability that both digits are even.

2. You are taking a 4-question true-or-false quiz. You do not know any of the answers. Use a simulation to find the probability that you guess exactly 3 out of 4 answers correctly.

3. A restaurant gives away a model car with each meal. You are equally likely to get any of the five cars. Use a simulation to find the probability that you get two of the same car after two meals.

4. Three friends are going bowling. Use a simulation to determine how many bowling orders are possible.

5. Conduct a simulation using a game spinner divided into 10 equal sections and numbered 1 to 10 to determine the probability of the spinner landing on an odd number three times in a row.

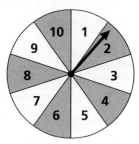

6. A bag of marbles contains 10 red marbles and 8 blue marbles. Some marbles spill out as shown.

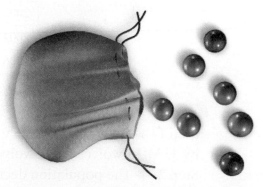

You randomly select two marbles from the marbles remaining in the bag. Use a simulation to determine the probability of selecting one red marble and one blue marble.

Make a Table

When to Use This Strategy A real-world problem may ask you to examine a set of data and draw a conclusion. In such a problem, you can *Make a Table* to organize the data.

Biology A wildlife preserve surveyed its wolf population in 1996 and counted 56 wolves. In 2000, there were 40 wolves. In 2002, there were 32 wolves. If the wolf population changes at a constant rate, in what year will there be fewer than 15 wolves?

Understand

Given the wolf population in 1996, 2000, and 2002, you want to find the year in which there will be fewer than 15 wolves.

Plan

Find the rate of change. *Make a Table* to organize the information in the problem. Use the rate of change to extend the table until the wolf population is less than 15.

Carry Out

From 2000 to 2002, the wolf population decreased by 8. Since the rate of decrease is constant, you can say that every 2 years, the population decreases by 8. In the beginning of 2006, there will be about 16 wolves. The population will be less than 15 later that year.

Year	Wolves
2000	40
2002	$40 - 8 = 32$
2004	$32 - 8 = 24$
2006	$24 - 8 = 16$

Check

Step 1 → For there to be 15 wolves, the population must decrease by $56 - 15$ wolves, or 41 wolves.

Step 2 → The population decreases by 4 wolves per year. Let x represent the number of years until there are 15 wolves.

Step 3 → Solve $4x = 41$. The value of x is about 10 years. So $1996 + 10 = 2006$.

⬤ Practice

1. **Multiple Choice** You are starting a business selling lemonade. You know that it costs $6 to make 20 c of lemonade and $7 to make 30 c of lemonade. How much will it cost to make 50 c of lemonade?

   A. $8
   B. $9
   C. $10
   D. $12

2. You have $10 saved and plan to save an additional $2 each week. How much will you have after 7 weeks?

3. A driver of a car slows to a stop. The decrease in speed is constant. When the driver first applies the brakes, the car is going 50 mi/h. After 5 s, the car is traveling 30 mi/h. About how long does it take the car to stop?

4. A family drives 127 miles on their first day of vacation. They drive an additional 35 miles each day after that.

   a. On what day will they have driven a total of 372 miles?
   b. How many total miles did they drive after the first 5 days?

5. A house plant starts at 13 in. and grows 4 in. each week. How tall will it be at the end of 7 weeks?

6. How many different groups of letters can be made with the following letter tiles?

Work a Simpler Problem

When to Use This Strategy If a problem seems to have many steps, you may be able to *Work a Simpler Problem* first. The result may give you a clue about the solution of the original problem.

When you simplify 3^{50}, what number is in the ones place?

Understand

You know that 3^{50} is a large number to calculate. You need to find the number in the ones place.

Plan

It is not easy to simplify 3^{50} with paper and pencil. Simplify easier expressions such as 3^2, 3^3, and 3^4, to see what number is in the ones place.

Carry Out

The table shows the values of the first 10 powers of 3.

Power	Value
3^1	3
3^2	9
3^3	27
3^4	81
3^5	243
3^6	729
3^7	2,187
3^8	6,561
3^9	19,683
3^{10}	59,049

Notice that the ones digits in the value column repeat in the pattern 3, 9, 7, and 1. Every fourth power of 3 has a ones digit of 1. Since 48 is divisible by 4, 3^{48} has a ones digit of 1. Then the ones digit of 3^{49} is 3 and the ones digit of 3^{50} is 9.

Check

When the exponent of 3 is 2, 6, or 10, the ones digit is 9. The numbers 2, 6, and 10 are divisible by 2 but not by 4. Since 50 is divisible by 2 but not by 4, the ones digit of 3^{50} is 9.

● Practice

1. a. What is the pattern for the ones digit of any power of 8?
   b. When you simplify 8^{63}, what number is in the ones place?

2. a. What is the pattern for the ones digit of any power of 7?
   b. When you simplify 7^{21}, what number is in the ones place?

3. The table shows the values of powers of 2 with even exponents from 10 to 20.

Power	Value
2^{10}	1,024
2^{12}	4,096
2^{14}	16,384
2^{16}	65,536
2^{18}	262,144
2^{20}	1,048,576

What is the ones digit of 2^{80}?

4. What is the value of $(-1)^{427}$? Explain.

5. When you simplify 10^{347}, what digit is in the ones place?

6. Find the sum of the first 10 powers of 10, that is, the sum of
$10^1 + 10^2 + 10^3 + \ldots 10^{10}$.

7. How many minutes are there in one week?

June						
1	2	3	4	5	6	7
8	9	10	11	12	13	14
15	16	17	18	19	20	21
22	23	24	25	26	27	28
29	30					

Work Backward

When to Use This Strategy You can use the strategy *Work Backward* when a problem asks you to find an initial value.

You and your friends are going to dinner and then to a concert that starts at 8:00 P.M., It will take $\frac{3}{4}$ h to drive to the restaurant and $1\frac{1}{4}$ h to eat and drive to the theater. You want to arrive at the theater 15 min before the concert starts. At what time should you leave?

Understand

Your goal is to find out what time you should leave home to arrive 15 min early for the 8:00 P.M. concert. It takes $\frac{3}{4}$ h to drive to the restaurant and $1\frac{1}{4}$ h to eat and drive to the theater.

Plan

You know that the series of events must end at 8:00 P.M. It makes sense to *Work Backward* to find when you must leave your house.

Carry Out

 Concert starts.
8:00 P.M.

 Arrive at theater.
7:45 P.M.

 Arrive at dinner.
6:30 P.M.

 Leave home.
5:45 P.M.

Working backward shows that when you leave at 5:45 P.M., you will get to the concert 15 min early.

Check

Find the total time it takes for the series of events to happen.

$\frac{3}{4} + 1\frac{1}{4} + \frac{1}{4} = 2\frac{1}{4}.$

Subtract $2\frac{1}{4}$ h from 8:00 P.M., and you get 5:45 P.M.

● Practice

1. After school today, you spent $1\frac{3}{4}$ h at band practice and then a half hour in the library. It took you 15 min to get home at 6:00 P.M. What time did you start practice?

2. Your friend spends one third of her money on lunch. You then give her $2.50 to repay a loan. After school, your friend spends $4.00 for a movie and $2.50 for a snack. She has $4.90 left. How much money did she have before lunch?

3. If you start with a number, add 5, and then multiply by 7, the result is 133. What was the original number?

4. A bakery uses 12 bags of flour on Monday, 8 bags on Tuesday, 14 bags on Wednesday, and half of the remaining bags on Thursday. After Thursday there are 3 bags of flour left. How many bags of flour did the bakery start with on Monday?

5. A concert begins at 7:00 P.M. The walk to the bus station will take 20 minutes. The bus ride to a friend's house is 30 minutes. From there it is a 17-minute walk to the concert. The opening act is set to perform for 45 minutes. What time should you leave if you want to make it to the concert after the opening act is finished?

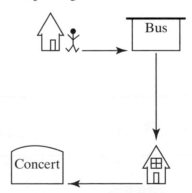

6. A delivery driver used $\frac{1}{3}$ of a tank of gas on his way to his first stop. He used $\frac{1}{8}$ of a tank from there to his second stop. He got $\frac{1}{2}$ a tank at the gas station and used another $\frac{1}{8}$ of a tank on the drive to the warehouse. His final gas gauge is shown.

How much gas did the driver start with?

Write an Equation

When to Use This Strategy You can *Write an Equation* to represent a real-world situation that involves two variables.

The cost of materials needed to make one toboggan is $8. A craftsman has a budget of $2,000. How many toboggans can he make?

Understand

Your goal is to find the number of toboggans the craftsman can make given his budget and the cost of materials.

Plan

Write an Equation to model the situation. Then solve the equation.

Carry Out

Write an equation to represent the number of toboggans.

Words	amount divided cost of is the number of budgeted by materials toboggans

Let b = amount budgeted. Let n = number of toboggans.

Equation

$$b \quad \div \quad \$8 \quad = \quad n$$

$$\frac{b}{8} = n$$

$$\frac{2{,}000}{8} = n \quad \leftarrow \text{Substitute } b \text{ for 2,000.}$$

$$250 = n \quad \leftarrow \text{Simplify.}$$

The craftsman can make 250 toboggans.

Check

The total cost of making 250 toboggans is 250 · $8, or $2,000. This equals the craftsman's budget. The answer checks.

● Practice

1. Family membership at a science museum costs $89 per year. The shows at the museum theater cost $22.50 per family each visit. How many shows can a family see if its yearly budget is $300?

2. **Multiple Choice** A pair of boots costs $10 more than twice the cost of a pair of shoes. The boots cost $76.50. How much do the shoes cost?
   A. $33.25
   B. $38.25
   C. $44.25
   D. $70.50

3. Your family's car can travel 23 mi using 1 gal of gas. To the nearest gallon, how many gallons of gas will your car need for a 540-mi trip?

4. An oven preheats at 15 degrees per minute. How long will it take for the oven to heat up to 375 degrees?

5. A courier service ships packages for $50 for the first 40 pounds. It costs an additional $0.79 for each additional pound. The weight of a package is shown below.

How much will it cost to ship the package?

What You've Learned

- In a previous course, you compared and ordered whole numbers.
- You used the properties of addition and multiplication to add, subtract, multiply, and divide whole numbers.
- You used the order of operations and the Distributive Property to simplify expressions with whole numbers.

Check Your Readiness

GO for Help

For Exercises	See Skills Handbook
1–2	p. 592
3–6	p. 594
7–11	p. 595
12–16	p. 596
17–21	p. 597

Comparing and Ordering Whole Numbers

Use > or < to compare the whole numbers.

1. 72 ■ 720   **2.** 3,972 ■ 3,927

Dividing Whole Numbers

Find each quotient.

3. 8)296   **4.** 9)684   **5.** 11)2,376   **6.** 68)14,552

Place Value and Decimals

Write the value of the underlined digit.

7. 24.3<u>5</u>   **8.** 4.08<u>6</u>   **9.** 17<u>9</u>.8   **10.** 59.0<u>3</u>   **11.** 1.046<u>7</u>

Reading and Writing Decimals

Write each number in words. Use *tenths, hundredths,* or *thousandths.*

12. 421.5   **13.** 5,006.25   **14.** 15.004   **15.** 0.329   **16.** 710.413

Rounding Decimals

Round to the nearest hundredth.

17. 34.124   **18.** 278.786   **19.** 3.602   **20.** 81.796   **21.** 16.999

What You'll Learn Next

- In this chapter, you will compare and order integers and rational numbers.

- You will use the properties of addition and multiplication to add, subtract, multiply, and divide integers and rational numbers.

- You will use the order of operations and the Distributive Property to simplify expressions with integers and rational numbers.

- You will estimate to find square and cube roots and determine whether a number is rational or irrational.

Key Vocabulary

- additive inverses (p. 10)
- cube root (p. 55)
- integers (p. 4)
- irrational number (p. 52)
- opposites (p. 4)
- perfect cube (p. 55)
- perfect square (p. 50)
- rational number (p. 26)
- real number (p. 52)
- repeating decimal (p. 22)
- square root (p. 50)
- terminating decimal (p. 21)

Comparing and Ordering Integers

© CONTENT STANDARD
7.NS.1.b

What You'll Learn

To compare and order integers and to find and add opposites

New Vocabulary integers, opposites

Why Learn This?

Most shipwrecks lie under water. You can use integers to describe distances above and below sea level.

Integers are the set of positive whole numbers, their opposites, and zero. The wreck of *La Belle*, a ship from the 1600s, lies 12 feet below sea level off the coast of Texas. You can use −12 to describe the wreck's depth.

Two numbers that are the same distance from 0 on a number line, but in opposite directions, are **opposites.** You can use integers to find opposites.

EXAMPLE **Finding an Opposite**

① Find the opposite of −12.

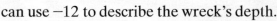

12 units   12 units

−12   −6   0   6   12

 **for Help**

For help with ordering whole numbers, see Skills Handbook p. 592.

The opposite of −12 is 12, because −12 and +12 are both twelve units from 0, but in opposite directions.

✓ Quick Check

1. Find the opposite of each number.

    a. −8   **b.** 13   **c.** −22

The sum of a number and its opposite is zero.

EXAMPLE **Adding Opposites**

2 What is the sum of −3 plus 3?
−3 and 3 are opposites, so they are additive inverses.
$-3 + 3 = 0$

✓ Quick Check

2. Find the sum.
   a. $8 + -8$ **b.** $3 + 3$ **c.** $-5 + 5$

You can compare and order integers by graphing.

EXAMPLE **Comparing Integers**

Test Prep Tip

Of two integers on a
number line, the one
farther to the right is
greater.

3 Compare −7 and 1 using <, =, or >.

−7 is 7 units to the left of 0.   1 is 1 unit to the right of 0.

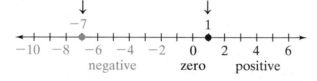

← Numbers increase in value from left to right

Since −7 is to the left of 1 on the number line, $-7 < 1$.

✓ Quick Check

3. Compare −8 and −2 using <, =, or >.

EXAMPLE **Ordering Integers**

4 **Climate** Order the cities on the map
from coldest to warmest by graphing.

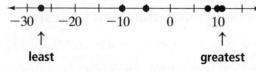

least   greatest

Lowest October Temperatures

ALASKA

Nome (−10°F)
Fairbanks (−27°F)
Anchorage (−5°F)
Valdez (8°F)
Juneau (11°F)
Kodiak (10°F)

SOURCE: National Weather Service

Coldest to warmest:
Fairbanks, Nome, Anchorage,
Valdez, Kodiak, Juneau.

✓ Quick Check

4. Order the numbers 3, −1, −4,
and 2 from least to greatest.

1. **Vocabulary** How are integers different from whole numbers?

2. **Number Sense** What is the name for a pair of numbers that have a sum of zero?

3. **Reasoning** Does every number have an opposite? Explain your thinking.

Find the opposite of each number.

4. 2   **5.** 4   **6.** 3   **7.** −2

Which number in each pair is farther away from zero?

8. 4, −5   **9.** 2, 5   **10.** −1, −3   **11.** −12, 11

Homework Exercises

For more exercises, see Extra Skills and Word Problems.

Find the opposite of each number. You may find a number line helpful.

GO for Help

For Exercises	See Examples
12–21	1
22–31	2
32–39	3
40–42	4

12. −1   **13.** −8   **14.** 15   **15.** 11   **16.** 90

17. −45   **18.** 20   **19.** −20   **20.** −123   **21.** 160

Find each sum.

22. 10 + −10   **23.** 11 + 11   **24.** −16 + 16   **25.** −1 + 1   **26.** 4 + 4

27. 7 + 7   **28.** −3 + 3   **29.** 5 + 5   **30.** 6 + 6   **31.** −10 + 10

Compare using <, =, or >.

32. 0 ■ −2   **33.** −6 ■ −3   **34.** −14 ■ 14   **35.** −23 ■ 0

36. −4 ■ −5   **37.** 17 ■ −18   **38.** 7 ■ −12   **39.** 5 ■ −1

Order the numbers from least to greatest.

40. −4, 8, −2, −6, 3   **41.** −2, 0, 7, −1, −5   **42.** 2, −3, −7, 1, 10

43. **Guided Problem Solving** Scores in a golf tournament are reported by the number of strokes each player is above or below par. The scores for five players are −12, +2, −7, +4, and −3. Order the scores from the lowest under par to the greatest over par.
  • Which score is farthest to the left on a number line?
  • Which score is the next-farthest to the left?

44. **Writing in Math** A friend does not know how to order integers. Explain how to order 12, −4, and −5 from least to greatest.

45. a. Which city has the highest normal temperature?

b. Which city has the greatest difference between its normal high and normal low temperatures?

Normal Temperatures for January (°F)

City	High	Low
Barrow, Alaska	−8	−20
Bismarck, N. Dak.	21	−1
Caribou, Maine	19	0
Duluth, Minn.	18	−1
Omaha, Nebr.	32	13

SOURCE: National Climatic Data Center.

Order from least to greatest.

46. 14, −15, −14, 12, −16

47. −3551, −3155, −3151, −3515

48. Sports In golf, the person with the lowest score is the winner. Rank the players at the right by ordering their scores from lowest to highest.

Player	Score
T. Woods	−12
V. Singh	−4
E. Els	+10
P. Mickelson	−3
R. Goosen	−5

49. Reasoning Write three numbers that are between −3 and −4. Are the numbers you wrote integers? Explain.

50. Challenge Since −5 and 5 are opposites, −5 + 5 = 0. You know that 6 is 1 more than 5, so what is the sum of −5 + 6?

Test Prep and Mixed Review
Practice

Multiple Choice

51. The table shows the lowest altitudes on four continents. Which continent has the lowest altitude?

Ⓐ Africa
Ⓑ Asia
Ⓒ Europe
Ⓓ North America

Lowest Altitudes

Continent	Altitude (ft below sea level)
Africa	−512
Asia	−1,348
Europe	−92
N. America	−282

52. Which number added to −7 gives a sum of 0?

Ⓕ 0   Ⓖ $\frac{1}{7}$ Ⓗ 7   Ⓙ 70

Write a number that makes each statement true.

For Exercises	See Skills Handbook
53–55	pp. 603–605

GO for Help

53. 45.3 cm = ▇ mm   **54.** 26.78 mL = ▇ L   **55.** 256 mg = ▇ g

Modeling Integer Addition and Subtraction

You can use models to add and subtract integers. Use chips of two different colors. Let one color represent positive integers and the other color represent negative integers.

ACTIVITY

1. Find 5 + 2.

Show 5 "+" chips.
Then add 2 "+" chips.

There are 7 "+" chips.
So 5 + 2 = 7.

2. Find −5 + (−2).

Show 5 "−" chips.
Then add 2 "−" chips.

There are 7 "−" chips.
So −5 + (−2) = −7.

To add integers with different signs, use zero pairs. These chips are a *zero pair* because  = 0. Removing a zero pair does not change the sum.

3. Find 5 + (−2).

Show 5 "+" chips.
Then add 2 "−" chips.

Pair the "+" and "−" chips.
Remove the pairs.

There are 3 "+" chips left.
So 5 + (−2) = 3.

 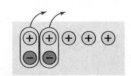 

4. Find −5 + 2.

Show 5 "−" chips.
Then add 2 "+" chips.

Pair the "+" and "−" chips.
Remove the pairs.

There are 3 "−" chips left.
So −5 + 2 = −3.

 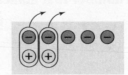 

ACTIVITY

1. Find $5 - 2$.

| Show 5 "+" chips. | Take away 2 "+" chips. | There are 3 "+" chips left. So $5 - 2 = 3$. |

2. Find $-5 - (-2)$.

| Show 5 "−" chips. | Take away 2 "−" chips. | There are 3 "−" chips left. So $-5 - (-2) = -3$. |

Sometimes you need to insert zero pairs in order to subtract.

3. Find $5 - (-2)$.

| Show 5 "+" chips. | Insert two zero pairs. Then take away 2 "−" chips. | There are 7 "+" chips left. So $5 - (-2) = 7$. |

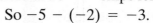

4. Find $-5 - 2$.

| Show 5 "−" chips. | Insert two zero pairs. Then take away 2 "+" chips. | There are 7 "−" chips left. So $-5 - 2 = -7$. |

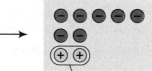

Exercises

Use chips or mental math to add or subtract the following integers.

1. $4 + 9$

2. $9 + (-3)$

3. $13 + (-8)$

4. $-14 + 6$

5. $-7 + (-12)$

6. $8 + (-11)$

7. $11 - 3$

8. $-4 - (-6)$

9. $5 - 12$

10. $-13 - 7$

11. $5 - (-9)$

12. $-8 - (-13)$

13. Explain how you can add: (a) two positive integers, (b) two negative integers, and (c) two integers with different signs.

Adding and Subtracting Integers

✓ Check Skills You'll Need

1. Vocabulary Review
On a number line, how far from zero is the opposite of a number?

Find the opposite of each number.

2. 73   **3.** −49

4. 22   **5.** 13

6. −424   **7.** −13

GO for Help
Lesson 1-1

© CONTENT STANDARDS

7.NS.1.a, 7.NS.1.b,
7.NS.1.c, 7.NS.1.d

Vocabulary Tip

The *absolute value* of a number is its distance from zero on a number line. The symbol for absolute value is a vertical bar on each side of the number.
$|2| = 2$ and $|-2| = 2$

What You'll Learn

To add and subtract integers and to solve problems involving integers

New Vocabulary additive inverses

Why Learn This?

You can add and subtract integers to keep track of money.

Suppose you have no money. You borrow and spend $10, and then you earn $10 babysitting to pay back the money you borrowed. You can add integers on a number line to see how much money you have.

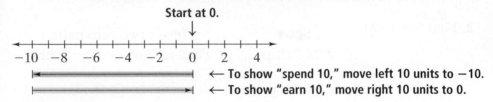

Start at 0.

← To show "spend 10," move left 10 units to −10.
← To show "earn 10," move right 10 units to 0.

The number line shows that the sum of −10 and 10 is 0. You are at zero where you started. Two numbers whose sum is 0 are **additive inverses.**

KEY CONCEPTS   **Adding Integers**

Start at zero. Move to the first integer. Find the absolute value of the second integer and move that distance. If the second integer is positive, move in the positive direction (right). If negative, move in the negative direction (left).

Examples $3 + 5 = 8$ $-3 + (-5) = -8$

Move to 3. $|5| = 5$. Move 5 to the right.   Move to −3. $|-5| = 5$. Move 5 to the left.

Examples $-3 + 5 = 2$ $3 + (-5) = -2$

Move to −3. $|5| = 5$. Move 5 to the right.   Move to 3. $|-5| = 5$. Move 5 to the left.

EXAMPLE **Adding Integers With a Number Line**

1 Use a number line to find each sum.

a. 5 + (−4)

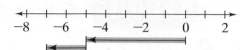

← Move to 5. |−4| = 4.
Move 4 to the left.

The sum is 1.

b. −5 + (−2)

← Move to −5. |−2| = 2.
Move 2 to the left.

The sum is −7.

✓ Quick Check

1. Use a number line to find each sum.

   a. −8 + 1   **b.** −1 + (−7)   **c.** −6 + 6

You can also add integers by using the absolute value of an integer.

EXAMPLE **Adding Integers**

Test Prep Tip

Check your answer by sketching a number line.

2 Find each sum.

   a. −18 + (−16) = −34   ← Both integers are negative. The sum is negative.

   b. −23 + 8

     $|-23| = 23$ and $|8| = 8$ ← Find the absolute value of each integer.

     23 − 8 = 15   ← Subtract the lesser absolute value from the greater.

     −23 + 8 = −15   ← The sum has the same sign as the integer with the
                       greater absolute value.

✓ Quick Check

2. Find each sum.

   a. −97 + (−65)   **b.** 21 + (−39)   **c.** 22 + (−22)

You can subtract integers, too. The number line shows that 9 − 5 = 4 and
9 + (−5) = 4. To subtract 5, add its opposite, −5.

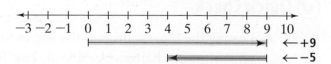

Subtract 5.   Add the opposite of 5.
9 − 5 = 4   9 + (−5) = 4

———— The answer is 4. ————

This result suggests a method for subtracting integers.

> **KEY CONCEPTS** Subtracting Integers
>
> To subtract an integer, add its additive inverse, which is its opposite.

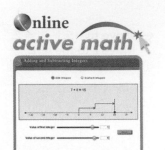

For: Integer Operations
Activity
Use: Interactive
Textbook, 1-2

EXAMPLES Subtracting Integers

3 Find $4 - 6$.

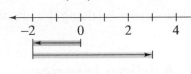

Start at 0. Move to 4.
Then add the opposite of 6,
which is -6.

$$4 - 6 = 4 + (-6) = -2$$

4 Find $-2 - (-5)$.

Start at 0. Move to -2.
Then add the opposite of -5,
which is 5.

$$-2 - (-5) = -2 + 5 = 3$$

✓ **Quick Check**

● **3.** Find $-6 - 1$. **4.** Find $14 - (-7)$.

You can use integers to work with measurements.

EXAMPLE Application: Weather

5 The temperature in Caribou, Maine, was 8°F at noon. By 10:00 P.M. the
temperature changed by –8°F. Find the temperature at 10:00 P.M.

$8 + (-8)$ ← Add to find the sum.

$8 - 8$ ← Subtract the absolute values.

The temperature at 10:00 P.M. is 0°F.

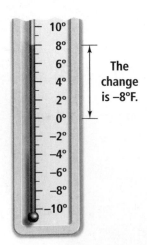

The
change
is –8°F.

✓ **Quick Check**

5. a. During the biggest drop of the Mean Streak roller coaster in Ohio,
your altitude changes by −155 ft. The Texas Giant™ in Texas has a
−137 ft change. You want to know how much farther you drop on
the Mean Streak. Which expression can you use to solve this
problem: $-155 - (-137)$, or $-137 - (-155)$?

b. How much farther do you drop on the Mean Streak?

1. **Vocabulary** The absolute values of two numbers that are additive inverses will __?__ be the same.
   Ⓐ always   Ⓑ sometimes   Ⓒ never

2. The sum of a number and -20 is 40. What is the number?

3. **Reasoning** When you add a positive number and a negative number, the positive addend will __?__ be less than the sum.
   Ⓐ always   Ⓑ sometimes   Ⓒ never

Find each missing number.

4. $-7 + \blacksquare = 0$ 5. $7 - \blacksquare = -1$ 6. $-15 - \blacksquare = 15$

Homework Exercises

For more exercises, see Extra Skills and Word Problems.

GO for Help

For Exercises	See Examples
7–12	1
13–18	2
19–25	3-5

Use a number line to find each sum.

7. $-5 + 4$ 8. $2 + (-8)$ 9. $-6 + 7$

10. $7 + 3$ 11. $-2 + (-3)$ 12. $-5 + (-5)$

Find each sum.

13. $-99 + 137$ 14. $27 + (-24)$ 15. $-42 + 42$

16. $-15 + 20$ 17. $-28 + (-32)$ 18. $126 + (-92)$

Find each difference. You may find a number line helpful.

19. $29 - 16$ 20. $-3 - (-3)$ 21. $17 - (-8)$

22. $-14 - 14$ 23. $12 - (-4)$ 24. $-15 - 2$

25. In the game of billiards called 14.1, players lose points if they receive penalties. Find the difference in the scores of the winner with 50 points and the opponent with -17 points.

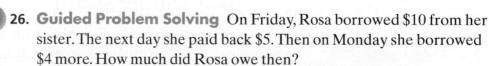

26. **Guided Problem Solving** On Friday, Rosa borrowed $10 from her sister. The next day she paid back $5. Then on Monday she borrowed $4 more. How much did Rosa owe then?
    • How much money did Rosa owe before Monday?
    • How much money did Rosa still need to repay?

27. **Temperature** The hottest temperature ever recorded in the United States was $134°F$, measured at Death Valley, California. The coldest temperature, $-80°F$, was recorded at Prospect Creek, Alaska. What is the difference between these temperatures?

Write an addition expression for each model. Then find the sum.

28.

29.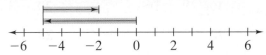

Algebra Find each value of *x*.

30. $-7 + 6 = x$ 31. $x + 2 = 0$ 32. $x - 3 = -6$

The continental United States has four time zones. Consider time changes as positive when going east and negative when going west. The time is given in your zone. Find the time in the indicated time zone.

33. 6:00 A.M.; 2 time zones east

34. 9:00 P.M.; 3 time zones west

35. midnight; 2 time zones west

36. 12:00 A.M.; 1 time zone east

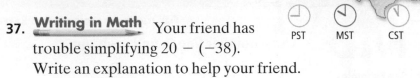

PST   MST   CST   EST

37. **Writing in Math** Your friend has trouble simplifying $20 - (-38)$. Write an explanation to help your friend.

38. **Challenge** You earn $5.25 an hour at your job in a restaurant but pay for any food you eat. On Friday, you receive a check for 7 hours of work, minus $8.90 for food. What is the amount on your check?

Test Prep and Mixed Review

Practice

Multiple Choice

39. Which expression is represented by the model below?

     -6   -4   -2   0   2   4   6

   Ⓐ $-5 + 0$ Ⓒ $-5 + 3$

   Ⓑ $-5 + 2$ Ⓓ $-5 + 5$

40. The chemical name for salt is sodium chloride. Its formula is NaCl. In NaCl, there is one sodium ion, Na^+, with a charge of $+1$, for every chlorine ion, Cl^-, with a charge of -1. What is the charge of NaCl?

   Ⓕ 0   Ⓗ 2

   Ⓖ 1   Ⓙ 11

GO for Help

For Exercises	See Lesson
41–43	1-1

Compare. Use <, =, or >.

41. $-4 \blacksquare -10$ 42. $-3 \blacksquare 3$ 43. $16 \blacksquare 23$

Modeling Integer Multiplication

To remember the rules for multiplying integers, you can think of the effects that different operations would have on your bank account. The algebra tiles in the diagrams below show groups of integers added to or taken away from a bank account. Think about whether each action would make you feel positive or negative.

ACTIVITY

1. Use algebra tiles to make a "bank account" like the one at the right. Using tiles, add two groups of 3 to your account. Does adding the tiles make you feel positive or negative? Write an equation to represent this operation.

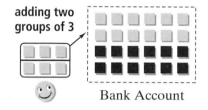

adding two groups of 3

Bank Account

2. Suppose you have to pay two video-rental late fees of $3 each. This is an example of adding negative integers to your account. Would this make you feel positive or negative? Use algebra tiles to model adding two groups of −3 to your account. Use the diagram below to write an equation for the operation.

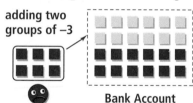

adding two groups of −3

Bank Account

3. Take away two groups of 4 from your account. Use the diagram below to write an equation representing this operation. Describe a situation that this operation might represent.

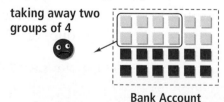

taking away two groups of 4

Bank Account

4. Suppose you have two library fines for $4 each. You *owe* this money, so you can use the integer −4 to represent each fine. If the librarian told you that you did not have to pay the fines, how would you feel? Use the diagram at the right to write an equation representing this operation.

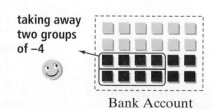

taking away two groups of −4

Bank Account

5. Use a table to summarize the rules for multiplying integers. Include all four possibilities. Describe any patterns you notice.

1-3 Multiplying and Dividing Integers

Check Skills You'll Need

1. Vocabulary Review
Two numbers that are *additive inverses* always have a sum of ___.

Find each sum.

2. 7 + (−3)

3. −4 + 9

4. −22 + (−13)

5. −17 + 17

for Help
Lesson 1-2

© CONTENT STANDARDS
7.NS.2, 7.NS.2.a, 7.NS.2.b

What You'll Learn

To multiply and divide integers and to solve problems involving integers

Why Learn This?

Balloonists watch their altitude when they fly. You can multiply integers to find change in altitude.

A balloon descends at a rate of 4 ft/min for 3 min. To multiply integers, think of multiplication as repeated addition.

$3(-4) = (-4) + (-4) + (-4) = -12$ ← **The balloon descends 12 ft.**

You can use number lines to multiply integers.

3(2) means three groups of 2.   3(−2) means three groups of −2.

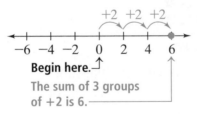

−3(2) is the opposite of three groups of 2.   −3(−2) is the opposite of three groups of −2.

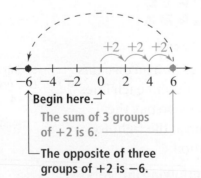
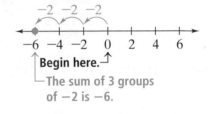

This pattern suggests the rules for multiplying integers.

KEY CONCEPTS   Multiplying Integers

The product of two integers with the same sign is positive. The product of two integers with different signs is negative.

Examples $-3(-2) = 6$ $3(-2) = -6$

EXAMPLE   Multiplying Integers

1 Find each product.

Vocabulary Tip

Integers are the set of positive whole numbers, their opposites, and zero.

a. $5(3) = 15$ ← same signs; positive product →   **b.** $-5(-3) = 15$

c. $5(-3) = -15$ ← different signs; negative product →   **d.** $-5(3) = -15$

✓ Quick Check

1. Simplify the expression $-4(-7)$.

Since $-2(5) = -10$, you know that $-10 \div (-2) = 5$. The rules for dividing integers are similar to the rules for multiplying.

KEY CONCEPTS   Dividing Integers

The quotient of two integers with the same sign is positive. The quotient of two integers with different signs is negative.

Examples $-10 \div (-2) = 5$ $10 \div (-2) = -5$

EXAMPLE   Dividing Integers

2 A rock climber is at an elevation of 10,100 feet. Five hours later, she is at 7,340 feet. Use the formula below to find the climber's vertical speed.

$$\text{vertical speed} = \frac{\text{final elevation} - \text{initial elevation}}{\text{time}}$$

$$= \frac{7{,}340 - 10{,}100}{5}$$ ← Substitute 7,340 for final elevation, 10,100 for initial elevation, and 5 for time.

$$= \frac{-2{,}760}{5} = -552$$ ← Simplify. The negative sign means the climber is descending.

The climber's vertical speed is -552 feet per hour.

✓ Quick Check

2. Find the vertical speed of a climber who goes from an elevation of 8,120 feet to an elevation of 6,548 feet in three hours.

Check Your Understanding

1. **Number Sense** A cave explorer descends at a rate of 6 m/min. Which expression CANNOT be used to find her depth after 4 min.?

Ⓐ $-6 + (-6) + (-6) + (-6)$ Ⓒ $-6(4)$

Ⓑ $\dfrac{-6}{4}$ Ⓓ $-6 - 6 - 6 - 6$

2. **Reasoning** The product of two integers is zero. What do you know about the value of at least one of the integers? Explain.

Find each missing number.

3. $-7 \times \blacksquare = -28$ 4. $-48 \div \blacksquare = 6$ 5. $\dfrac{\blacksquare}{-4} = -20$

Find each product or quotient.

6. $-2(-13)$ 7. $22 \div (-11)$ 8. $-4(9)$ 9. $-25 \div 5$

Homework Exercises

For more exercises, see Extra Skills and Word Problems.

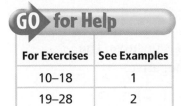

For Exercises	See Examples
10–18	1
19–28	2

Find each product.

10. -5×4 11. $12(3)$ 12. $6(-6)$

13. $-7 \cdot (-3)$ 14. $-21 \times (-4)$ 15. $3(-33)$

16. $-12(-17)$ 17. $-35 \cdot 24$ 18. $-102(6)$

Find each quotient.

19. $\dfrac{36}{12}$ 20. $\dfrac{14}{-2}$ 21. $-42 \div 3$

22. $-80 \div -20$ 23. $-8\overline{)64}$ 24. $\dfrac{-27}{-9}$

25. $96 \div (-12)$ 26. $\dfrac{-195}{13}$ 27. $\dfrac{-242}{-1}$

28. **Hiking** In four hours, a hiker in a canyon goes from 892 ft to 256 ft above the canyon floor. Find the hiker's vertical speed.

29. **Guided Problem Solving** A submarine takes 6 min to dive from a depth of 29 m below the water's surface to 257 m below the surface. Find the submarine's vertical speed.

$$\text{vertical speed} = \frac{\text{final depth} - \text{initial depth}}{\text{time}} = \frac{\blacksquare - (-29)}{\blacksquare}$$

30. **Birds** A hawk soars at an altitude of 1,800 ft. If the hawk descends to the ground in 45 min, what is its vertical speed?

Algebra Find each value of *x*.

31. $x \cdot 9 = -9$ **32.** $x \div 3 = -5$ **33.** $\frac{-8}{x} = 4$

34. **Writing in Math** Explain how you would decide whether the product of three numbers is positive or negative.

35. **Hobbies** A scuba diver is 180 ft below sea level and rises to the surface at a rate of 30 ft/min. How long will the diver take to reach the surface?

36. **Open-Ended** Describe a situation that can be represented by the expression $4(-2)$.

37. In July, a sporting goods store offers a bike for $278. Over the next five months, the store reduces the price of the bike $15 each month.
  a. Write an expression for the total change in price after the five months of discounts.
  b. What is the price of the bike at the end of five months?

38. **Challenge** A bank customer has $172 in a bank account. She withdraws $85 per month for the next 3 months. She also writes 4 checks for $45.75 each. How much money should she deposit to ensure that her balance is at least $25 at the end of the 3 months?

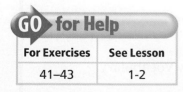 **Test Prep and Mixed Review**   **Practice**

Multiple Choice

39. Which model best represents the expression $2 \times (-4)$?

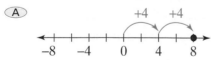

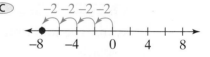

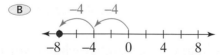

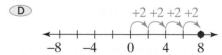

40. One day in January, five different cities had temperatures of $-12°F$, $5°F$, $-16°F$, $0°F$, and $73°F$. Which list shows the temperatures from least to greatest?
  Ⓕ $-16°F$, $5°F$, $-12°F$, $0°F$, $73°F$
  Ⓖ $0°F$, $5°F$, $-12°F$, $-16°F$, $73°F$
  Ⓗ $-16°F$, $-12°F$, $0°F$, $5°F$, $73°F$
  Ⓙ $73°F$, $-16°F$, $-12°F$, $0°F$, $5°F$

For Exercises	See Lesson
41–43	1-2

Find each sum or difference.

41. $-19 + (-23)$ **42.** $55 - (-33)$ **43.** $54 + (-18)$

Find each sum or difference.

1. $-89 + 23$

2. $33 - (-11)$

3. $-45 - (-16)$

Find each product or quotient.

4. $-88 \div 22$

5. $3 \cdot (-11)$

6. $-45 \div (-15)$

Compare using <, =, or >.

7. $-4 \blacksquare -5$

8. $-2 \blacksquare 0$

9. $|-7| \blacksquare |7|$

10. Weather The temperature at noon was 18°F. It dropped 3°F every hour for 5 hours. What was the temperature at 5:00 P.M.? Write the expression you used to find the temperature.

Vocabulary Builder

Learning New Math Terms

Your textbook has many features designed to help you as you read. When you aren't sure what a word means, keep these hints in mind.

- **Look for new vocabulary.** New vocabulary words are listed at the beginning of lessons. The first time vocabulary words are used in a lesson they look like **these words.**
- **Review the key concepts.** Important mathematical terms are explained in Key Concepts boxes.
- **Look for vocabulary tips.** They help you remember what a word means.
- **Use the glossary.** This book contains a glossary, which defines words and refers you to the page where the word is explained.
- **Read carefully.** If necessary, reread a section with new vocabulary until you understand all the information.

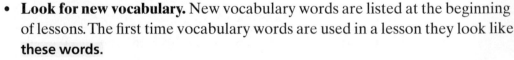
Exercises

Look through Lessons 1-1 to 1-3. Write down the page numbers where these items appear.

1. Vocabulary Tip

2. Key Concepts

3. New Vocabulary

© **CONTENT STANDARDS**
7.NS.2.d, 7.EE.3, 8.NS.1

What You'll Learn

To convert between fractions and decimals

New Vocabulary terminating decimal, repeating decimal

Why Learn This?

When you order sandwich meat at a delicatessen, you may ask for half a pound. The scales at a deli often use decimal measures. You can convert between fractions and decimals to make sure you are receiving the correct amount.

You write a fraction as a decimal by dividing the numerator by the denominator.
A decimal that stops, or terminates, is a **terminating decimal.**

EXAMPLE **Writing a Terminating Decimal**

1 **Science** The pull of gravity is weaker on the moon than on Earth. The fraction $\frac{4}{25}$ represents the ratio of the moon's gravity to Earth's gravity. Use long division to write this fraction as a decimal.

$$\frac{4}{25} \text{ or } 4 \div 25 = 25\overline{)4.00}$$

$$\begin{array}{r} 0.16 \quad \leftarrow \text{quotient} \\ 25\overline{)4.00} \\ \underline{-25} \\ 150 \\ \underline{-150} \\ 0 \quad \leftarrow \text{The remainder is 0.} \end{array}$$

The ratio of the moon's gravity to Earth's gravity as a decimal is 0.16. This is a terminating decimal because the division process stops when the remainder is 0. If you continue to divide, the rest of the digits in the quotient will be zeros.

Quick Check

1. The fraction of nitrogen in a chemical sample is $\frac{5}{8}$. Write the fraction as a decimal.

If the same block of digits in a decimal repeats without end, the decimal is a **repeating decimal.** The repeating block can include one or more digits.

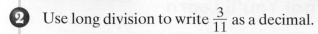

$5.355555555555\ldots = 5.3\overline{5}$ ← The digit 5 repeats.

$0.171717171717\ldots = 0.\overline{17}$ ← The digits 17 repeat.

EXAMPLE **Writing a Repeating Decimal**

② Use long division to write $\frac{3}{11}$ as a decimal.

Method 1 Paper and Pencil

$$\frac{3}{11} \text{ or } 3 \div 11 = 11\overline{)3.00000}$$

```
        0.27272    ← The digits 27 repeat.
  11)3.00000
     -22
      ───
       80
      -77
       ──
       30
      -22
       ──
       80
      -77
       ──
       30    ← There will always be a remainder
                 of 30 or 80.
```

Method 2 Calculator

3 ⬚ 11 ⬚ 0.27272727273

So $\frac{3}{11} = 0.\overline{27}$.

✓ Quick Check

● **2.** Write $\frac{5}{9}$ as a decimal.

You can write a terminating decimal as a fraction or a mixed number by writing the digits to the right of the decimal point as a fraction.

EXAMPLE **Writing a Decimal as a Fraction**

③ Write 1.325 as a mixed number with a fraction in simplest form.

Since $0.325 = \frac{325}{1,000}$, $1.325 = 1\frac{325}{1,000}$.

$$1\frac{325}{1,000} = 1\frac{325 \div 25}{1,000 \div 25}$$ ← Use the GCF to write the fraction in simplest form.

$$= 1\frac{13}{40}$$

✓ Quick Check

● **3.** Write each decimal as a mixed number in simplest form.
　a. 1.364　　　　　**b.** 2.48　　　　　**c.** 3.6

To compare fractions and decimals, you can write the decimals as fractions or the fractions as decimals. You can decide which is easier for different numbers.

GO for Help

For help with place value and decimals, go to Skills Handbook p. 595.

EXAMPLE **Ordering Fractions and Decimals**

4 Order from greatest to least: 2, 2.55, $2\frac{6}{18}$.

$$2\frac{6}{18} = 2\frac{1}{3} = 2.\overline{3} \quad \leftarrow \quad \text{Use a calculator to change the}$$
$$\text{mixed number to a decimal.}$$

Use a number line to find each decimal number's relative position.

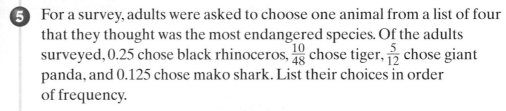

So the order of the numbers from greatest to least is 2.55, $2\frac{6}{18}$, and 2.

✓ Quick Check

4. Order from greatest to least: $1\frac{3}{8}$, $1\frac{7}{15}$, 1.862.

You can order rational numbers to analyze data results.

Careers Journalists gather information, analyze data, and write reports.

EXAMPLE **Application: Surveys**

5 For a survey, adults were asked to choose one animal from a list of four that they thought was the most endangered species. Of the adults surveyed, 0.25 chose black rhinoceros, $\frac{10}{48}$ chose tiger, $\frac{5}{12}$ chose giant panda, and 0.125 chose mako shark. List their choices in order of frequency.

First write all 4 ratios as decimals.

black rhinoceros: 0.25

tiger: $\frac{10}{48} = \frac{5}{24} = 0.208\overline{3}$ ⎫

giant panda: $\frac{5}{12} = 0.41\overline{6}$ ⎬ ← Use a calculator to change the fractions to decimals.

mako shark: 0.125 ⎭

Since $0.41\overline{6} > 0.25 > 0.208\overline{3} > 0.125$, the order of frequency was giant panda, black rhinoceros, tiger, and mako shark.

✓ Quick Check

5. In a survey about pets, $\frac{2}{5}$ of students prefer cats, 0.33 prefer dogs, $\frac{3}{25}$ prefer birds, and 0.15 prefer fish. List the choices in order of preference.

1. **Vocabulary** What is the difference between a terminating decimal and a repeating decimal?

2. **Reasoning** Is a remainder of 0 the same as no remainder? Explain.

Write each decimal as a mixed number or a fraction in simplest form.

3. 1.375   4. 0.44   5. 3.99

6. **Reasoning** Is 3.03003000300003 . . . a repeating decimal? Explain.

7. Order the following numbers from least to greatest: $1.\overline{9}$, $1\frac{1}{3}$, 2, 0.5.

Homework Exercises

For more exercises, see Extra Skills and Word Problems.

For Exercises	See Examples
8–15	1–2
16–23	3
24–28	4–5

GO for Help

Write each fraction as a decimal.

8. $\frac{2}{5}$ 9. $\frac{4}{5}$ 10. $\frac{3}{8}$ 11. $\frac{2}{3}$

12. $\frac{3}{4}$ 13. $\frac{1}{8}$ 14. $\frac{7}{11}$ 15. $\frac{3}{16}$

Write each decimal as a mixed number or a fraction in simplest form.

16. 0.125   17. 0.66   18. 2.5   19. 3.75

20. 0.32   21. 0.19   22. 0.8   23. 0.965

Order from greatest to least.

24. $\frac{9}{22}$, 0.83, $\frac{7}{8}$, 0.4, $\frac{44}{44}$ 25. 3.84, 3.789, 3, $3\frac{41}{50}$

26. $\frac{2}{3}$, 0.67, $\frac{5}{9}$, 0.58, $\frac{7}{12}$ 27. $0.1\overline{2}$, 0.1225, $\frac{3}{25}$, $\frac{7}{125}$

28. **Biology** DNA content in a cell is measured in picograms (pg). A sea star cell has $\frac{17}{20}$ pg of DNA, a scallop cell has $\frac{19}{20}$ pg, a red water mite cell has 0.19 pg, and a mosquito cell has 0.24 pg. Order the DNA contents from greatest to least.

29. **Guided Problem Solving** On an adventure trail, you biked 12 mi, walked 4 mi, ran 6 mi, and swam 2 mi. What fraction of the total distance did you bike? Write this number as a decimal.
    • The total distance of the adventure trail is ■ mi.
    • You biked ■ mi. As a fraction, this is ■ of the total distance.

30. **Music** To compose music on a computer, you can write notes as decimals. What decimals should you enter for a half note, a quarter note, an eighth note, and a sixteenth note?

Greenland is the world's largest island.

Algebra Compare. Use <, =, or >. (*Note: n* is a value greater than 1.)

31. $\frac{1}{n}$ ▇ $\frac{n}{n}$ **32.** 1 ▇ $\frac{n}{1}$ **33.** n ▇ $\frac{1}{n}$ **34.** $\frac{n}{n^2}$ ▇ $\frac{1}{n}$

35. Number Sense Examine the fractions $\frac{2}{3}$, $\frac{3}{3}$, $\frac{4}{3}$, $\frac{5}{3}$, and $\frac{6}{3}$. Explain when a denominator of 3 will result in a repeating decimal.

36. Geography About 12,500 icebergs break away from Greenland each year. Of these, about 375 float into the Atlantic Ocean.
   a. What fraction of the icebergs float into the Atlantic Ocean?
   b. Write your answer for part (a) as a decimal.
   c. What fraction of the icebergs do *not* float into the Atlantic?

For Exercises 37–39, use the table at the right.

37. For each state, write a fraction that shows the ratio $\frac{\text{number of people under age 18}}{\text{total population}}$.

38. For most of the states, would $\frac{1}{2}$, $\frac{1}{3}$, or $\frac{1}{4}$ best describe the fraction of the population that is under age 18?

39. Calculator Order the states from least to greatest fraction under age 18.

Population (thousands)

State	Total	Under Age 18
N.Y.	19,227	4,572
Texas	22,490	6,267
Calif.	33,893	9,596
Fla.	17,397	4,003
Ohio	11,459	2,779

SOURCE: U.S. Census Bureau.

40. Writing in Math Describe some everyday situations in which you need to change fractions to decimals.

41. Challenge Divide 50 by these numbers: 100, 10, 1, 0.1, 0.01, 0.001. Explain how the quotient changes as the divisor approaches 0.

Test Prep and Mixed Review   **Practice**

Multiple Choice

42. Bennie's teacher gave him a score of $\frac{34}{40}$ on his quiz. What decimal is equivalent to the score Bennie received?
   Ⓐ 85.0   Ⓒ 0.85
   Ⓑ 8.50   Ⓓ 0.085

43. Rahmi has 150 sheets of paper. He uses 6 sheets each to make 4 copies of a short story he wrote. Which expression shows how many sheets he has left?
   Ⓕ $150 + 6 + 4$ Ⓗ $150 + (-6) + (-4)$
   Ⓖ $150 + (6 \div (-4))$ Ⓙ $150 + (4 \cdot (-6))$

Find each product or quotient.

44. $13 \times (-3)$ **45.** $-72 \div (-24)$ **46.** $-12 \cdot (-12)$

47. $54 \div (-18)$ **48.** $-121 \div (-11)$ **49.** $-15(4)$

Go for Help

For Exercises	See Lesson
44–49	1-3

✓ Check Skills You'll Need

1. **Vocabulary Review** Is 1.234 a repeating decimal or a terminating decimal? Explain.

Write each fraction as a decimal.

2. $\frac{3}{4}$ 3. $-\frac{7}{9}$

4. $1\frac{1}{3}$ 5. $\frac{12}{48}$

 **for Help**
Lesson 1-4

What You'll Learn

To compare and order rational numbers

New Vocabulary rational number

Why Learn This?

Rational numbers are part of everyday life. You see them on price tags, highway signs, and charts. Rational numbers can be written in different forms. To compare rational numbers, it is easier to convert them into the same form.

A **rational number** is a number that can be written as a quotient of two integers, where the divisor is not 0. Examples are $\frac{2}{5}$, $0.\overline{3}$, -6, and $3\frac{1}{2}$.

© CONTENT STANDARDS
7.NS.2.b, 7.NS.2.d, 8.NS.1

EXAMPLE **Comparing Rational Numbers**

1 Compare $-\frac{1}{2}$ and $-\frac{3}{4}$.

Method 1

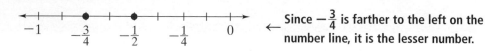

← Since $-\frac{3}{4}$ is farther to the left on the number line, it is the lesser number.

So $-\frac{3}{4} < -\frac{1}{2}$.

GO for Help

For help with comparing and ordering fractions and decimals, go to Lesson 1-4, Example 4.

Method 2

$-\frac{1}{2} = \frac{-1}{2}$ ← Rewrite $-\frac{1}{2}$ with -1 in the numerator.

$= \frac{-1 \times 2}{2 \times 2}$ ← The LCD is 4. Write an equivalent fraction.

$= \frac{-2}{4} = -\frac{2}{4}$ ← The fraction $-\frac{2}{4}$ is equivalent to $\frac{-2}{4}$.

Since $-\frac{3}{4} < -\frac{2}{4}$, $-\frac{3}{4} < -\frac{1}{2}$.

✓ Quick Check

1. Compare $-\frac{2}{3}$ and $-\frac{1}{6}$. Use $<$, $=$, or $>$.

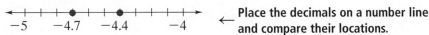

EXAMPLE Comparing Decimals

2 **a.** Compare -4.4 and 4.7.

$-4.4 < 4.7$ ← Any negative number is less than a positive number.

b. Compare -4.4 and -4.7.

$$\xleftarrow{\hspace{0.3em}}\!\!\!+\!\!+\!\!+\!\!\bullet\!\!+\!\!+\!\!\bullet\!\!+\!\!+\!\!+\!\!+\!\!\xrightarrow{\hspace{0.3em}}$$
$$\quad -5 \quad -4.7 \;\; -4.4 \qquad -4$$

← Place the decimals on a number line and compare their locations.

$-4.4 > -4.7$ since -4.4 is to the right of -4.7.

✓ Quick Check

2. Compare -4.2 and -4.9. Use $<$, $=$, or $>$.

When you compare and order decimals and fractions, it is often helpful to write the fractions as decimals.

EXAMPLE Ordering Rational Numbers

3 **Multiple Choice** The peaks of four mountains or seamounts are located either below or above sea level as follows: $\frac{1}{4}$ mi, -0.2 mi, $-\frac{2}{9}$ mi, 1.1 mi. Which list shows the order of numbers from least to greatest?

Ⓐ $\frac{1}{4}, -0.2, -\frac{2}{9}, 1.1$ Ⓒ $-\frac{2}{9}, -0.2, \frac{1}{4}, 1.1$

Ⓑ $\frac{1}{4}, -\frac{2}{9}, 1.1, -0.2$ Ⓓ $-0.2, -\frac{2}{9}, 1.1, \frac{1}{4}$

Order these numbers from least to greatest: $\frac{1}{4}, -0.2, -\frac{2}{9}, 1.1$.

$\dfrac{1}{4} = 1 \div 4 = 0.250$ ← Write as a decimal. Use long division if it helps.

$-\dfrac{2}{9} = -2 \div 9 = -0.22222\ldots = -0.\overline{2}$ ← Write as a repeating decimal.

You can use a number line to order the numbers.

$$-0.4 \;\; -0.2 \quad 0 \quad 0.2 \quad 0.4 \quad 0.6 \quad 0.8 \quad 1.0 \quad 1.2$$

$$\frac{-4}{10} \quad \frac{-2}{10} \quad 0 \quad \frac{2}{10} \quad \frac{4}{10} \quad \frac{6}{10} \quad \frac{8}{10} \quad 1 \quad 1\frac{2}{10}$$

$$-\frac{2}{9} \quad -0.2 \qquad \frac{1}{4} \qquad\qquad 1.1$$

$-0.\overline{2} < -0.2 < 0.25 < 1.1$ ← Compare the decimals.

In order, the numbers are $-\frac{2}{9}, -0.2, \frac{1}{4}$, and 1.1. The answer is C.

Test Prep Tip

Sometimes it is easier to order rational numbers when they are all written as decimals.

✓ Quick Check

3. The following temperatures were recorded during a science project: $12\frac{1}{2}°C, -4°C, 6.55°C$, and $-6\frac{1}{4}°C$. Order the temperatures from least to greatest.

1. **Vocabulary** In your own words, define *rational number*.

Compare. Use <, =, or >.

2. $2\frac{1}{5}$ ▦ $3\frac{1}{3}$

3. $-3\frac{1}{2}$ ▦ $-3\frac{3}{4}$

4. -6.1 ▦ -6

Order from least to greatest.

5. $-236, -7\frac{1}{7}, 0, \frac{41}{99}, -3.\overline{3}$

6. $-8, -5\frac{1}{3}, -8.22, -8\frac{1}{3}, \frac{16}{42}$

Homework Exercises

For more exercises, see Extra Skills and Word Problems.

Compare. Use <, =, or >.

GO for Help

For Exercises	See Examples
7–12	1
13–18	2
19–22	3

7. $-\frac{1}{7}$ ▦ $-\frac{6}{7}$

8. $-\frac{3}{4}$ ▦ -3

9. $-\frac{1}{2}$ ▦ $-\frac{2}{10}$

10. $-\frac{3}{4}$ ▦ -1

11. $-\frac{1}{2}$ ▦ $-\frac{5}{6}$

12. $-\frac{4}{5}$ ▦ $-\frac{1}{3}$

13. 5.2 ▦ -8.3

14. -6.5 ▦ 6.2

15. -4.9 ▦ -4.3

16. 1.09 ▦ -1.90

17. -1.22 ▦ -6.5

18. -10.2 ▦ -10.23

Order from least to greatest.

19. $\frac{3}{2}, 0.25, -\frac{3}{4}, -1.0$

20. $\frac{7}{3}, 2.4, -\frac{6}{25}, -1.34$

21. $\frac{6}{11}, -1.5, 0.545, \frac{1}{2}$

22. $\frac{7}{6}, \frac{11}{12}, \frac{14}{24}, 1$

23. **Guided Problem Solving** You are skier A, the first skier in a skiing event with three other skiers. Compared to your time, skier B is slower, by a time of +00:28. Skier C has a time of +02:13, and skier D has a time of −01:24. Who is the fastest skier?
    - Since all times are compared to yours, what is your time?
    - What is the order of times, from fastest to slowest?

24. The table below shows melting points of four elements. Which element has the highest melting point?

Melting Points

Element	Krypton	Argon	Xenon	Helium
Melting Point (°C)	−157.36	−189.35	−111.79	−272.2

Compare. Use <, =, or >.

25. -5.8 ▇ $-5\frac{9}{10}$ **26.** $-6\frac{11}{50}$ ▇ -6.21 **27.** -10.42 ▇ $-10.4\overline{2}$

28. <u>**Writing in Math**</u> Compare $-\frac{5}{8}$ and $-\frac{3}{4}$. Is it easier to find common denominators or to write decimal equivalents? Explain.

29. **Animals** About $\frac{1}{25}$ of a toad's eggs survive to adulthood. About 0.25 of a frog's eggs and $\frac{1}{5}$ of a green turtle's eggs survive to adulthood. Which animal's eggs have the highest survival rate?

30. **Money** Here is part of Mr. Lostcash's checkbook register. Order his balances from greatest to least.

Description	Debits (−)	Credits (+)	Balance
Paycheck		122.18	122.18
Sneakers	95.00		27.18
Two outfits	68.09		−40.91
Paycheck		122.18	81.27
Insufficient funds fee	25.00		56.27
Three CDs	59.97		−3.70

31. **Challenge** Evaluate $\frac{m-n}{-12}$ for $m = -3$ and $n = 6$.

Test Prep and Mixed Review   Practice

Multiple Choice

32. Harry's teacher subtracts points for spelling and grammar errors on math quizzes and tests. Harry's scores for 4 quizzes were $\frac{9}{11}, -\frac{10}{50}, \frac{3}{4},$ and $-\frac{20}{30}$. Which of the following shows the scores in increasing order?

   Ⓐ $\frac{9}{11}, \frac{3}{4}, -\frac{10}{50}, -\frac{20}{30}$

   Ⓑ $-\frac{10}{50}, -\frac{20}{30}, \frac{9}{11}, \frac{3}{4}$

   Ⓒ $\frac{3}{4}, -\frac{20}{30}, \frac{9}{11}, -\frac{10}{50}$

   Ⓓ $-\frac{20}{30}, -\frac{10}{50}, \frac{3}{4}, \frac{9}{11}$

33. Serena converts $\frac{4}{7}$ to a decimal and is surprised by the number of repeating digits. How many digits are in the repeating block?

   Ⓕ 4   Ⓖ 5   Ⓗ 6   Ⓙ 7

GO for Help

For Exercises	See Lesson
34–37	1-4

Write each fraction as a decimal.

34. $\frac{5}{9}$ **35.** $\frac{5}{10}$ **36.** $\frac{5}{11}$ **37.** $\frac{5}{12}$

Repeating Decimals

Every rational number has a decimal expansion. Earlier in this chapter, you learned that you can write the decimal expansion of a fraction by dividing the numerator by the denominator. You also learned how to write a terminating decimal as a fraction. You can use algebra to write a repeating decimal as a fraction.

EXAMPLE   Writing a Repeating Decimal as a Fraction

In a recent survey, $0.\overline{45}$ of those asked chose blue as their favorite color. Write $0.\overline{45}$ as a fraction in simplest form.

Step 1 Represent the given decimal with a variable.

$$n = 0.\overline{45}$$

Step 2 Multiply by 10^d, where $d =$ the number of digits that repeat. In this case, multiply by 10^2 or 100. Since 2 digits repeat in $0.\overline{45}$.

$$100n = 45.\overline{45}$$

Step 3 Subtract to eliminate the repeating part.

$$100n = \quad 45.454545 \ldots$$
$$\underline{- \quad n = - \quad 0.454545 \ldots} \quad \leftarrow \text{Use the Subtraction Property of Equality.}$$
$$99n = \quad 45.000000 \ldots \quad \leftarrow \text{Simplify.}$$
$$99n = \quad 45$$

Step 4 Solve the new equation.

$$\frac{99n}{99} = \frac{45}{99} \qquad \leftarrow \text{Divide each side by 99.}$$
$$n = \frac{45}{99} = \frac{5}{11} \quad \leftarrow \text{Simplify using the GCF, 9.}$$

The repeating decimal $0.\overline{45}$ equals $\frac{5}{11}$.

Exercises

Write each repeating decimal as a fraction in simplest form.

1. $0.\overline{5}$ **2.** $0.\overline{7}$ **3.** $0.\overline{24}$ **4.** $0.\overline{15}$ **5.** $0.\overline{135}$ **6.** $0.\overline{282}$

7. **Writing in Math** Explain why a repeating decimal is a rational number. Justify your answer with an example.

Modeling Addition and Subtraction of Rational Numbers

You already know how to use a number line to add and subtract integers. You also know how to add positive decimals, fractions, and mixed numbers. You can use these skills to add and subtract any rational numbers on a number line.

ACTIVITY

1. The sum $\frac{1}{2} + \left(-\frac{3}{4}\right)$ can be represented on a horizontal number line diagram.

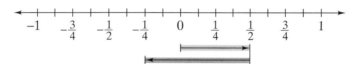

   Copy the number line diagram and label the parts that represent $\frac{1}{2}$ and $\left(-\frac{3}{4}\right)$.

2. What is the sum of these two fractions?

3. Can you use the same number line diagram to represent $\frac{1}{2} - \frac{3}{4}$?

4. Represent each sum or difference on a horizontal number line. Then find each sum or difference.

   a. $-\frac{3}{4} + \frac{5}{8}$ c. $\frac{3}{4} + \left(-\frac{1}{2}\right)$

   b. $\frac{1}{4} - \left(-\frac{3}{4}\right)$ d. $-\frac{1}{4} - \frac{5}{8}$

5. Use a horizontal number line like the one below to represent the sum of $-2.25 + 1.75$.

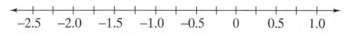

6. The vertical number line at the right represents $-0.5 - (-1.2)$.
   a. How else could you write this expression?
   b. What is the value of this expression?

7. Represent $-1\frac{1}{4} - 5\frac{1}{2}$ on a vertical number line diagram and find the difference.

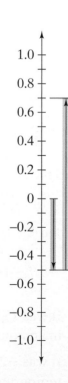

ACTIVITY

The altitude at sea level is 0 meters. A scuba diver is standing on a platform 3.1 meters above sea level on a boat in the ocean.

1. Draw a diagram. At what altitude are the diver's feet?

2. The diver jumps into the water and stops at the top of a kelp plant 8.25 meters below sea level. Add this information to your diagram.

3. Find the absolute value of the difference between 3.1 and −8.25 to determine the distance the diver descended.

4. The diver follows the kelp plant down to its base at 21.3 meters below sea level. Complete your diagram.

5. Simplify the expression $3.1 - (-21.3)$ to find the total distance the diver descended.

Exercises

Represent each sum or difference on a horizontal or vertical number line diagram. Then find each sum or difference.

1. $3.5 + (-2.8)$

2. $-\frac{3}{4} + \left(-\frac{7}{8}\right)$

3. $-2.8 + 3.5$

4. $2.1 - (-1.7)$

5. $-1\frac{5}{8} - \left(-4\frac{3}{8}\right)$

6. $1\frac{1}{4} - 2\frac{7}{8}$

Find the sum or difference.

7. $-16 - 26.6$

8. $-15.2 + 15.2$

9. $-9\frac{4}{5} - 4\frac{3}{5}$

10. $15\frac{1}{5} - \left(-15\frac{1}{5}\right)$

11. $-9.7 - (-8.8)$

12. $8\frac{3}{8} + \left(-6\frac{1}{4}\right)$

13. It was 75.5°F at 2 P.M. and then the temperature dropped 15.1°F in an hour. What was the temperature at 3 P.M.?

14. It was −20.5°F at 6 A.M. and 22°F at noon. How much did the temperature change?

 **Adding and Subtracting Rational Numbers**

y

Check Skills You'll Need

1. **Vocabulary Review**
   A __?__ is the quotient of two integers, where the divisor is not zero.

Write each fraction as a decimal.

2. $\frac{1}{2}$ 3. $\frac{1}{3}$

4. $\frac{1}{4}$ 5. $\frac{1}{5}$

6. $\frac{1}{6}$ 7. $\frac{1}{8}$

 **for Help**
Lesson 1-4

© **CONTENT STANDARDS**
7.NS.1, 7.NS.1.b, 7.NS.1.c,
7.NS.1.d, 7.NS.3

Vocabulary Tip

Distance is a positive quantity. This is why you need to find the absolute value of the difference. The absolute value of all numbers, except zero, is positive.

What You'll Learn

To add and subtract rational numbers

Why Learn This?

You can add and subtract rational numbers to find differences in temperatures.

Temperatures in cold climates can change from being above zero to being below zero in a day. One day in 1939, the temperature in Rochester, Minnesota, dropped from 3.3°C to −30°C in less than 24 hours. To find the difference in temperatures, you can find the distance between the two temperatures on a number line.

KEY CONCEPTS **Distance on a Number Line**

The distance between two numbers on a number line is the absolute value of their difference.

Find the distance between –1.4 and 2.8.

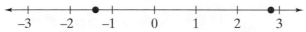

You can subtract –1.4 from 2.8 or you can subtract 2.8 from –1.4 before you find the absolute value of the difference.

Example $2.8 - (-1.4)$
$\quad\quad\quad 2.8 + (1.4)$ ← Add the opposite of $-\frac{1}{4}$.
$\quad\quad\quad 4.2$ ← This is the difference.
$\quad\quad\quad |4.2| = 4.2$ ← Find the absolute value of the difference.

The distance is 4.2.

Check by counting the distance on the number line.

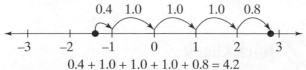

$0.4 + 1.0 + 1.0 + 1.0 + 0.8 = 4.2$

Whether you find the absolute value of the difference of the two points or you count on the number line, the distance is 4.2.

Video Tutor Help

PearsonSuccessNet.com

You know how to add and subtract integers and you know how to add and subtract positive decimals, fractions, and mixed numbers. You can use these skills to add and subtract rational numbers.

EXAMPLE **Adding Rational Numbers**

① Same Sign The sum of two positive rational numbers is positive. The sum of two negative rational numbers is negative.

a. $1\frac{3}{4} + 2\frac{1}{8}$ ← Both numbers are positive. The sum is $3\frac{7}{8}$.

b. $-3.5 + (-4.25)$ ← Both numbers are negative. The sum is -7.75.

Different Sign Find the absolute value of each addend. Subtract the lesser from the greater. The sum has the sign of the addend with the greater absolute value.

c. $1\frac{3}{4} + \left(-2\frac{1}{8}\right)$ ← $\left|1\frac{3}{4}\right| = 1\frac{3}{4}, \left|-2\frac{1}{8}\right| = 2\frac{1}{8}$

$2\frac{1}{8} - 1\frac{3}{4} = \frac{3}{8}$

$2\frac{1}{8} > 1\frac{3}{4}$, so the sum is $-\frac{3}{8}$.

d. $-3.5 + 4.25$ ← $|-3.5| = 3.5, |4.25| = 4.25$

$4.25 - 3.5 = 0.75$

$4.25 > 3.5$, so the sum is 0.75.

✓ Quick Check

1. Find each sum.

a. $-6.25 + (-8.55)$ b. $4\frac{3}{5} + \left(-3\frac{2}{5}\right)$ c. $-5.35 + 1.25$

EXAMPLE **Subtracting Rational Numbers**

Vocabulary Tip

The sum of a number and its opposite is zero.

② To subtract a rational number, add its opposite.

a. Find $6\frac{2}{3} - \left(-3\frac{1}{3}\right)$.

$6\frac{2}{3} + \left(3\frac{1}{3}\right)$ ← Add the opposite of $-3\frac{1}{3}$.

10

b. Find $-4.68 - (-5.79)$.

$-4.68 + (5.79)$ ← Add the opposite of -5.79.

1.11

✓ Quick Check

2. Find each difference.

a. $-3\frac{2}{5} - \left(-2\frac{4}{5}\right)$ b. $4.35 - (-8.27)$ c. $-13.45 - 12.25$

You can subtract rational numbers to find temperature differences.

EXAMPLE **Application: Temperature**

3 The temperature was 3.5°C at noon and −2.7°C at 6:00 P.M. Find the change in the temperatures.

$3.5 - (-2.7)$ ← **Subtract to find the difference.**
$3.5 + 2.7$ ← **Add the opposite of −2.7.**
6.2
The change in the temperatures is 6.2°C.

✔ Quick Check

3. What is the temperature difference between −2.5°F and −6°F?

✔ Check Your Understanding

1. **Vocabulary** On a number line, the __?__ of the difference of two rational numbers is the distance between them on a number line.

2. **Reasoning** The sum of two negative numbers will __?__ be negative.

3. **Number Sense** 68.97 is a rational number. What is its opposite?

Find each sum or difference.

4. $-\dfrac{3}{4} + \dfrac{3}{8}$

5. $0.25 - (-0.75)$

6. $-3\dfrac{1}{9} - \left(-5\dfrac{5}{9}\right)$

Homework Exercises

For more exercises, see Extra Skills and Word Problems.

GO for Help

For Exercises	See Examples
7–12	1
13–18	2
19–20	3

Find each sum.

7. $27.9 + (-3.1)$

8. $5\dfrac{2}{5} + \left(-8\dfrac{4}{5}\right)$

9. $-6.47 + (-4.39)$

10. $2\dfrac{1}{3} + \left(-3\dfrac{2}{3}\right)$

11. $4.5 + (-3.8)$

12. $-3.8 + 4.5$

Find each difference.

13. $2\dfrac{1}{3} - \left(-3\dfrac{2}{3}\right)$

14. $4.5 - (-3.8)$

15. $-3.8 - 4.5$

16. $17.3 - (-6.9)$

17. $7\dfrac{2}{7} - \left(-2\dfrac{3}{7}\right)$

18. $-2.45 - (-3.94)$

19. The temperature was −1.5°C at 6:00 A.M. and 4.7°C at noon. What is the difference between the two temperatures?

20. Nitrogen and oxygen are the two main gases in air. Nitrogen freezes at −345.8°F and oxygen freezes at −361.1°F. What is the difference between their freezing points?

21. Guided Problem Solving Josie's checking account balance is $535.23. She deposits a check for $97.83. She then writes a check for $299.98 for a new bicycle and uses her debit card to withdraw $40.00. What is her checking account balance now?
- What is the balance after she deposits the check?
- What is the total of the check she wrote and her withdrawal?

GO Online
Homework Video Tutor
PearsonSuccessNet.com

22. A diver climbs a 12 ft tower and walks $6\frac{3}{4}$ ft to the end of the diving board. Then he jumps $5\frac{1}{2}$ ft above the board and dives into the water. The water level is $1\frac{1}{4}$ ft below the base of the tower. How far does the diver travel from the top of the dive to the water?

23. Data Analysis Both Barrow, Alaska, and Needles, California, have desert climates. The average low temperature in January is $-28.6°F$ for Barrow and $43.5°F$ for Needles. Find the difference between these temperatures.

24. Writing in Math Explain how what you know about adding and subtracting integers, fractions, and decimals helps you add and subtract rational numbers.

Desert near Needles, California

25. Challenge A deep-sea diver went to a depth of 50.5 m below sea level and stayed there for 30 minutes. The diver then descended another 13.7 m and remained there for 25 minutes. How far does the diver need to ascend to reach a level of 30.6 m below sea level?

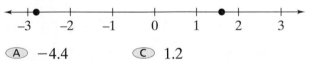
Test Prep and Mixed Review
Practice

Multiple Choice

26. What is the approximate distance between the two points on the number line?

```
←——•—+—+—+—+—•—+—→
   -3  -2  -1   0   1   2   3
```

  Ⓐ −4.4   Ⓒ 1.2
  Ⓑ −1.2   Ⓓ 4.4

27. Which lists these elements in descending order of their melting points?

  Ⓕ mercury, nitrogen, sodium
  Ⓖ sodium, mercury, nitrogen
  Ⓗ sodium, nitrogen, mercury
  Ⓙ nitrogen, mercury, sodium

Element	Melting Point
Mercury (Hg)	−38.8°C
Nitrogen (N)	−209.86°C
Sodium (Na)	97.81°C

GO for Help

For Exercises	See Skills Handbook
28–31	p. 602

Add or subtract. Write answers in simplest form.

28. $\frac{8}{11} + \frac{5}{11}$ **29.** $\frac{4}{7} - \frac{1}{7}$ **30.** $2\frac{3}{8} + \frac{7}{8}$ **31.** $1\frac{9}{10} - \frac{3}{10}$

Using Tables to Compare Data

Analyzing data is easier if the data are organized. You can rearrange a table to organize and display data.

An experiment with seeds resulted in the data recorded in the table. Analyze the data and redraw the table to show which seed types sprouted most frequently.

Seed Type	A	B	C	D	E	F	G	H	I
Number Sprouted	15	5	22	17	18	21	14	18	8
Number Planted	48	20	44	35	52	63	55	35	15

1. For each seed type, find the fraction $\dfrac{\text{number sprouted}}{\text{number planted}}$.

2. Compare the fractions. Order the seed types from most frequently sprouted to least frequently sprouted. (*Hint:* Convert to decimals.)

3. Redraw the table showing the seed types in order from most frequently sprouted to least frequently sprouted.

✓ Checkpoint Quiz 2

Lessons 1-4 through 1-6

Write each fraction as a decimal.

1. $\dfrac{4}{5}$

2. $\dfrac{4}{7}$

3. $\dfrac{4}{9}$

Compare. Use <, =, or >.

4. $\dfrac{2}{3}$ ■ $-\dfrac{2}{3}$

5. -5.56 ■ -3.36

6. $\dfrac{2}{5}$ ■ 0.4

Find each sum or difference.

7. $-6\dfrac{3}{4} + 1\dfrac{2}{3}$

8. $-4.23 + 16.34$

9. $-3\dfrac{5}{6} - \left(-3\dfrac{5}{6}\right)$

10. On a January morning in 1943, the temperature in Spearfish, SD, changed from $-20°C$ to $22.8°C$ in 2 minutes. By how many degrees Celsius did the temperature change?

1-7 Multiplying Rational Numbers

✓ Check Skills You'll Need

1. Vocabulary Review
For two integers, *a* and *b*, the __?__ says that $a \times b = b \times a$.

Find each product.

2. $1 \cdot 2$ **3.** $-2 \cdot 3$

4. $3 \cdot -4$ **5.** $-4 \cdot -5$

6. $-5 \cdot -6$ **7.** $-6 \cdot 7$

 **for Help**

Lesson 1-3

© CONTENT STANDARDS
7.NS.2, 7.NS.2.a,
7.NS.2.c, 7.NS.3

What You'll Learn

To use number lines and properties to understand multiplication of rational numbers and to multiply rational numbers

Why Learn This?

You can multiply rational numbers to represent situations with money.

Suppose you borrow $8.75 from your parents every week for 8 weeks to cover bus fare and have not yet repaid them. You can calculate your debt to your parents by multiplying -8.75×8.

KEY CONCEPTS Multiplying Rational Numbers

The number line below shows the product $\left(2\frac{1}{2}\right) \cdot \left(-1\frac{1}{2}\right)$.

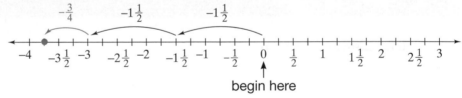

begin here

The Distributive Property explains why $2\frac{1}{2} \cdot \left(-1\frac{1}{2}\right)$ is equal to $2 \cdot \left(-1\frac{1}{2}\right) + \frac{1}{2} \cdot \left(-1\frac{1}{2}\right)$.

The number line above illustrates $2 \cdot \left(-1\frac{1}{2}\right) + \frac{1}{2} \cdot \left(-1\frac{1}{2}\right)$, because there are 2 groups of $\left(-1\frac{1}{2}\right)$ and $\frac{1}{2}$ group of $\left(-1\frac{1}{2}\right)$.

The sum of $2\frac{1}{2}$ groups of $-1\frac{1}{2}$ is $-3\frac{3}{4}$, and is equal to the product $\left(2\frac{1}{2}\right) \cdot \left(-1\frac{1}{2}\right)$, so $\left(2\frac{1}{2}\right) \cdot \left(-1\frac{1}{2}\right) = 3\frac{3}{4}$.

The rules for multiplying rational numbers are the same as those for multiplying integers.

Multiplying Positive Rational Numbers

1 When both factors are positive, the product is positive.

Find $\left(4\frac{3}{4}\right)\left(2\frac{1}{2}\right)$.

Vocabulary Tip

The Distributive Property shows how multiplication affects addition or subtraction:
$a(b + c) = ab + ac$.

$$\left(4\frac{3}{4}\right)\left(2\frac{1}{2}\right) = \left(4\frac{3}{4}\right)\left(2 + \frac{1}{2}\right) \quad \leftarrow \text{Write } 2\frac{1}{2} \text{ as a sum.}$$

$$= \left(4\frac{3}{4} \cdot 2\right) + \left(4\frac{3}{4} \cdot \frac{1}{2}\right) \quad \leftarrow \text{Use the Distributive Property.}$$

$$= \left(9\frac{1}{2}\right) + \left(2\frac{3}{8}\right) \quad \leftarrow \text{Multiply.}$$

$$= 11\frac{7}{8} \quad \leftarrow \text{Add.}$$

✓ Quick Check

1. Find the product. Write your answer in simplest form.

  a. $4.75 \cdot 2.2$ **b.** $\left(8\frac{2}{5}\right)\left(\frac{15}{24}\right)$ **c.** $3.7 \cdot 5.1$

EXAMPLE **Multiplying Negative Rational Numbers**

2 When both factors are negative, the product is positive.

Find $(-3.2)(-4.1)$.

$$(-3.2)(-4.1) = (-1 \cdot 3.2)(-1 \cdot 4.1) \quad \leftarrow \text{Write the negative factors as products.}$$

$$= -1 \cdot (3.2 \cdot -1) \cdot 4.1 \quad \leftarrow \text{Use the Associative Property of Multiplication.}$$

$$= -1 \cdot (-1 \cdot 3.2) \cdot 4.1 \quad \leftarrow \text{Use the Commutative Property of Multiplication.}$$

$$= (-1 \cdot -1) \cdot (3.2 \cdot 4.1) \quad \leftarrow \text{Use the Associative Property of Multiplication.}$$

$$= (1) \cdot (3.2 \cdot 4.1) \quad \leftarrow (-1)(-1) = 1$$

$$= 13.12 \quad \leftarrow \text{Multiply.}$$

✓ Quick Check

2. Find the product.

  a. $\left(-2\frac{2}{3}\right)\left(-2\frac{1}{4}\right)$ **b.** $-7.5 \cdot (-3.1)$ **c.** $\left(-2\frac{2}{5}\right)\left(-1\frac{1}{3}\right)$

EXAMPLE **Multiplying With Different Signs**

3 When both factors have different signs, the product is negative.

Find $(-6.3)(2.2)$.

$$
\begin{aligned}
(-6.3)(2.2) &= (-1 \cdot 6.3)(2.2) &&\leftarrow \textbf{Write the negative factor as a product.}\\
&= -1 \cdot (6.3 \cdot 2.2) &&\leftarrow \textbf{Use the Associative Property of Multiplication.}\\
&= -1 \cdot (13.86) &&\leftarrow \textbf{Multiply.}\\
&= -13.86 &&\leftarrow \textbf{Simplify.}
\end{aligned}
$$

✓ Quick Check

3. Find the product.

   a. $\left(-\frac{3}{5}\right)\left(4\frac{1}{6}\right)$

   b. $-8.5 \cdot (1.2)$

   c. $\left(-1\frac{11}{16}\right)\left(\frac{8}{9}\right)$

EXAMPLE **Application: Freediving**

4 Freediving is an underwater activity in which the diver does not use scuba gear. When James freedives, he can descend $1\frac{1}{3}$ ft per second below sea level. How far below sea level can James descend in 5 seconds?

$$
\begin{aligned}
\left(-1\frac{1}{3}\right)(5) &= \left(-\frac{4}{3}\right)\left(\frac{5}{1}\right) &&\leftarrow \textbf{Use multiplication to write an expression for the amount.}\\
&= \left(-\frac{20}{3}\right) &&\leftarrow \textbf{Multiply to find the distance below sea level.}\\
&= -6\frac{2}{3} &&\leftarrow \textbf{Simplify.}
\end{aligned}
$$

James descends to $-6\frac{2}{3}$ ft.

✓ Quick Check

4. a. Marta is conducting a science experiment. She changes the temperature of a chemical solution by $-\frac{3}{4}°$F each minute. What is the total change in the temperature of the chemical solution after 11 minutes?

   b. Ines has her gym membership fee of $24.95 deducted from her savings account each month. After 6 months, what is the total change of the amount of money in her savings account?

1. **Vocabulary** The Commutative Property of Multiplication lets you change the __?__ of the factors when you are multiplying.
   Ⓐ sign   Ⓑ names   Ⓒ order

2. **Reasoning** The product of two negative numbers will __?__ be negative.
   Ⓐ always   Ⓑ sometimes   Ⓒ never

3. **Number Sense** If you multiply 7 by -1 five times, will the product be positive or negative?

Find each product.

4. $-\dfrac{3}{4} \cdot \dfrac{2}{5}$

5. $(0.32)(-0.75)$

6. $\left(-\dfrac{12}{15}\right)\left(-1\dfrac{1}{4}\right)$

Homework Exercises

For more exercises, see **Extra Skills and Word Problems.**

GO for Help

For Exercises	See Examples
7–9	1
10–12	2
13–15	3
16–24	1-3
25	4

Find each product.

7. 3.25×4.2

8. $\left(3\dfrac{1}{4}\right)\left(2\dfrac{2}{3}\right)$

9. $2.6 \cdot 1.5$

10. $\left(-3\dfrac{3}{5}\right)\left(-2\dfrac{3}{4}\right)$

11. $-4.5 \cdot (-6.2)$

12. $\left(-5\dfrac{2}{3}\right)\left(-1\dfrac{1}{2}\right)$

13. $\left(-3\dfrac{1}{5}\right)\left(\dfrac{3}{8}\right)$

14. $-1.2 \cdot (1.2)$

15. $\left(-1\dfrac{1}{6}\right)\left(\dfrac{5}{7}\right)$

16. $\left(-\dfrac{3}{5}\right)\left(4\dfrac{1}{6}\right)$

17. $-8.5 \cdot (-1.2)$

18. $\left(1\dfrac{11}{16}\right)\left(-\dfrac{8}{9}\right)$

19. $\left(1\dfrac{3}{5}\right)\left(\dfrac{15}{16}\right)$

20. $-4.5 \cdot (2.3)$

21. $\left(-2\dfrac{2}{7}\right)\left(-1\dfrac{3}{4}\right)$

22. $\left(-\dfrac{15}{16}\right)\left(1\dfrac{3}{5}\right)$

23. $2.3 \cdot (4.5)$

24. $\left(-1\dfrac{3}{4}\right)\left(2\dfrac{2}{7}\right)$

25. After a skydiver's parachute opens, he or she descends at a rate of about $8\dfrac{4}{5}$ yd per second. In seven seconds, how many yards will a skydiver with an open parachute descend?

26. **Guided Problem Solving** Jolene graduated from college last year. When she starts her first job, she begins to repay her student loan. Every month she makes a payment of $124.18 from her checking account. She has done this for 7 months so far. This month she decides to make a payment that is $1\dfrac{1}{2}$ times her usual payment. What change to her checking account balance is made by these 8 payments?
    • What expression can you write for the first 7 payments?
    • What expression can you write for the eighth payment?
    • What expression can you write for the 8 payments?

27. **Mental Math** Richard's cell phone bill is $29.99 a month. Each month this amount is automatically taken from his checking account. In 6 months, what is the change to his checking account for his cell phone bills?

28. Rhoda is sewing 22 beanbags for a fundraiser for the school band. She uses $6\frac{1}{4}$ oz of beans for each bag. How many ounces of beans does she use to make all 22 beanbags?

29. **Writing in Math** Use properties of mathematics to explain why $3\frac{1}{2} \cdot \left(-2\frac{1}{2}\right)$ and $\left(2\frac{1}{2}\right) \cdot \left(-3\frac{1}{2}\right)$ have the same value.

30. **Challenge** A submarine is cruising at a depth of 448.6 m. The captain issues this order:

    "Drop 42.5 m and stay at that level for 10 min. Repeat 4 more times."

    What is the submarine's depth after these moves?

Test Prep and Mixed Review

Practice

Multiple Choice

31. Mrs. Martinez writes 3 checks for $17.50 for school lunches for her children. Which expression shows how these checks change her checking account balance?
    - Ⓐ $3 \times (-17.50)$
    - Ⓑ $-3 \times (-17.50)$
    - Ⓒ $(-17.50) + 3$
    - Ⓓ 3×17.50

32. Which gives these rational numbers in order from greatest to least?

    $$\frac{3}{4}, 0.34, 3.4, 0.43, 0.043$$

    - Ⓕ $\frac{3}{4}, 0.34, 3.4, 0.43, 0.043$
    - Ⓖ $0.043, 0.34, 0.43, \frac{3}{4}, 3.4$
    - Ⓗ $3.4, \frac{3}{4}, 0.43, 0.34, 0.043$
    - Ⓙ $0.34, 3.4, \frac{3}{4}, 0.043, 0.43$

GO for Help

For Exercises	See Skills Handbook
33–36	p. 598

Multiply.

33. 0.05×3.2

34. 75.6×3.4

35. 0.5×0.708

36. 1.9×3.02

© **CONTENT STANDARDS**
7.NS.2, 7.NS.2.b,
7.NS.2.c, 7.NS.3

What You'll Learn

To use the rules for dividing integers to divide rational numbers and to solve problems by dividing rational numbers

Why Learn This?

In many places, a well is the source of water. Many wells today are drilled deep underground. Rational numbers can be used to show depths of wells.

Suppose some drillers want to drill a water well 212.5 m deep. If they plan to work for 5 days, they can divide the rational number −212.5 by 5 to determine the depth they need to drill each day.

KEY CONCEPTS **Dividing Rational Numbers**

You already know how to divide integers.

Two Numbers	Sign of Quotient	Examples
Same Sign	Quotient is positive.	$16 \div 2 = 8$ $-16 \div (-2) = 8$
Opposite Signs	Quotient is negative.	$-16 \div 2 = (-8)$ $16 \div (-2) = (-8)$

EXAMPLE **Dividing Rational Numbers: Same Sign**

1 **a.** Find $2.064 \div 0.24$.

Vocabulary Tip

The quotient is the result of dividing a dividend by a divisor. Remember that a divisor can never be zero.

$$0.24\overline{)2.064} \quad \rightarrow \quad 24\overline{)206.4}$$

↑
Multiply the divisor and the dividend by 100 to make the divisor a whole number.

Place the decimal point in the
← quotient above the decimal
point in the dividend.

$$\begin{array}{r} 8.6 \\ 24\overline{)206.4} \\ \underline{192} \\ 144 \\ \underline{144} \\ 0 \end{array}$$

b. Find $-\frac{5}{6} \div -\frac{2}{3}$.

$$-\frac{5}{6} \div -\frac{2}{3} = -\frac{5}{6} \times -\frac{3}{2} \quad \leftarrow \text{Multiply by the reciprocal of the divisor.}$$

$$= -1\left(\frac{5}{6}\right) \times -1\left(\frac{3}{2}\right) \quad \leftarrow \text{Write the rational numbers as products with } -1.$$

$$= -1 \times \left(\frac{5}{6} \times -1\right) \times \left(\frac{3}{2}\right) \quad \leftarrow \text{Use the Associative Property.}$$

$$= -1 \times \left(-1 \times \frac{5}{6}\right) \times \left(\frac{3}{2}\right) \quad \leftarrow \text{Use the Commutative Property.}$$

$$= (-1 \times -1) \times \left(\frac{5}{6} \times \frac{3}{2}\right) \quad \leftarrow \text{Use the Associative Property.}$$

$$= 1 \times \left(\frac{5}{6} \times \frac{3}{2}\right) \quad \leftarrow -1 \times -1 = 1$$

$$= \frac{5}{6} \times \frac{3}{2} \quad \leftarrow \text{Multiply and simplify.}$$

$$= \frac{15}{12} \text{ or } 1\frac{1}{4}$$

For: Dividing Fractions Activity

Use: Interactive Textbook, 1-8

✓ Quick Check

1. Find each quotient.

    a. $16.9 \div 1.3$ **b.** $-\frac{2}{3} \div -\frac{1}{6}$

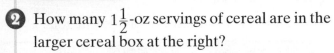

EXAMPLE   **Application: Meal Planning**

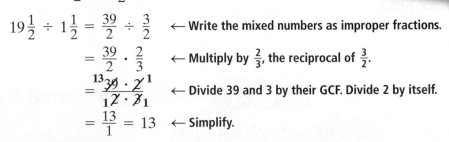

2 How many $1\frac{1}{2}$-oz servings of cereal are in the larger cereal box at the right?

To find how many $1\frac{1}{2}$-oz servings are in $19\frac{1}{2}$ oz, divide $19\frac{1}{2}$ by $1\frac{1}{2}$.

$$19\frac{1}{2} \div 1\frac{1}{2} = \frac{39}{2} \div \frac{3}{2} \quad \leftarrow \text{Write the mixed numbers as improper fractions.}$$

$$= \frac{39}{2} \cdot \frac{2}{3} \quad \leftarrow \text{Multiply by } \frac{2}{3}, \text{ the reciprocal of } \frac{3}{2}.$$

$$= \frac{\overset{13}{\cancel{39}} \cdot \overset{1}{\cancel{2}}}{\underset{1}{\cancel{2}} \cdot \underset{1}{\cancel{3}}} \quad \leftarrow \text{Divide 39 and 3 by their GCF. Divide 2 by itself.}$$

$$= \frac{13}{1} = 13 \quad \leftarrow \text{Simplify.}$$

There are thirteen $1\frac{1}{2}$-oz servings in the larger cereal box.

✓ Quick Check

2. One can of iced tea holds 12 fl oz. A 2-liter bottle holds $67\frac{3}{5}$ fl oz. How many cans of iced tea will you need to fill a 2-liter bottle?

Dividing Rational Numbers: Different Sign

3 Find $-3\frac{5}{6} \div 2\frac{1}{3}$.

$$-3\frac{5}{6} \div 2\frac{1}{3} = -\frac{23}{6} \div \frac{7}{3} \qquad \leftarrow \text{Write both mixed numbers as fractions.}$$

$$= \left(-1 \times \frac{23}{6}\right) \div \frac{7}{3} \qquad \leftarrow \text{Write the negative number as a product with } -1.$$

$$= \left(-1 \times \frac{23}{6}\right) \times \frac{3}{7} \qquad \leftarrow \text{Multiply by the reciprocal of the divisor.}$$

$$= -1 \times \left(\frac{23}{6} \times \frac{3}{7}\right) \qquad \leftarrow \text{Use the Associative Property.}$$

$$= -1 \times \left(\frac{23}{14}\right) \qquad \leftarrow \text{Multiply.}$$

$$= -\frac{23}{14} \text{ or } -1\frac{9}{14} \qquad \leftarrow \text{Simplify.}$$

✓ Quick Check

3. Find each quotient.

a. $-\frac{3}{4} \div \frac{1}{8}$ **b.** $5\frac{4}{9} \div -\frac{7}{10}$ **c.** $-43.68 \div 5.6$

You can divide rational numbers to help solve problems about money.

EXAMPLE **Paying Bills**

4 Denise takes her father's old bicycle to a shop to be restored. The shop owner charges Denise $205.20 for the work on the bicycle. The owner wants Denise to pay the bill in full in $4\frac{1}{2}$ months. What amount does Denise need to pay each month to settle the bill? What will her payments be?

$$-205.20 \div 4.5 \qquad \leftarrow \text{Express both numbers as decimals.}$$
$$-45.6 \qquad \leftarrow \text{Divide.}$$

Check

$$4.5 \times -45.6 = (4 \times -45.6) + (0.5 \times -45.6) \leftarrow \text{Use the Distributive Property.}$$
$$= -182.40 + -22.80 \qquad \leftarrow \text{Multiply.}$$
$$= -205.20 \qquad \leftarrow \text{Simplify.}$$

Checking the answer helps you see that Denise will make 4 payments of $45.60 and 1 payment of $22.80 to the shop owner.

✓ Quick Check

4. Solve.

a. Lucy owes $125.40 for repairs on her laptop. She agrees to pay this back in $5\frac{1}{2}$ weeks. By what amount will her checking account change each week to do this?

b. Randy borrows $315.25 from his mother to buy a tablet computer. He promises to pay her back in $6\frac{1}{2}$ months. If he does this, what will his last payment be?

1. **Vocabulary** The Associative Property of Multiplication lets you change the __?__ of the factors when you are multiplying.
   - Ⓐ sign
   - Ⓑ grouping
   - Ⓒ order
   - Ⓓ value

2. The quotient of a negative number and a positive number will __?__ be negative.
   - Ⓕ always
   - Ⓖ sometimes
   - Ⓗ never
   - Ⓙ not

3. **Reasoning** You know that the opposite of a negative is a positive and the opposite of a positive is a negative. What is the opposite of the opposite of a negative?

Find each quotient. Simplify your answers.

4. $-\dfrac{3}{4} \div \dfrac{3}{10}$

5. $(0.72) \div (-0.24)$

6. $\left(-1\dfrac{2}{5}\right) \div \left(-1\dfrac{5}{10}\right)$

Homework Exercises

For more exercises, see Extra Skills and Word Problems.

Find each product.

GO for Help

For Exercises	See Examples
7–12	1-2
13–18	3
19–21	1-3
22	4

7. $13.65 \div 2.1$

8. $-8\dfrac{2}{3} \div -2\dfrac{2}{3}$

9. $-3.9 \div -1.5$

10. $-9\dfrac{9}{10} \div \left(-2\dfrac{3}{4}\right)$

11. $-27.9 \div (-6.2)$

12. $8\dfrac{1}{2} \div 1\dfrac{1}{2}$

13. $\left(-5\dfrac{1}{3}\right) \div \left(\dfrac{2}{3}\right)$

14. $3.7 \div (-3.7)$

15. $\left(-\dfrac{5}{6}\right) \div \left(\dfrac{5}{7}\right)$

16. $-\dfrac{4}{5} \div \left(\dfrac{8}{11}\right)$

17. $-20.4 \div 1.2$

18. $3 \div (-0.375)$

19. $1\dfrac{4}{5} \div \dfrac{5}{6}$

20. $-15.64 \div 2.3$

21. $\left(6\dfrac{2}{5}\right) \div \left(-1\dfrac{3}{5}\right)$

22. Mrs. Balick owes the dentist $342. She wants to have her payments taken from her checking account over the next $7\dfrac{1}{2}$ months. By what amount will her account change each month for the first 7 months?

 23. **Guided Problem Solving** A caver uses a rope to explore a deep cave. Each step moves the caver $-1\dfrac{1}{4}$ ft down the wall of the cave. After 16 steps, the caver reaches a narrow ledge. How many more steps are needed for the caver to move a total of -35 ft down into the cave?
   - What is the distance to the ledge?
   - After reaching the ledge, how much farther does the caver need to go?
   - Is the number of steps positive or negative?

24. **Mental Math** Mr. Jameson notices that his checking account has a change of −$45.00 after he writes 5 checks for the same amount. By how much does each check change his account?

25. Lucille had 48 oz of dried blueberries. Each batch of muffins uses 3.6 oz of dried blueberries. After making several batches, 30 oz of the dried blueberries are left. How many batches of muffins did she make?

26. **Reasoning** By what number can you divide a rational number to get a number that is twice the opposite of the rational number?

27. **Writing in Math** The rules for finding the sign of the quotient when dividing rational numbers are the same as the rules for finding the sign of the product when multiplying rational numbers. Explain why.

28. **Challenge** A chemist is cooling a reaction mixture with an ice and salt bath. The temperature of the mixture starts at 97.5°C and changes by −7.5°C every 3.5 min for 35 min. Then the temperature changes more slowly, by −3.5°C every 7.5 min. How long does the mixture stay in the ice and salt bath to reach a temperature of 5°C?

Test Prep and Mixed Review

Practice

Multiple Choice

29. Jason rappelled down a $132\frac{1}{2}$ ft cliff in 4 equal moves. What expression does NOT show his change in position during each move?

   Ⓐ $-132\frac{1}{2} \div 4$

   Ⓑ $-132.5 \div 4$

   Ⓒ -132.5×4

   Ⓓ $-132.5 \times \frac{1}{4}$

30. If the product of −3.2 and −2.3 is divided by −23, the result is ? .
   Ⓕ a counting number
   Ⓖ an integer
   Ⓗ a negative rational number
   Ⓙ a positive rational number

31. In which expression can zero NOT be substituted for b?
   Ⓐ $a + b = c$ Ⓒ $a^2 + b^2 = c^2$
   Ⓑ $a \div b = c$ Ⓓ $a \cdot c = b$

For Exercises	See Lesson
32–35	1-7

Find each product.

32. $-3.6 \times (-2.4)$ 33. $-2\frac{1}{3} \cdot 1\frac{2}{3}$ 34. $4.4 \times (-1.6)$ 35. $\left(-\frac{7}{8}\right)\left(1\frac{1}{3}\right)$

Choosing Operations

Flying Flags! At a flag factory, bolts holding $72\frac{3}{4}$ yd of fabric are placed on a cutting machine. The machine cuts off $\frac{3}{4}$ yd for a flag every 10 seconds. When a bolt is used up, how many flags have been cut off?

What You Might Think

What do I know? What do I want to find out?

How do I show the main idea?

Can I estimate the answer?

How do I solve the problem? What is the answer?

Is the answer reasonable?

What You Might Write

When the bolt is used up, $72\frac{3}{4}$ yd have been used. Each flag is $\frac{3}{4}$ yd. I want to know how many flags have been cut off.

I can write an expression with rational numbers.
$$72\frac{3}{4} \div \left(\frac{3}{4}\right)$$

Each flag is less than 1 yd, so there should be more than 72 flags cut off.

$72\frac{3}{4} \div \frac{3}{4}$ ← This is the division.

$\frac{291}{4} \div \frac{3}{4}$ ← Write the mixed number as a fraction.

$\frac{291}{4} \times \frac{4}{3}$ ← Multiply by the reciprocal of the divisor.

97 ← The number of flags

Yes, 97 is more than 72.

Think It Through

1. Suppose your answer was $54\frac{9}{16}$. How does your estimate help you decide to check your work?

2. **Number Sense** The expression above uses negative rational numbers to represent changes in a bolt of fabric. Explain why this makes sense.

3. **Reasoning** Explain why the answer is a positive number.

Exercises

Solve each problem. For Exercises 4 and 5, answer the questions first.

4. As pioneers headed west in the 1800s, differences in elevations made travel difficult. The table below shows the highest and lowest elevations in some of the places the pioneers sought to go. What is the greatest elevation difference? Which state has the greatest elevation difference?

State	Highest Elevation (ft)	Lowest Elevation (ft)
Wyoming	13,804	3,099
California	14,494	−282
Nevada	13,140	479
Oklahoma	4,973	289
Oregon	11,239	0

   a. What do you know? What do you want to find out?

   b. How can you use reasoning to make your work more efficient?

5. In May, 1860, the longest run in the history of the Pony Express was made using four horses. The table shows the distances run by the horses.

Horse	Distance (miles)
1	60
2	35
3	37
4	30

   What was the total distance? What fraction of the distance did each horse run?

   a. What do you know? What do you want to find out?

   b. How can you change the table to help find the answer?

6. Early settlers often sold their furniture to lighten their wagons. Suppose a settler sold furniture for 0.2 times the amount he paid. If he sold a chair for $3.80, what was his loss?

7. In the 1850s, a wind wagon was invented that was half sailboat and half wagon. The wind wagon took about 133 days to travel 1,968 mi. After 19 days, what fraction of the trip was over?

8. The Mississippi River is 3.2 times longer than the Platte-South Platte River. The Mississippi River is 2,340 mi long. How long is the Platte-South Platte River? What is the difference in their lengths?

CONTENT STANDARDS

8.NS.1, 8.NS.2, 8.EE.2

✓ Check Skills You'll Need

1. **Vocabulary Review** How is a *terminating decimal* different from a *repeating decimal*?

Classify each decimal as *terminating* or *repeating*.

2. 1.276   3. $3.\overline{35}$

4. $8.1\overline{6}$ 5. 12.1212

 **for Help**
Lesson 1-4

What You'll Learn

To find and estimate square roots and to classify numbers as rational or irrational

New Vocabulary perfect square, square root, irrational numbers, real numbers

Why Learn This?

Not every situation can be modeled using the four basic operations. For example, you need square roots to relate the time and distance a skydiver falls.

A number that is the square of a whole number is a **perfect square.**
The **square root** of a number is another number that when multiplied by itself is equal to the given number.

In the diagram at the right, 16 square tiles form a square with 4 tiles on each side. Since $4 \cdot 4 = 16$ and $-4 \cdot (-4) = 16$, 16 has two square roots, 4 and -4. Since $4^2 = 16$, 16 is a perfect square.

$4^2 = 16$

EXAMPLE Finding Square Roots of Perfect Squares

Perfect Squares

n	n^2
0	0
1	1
2	4
3	9
4	16
5	25
6	36
7	49
8	64
9	81
10	100
11	121
12	144

1 Find the two square roots of 25.

$5 \cdot 5 = 25$ and $-5 \cdot (-5) = 25$

The square roots of 25 are 5 and -5.

✓ Quick Check

1. Find the square roots of each number.
   a. 36   **b.** 1   **c.** $\frac{1}{16}$

The symbol $\sqrt{}$ means the square root of a number. In this book, $\sqrt{}$ means the nonnegative square root, unless stated otherwise. So $\sqrt{9}$ means the nonnegative square root of 9, or 3, and $-\sqrt{9}$ means the opposite of the nonnegative square root of 9, or -3.

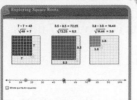
EXAMPLE **Estimating a Square Root**

2 Estimate the value of $\sqrt{28}$ to the nearest integer and to the nearest tenth.

To estimate $\sqrt{28}$ to the nearest integer, find the closest perfect square greater than 28 and the closest perfect square less than 28.

$$\sqrt{16} \quad \sqrt{25} \; \sqrt{28} \; \sqrt{36} \qquad \sqrt{49}$$

<—|————————|———●——|——————————|——>
  4   5   6   7

The perfect squares closest to 28 are 25 and 36. Since 28 is closer to 25 than it is to 36, $\sqrt{28}$ must be closer to 5 than to 6. So $\sqrt{28} \approx 5$.

To estimate $\sqrt{28}$ to the nearest tenth, find two squares between 5 and 6 that are closest to 28. Start with $5.1^2, 5.2^2$, and so on.

$$\sqrt{26.01} \quad \sqrt{27.04} \quad \sqrt{28.09} \quad \sqrt{29.16}$$

<—|—————————|————————●—|———————|——>
  5.1^2 5.2^2 5.3^2 5.4^2
                              $\sqrt{28}$

The squares closest to 28 are 27.04 and 28.09. Since 28 is closer to 28.09 than it is to 27.04, $\sqrt{28}$ must be closer to 5.3 than to 5.2. So, $\sqrt{28} \approx 5.3$.

✓ Quick Check

2. Estimate the value of $\sqrt{38}$ to the nearest integer and to the nearest tenth.

You can compare square roots in the same way you compare integers.

EXAMPLE **Comparing Square Roots**

3 Which is greater, $\sqrt{18}$ or 4.4?
First, estimate the value of the square root to the nearest tenth.
$\sqrt{18} \approx 4.2$
Since $4.2 < 4.4, \sqrt{18} < 4.4$.

✓ Quick Check

3. Which is greater $\sqrt{20}$ or 4.7?

Finding a number's square root is the inverse of finding its square. So $\sqrt{3^2} = 3$.

EXAMPLE **Application: Surface Area of a Sphere**

4 The formula S.A. $= 13r^2$ approximates the surface area of a sphere with radius r. Find the radius of a sphere with S.A. 780 square units.

$$S.A. = 13r^2 \qquad \leftarrow \textbf{Use the formula for the surface area of a sphere.}$$
$$780 = 13r^2 \qquad \leftarrow \textbf{Substitute 780 for S.A.}$$
$$\frac{780}{13} = r^2 \qquad \leftarrow \textbf{Divide each side by 13 to isolate } r.$$

To find $\sqrt{60}$ on your calculator, press $\boxed{\sqrt{}}$. Enter 60. Then press $\boxed{=}$.

$$60 \approx r^2 \qquad \leftarrow \textbf{Simplify.}$$
$$\sqrt{60} \approx \sqrt{r^2} \qquad \leftarrow \textbf{Find the positive square root of each side. Use a calculator.}$$
$$7.7 \approx r \qquad \leftarrow \textbf{Round to the nearest tenth.}$$

The radius of a sphere with surface area 780 square units is about 7.7 units.

✓ Quick Check

4. Use the formula S.A. $= 13r^2$ to find the radius of a sphere with a surface area of 520 square units. Round to the nearest tenth of a unit.

Irrational numbers are numbers that cannot be written in the form $\frac{a}{b}$, where a is any integer and b is any nonzero integer. Rational and irrational numbers form the set of **real numbers.** The diagram below shows the relationships among sets of numbers.

Vocabulary Tip

The word *rational* has the word *ratio* in it.
The word *irrational* means "not rational."

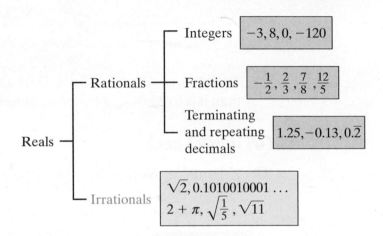

The decimal expansion of irrational numbers do not terminate or repeat. The decimal digits of $\pi = 3.14159265359\ldots$ do not terminate or repeat, so π is an irrational number. Irrational numbers can also include decimals that have a pattern in their digits, like $0.02022022202222\ldots$

For any integer n that is not a perfect square, $\sqrt{n}$ is irrational.

EXAMPLE Classifying Real Numbers

GO for Help

For help with terminating and repeating decimals, go to Lesson 1-4, Examples 2–3.

5 Is each number *rational* or *irrational*? Explain.

a. $0.818118111\ldots$ Irrational; the decimal does not terminate or repeat.

b. $-0.\overline{81}$ Rational; the decimal repeats.

c. $1\frac{2}{9}$ Rational; the number can be written as the ratio $\frac{11}{9}$.

d. $\sqrt{2}$ Irrational; 2 is not a perfect square.

✓ Quick Check

5. Is $0.\overline{6}$ *rational* or *irrational*? Explain.

Vocabulary Write all the possible names for each number. Choose from the terms *rational number*, *irrational number*, *real number*, and *perfect square*.

1. $\sqrt{6}$ 2. $-0.\overline{6}$ 3. $\frac{1}{6}$ 4. 25

Find the positive and negative square roots of each number.

5. 4   6. $\frac{1}{4}$ 7. 100   8. $\frac{1}{100}$

Homework Exercises

For more exercises, see Extra Skills and Word Problems.

Find the square roots of each number.

9. 49   10. 900   11. $\frac{1}{36}$ 12. $\frac{1}{121}$ 13. $\frac{4}{25}$

Estimate the value of each expression to the nearest integer.

14. $\sqrt{3}$ 15. $\sqrt{10}$ 16. $-\sqrt{22}$ 17. $-\sqrt{120}$

Which number is greater?

18. $\sqrt{26}, 5.2$ 19. $7.3, \sqrt{55}$ 20. $\sqrt{44}, 6.4$ 21. $10.3, \sqrt{104}$

Use $s = 20\sqrt{273 + T}$ to estimate the speed of sound s in meters per second for each Celsius temperature T. Estimate square roots to the nearest tenth.

22. 0°C   23. 20°C   24. −10°C   25. 70°C

Is each number *rational* or *irrational*? Explain.

26. −0.6   27. $\sqrt{40}$ 28. 0.606606660…   29. $-\sqrt{144}$

30. **Guided Problem Solving** The area of a square postage stamp is $\frac{81}{100}$ in.^{2}. What is the side length of the stamp?
 - What is the formula for the area of a square?
 - How can you use the formula to find the side length of a square?

31. **Boxing** The area of a square boxing ring is 484 ft^2. What is the perimeter of the boxing ring?

32. **Open-Ended** Give an example of an irrational number that is less than 2 and greater than 1.5. Explain how you know the number is irrational.

33. **Writing in Math** Explain how you can approximate $\sqrt{30}$.

For Exercises	See Examples
9–13	1
14–17	2
18–21	3
22–25	4
26–29	5

Find the value of each expression.

34. $(\sqrt{36})^2$ **35.** $\sqrt{(10)^2}$ **36.** $\sqrt{(3.2)^2}$ **37.** $(\sqrt{a})^2$

38. The area of a square is $\frac{25}{36}$ in.² What is the length of its side?

39. Ferris Wheels The formula $d = 1.23\sqrt{h}$ represents the distance in miles d you can see from h feet above ground. On the London Eye Ferris Wheel, you are 450 ft above ground. To the nearest tenth of a mile, how far can you see?

40. Number Sense For what values of n is $\sqrt{n}$ a rational number?

41. Error Analysis A student evaluated the expression $\sqrt{4 + 9}$ and got the answer 5. What error did the student make?

42. Challenge Explain how you know that the number 123,456,789,101,112 cannot be a perfect square. (*Hint:* What is the units digit?)

Test Prep and Mixed Review   **Practice**

Multiple Choice

43. The area of a square is 150 square centimeters. Which best represents the side length of the square?

    Ⓐ 11.7 cm   Ⓒ 2.9 cm

    Ⓑ 12.2 cm   Ⓓ 13 cm

44. A submarine is 500 feet below sea level and rises to the surface at 35 ft/s. About how long will the submarine take to reach the surface?

    Ⓕ 13.7 seconds   Ⓗ 14.3 seconds

    Ⓖ 13.9 seconds   Ⓙ 14.9 seconds

45. Which of the following inequalities correctly compares two numbers?

    Ⓐ $\sqrt{97} < 9.9$ Ⓒ $\sqrt{97} < 9.5$

    Ⓑ $\sqrt{97} \le 9.7$ Ⓓ $\sqrt{97} \le 9.3$

Write the decimal expansion of each fraction.

46. $\frac{27}{36}$ **47.** $\frac{20}{64}$

48. $\frac{88}{121}$ **49.** $\frac{196}{144}$

GO for Help

For Exercises	See Lesson
46–49	1-4

What You'll Learn

To find cube roots and to solve cube root equations

New Vocabulary perfect cube, cube root

Why Learn This?

The large cube at the right is made up of smaller unit cubes. You can use this type of model to help you understand perfect cubes and cube roots.

A cube number is a power with an exponent of 3. A number that is the cube of a whole number is a **perfect cube**. For example, $3 \cdot 3 \cdot 3$, or 3^3, is 27. So 27 is a perfect cube.

The **cube root** of a number is a number that, when used as a factor three times, is equal to the given number. Since 3^3, or $3 \cdot 3 \cdot 3$, is 27, 3 is the cube root of 27.

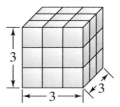

Perfect Cubes

n	n^3
0	0
1	1
2	8
3	27
4	64
5	125
6	216
7	343
8	512
9	729
10	1,000

EXAMPLE **Finding Cube Roots of Perfect Cubes**

1 Find the cube root of each number.

   a. 8 $2 \cdot 2 \cdot 2 = 8$ ← The cube root of 8 is 2.

   b. -125 $-5 \cdot -5 \cdot -5 = -125$ ← The cube root of -125 is -5.

   c. $\frac{1}{64}$ $\frac{1}{4} \cdot \frac{1}{4} \cdot \frac{1}{4} = \frac{1}{64}$ ← The cube root of $\frac{1}{64}$ is $\frac{1}{4}$.

✓ Quick Check

1. Find the cube root of each number.
     a. 216   **b.** -1 **c.** $\frac{1}{27}$

The inverse of cubing a number is finding its cube root. The symbol $\sqrt[3]{}$ means the cube root of a number. For example, $\sqrt[3]{1,000}$ means the cube root of 1,000, or 10.

EXAMPLE **Finding the Side Length of a Cube**

2 **Measurement** A cube-shaped packing box has a volume of 64 cubic feet. What is the side length of the box?

64 ft³

Vocabulary Tip

Volume is the number of unit cubes needed to fill a solid. Volume is measured in cubic units.

The formula for the volume V of a cube is $V = s^3$, where s is the length of one side of the cube.

Method 1 Solve an Equation

$V = s^3$	← **Volume formula**
$64 = s^3$	← **Substitute 64 for V.**
$\sqrt[3]{64} = \sqrt[3]{s^3}$	← **Find the cube root of each side.**
$3\ \boxed{\sqrt[x]{}}\ 64\ \boxed{=}\ 4$	← **Use a calculator.**
$4 = s$	

Method 2 Mental Math

The volume of the box is 64 cubic feet. Since $4^3 = 64$, $\sqrt[3]{64} = 4$.

The side length of the box is 4 feet.

✓ Quick Check

2. A different cube-shaped packing box has a volume of 125 cubic feet. What is the side length of the box?

To find the cube root of a fraction, find the cube root of the numerator and the cube root of the denominator.

EXAMPLE **Solving a Cube Root Equation**

3 Solve $x^3 = \dfrac{8}{343}$.

$$x^3 = \frac{8}{343}$$

$$\sqrt[3]{x^3} = \sqrt[3]{\frac{8}{343}} \qquad \leftarrow \textbf{Find the cube root of each side.}$$

$$= \frac{\sqrt[3]{8}}{\sqrt[3]{343}} \qquad \leftarrow \begin{array}{l}\textbf{Find the cube root of the numerator.}\\ \textbf{Find the cube root of the denominator.}\end{array}$$

$$x = \frac{2}{7} \qquad \leftarrow \textbf{Simplify. } \textit{Think:} \textbf{ } 8 = 2 \cdot 2 \cdot 2 \textbf{ and } 343 = 7 \cdot 7 \cdot 7.$$

✓ Quick Check

3. Solve $x^3 = \dfrac{27}{216}$.

Check Your Understanding

1. **Reasoning** The volume of a cube is 512 cubic inches. What is the length of its side? Explain your reasoning.

Find the cube root of each number.

2. 729   3. 0   4. -8 5. $\dfrac{1}{1,000}$

Homework Exercises

For more exercises, see Extra Skills and Word Problems.

Find the cube root of each number.

6. 343   7. 1   8. -27

9. $\dfrac{1}{125}$ 10. -216 11. $\dfrac{8}{343}$

GO for Help

For Exercises	See Examples
6–11	1
12–19	2, 3

Solve each equation by finding the value of x.

12. $x^3 = 512$ 13. $x^3 = 125$ 14. $x^3 = -1,000$

15. $x^3 = \dfrac{27}{125}$ 16. $x^3 = \dfrac{512}{729}$ 17. $x^3 = \dfrac{343}{1,000}$

18. A cube-shaped gift box has a volume of 8 cubic inches. What is the side length of the box?

19. A cube-shaped planter holds $\dfrac{27}{512}$ cubic feet of potting soil. What is the side length of the planter?

20. **Guided Problem Solving** Find the cube root of 0.008.
    - Can you rename the decimal as a fraction?
    - Write your answer as a decimal. Check by cubing your answer.

21. Find the cube root of 0.216.

22. **Writing in Math** Is 0.3 the cube root of 0.27? Explain.

23. **a.** Copy and complete the table below.

x	1	2	3	4	5	6	7	8	9	10
x^2										
x^3										

b. Are any of the numbers both a perfect square and a perfect cube?
c. When x is a perfect square, what is true about the cube of x?

Find the value of each expression.

24. $(\sqrt[3]{64})^3$

25. $\sqrt[3]{9^3}$

26. $(\sqrt[3]{n})^3$

Draw and label a cube to model each volume.

27. 1 cubic inch

28. 8 cubic feet

29. 125 cubic meters

30. Number Sense For what values of n does $\sqrt[3]{n}$ have the following values?
 a. positive
 b. 0
 c. negative

31. Error Analysis A student evaluated the expression $3\sqrt{\dfrac{8}{64}}$ and got $\dfrac{1}{8}$. What error did the student make?

 **for Help**

For help using a calculator to find a cube root, see Example 2.

32. Use a calculator to estimate $\sqrt[3]{350}$ to the nearest hundredth.

33. Challenge Estimate the value of the expression $\sqrt[3]{100}$ to the nearest integer. Explain your reasoning.

Test Prep and Mixed Review

Practice

Multiple Choice

34. The model represents $\sqrt[3]{27} = 3$. Which model can be used to represent $\sqrt[3]{1,000}$?
 Ⓐ $100 \times 10 \times 1$ rectangular prism
 Ⓑ $25 \times 10 \times 4$ rectangular prism
 Ⓒ $20 \times 10 \times 5$ rectangular prism
 Ⓓ $10 \times 10 \times 10$ rectangular prism

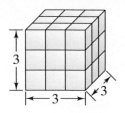

35. Luisa bought 50 tiles on sale. Each one measured 1 square foot. What is the largest square floor she can tile?
 Ⓕ $1\,\text{ft} \times 1\,\text{ft}$
 Ⓖ $7\,\text{ft} \times 7\,\text{ft}$
 Ⓗ $8\,\text{ft} \times 8\,\text{ft}$
 Ⓙ $50\,\text{ft} \times 50\,\text{ft}$

36. Which of the following inequalities is NOT true?
 Ⓐ $\sqrt{64} > \sqrt[3]{64}$
 Ⓑ $\sqrt{64} \geq \sqrt[3]{64}$
 Ⓒ $\sqrt{0} < \sqrt[3]{0}$
 Ⓓ $\sqrt{1} \leq \sqrt[3]{1}$

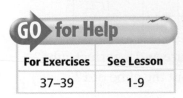 **for Help**

For Exercises	See Lesson
37–39	1-9

Estimate the value of each expression to the nearest tenth.

37. $\sqrt{18}$

38. $\sqrt{30}$

39. $\sqrt{85}$

🌐**nline** lesson quiz, PearsonSuccessNet.com

Writing Gridded Responses

Some tests call for gridded responses. You find a numerical answer. Then you write the answer at the top of the grid and fill in the corresponding bubbles below. You must use the grid correctly.

EXAMPLES

1. The distance between −0.1 and 0.4 on a number line is 0.5. Record this answer.

   You can write the answer as 0.5 or .5. Here are the two ways to enter these answers.

2. Cindy had $19.25 before she went shopping. She spent $18.50 on purchases that day. How much money, in dollars, did she have left?

$$\begin{array}{r} 19.25 \\ - 18.50 \\ \hline 0.75 \end{array}$$

The answer is 0.75. You grid this as 0.75 or .75.

Exercises

Write the number you would grid for each answer. If you have a grid, complete it.

1. A bottle of apple juice holds 3.79 L. A bottle of orange juice holds 1.89 L. How many more liters does the bottle of apple juice hold?

2. You are organizing a pet show. On the first morning, 40 dogs will be shown. For each dog, you will allow one and a half minutes to set up and four minutes for showing. How many minutes will the morning session last?

3. What is the distance between −41 and 41 on a number line?

Chapter 1 Review

Vocabulary Review

additive inverses (p. 10)
cube root (p. 55)
integers (p. 4)
irrational number (p. 52)

opposites (p. 4)
perfect cube (p. 55)
perfect square (p. 50)
rational number (p. 26)

real number (p. 52)
repeating decimal (p. 22)
square root (p. 50)
terminating decimal (p. 21)

Choose the correct term to complete each sentence.

1. When you divide 4 by 7, the quotient is a ? .

2. The quotient of two integers where the divisor is never zero is called a ? .

3. When you divide 3 by 8, the quotient is a ? .

4. Two numbers with the same absolute value and different signs are ? .

Go Online

For vocabulary quiz
PearsonSuccessNet.com

5. The numbers $-2, 0,$ and 7 are ? , but the numbers -2.5 and 3.7 are not.

Skills and Concepts

Lesson 1-1
- To compare and order integers and to find and add opposites.

Opposites are two numbers that are the same distance from 0 on a number line, but in opposite directions. **Integers** are the set of positive whole numbers, their opposites, and zero.

Compare. Use <, =, or >.

6. $-7 \blacksquare 7$ 7. $3 \blacksquare 3$ 8. $9 \blacksquare -4$ 9. $8 \blacksquare -15$

Lessons 1-2, 1-3
- To add and subtract integers and to solve problems involving integers
- To multiply and divide integers and to solve problems involving integers

The sum of two positive integers is positive. The sum of two negative integers is negative. To find the sum of two integers with different signs, find the absolute value of each integer. Subtract the lesser absolute value from the greater. The sum has the sign of the integer with the greater absolute value. To subtract an integer, add its opposite.

The product or quotient of two integers with the same sign is positive. The product or quotient of two integers with different signs is negative.

Simplify.

10. $14 + (-8)$ 11. $17 - (-12)$ 12. $-5 \cdot 6$ 13. $125 \div (-5)$

Lessons 1-4, 1-5

- To convert between fractions and decimals
- To compare and order rational numbers

To write a fraction as a decimal, you divide the numerator by the denominator. When the division ends with a remainder of 0, the quotient is a **terminating decimal**. When the same block of digits in a decimal repeats without end, the quotient is a **repeating decimal**. A **rational number** can be written as the quotient of two integers, where the denominator is not zero.

Write each fraction as a decimal, and then order from least to greatest.

14. $\frac{3}{4}, 0.\overline{3}, -\frac{7}{8}$ **15.** $2.7, -0.3, -\frac{4}{11}$ **16.** $-\frac{5}{6}, 2.2, -0.5$

Lessons 1-6, 1-7, 1-8

- To add and subtract rational numbers
- To use number lines and properties to understand multiplication of rational numbers and to multiply rational numbers
- To use the rules for dividing integers to divide rational numbers and to solve problems by dividing rational numbers

The rules for signs of rational numbers are the same as for integers.

The sum of two positive rational numbers is positive. The sum of two negative rational numbers is negative. To subtract a rational number, add its opposite. The product or quotient of two rational numbers with the same sign is positive. The product or quotient of two rational numbers with different signs is negative.

Simplify.

17. $-\frac{1}{3} + \left(\frac{2}{3}\right)$ **18.** $2.5 - (-1.3)$ **19.** $\left(-\frac{1}{5}\right)\left(\frac{10}{13}\right)$ **20.** $-1\frac{2}{5} \div \left(\frac{1}{5}\right)$

Lessons 1-9, 1-10

- To find and estimate square roots and to classify numbers as rational or irrational
- To find cube roots and to solve cube root equations

Irrational numbers are numbers that cannot be written as fractions using integers. The square of a whole number is a **perfect square**. The inverse of squaring a number is finding its **square root**. The cube of a whole number is a **perfect cube**. The inverse of cubing a number is finding its **cube root**.

Simplify each expression.

21. $\sqrt{81}$ **22.** $\sqrt{\frac{100}{121}}$ **23.** $\sqrt[3]{125}$ **24.** $\sqrt[3]{\frac{1}{8}}$

25. $\sqrt{\frac{1}{9}}$ **26.** $\sqrt{\frac{4}{25}}$ **27.** $\sqrt[3]{-\frac{8}{27}}$ **28.** $\sqrt[3]{0}$

Chapter 1 Test

Go Online

For online chapter test
PearsonSuccessNet.com

Find the opposite of each number.

1. -8 2. 16 3. 176 4. -48

Find each sum.

5. $-6 + 6$ 6. $67 + (-67)$

Compare using <, =, or >.

7. $-17 \blacksquare -3$ 8. $-24 \blacksquare -24$
9. $-8 \blacksquare 0$ 10. $16 \blacksquare -4$

Find each sum.

11. $-3 + (-9)$ 12. $37 + (-14)$
13. $-37 + 14$ 14. $2 + 49$

Find each difference.

15. $-71 - (-3)$ 16. $-36 - (-36)$
17. $8 - 10$ 18. $14 - (-4)$

19. **Money** You have a balance of $213 in a savings account. You withdraw $68 one day and $128 the next day without making any deposits. What is your new balance?

Find each product.

20. $-4 \times (-8)$ 21. $15 \times (-4)$
22. -7×14 23. 14.8×12

Find each quotient.

24. $-72 \div (-3)$ 25. $-37 \div (-37)$
26. $56 \div -7$ 27. $-144 \div 24$

28. **Reasoning** Is each statement true or false?
   a. The product of two integers with different signs can be positive or negative.
   b. The sum of two integers with different signs can be positive or negative.

Write each fraction as a decimal.

29. $\frac{2}{5}$ 30. $\frac{4}{11}$

Order from greatest to least.

31. $7.5, -8.3, 0, 5.7$

32. $\frac{2}{3}, -\frac{3}{2}, 1\frac{2}{3}, -3\frac{1}{2}$

33. **Writing in Math** Summarize the rules for signs when operating with rational numbers. Give an example for each.

Find each sum or difference.

34. $-2.6 + 1.5$ 35. $\frac{6}{7} - \left(-\frac{6}{7}\right)$
36. $-8.4 - (-1.3)$ 37. $-\frac{3}{5} + \left(-\frac{3}{5}\right)$

Find each product.

38. $\left(-\frac{5}{6}\right)\left(-\frac{3}{8}\right)$ 39. $3.7 \times (-1.4)$
40. -3.7×1.4 41. $\frac{2}{3} \times \frac{3}{7}$

Find each quotient.

42. $\left(-\frac{7}{10}\right) \div \left(-\frac{3}{5}\right)$ 43. $-3.6 \div (-3.6)$
44. $\frac{5}{8} \div \frac{3}{4}$ 45. $1.4 \div (-0.7)$

46. **Weather** If the temperature drops from $13.5°F$ to $-13.5°F$, what is the change in temperature?

Find the two square roots of each number.

47. 144 48. 400 49. $\frac{25}{36}$

50. **Windows** The area of a square window is $1,296$ in.^{2}. What is the perimeter of the window?

Find the cube root of each number.

51. $1,331$ 52. $\frac{1}{512}$ 53. $-\frac{8}{729}$

54. **Open-Ended** Give an example of an integer that is less than $\sqrt[3]{-64}$ and greater than $\sqrt[3]{-343}$. Explain your reasoning.

Reading Comprehension

Read each passage and answer the questions that follow.

> **Summer Camp News** The Blue and Green teams have a fishing contest as an activity this year. In order, the Blues catch 15, 8, 5, 7, and 11 fish and the Greens catch 12, 9, 11, 5, and 7 fish in the first five days of camp. The two teams also play golf together. The best Blue score is –4 and the best Green score is –1. The campers will enjoy cooking out every evening for the 12 days of camp!

1. What integer describes the change in the number of fish the Greens catch between the third and fourth days of camp?
   - (A) −16
   - (B) −6
   - (C) 6
   - (D) 16

2. In golf, lower scores are better scores. Why is the Blue golf score better than the Green golf score?
   - (F) $-4 + -1 = -5$
   - (G) $-4 \div -1 = 4$
   - (H) $-4 > -1$
   - (J) $-4 < -1$

3. Predict the final fishing results based on the results for the first five days.
   - (A) The Blues will catch about 12 more fish than the Greens.
   - (B) The Greens will catch about 12 more fish than the Blues.
   - (C) The Blues and the Greens will catch about the same number of fish.
   - (D) The Blues and the Greens will catch exactly the same number of fish.

4. During the first two days of camp, which team caught more fish? How many more?
   - (F) Blue, 2 more
   - (G) Blue, 23 more
   - (H) Green, 3 more
   - (J) Green, 21 more

> **Parity** We say that two integers have the same *parity* if they are both even or both odd. So 2 and 12 have the same parity, and 51 and 139 have the same parity. If one number is even and the other number is odd, then we say they have different or opposite parities. 2 and 51 have opposite parities.

5. Two integers have the same parity. Describe the parity of their sum.
   - (A) same as the two numbers
   - (B) opposite of the two numbers
   - (C) same if the numbers are odd
   - (D) opposite if the numbers are odd

6. Two integers have the same parity. Describe the parity of their difference.
   - (F) same as the two numbers
   - (G) opposite of the two numbers
   - (H) same only if the numbers are even
   - (J) same only if the numbers are odd

7. Two integers have the same parity. Describe the parity of their product.
   - (A) same as the two numbers
   - (B) opposite of the two numbers
   - (C) same only if the numbers are odd
   - (D) opposite only if the numbers are odd

8. Two integers have different parity. Describe their product.
   - (F) always even
   - (G) always odd
   - (H) sometimes even
   - (J) odd if the smaller number is odd

CHAPTER 2

Exponents

What You've Learned

- In a previous course, you wrote and simplified expressions with exponents.
- You multiplied and divided by powers of ten.
- You multiplied and divided decimals by decimals.

Check Your Readiness

GO for Help

For Exercises	See
1–12	Lesson 1-9
13–18	p. 601
19–24	pp. 598, 600

Using Exponents
Write using exponents.

1. $7 \cdot 7 \cdot 7 \cdot 7 \cdot 7$ **2.** $5 \cdot 5 \cdot c \cdot c$ **3.** $a \cdot a \cdot b \cdot b \cdot b$

4. $x \cdot y \cdot x \cdot y \cdot x$ **5.** $(3x) \cdot (3x) \cdot (3x)$ **6.** $c \cdot d \cdot g \cdot d \cdot g$

Simplify each expression.

7. 4^2 **8.** $(-4)^2$ **9.** -4^2

10. $-(-2)^5$ **11.** 10^2 **12.** 10^3

Multiplying and Dividing by Powers of Ten
Multiply or Divide.

13. 100×7.32 **14.** 75.2×0.01 **15.** $204.8 \div 10{,}000$

16. $1.03 \div 0.001$ **17.** 0.001×0.7 **18.** $45.3 \div 0.1$

Multiplying Decimals and Dividing Decimals by Decimals
Multiply or Divide.

19. $22.4 \div 8$ **20.** 8.2×9.5 **21.** $25.85 \div 5.5$

22. $163.2 \div 17$ **23.** 6.5×0.4 **24.** 1.4×12.5

What You'll Learn Next

- In this chapter, you will write numbers in both standard form and scientific notation.

- You will multiply powers with the same base and numbers in scientific notation.

- You will divide powers with the same base and numbers in scientific notation.

- Applying what you learn, you will use scientific notation to describe and compare distances.

Key Vocabulary

- scientific notation (p. 66)

What You'll Learn

To write numbers in both standard form and scientific notation

New Vocabulary scientific notation

Why Learn This?

When you are dealing with very large or very small numbers in science, it is helpful to be able to write them in a shorter form.

Written in standard form, or standard notation, the volume of Earth is about 259,000,000,000 cubic miles. Using scientific notation, you can write the number as 2.59×10^{11}.

Scientific Notation		**Standard Form**
2.59×10^{11}	=	$259,000,000,000$

KEY CONCEPTS **Scientific Notation**

A number is in **scientific notation** if the first factor is greater than or equal to 1 and less than 10 and the second factor is a power of 10.

Examples 1×10^8 1.54×10^7 9.99×10^4

Multiplying a number by 10^n, when n is positive, moves the decimal point n places to the right.

EXAMPLE **Writing in Standard Form**

1 **Science** The temperature at the sun's core is about 1.55×10^7 degrees Celsius. Write the temperature in standard form.

$$1.55 \times 10^7 = 1.5500000. \leftarrow \text{Move the decimal point 7 places to the right.}$$
$$\text{Insert zeros as necessary.}$$
$$= 15,500,000$$

The temperature at the sun's core is 15,500,000°C.

 Calculator Tip

1.55E7 on a calculator means 1.55×10^7.

✓ **Quick Check**

1. Write 7.66×10^6 km², the area of Australia, in standard form.

To write a number in scientific notation, determine the first factor. Then write the second factor as a power of 10.

EXAMPLE **Writing in Scientific Notation**

2 A supercomputer can perform 135,300,000,000,000 operations per second. Write this quantity in scientific notation.

$135{,}300{,}000{,}000{,}000 = 1.35{,}300{,}000{,}000{,}000.$ ← **Move the decimal point 14 places to the left.**

$= 1.353 \times 10^{14}$ ← **Use 14 as the exponent of 10.**

The supercomputer can perform 1.353×10^{14} operations per second.

✓ Quick Check

2. Write 3,476,000 m, the moon's diameter, in scientific notation.

Numbers in scientific notation can have negative exponents. Multiplying a number by 10^n, when n is negative, moves the decimal point n places to the left.

EXAMPLE **Scientific Notation With Negative Exponents**

3 **Biology** Fingernails grow about 1.23×10^{-2} centimeter per day. Write this rate in standard form.

$1.23 \times 10^{-2} = .01.23$ ← **Move the decimal point 2 places to the left to make 1.23 less than 1.**

Fingernails grow about 0.0123 centimeter per day.

✓ Quick Check

3. Write 2.5×10^{-4} inch, the diameter of a cell, in standard form.

To write a number that is less than 1 in scientific notation, determine the first factor by moving the decimal point. Then write the second factor as a negative power of ten.

EXAMPLE **Numbers Less Than 1**

4 Write the quantity 0.0000076 in scientific notation.

$0.0000076 = 0.000007.6$ ← **Move the decimal point 6 places to the right to get a factor greater than 1 but less than 10.**

$= 7.6 \times 10^{-6}$ ← **Use −6 as the exponent of 10.**

✓ Quick Check

4. Write 0.0000035 in scientific notation.

1. **Vocabulary** A number is in scientific notation if the first factor is greater than or equal to _?_ and less than 10.

2. **Reasoning** Explain why 1.55×10^6 does not have six zeros when it is written in standard form.

3. **Number Sense** Is 8×10^{-5} greater than or less than 0? Explain.

4. When 123.4 and 654.321 are written in scientific notation, will the exponents of 10 be the same? Explain.

Homework Exercises

For more exercises, see Extra Skills and Word Problems.

Write each number in standard form.

5. 3×10^3 6. 5.08×10^4 7. 4.1×10^8 8. 7.145×10^9

9. **Whales** Write the average weight of a blue whale, 2.6×10^5 lb, in standard form.

Write each number in scientific notation.

10. 4,000   11. 17,200   12. 180,000   13. 343,502

14. **Space Travel** NASA's Apollo program lasted nine years (1963–1972) and included six moon landings. Write the cost of the Apollo project, $25,000,000,000, in scientific notation.

Write each number in standard form.

15. 2.5×10^{-3} 16. 5.12×10^{-5} 17. 1.05×10^{-2} 18. 3×10^{-7}

19. Write the size of a grain of very fine sand, about 9.35×10^{-3} cm, in standard form.

Write each number in scientific notation.

20. 0.00581   21. 0.00105   22. 0.0000078

23. 0.00002   24. 0.000000132   25. 0.000000009

GPS 26. **Guided Problem Solving** The human eye's retina has about 130 million light-sensitive cells. Write this number in scientific notation.
- What is 130 million written in standard form?
- Should you move the decimal point to the right or to the left?
- How many places should you move the decimal point?

GO for Help

For Exercises	See Example
5–9	1
10–14	2
15–19	3
20–25	4

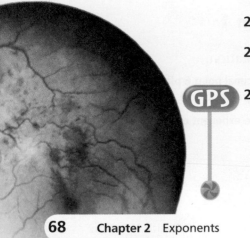

Find each value of n.

27. $1.0035 \times 10^n = 100,350,000$

28. $56,194 = n \times 10^4$

29. $0.000008 = 8 \times 10^n$

30. $n \times 10^{-9} = 0.000000004802$

31. The population of the United States is expected to be 392 million people by 2050. Write this number in scientific notation.

32. Error Analysis Explain how you know that 492×10^5 is not in scientific notation.

33. Astronomy When the sun emits a solar flare, the blast wave can travel through space at 3×10^6 km/h. Use the formula $d = rt$ to find how far the wave will travel in 30 min.

34. Which number is greater, 3.14×10^{99} or 3×10^{100}?

35. Heat For a 10-minute shower, you use about 5,500 kilocalories to heat 50 gallons of water. (The prefix *kilo-* means 1,000 or 10^3.)
a. About how many calories do you use in a 5-minute shower?
b. Write your answer to part (a) in scientific notation.

36. Writing in Math A number written in scientific notation is multiplied by 100. Explain what happens to the exponent of 10.

37. Challenge Write $10^{29} - 10^{28}$ in scientific notation.

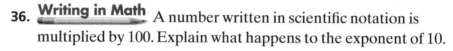

Test Prep and Mixed Review   **Practice**

Multiple Choice

38. The moon is about 380,000 kilometers from Earth. Which expression represents this measurement in scientific notation?
Ⓐ 3.8×10^3 km
Ⓒ 3.8×10^5 km
Ⓑ 3.8×10^4 km
Ⓓ 3.8×10^6 km

39. The temperature was -2.7 degrees Celsius at 7 A.M. and 9.2 degrees Celsius at 1 P.M. What is the difference between the two temperatures?
Ⓕ 6.5 degrees
Ⓗ 11.5 degrees
Ⓖ 6.9 degrees
Ⓙ 11.9 degrees

40. Maya grows 18 plants in her garden. Some are tomatoes, and the rest are squash. She grows twice as many tomato plants as squash plants. How many squash plants does she grow?
Ⓐ 3
Ⓑ 6
Ⓒ 9
Ⓓ 12

GO for Help

For Exercises	See Lesson
41–43	1-10

Solve each equation.

41. $x^3 = 512$

42. $x^3 = \dfrac{8}{125}$

43. $x^3 = \dfrac{1}{729}$

Writing Measurements

When you write very large or very small numbers in scientific notation, you write the numbers as multiples of powers of ten. In the metric system of measurement, you can use prefixes to indicate powers of ten. The table shows common prefixes and their meanings.

For example, the prefix *kilo-* means 10^3. You can write 2 kilometers as 2×10^3, or 2,000, meters. Similarly, you can write 4,000 meters as 4×10^3 meters, or 4 kilometers. Note that the symbol for kilo- is *k*, so the abbreviation for kilometers is km.

Prefix	Symbol	Meaning
micro-	μ	10^{-6}
milli-	m	10^{-3}
centi-	c	10^{-2}
kilo-	k	10^3
mega-	M	10^6

ACTIVITY

1. Use a metric prefix to write 3,100 grams (g) in kilograms (kg).

2. Use a metric prefix to write 0.0052 meters (m) in millimeters (mm).

3. Use a metric prefix to write 64,200,000 bytes (b) in megabytes (Mb).

4. Copy the table below. Fill in each of the facts about Thomson's gazelles using both scientific notation and metric prefixes.

Thomson's Gazelles

Characteristic	Measure	Scientific Notation	Metric Prefixes
Average mass	21,500 g	■ g	■
Average height	0.63 m	■ m	■
Possible diameter of a single hair	0.00005 m	■ m	■
Distance a herd can travel in a day	16,000 m	■ m	■

5. Make a table like the one above for an animal or insect of your choice. Write all measures using both scientific notation and metric prefixes.

6. The average diameter of a human hair is about 80 micrometers. Use scientific notation or measurements with metric prefixes to compare it to the diameter of a gazelle's hair. Explain your choice.

7. Suppose you want to compare the mass of an elephant to the mass of a whale. Would you write the measures in scientific notation or using metric prefixes? Explain your choice.

Exploring Exponents

You can explore the properties of exponents by looking for patterns.

ACTIVITY

1. Copy and complete the table below.

Two Exponents	Product as a Repeated Factor	Standard Form	Single Exponent
$2^1 \cdot 2^1$	$2 \cdot 2$	4	2^2
$2^1 \cdot 2^2$	■	■	■
$2^2 \cdot 2^2$	$2 \cdot 2 \cdot 2 \cdot 2$	16	■
$2^2 \cdot 2^3$	■	■	■

2. **a. Patterns** Look at the first row in the table. What relationship do you see between the sum of the exponents in the first cell and the exponent in the last cell?

   b. Does this relationship hold for the other rows in the table?

3. Add the following rows to your table and fill in the missing cells.

$3^3 \cdot 3^4$	■	■	■
$5^5 \cdot 5^2$	■	■	■
$x^2 \cdot x^3$	■	■	■

4. Based on the pattern you observed in your table, write the product of $9^3 \cdot 9^8$ as a single exponent.

5. Write a general rule that you can use to find the product of two exponents such as $a^m \cdot a^n$.

Exercises

Write each expression using a single exponent. Check your answers.

1. $4^2 \cdot 4^2$ 2. $10 \cdot 10^2$

3. $b^3 \cdot b$ 4. $x^7 \cdot x^5$

2-2 Exponents and Multiplication

What You'll Learn

To multiply powers with the same base

Why Learn This?

Computer programmers often use exponents with base 2, base 8, or base 16 to express numbers. To perform calculations within these number systems, you need to know how to multiply with exponents.

You can write the expression $3^2 \cdot 3^4$ using a single exponent.

$$3^2 \cdot 3^4 = (3 \cdot 3)(3 \cdot 3 \cdot 3 \cdot 3) = 3^6$$

The two factors of 3 together with four factors of 3 give a total of six factors of 3. Notice that the exponent 6 is equal to the sum of the exponents 2 and 4.

KEY CONCEPTS Multiplying Powers With the Same Base

To multiply numbers or variables with the same base, add the exponents.

Arithmetic	**Algebra**
$3^2 \cdot 3^7 = 3^{(2 + 7)} = 3^9$	$a^m \cdot a^n = a^{(m + n)}$

Vocabulary Tip

The word *power* can be used in two ways. The expression a^n is a power. You can also read a^n as "a to the nth power."

EXAMPLE Multiplying Powers

1 Write the expression $(-2)^3 \cdot (-2)^5$ using a single exponent.

$$(-2)^3 \cdot (-2)^5 = (-2)^{(3 + 5)} \quad \leftarrow \text{Add the exponents.}$$
$$= (-2)^8 \quad \leftarrow \text{Simplify the exponent.}$$

✓ Quick Check

1. Write each expression using a single exponent.
  a. $6^2 \cdot 6^3$ **b.** $(-4) \cdot (-4)^7$ **c.** $3 \cdot 3^2 \cdot 3^3$

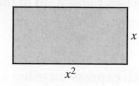 **Application: Geometry**

Vocabulary Tip

Terms raised to the second power are often referred to as *squared*, while terms to the third power are said to be *cubed*.

2 Multiple Choice Find the area of the rectangle.

x^2

x

Ⓐ x^2 Ⓑ x^3 Ⓒ $2x^2$ Ⓓ $2x^3$

Recall that the area of a rectangle is $A = \ell \cdot w$, where ℓ is the length and w is the width.

Let $\ell = x^2$ and $w = x$.

$A = \ell \cdot w$ ← Write the area formula.

$A = x^2 \cdot x$ ← Substitute x^2 for ℓ and x for w.

$A = x^{(2+1)}$ ← Add the exponents.

$A = x^3$ ← Simplify.

The area of the rectangle is $A = x^3$.

The correct answer is choice B.

✓ Quick Check

2. A square has a side length of n^3. Find the area of the square.

n^3

EXAMPLE Using the Commutative Property

📱 **Calculator Tip**

When using a calculator to evaluate expressions with exponents, be sure to use parentheses when needed.

3 Simplify the expression $-3x^2 \cdot 5x^4$.

$-3x^2 \cdot 5x^4 = -3 \cdot 5 \cdot x^2 \cdot x^4$ ← Use the Commutative Property of Multiplication.

$= -15x^{(2+4)}$ ← Add the exponents of powers with the same base.

$= -15x^6$ ← Simplify.

✓ Quick Check

3. Simplify each expression.
   a. $2a^2 \cdot 3a$ **b.** $x^{10} \cdot x^3$ **c.** $-4y^5 \cdot -3y^5$

For Exercises 1 and 2, fill in the blank.

1. $(8)^3 \cdot (\blacksquare^4) = 8^7$

2. $5^3 \cdot 5^{\blacksquare} = 5^6$

Write each expression using a single exponent.

3. $(-6)^2 \cdot (-6)^2$

4. $(-2)^8 \cdot (-2)^3$

5. $7^2 \cdot 7^8$

6. $4^5 \cdot 4^6$

7. **Error Analysis** A student simplified $5^2 \cdot 5^4$. His work is shown below. Explain the student's error.

$$5^2 \cdot 5^4 = 5 \cdot 5^{(2+4)} = 25^6$$

8. **Mental Math** Write a product of two powers that is equal to 3^6.

Homework Exercises

For more exercises, see Extra Skills and Word Problems.

Write each expression using a single exponent.

GO for Help

For Exercises	See Example
9–16	1
17	2
22–33	3

9. $y^3 \cdot y^5$

10. $m^{10} \cdot m^{100}$

11. $3.4^3 \cdot 3.4^{10}$

12. $12^5 \cdot 12^{50}$

13. $4.5^{10} \cdot 4.5^{10}$

14. $(-5)^5 \cdot (-5)$

15. $0.4^5 \cdot 0.4^{10}$

16. $x \cdot x^0$

17. **Earth Science** The Hudson River in New York is about 2^9 km long. The Columbia River in Oregon is 2^2 times longer. How long is the Columbia River? Write your answer with exponents.

18. **Guided Problem Solving** An architect is designing a deck. It will be $5x$ ft long and $2x$ ft wide. Write an expression for the area of the deck when it is completed.
    - Use the area formula $A = \ell w$.
    - Simplify the expression.

19. **Open-Ended** Give three different ways to write 4^{12} as the product of two powers.

20. **Writing in Math** Explain why you *cannot* write $5^3 \cdot 7^9$ as $(35)^{12}$.

21. Double the number 2^5. Write your answer as a single exponent.

Write each expression using a single exponent.

22. $4^x \cdot 4^t$ 23. $3^m \cdot 3^n$ 24. $1.5^8 \cdot 1.5^t$

25. $(-4)^x \cdot (-4)^y$ 26. $2^3 \cdot 2 \cdot 2^8$ 27. $a^5 \cdot a^4 \cdot a$

28. $9^{12} \cdot 9^6 \cdot 9^3$ 29. $3^a \cdot 3^{2a} \cdot 3^{3a}$ 30. $xy \cdot x^2y^3$

31. $c^2d \cdot cd^3$ 32. $x \cdot x^3 \cdot x^5$ 33. $3x^2 \cdot x^5 \cdot x$

34. **Geometry** The formula for the area of a square is $A = s^2$.
    What is the area of a square with sides that are $3x^2$ cm?

Use <, >, or = to complete each statement.

35. $4^6 \ \blacksquare \ 4^3 \cdot 4^2$ 36. $36 \ \blacksquare \ 6^2 \cdot 6^2$ 37. $5^{16} \ \blacksquare \ 5^8 \cdot 5^2$

38. A milligram is 10^{-3} grams. A kilogram is 10^3 grams. How many
    milligrams are in a kilogram?

39. **Challenge** If $(h + h) \cdot (h \cdot h) = 16$, what is the value of h?

Test Prep and Mixed Review   Practice

Multiple Choice

40. Look for a pattern in the table at
    the right. Based on the pattern in
    the table, what value of x makes the
    statement $4^{15} = 2^x$ true?

Powers of 4	Powers of 2
$4^2 = 16$	$2^4 = 16$
$4^3 = 64$	$2^6 = 64$
$4^4 = 256$	$2^8 = 256$
$4^5 = 1024$	$2^{10} = 1024$

    Ⓐ 15
    Ⓑ 20
    Ⓒ 30
    Ⓓ 7.5

41. According to a 2013 estimate, the population of India is about 1,220,800,000.
    Which is India's population written in scientific notation?

    Ⓕ 1.2208×10^7
    Ⓖ 1.2208×10^8
    Ⓗ 1.2208×10^9
    Ⓙ 1.2208×10^{10}

Find each quotient.

42. $-3\frac{1}{2} \div 1\frac{1}{4}$ 43. $30.6 \div -0.18$ 44. $12\frac{4}{5} \div -3\frac{1}{5}$

GO for Help

For Exercises	See Lesson
42–44	1-8

2-3 Multiplying with Scientific Notation

© **CONTENT STANDARD**

8.EE.4

GO for Help

For help with scientific notation, go to Lesson 2-1, Example 2.

What You'll Learn

To multiply numbers written in scientific notation and choose appropriate units of measure

Why Learn This?

Astronomers use scientific notation when they work with very large numbers. To calculate using scientific notation, you must know how to multiply with exponents.

The rule for multiplying powers with the same base applies to multiplying numbers in scientific notation.

EXAMPLE Multiplying With Scientific Notation

1. Multiply $(5 \times 10^6)(9 \times 10^3)$. Write the product in scientific notation.

$$(5 \times 10^6)(9 \times 10^3) = (5 \times 9) \times (10^6 \times 10^3) \leftarrow \text{Use the associative and commutative properties.}$$
$$= 45 \times (10^6 \times 10^3) \leftarrow \text{Multiply 5 and 9.}$$
$$= 45 \times 10^9 \leftarrow \text{Add the exponents of the powers of 10.}$$
$$= 4.5 \times 10^1 \times 10^9 \leftarrow \text{Write 45 in scientific notation.}$$
$$= 4.5 \times 10^{10} \leftarrow \text{Add the exponents.}$$

✓ Quick Check

1. Multiply. Write each product in scientific notation.

   a. $(2 \times 10^6)(4 \times 10^3)$ **b.** $(3 \times 10^5)(2 \times 10^8)$ **c.** $12(8 \times 10^{20})$

Multiplying large or small numbers in scientific notation is easier than multiplying the same numbers in standard form.

EXAMPLE **Application: Science**

2 **Multiple Choice** A light-year, the distance light travels in one Earth year, is about 5.9×10^{12} miles. A mile is 5.28×10^3 feet. How many feet are in a light-year?

(A) 31.2×10^{15} (C) 3.12×10^{15}

(B) 31.2×10^{16} (D) 3.12×10^{16}

$(5.9 \times 10^{12})(5.28 \times 10^3)$ ← **Multiply by the conversion factor.**

$(5.9 \times 5.28) \times (10^{12} \times 10^3)$ ← **Associative and Commutative properties**

$31.2 \times (10^{12} \times 10^3)$ ← **Multiply 5.9 and 5.28. Round to the nearest tenth.**

31.2×10^{15} ← **Add the exponents of the powers of 10.**

$(3.12 \times 10^1) \times 10^{15}$ ← **Write 31.2 in scientific notation.**

3.12×10^{16} ← **Add the exponents.**

There are 3.12×10^{16} feet in a light-year. The correct answer is choice D.

✓ **Quick Check**

2. **Astronomy** The speed of light is about 3.0×10^5 kilometers/second. Use the formula $d = r \cdot t$ to find the distance light travels in an hour, which is 3.6×10^3 seconds.

Often the size of the unit is close to the measurement of the object. You can also choose units that are much greater or smaller by multiplying with scientific notation.

EXAMPLE **Choosing Units with Scientific Notation**

3 Choose the most reasonable unit to describe the quantity. Then use scientific notation to describe the quantity using the other unit.

   a. The mass of a nickel is 5 _____. (g, mg) 5 g

$$5 \text{ g} \times \left(\frac{10^3 \text{ mg}}{1 \text{ g}} \right) = 5 \times 10^3 \text{ mg} \quad \leftarrow \textbf{Multiply by a conversion factor.}$$

   b. The length of a football field is about 91 _____. (km, m) 91 m

$$91 \text{ m} \times \left(\frac{10^{-3} \text{ km}}{1 \text{ m}} \right) = 91 \times 10^{-3} \text{ km} \quad \leftarrow \textbf{Multiply by a conversion factor.}$$

$$= 9.1 \times 10^{-2} \text{ km} \quad \leftarrow \textbf{Simplify.}$$

✓ **Quick Check**

3. Choose the most reasonable unit to describe the quantity. Then use scientific notation to describe the quantity using the other unit.

   A pencil is 7 _____ long. (cm, m)

For Exercises 1–4, fill in the blank.

1. $(3 \times 10^4)(6 \times 10^{12}) = 1.8 \times 10^{\blacksquare}$

2. $7(1.8 \times 10^7) = \blacksquare \times 10^8$

3. $(1.9 \times 10^5)(6.4 \times 10^3) = 1.216 \times \blacksquare^9$

4. $5(3.2 \times 10^7) = 1.6 \times 10^{\blacksquare}$

5. The speed of light is about 3.00×10^5 km/s. A kilometer is about 0.621 mi. Written in scientific notation, what is the speed of light in miles per second?

6. **Reasoning** Choose the most reasonable unit to complete each of the following sentences. Then use scientific notation to describe each quantity using another unit.
   a. The distance between two cities is 36 _____. (m, km)
   b. The mass of a teaspoon of salt is 6 _____. (g, kg)

For more exercises, see Extra Skills and Word Problems.

Multiply. Write each product in scientific notation.

GO for Help

For Exercises	See Examples
7–12	1, 2
13–14	3
15	2

7. $(2 \times 10^3)(4 \times 10^6)$

8. $(7 \times 10^2)(9 \times 10^5)$

9. $90(8 \times 10^9)$

10. $(3 \times 10^5)(5 \times 10^7)$

11. $(9 \times 10^5)(5 \times 10^9)$

12. $(5.1 \times 10^4)(2 \times 10^7)$

Choose the most reasonable unit to describe the quantity. Then use scientific notation to describe the quantity using the other unit.

13. The thickness of a quarter is 1.75 _____. (cm, mm)

14. The mass of a banana is 2×10^2 _____. (g, kg)

15. **Earth Science** There are about 4.8×10^{19} ft^3 of water on Earth. One cubic foot of water contains about 9.47×10^{26} water molecules. About how many water molecules are there on Earth?

GPS **16.** **Guided Problem Solving** Einstein's famous equation states that $E = mc^2$. E represents energy, m represents mass, and c represents the speed of light. Find the value of E (in joules) when m is equal to 1 kilogram and c is equal to 3.0×10^8 meters per second.
   • How can you write Einstein's law without using exponents?
   • Evaluate c^2 for $c = 3.0 \times 10^8$.

17. **Open-Ended** The area of a small garden is 8 m². Write this area in two other ways using different units and scientific notation.

18. **Writing in Math** Explain why multiplying large or small numbers in scientific notation is easier than multiplying the same numbers in standard form.

19. Double the number 3.4×10^{12}. Write the answer in scientific notation.

20. **Geography** The Sahara is a desert of about 3.5 million square miles. There are about 2.79×10^7 square feet in a square mile. About how many square feet does the Sahara cover? Write your answer in scientific notation.

21. **Chemistry** The mass of an electron is about 9.1×10^{-31} kg. A kilogram is equal to 1×10^6 mg. What is the mass of an electron in milligrams?

22. The radius of Venus is about 6.05×10^3 km. Use the formula S.A. $= 4\pi r^2$ to approximate the surface area of Venus.

23. **Challenge** What is $(9.7 \times 10^{-5})(7.8 \times 10^5)(3.3 \times 10^{10})$?

Test Prep and Mixed Review
Practice

Multiple Choice

24. The volume of Earth is 1.08×10^{12} km³. The volume of Jupiter is 1,320 times that of Earth. Which is NOT a way to express the volume of Jupiter in cubic kilometers?
    - Ⓐ 142.6×10^{13}
    - Ⓒ 14.26×10^{13}
    - Ⓑ 14.3×10^{14}
    - Ⓓ 1.43×10^{15}

25. Which statement below is true?
    - Ⓕ $1.5 \times 10^2 = 1.5 \times 10^{-2}$
    - Ⓗ $1.5 \times 10^2 < 1.5 \times 10^{-2}$
    - Ⓖ $1.5 \times 10^2 = 15 \times 10$
    - Ⓙ $1.5 \times 10^2 > 5.1 \times 10^3$

GO for Help

For Exercises	See Lesson
26–28	1-10

Solve each equation by finding the value of x.

26. $x^3 = 216$

27. $x^3 = \dfrac{64}{27}$

28. $x^3 = \dfrac{343}{1000}$

Calculations With Scientific Notation

Calculators use scientific notation as a shorthand way to write very large numbers. If you enter a number with too many digits for a calculator to display, the calculator will use scientific notation to display the rounded number.

2346549887051 [ENTER] *2.346549887E12* ← The display shows the number rounded.

The number in the display is $2.346549887 \times 10^{12}$. The 12 after the E is the exponent on 10.

You can use your calculator to simplify expressions in scientific notation.

EXAMPLES **Calculating With Scientific Notation**

1 Use a calculator to find $(7.6 \times 10^6)(3.52 \times 10^3)$.

$(7.6 \times 10^6) (3.52 \times 10^3)$

7.6 [EE] 6 [X] 3.52 [EE] 3 ← Use [EE] to enter the exponent of the power of 10.

2.6752E10

The product is 2.6752×10^{10}.

2 Use a calculator to find $(2.8 \times 10^{12}) + (4.9 \times 10^{15})$.

2.8 [EE] 12 [+] 4.9 [EE] 15

4.9028E15

The sum is 4.9028×10^{15}.

Exercises

Use a calculator to simplify. Write your answer in scientific notation.

1. $(3.5 \times 10^{12})(2.3 \times 10^9)$

2. $(2.99 \times 10^{16})(4.36 \times 10^{12})$

3. $(2.75 \times 10^4)^2$

4. $(5.54 \times 10^6) + (1.38 \times 10^6)$

5. $(4.02 \times 10^{13}) - (2.01 \times 10^{13})$

6. $(9.22 \times 10^{11})^3$

7. Mental Math Simplify 10^{20}. Check your answer with a calculator.

8. Find the area of a square with side length 1.5×10^4 units.

Write each number in standard form.

1. 6×10^5 **2.** 8.02×10^{-4} **3.** 4×10^{-3}

Write each number in scientific notation.

4. 90,000   **5.** 3,900   **6.** 0.00301

Write each expression using a single exponent.

7. $4.7^6 \cdot 4.7^{15}$ **8.** $(-4a)^2(-4a)^2$ **9.** $xy^5 \cdot x^3 y^7$

Multiply. Write each product in scientific notation.

10. $50(6 \times 10^3)$ **11.** $(3 \times 10^7)(5 \times 10^4)$ **12.** $(4 \times 10^4)(9 \times 10^2)$

Simplify each expression.

13. $7f^5 \cdot 4f^3$ **14.** $(3.1g^6)(5g^2)$ **15.** $(-8h^8)(2.2h^{10})$

16. Choose the most reasonable unit to describe the quantity. Then use scientific notation to describe the quantity using the other unit. The diameter of a quarter is about 2.4 _____. (cm, km)

MATH AT WORK

Automotive Mechanic

Automotive mechanics diagnose and repair mechanical problems. An automotive mechanic must inspect a car and analyze its problems to determine the necessary adjustments to make.

The ability to reason is a skill that an auto mechanic uses to diagnose problems quickly and accurately. Mechanics also use estimating skills to determine the approximate cost of repairs. The mechanic wants to make sure that he or she charges enough for the work, yet does not overcharge the customer.

Go Online For more information on automotive mechanics
PearsonSuccessNet.com

What You'll Learn

To divide powers with the same base and to simplify expressions with negative exponents

Why Learn This?

Nanorobots are microscopic machines that may soon be used to fight illness inside the human body. When working with very small numbers, such as the length of a nanorobot, you often divide expressions with exponents.

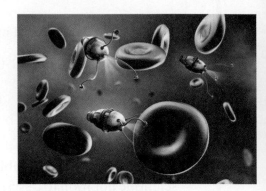

You can divide powers with the same base by writing out all the factors.

$$\frac{7^5}{7^3} = \frac{\cancel{7}^1 \cdot \cancel{7}^1 \cdot \cancel{7}^1 \cdot 7 \cdot 7}{{}_1\cancel{7} \cdot {}_1\cancel{7} \cdot {}_1\cancel{7}} = \frac{7 \cdot 7}{1} = 7^2$$

Notice that $5 - 3 = 2$. This example suggests the following rule.

KEY CONCEPTS **Dividing Powers With the Same Base**

To divide nonzero numbers or variables with the same nonzero base, subtract the exponents.

Arithmetic	**Algebra**
$\frac{8^5}{8^3} = 8^{(5-3)} = 8^2$	$\frac{a^m}{a^n} = a^{(m-n)}$, where $a \neq 0$

EXAMPLE **Dividing Powers**

1 Write $\frac{m^{12}}{m^5}$ using a single exponent.

$$\frac{m^{12}}{m^5} = m^{(12-5)} \qquad \leftarrow \text{Subtract exponents with the same base.}$$
$$= m^7 \qquad\qquad \leftarrow \text{Simplify.}$$

✓ Quick Check

● **1.** Write $\frac{w^8}{w^5}$ using a single exponent.

What does the exponent 0 mean? Consider finding the quotient $\frac{3^5}{3^5}$.

If you subtract exponents, $\frac{3^5}{3^5} = 3^{(5-5)} = 3^0$.

If you write factors, $\quad \frac{3^5}{3^5} = \frac{\cancel{3}^1 \cdot \cancel{3}^1 \cdot \cancel{3}^1 \cdot \cancel{3}^1 \cdot \cancel{3}^1}{_1\cancel{3} \cdot _1\cancel{3} \cdot _1\cancel{3} \cdot _1\cancel{3} \cdot _1\cancel{3}}$

$$= \frac{1}{1} = 1.$$

Notice that $\frac{3^5}{3^5} = 3^0$ and $\frac{3^5}{3^5} = 1$. This suggests the following rule.

Read 3^0 as "3 to the zero power."

KEY CONCEPTS   **Zero as an Exponent**

For any nonzero number a, $a^0 = 1$.

Example $9^0 = 1$

EXAMPLE   **Expressions With a Zero Exponent**

2 Simplify each expression.

   a. $(-8)^0$ **b.** $3m^0$

     $(-8)^0 = 1$ ← Simplify. → $3m^0 = 3 \cdot 1 = 3$

✓ Quick Check

2. Simplify each expression.

   a. $(-9)^0$ **b.** $(2r)^0$ **c.** $2r^0$

GO **nline**

Video Tutor Help

PearsonSuccessNet.com

To understand negative exponents, consider finding the quotient $\frac{6^2}{6^5}$.

If you subtract exponents, $\frac{6^2}{6^5} = 6^{(2-5)} = 6^{-3}$.

If you write factors, $\frac{6^2}{6^5} = \frac{\cancel{6}^1 \cdot \cancel{6}^1}{_1\cancel{6} \cdot _1\cancel{6} \cdot 6 \cdot 6 \cdot 6}$

$$= \frac{1}{6 \cdot 6 \cdot 6} = \frac{1}{6^3}.$$

Notice that $\frac{6^2}{6^5} = 6^{-3}$ and $\frac{6^2}{6^5} = \frac{1}{6^3}$. This suggests the following rule.

KEY CONCEPTS   **Negative Exponents**

For any nonzero number a and integer n, $a^{-n} = \frac{1}{a^n}$.

Example $8^{-5} = \frac{1}{8^5}$

To simplify an expression with negative exponents, you can first write the expression with a positive exponent.

EXAMPLE **Expressions With Negative Exponents**

3 Simplify each expression.

a. 3^{-2} **b.** $(y)^{-6}$

$3^{-2} = \dfrac{1}{3^2}$ ← Use a positive exponent. → $(y)^{-6} = \dfrac{1}{y^6}$

$= \dfrac{1}{9}$ ← Simplify.

✓ Quick Check

3. Simplify each expression.

a. 3^{-1} **b.** w^{-4} **c.** $(-2)^{-3}$

● More Than One Way

Simplify the expression $4^3 \cdot 4^{-5}$.

Tina's Method

I can rewrite the expression with positive exponents.

$4^3 \cdot 4^{-5} = 4^3 \cdot \dfrac{1}{4^5}$ ← Use a positive exponent.

$= \dfrac{4^3}{4^5}$ ← Multiply fractions.

$= 4^{(3-5)}$ ← Subtract exponents with the same base.

$= 4^{-2}$ ← Simplify.

$= \dfrac{1}{4^2}$ ← Use a positive exponent.

$= \dfrac{1}{16}$ ← Simplify.

So the expression is equal to $\dfrac{1}{16}$.

Eric's Method

To multiply numbers with the same base, I can add the exponents.

$4^3 \cdot 4^{-5} = 4^{(3 + (-5))}$ ← Add the exponents.

$= 4^{-2}$ ← Simplify.

$= \dfrac{1}{4^2}$ ← Use a positive exponent.

$= \dfrac{1}{16}$ ← Simplify.

So the expression is equal to $\dfrac{1}{16}$.

Choose a Method

Simplify the expression $5^2 \cdot 5^{-5}$.

1. **Reasoning** Is $(-1)^0$ a positive or a negative number? Explain.

2. **Mental Math** Find the value of $\dfrac{123^5}{123^4}$.

Write out the factors of each expression. Then simplify using a single exponent. Exercise 3 has been started for you.

3. $\dfrac{2^6}{2^5} = \dfrac{2 \cdot 2 \cdot 2 \cdot 2 \cdot 2 \cdot 2}{2 \cdot 2 \cdot 2 \cdot 2 \cdot 2}$

4. $\dfrac{3^4}{3^2}$

5. $\dfrac{8^5}{8^2}$

Homework Exercises

For more exercises, see Extra Skills and Word Problems.

GO for Help

For Exercises	See Examples
6–13	1
14–22	2-3

Write each expression using a single exponent.

6. $\dfrac{a^5}{a^3}$

7. $\dfrac{x^9}{x^5}$

8. $\dfrac{c^7}{c^2}$

9. $\dfrac{(-1)^5}{(-1)^4}$

10. $\dfrac{23^{12}}{23^8}$

11. $\dfrac{135^{10}}{135^1}$

12. $\dfrac{(-7)^{99}}{(-7)^{98}}$

13. $\dfrac{(-9)^{32}}{(-9)^{15}}$

14. **Zoology** The slowest mammal on Earth is the sloth. A sloth might move along a tree at a maximum rate of just 3^{-1} m each minute. At this rate, how long will it take a sloth to climb a tree that is 33 m tall?

Simplify each expression.

15. 4^0

16. $(-3)^0$

17. u^0

18. $(3t)^0$

19. 10^{-2}

20. b^{-6}

21. x^{-4}

22. 7^{-1}

23. **Guided Problem Solving** Snow is falling at an average rate of 2^{-2} cm each hour. At this rate, how long will it take 2^2 cm of snow to fall?
   - **Make a Plan** Use the formula time $= \dfrac{\text{distance}}{\text{rate}}$.
   - **Carry Out the Plan** Divide powers with the same base. Simplify.

24. **Earth Science** Earth's crust is divided into large pieces called tectonic plates. The Pacific tectonic plate is moving northwest at a rate of about 4^{-2} m each year. At this rate, how long will it take the plate to move 4^6 m (about 2.5 miles)?

GO Online
Homework Video Tutor
PearsonSuccessNet.com

Complete each equation.

25. $\dfrac{4^{\blacksquare}}{4^2} = 4^{10}$

26. $\dfrac{x^6}{x^{\blacksquare}} = x^4$

27. $\dfrac{14x^5}{7x^3} = 2x^{\blacksquare}$

28. $\dfrac{1}{c^7} = c^{\blacksquare}$

Use $w = -1$ and $x = 2$. Simplify each expression.

29. $(w + x)^{-4}$

30. x^w

31. $-2^{w + 2x}$

32. $(2x)^{w + 1}$

33. Error Analysis A student wrote that $-3^0 = 1$. What error did the student make?

Writing in Math Is each statement *true* or *false*? Explain your reasoning.

34. $4^0 = 4^{-1}$

35. $8^{-1} = (-8)^1$

36. $2^1 \cdot 2^{-1} = 2^0$

37. $(-2)^{-1} = 2$

38. Astronomy The Moon is moving away from Earth at a rate of more than 3^{-5} m each year. At this rate, how long will it take the Moon to move 34 m away from Earth?

39. Challenge You can divide a polynomial by a monomial by dividing each term of the numerator by the denominator.

Sample $\dfrac{6x^4 + 10x^3}{2x^2} = \dfrac{6x^4}{2x^2} + \dfrac{10x^3}{2x^2}$
$= 3x^2 + 5x$

a. $\dfrac{6n^5 - 12n^2}{3n^2}$

b. $\dfrac{4m^9 + 6m^6 + 2m^3}{2m^3}$

Test Prep and Mixed Review

Practice

Gridded Response

40. A garden snail is moving at a rate of 4^{-3} m/s. At this speed, how many seconds will it take the snail to move across a garden that is 4^2 m wide?

41. A certain pattern, or rule, is represented by the ordered pairs in the table below. What is the value of y when $x = 12$?

x	1	3	5	7
y	-2	7	23	47

42. Molly's teacher gave her a score of $\dfrac{27}{40}$ on her math test. What decimal is equivalent to the score Molly received? Round your answer to the nearest whole percent.

Find the square roots of each number.

For Exercises	See Lesson
43–46	1-9

43. 121

44. 625

45. $\dfrac{1}{144}$

46. $\dfrac{1}{81}$

Power Rules

You can use the rules for multiplying exponents to simplify an expression such as $(4^3)^2$.

$$(4^3)^2 = 4^3 \cdot 4^3$$
$$= 4^{(3 + 3)} = 4^6$$

Since $6 = 3 \cdot 2$, $(4^3)^2 = 4^{(3 \cdot 2)} = 4^6$. This suggests that to raise a power to a power, you multiply the exponents.

EXAMPLE   Raising a Power to a Power

1 Write each expression using a single exponent.

a. $(3^{-4})^5$

$(3^{-4})^5 = 3^{(-4 \cdot 5)}$
$= 3^{-20}$

b. $(x^{-2})^{-3}$

$(x^{-2})^{-3} = x^{(-2 \cdot -3)}$
$= x^6$

You can raise a product to a power using repeated multiplication.

$(2w)^3 = (2w) \cdot (2w) \cdot (2w)$ ← Write out the factors of the power.

$= 2 \cdot 2 \cdot 2 \cdot w \cdot w \cdot w$ ← Use the Commutative Property to rearrange the factors.

$= 2^3 \cdot w^3 = 2^3w^3$ ← Write the factors as a product.

Notice that $(2w)^3 = 2^3w^3$. This suggests that to raise a product to a power, you raise each factor to the power.

EXAMPLE   Raising a Product to a Power

2 Simplify $(3y^3)^2$.

$(3y^3)^2 = 3^2(y^3)^2$
$= 3^2y^6 = 9y^6$

Exercises

Write each expression using a single exponent.

1. $(3^3)^7$

2. $(9^2)^{-5}$

3. $(w^{-2})^{-6}$

4. $(r^2)^3$

Simplify each expression.

5. $(3x)^2$

6. $(a^2b^3)^4$

7. $(10x^5)^2$

8. $(y^2 \cdot 2^2)^4$

Solving Equations

Rectangles based on the Golden Ratio ($1.618w : w$, where w is the width of the rectangle) are pleasing to the eye. Suppose you want a rectangular tiled patio using the Golden Ratio for a circular hot tub with a diameter that is one half of the rectangle's width. How many square feet of patio will be tiled if the patio's width is 25 feet?

What You Might Think

What do I know? What am I trying to find out?

How can I visualize the problem?

How can I write an equation for the area of the patio that needs to be tiled?

What is the area when $w = 25$?

What You Might Write

The patio has a length to width ratio of $1.618w : w$. A circle with diameter $\frac{1}{2}w$ is removed. I want to find the area of the patio when $w = 25$ feet.

Draw a diagram.

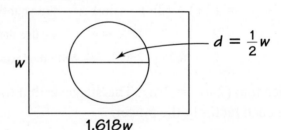

$$1.618w$$

Find the rectangle's area and subtract the circle's area. The radius of the circle is half the diameter. Use 3.14 for π.

$$\ell w - \pi r^2 = (1.618w)(w) - \pi(\tfrac{1}{4}w)^2$$
$$= 1.618w^2 - (3.14)\frac{w^2}{16}$$

$$1.618(25)^2 - (3.14)\frac{25^2}{16} = 888.59375$$

I will need about 889 square feet of tile.

Think It Through

1. In buying tile, you should buy 10% more than the area to be covered. Will 1,000 square feet be enough? Explain.

Exercises

Solve each problem. For Exercises 2 and 3, answer the questions first.

2. Wanda likes to set up and knock down dominoes arranged as shown at the right. She says you can find out how many dominoes you need for n rows by adding $1 + 2 + 3 + \ldots + n$. Jake says you can find it by evaluating $\frac{1}{2}(n^2 + n)$. Who is correct?

   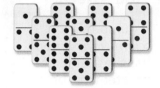

   a. What are you trying to find?

   b. Try both expressions for the first ten rows. What do you notice?

3. **Science** Gravitational pull varies among the different planets in our solar system. Since your weight depends on gravitational pull, it also varies from planet to planet. Use the table below to find your weight on Jupiter if you weigh 110 lb on Earth.

Planet	Gravitational Pull (compared to Earth)
Mercury	0.38
Venus	0.91
Mars	0.38
Jupiter	2.36
Saturn	0.91
Uranus	0.89
Neptune	1.12

   a. What do you know? What do you want to find out?

   b. How is your weight on Jupiter related to your weight on Earth?

4. On a clear day, the distance d in miles you can see across the ocean from a height of h feet is given by $h = \frac{2}{3}d^2$. Jaime is learning to parasail with his friends. If beginning parasailers usually go up about 150 feet, how far can Jaime see when he is in the air?

5. Suppose your father goes skydiving for his birthday. He jumps from a plane at 10,000 feet and opens his parachute at 5,000 feet. How much time passes before he opens his parachute? Use the equation $t = 0.25\sqrt{d}$, where t is the time in seconds a falling object takes to fall d feet.

Dividing with Scientific Notation

for Help

For help with scientific notation, go to Lesson 2-1, Example 1.

What You'll Learn

To divide and compare numbers written in scientific notation.

Why Learn This?

Earth's mass is almost 6×10^{24} kg, and the mass of Jupiter is almost 2×10^{27} kg. You can divide the mass of Jupiter by the mass of Earth to find how many times greater Jupiter's mass is than Earth's. The rule for dividing powers with the same base applies to dividing numbers in scientific notation.

EXAMPLE **Dividing Numbers in Scientific Notation**

1 Simplify $(6.5 \times 10^6) \div (7.3 \times 10^2)$. Write the quotient in scientific notation.

$$(6.5 \times 10^6) \div (7.3 \times 10^2) = \frac{6.5 \times 10^6}{7.3 \times 10^2} \qquad \leftarrow \text{Write a fraction.}$$

$$= \frac{6.5}{7.3} \times \frac{10^6}{10^2} \qquad \leftarrow \begin{array}{l}\text{Separate the coefficients}\\\text{and the powers of ten.}\end{array}$$

$$\approx 0.89 \times \frac{10^6}{10^2} \qquad \leftarrow \text{Divide the coefficients.}$$

$$= 0.89 \times 10^4 \qquad \leftarrow \text{Subtract the exponents.}$$

$$= 8.9 \times 10^{-1} \times 10^4 \qquad \leftarrow \begin{array}{l}\text{Write 0.89 in scientific}\\\text{notation.}\end{array}$$

$$= 8.9 \times 10^3 \qquad \leftarrow \text{Add the exponents.}$$

✓ Quick Check

1. Simplify. Write each quotient in scientific notation.

  a. $\dfrac{7.9 \times 10^5}{2.3 \times 10^3}$
  b. $\dfrac{4.8 \times 10^4}{2.95 \times 10^6}$
  c. $\dfrac{3.7 \times 10^7}{5.2 \times 10^2}$

EXAMPLE **Application: Astronomy**

2 **Gridded Response** The distance between the sun and a comet is about 2.79×10^8 miles. Light travels about 1.1×10^7 miles per minute. Use the formula time $= \frac{\text{distance}}{\text{speed}}$ to estimate how many minutes sunlight takes to reach the comet. Write your answer in standard form and round to the nearest tenth.

$$\text{time} = \frac{\text{distance}}{\text{speed}} \quad \leftarrow \textbf{Use the formula for time.}$$

$$= \frac{2.79}{1.1} \times \frac{10^8}{10^7} \quad \leftarrow \begin{array}{l}\textbf{Substitute. Write as a} \\ \textbf{product of quotients.}\end{array}$$

$$= \frac{2.79}{1.1} \times 10^1 \quad \leftarrow \textbf{Subtract exponents.}$$

$$\approx 2.54 \times 10^1 \quad \leftarrow \textbf{Divide.}$$

Sunlight takes about 2.54×10^1 minutes, or 25.4 minutes, to reach the comet.

✓ Quick Check

2. **Astronomy** The distance between the sun and Earth is about 9.3×10^7 miles. Light travels about 1.1×10^7 miles per minute. Estimate how long sunlight takes to reach Earth. Write your answer in standard form and round to the nearest tenth.

The rule for dividing numbers in scientific notation applies when one of the numbers is in standard form.

EXAMPLE **Dividing by Numbers in Standard Form**

3 Divide. Write each quotient in scientific notation.

a. $(-7.1 \times 10^3) \div 6.3 = \dfrac{-7.1 \times 10^3}{6.3} \quad \leftarrow \textbf{Write as a fraction.}$

$$= \frac{-7.1}{6.3} \times 10^3 \quad \leftarrow \begin{array}{l}\textbf{Write as a product of quotients} \\ \textbf{and a power of 10.}\end{array}$$

$$\approx -1.1 \times 10^3 \quad \leftarrow \textbf{Divide.}$$

b. $4.2 \div (5.5 \times 10^9) = \dfrac{4.2}{5.5 \times 10^9} \quad \leftarrow \textbf{Write as a fraction.}$

$$= \frac{4.2}{5.5} \times 10^{-9} \quad \leftarrow \begin{array}{l}\textbf{Write as a product of quotients} \\ \textbf{and a power of 10.}\end{array}$$

$$\approx 0.76 \times 10^{-9} \quad \leftarrow \textbf{Divide.}$$

$$= 7.6 \times 10^{-1} \times 10^{-9} \quad \leftarrow \textbf{Write 0.76 in scientific notation.}$$

$$= 7.6 \times 10^{-10} \quad \leftarrow \textbf{Add the exponents.}$$

✓ Quick Check

3. Divide. Write each quotient in scientific notation.

a. $\dfrac{6.2 \times 10^6}{4.1}$ **b.** $\dfrac{-3.5 \times 10^3}{5}$ **c.** $\dfrac{17}{1.4 \times 10^8}$

Vocabulary Tip

Remember that *ordering* can mean placing values in order from least to greatest *or* from greatest to least. Be sure to read the question carefully to determine which you need to do.

EXAMPLE Ordering Numbers

4 Order $6.2 \times 10^{-4}, 6.2 \times 10^4, 7.5 \times 10^4$ and 6.5×10^3 from least to greatest.

$6.2 \times 10^{-4}, \ 6.5 \times 10^3, \ 7.5 \times 10^4, \ 6.2 \times 10^4 \leftarrow$ Order the numbers from least to greatest power of 10.

$6.2 \times 10^{-4}, \ 6.5 \times 10^3, \ 6.2 \times 10^4, \ 7.5 \times 10^4 \leftarrow$ Order the numbers with the same power of 10 from least to greatest using the first factor.

✓ Quick Check

4. Order the numbers from least to greatest.

a. $3 \times 10^6, \ 3.11 \times 10^5, \ 3 \times 10^{-6}, \ 3.8 \times 10^{-5}$

b. $1.8 \times 10^{-2}, \ 1.5 \times 10^3, \ 1.5 \times 10^4, \ 1.7 \times 10^{-2}$

You can use division to find how many times greater one number is than another. Write a fraction with the greater number as the numerator and the lesser number as the denominator. Then divide and simplify.

EXAMPLE Comparing Numbers in Scientific Notation

5 Estimate how many times greater 4×10^9 is than 9×10^7.

Write a fraction with the greater number as the numerator. Then divide.

$$\frac{4 \times 10^9}{9 \times 10^7} = \frac{4}{9} \times \frac{10^9}{10^7} \quad \leftarrow \textbf{Write as a product of quotients.}$$

$$\approx 0.44 \times 10^2 \quad \leftarrow \begin{array}{l}\textbf{Divide the coefficients, and divide the} \\ \textbf{powers of ten.}\end{array}$$

$$= 4.4 \times 10^{-1} \times 10^2 \quad \leftarrow \textbf{Write 0.44 in scientific notation.}$$

$$= 4.4 \times 10^1 \quad \leftarrow \textbf{Add exponents.}$$

$$= 44 \quad \leftarrow \textbf{Simplify.}$$

So 4×10^9 is about 44 times greater than 9×10^7.

✓ Quick Check

5. Estimate how many times greater 5.5×10^{18} is than 8×10^{17}. Round to the nearest tenth.

Fill in the blank.

1. $\dfrac{9 \times 10^5}{\blacksquare \times 10^5} = 3$

2. $\dfrac{8 \times 10^{-3}}{4 \times 10^{\blacksquare}} = 2$

3. $\dfrac{2.5 \times 10^{\blacksquare}}{2.5 \times 10^5} = 100$

Which number is greater?

4. 9×10^3 or 9.01×10^4 5. 8×10^7 or 6×10^8 6. 2.1×10^{-3} or 1.2×10^{-4}

7. **Reasoning** If you divide a number in scientific notation by 3, why do you only divide the first factor by 3?

8. **Mental Math** How many times greater is 8×10^3 than 4?

Homework Exercises

For more exercises, see **Extra Skills and Word Problems.**

GO **for Help**

For Exercises	See Examples
9–12	1-3
13–15	4
16–17	5

Divide. Write each quotient in scientific notation.

9. $\dfrac{2.1 \times 10^3}{0.5 \times 10^2}$ 10. $\dfrac{8.5 \times 10^3}{6.1 \times 10^5}$ 11. $\dfrac{3.9 \times 10^{-3}}{3}$ 12. $\dfrac{4}{2 \times 10^9}$

Which number in each pair is greater?

13. 2×10^4 or 2.1×10^3 14. 8×10^{-3} or 4×10^2 15. 6.2×10^7 or 5.8×10^7

Estimate how many times greater the first number is than the second number.

16. $8 \times 10^{12}, 4 \times 10^{10}$ 17. $2 \times 10^6, 4 \times 10^3$

18. **Guided Problem Solving** China has about 1.3×10^9 people. One of the world's smallest nations, the Marshall Islands, has a population of just 5.9×10^4 people. How many times greater is China's population than the Marshall Islands' population?
    - **Make a Plan** Write a ratio comparing China's population to the Marshall Islands' population.
    - **Carry Out the Plan** Divide and write the quotient in scientific notation. Simplify.

19. The sun's diameter is 1.39×10^6 kilometers. Earth's diameter is 1.28×10^4 kilometers. How many times greater is the sun's diameter than Earth's diameter?

GO Online
Homework Video Tutor
PearsonSuccessNet.com

Divide. Write each quotient in scientific notation.

20. $\dfrac{1.9 \times 10^{-1}}{9.8 \times 10^7}$ 21. $\dfrac{4.4 \times 10^{11}}{9 \times 10^2}$ 22. $\dfrac{7 \times 10^3}{5.1 \times 10^{-4}}$

Estimate how many times the first number is than the second number. Round to the nearest integer.

23. $-1.8 \times 10^5, -3.5 \times 10^3$ 24. $8 \times 10^{-6}, 9 \times 10^{-8}$

25. **Speed of Sound** At sea level, the speed of sound is about 761 miles per hour, or $\dfrac{4.02 \times 10^6 \text{ feet}}{3.6 \times 10^3 \text{ seconds}}$. What is this speed in feet per second? Write your answer in scientific notation.

 **Is each statement *true* or *false*? Explain your reasoning.**

26. $1.3 \times 10^{-5} > 1.3 \times 10^{-3}$ 27. $2.8 \times 10^5 > 1.6 \times 10^4$

28. **Space Travel** The space probe *Pioneer 10* was 12.1×10^9 km from Earth in 2002. Its radio signal traveled at 3.0×10^5 km/s. How many hours did its signal take to reach Earth?

29. **Challenge** According to the U.S. Treasury, the United States had a federal debt of 1.58×10^{13} dollars in 2012. This is approximately $50,450 of debt per U.S. citizen. Based on this information, approximately how many U.S. citizens were there in the year 2012? Write your answer in scientific notation.

Careers Test pilots often fly airplanes faster than the speed of sound. When they fly near the speed of sound, a cloud of condensation may form because of a rapid drop in air pressure and temperature.

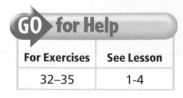

Test Prep and Mixed Review   **Practice**

Multiple Choice

30. The distance from the sun to Saturn is about 8.88×10^8 miles. The speed of light is about 1.1×10^7 miles per minute. Which is the best estimate for the number of seconds it takes for sunlight to reach Saturn. Use the formula time $= \dfrac{\text{distance}}{\text{speed}}$.
    Ⓐ 8.07×10^3 Ⓑ 8.07×10 Ⓒ 4.84×10^3 Ⓓ 4.84×10^2

31. Lydia is making centerpieces for the school band's annual fundraiser dinner. For each centerpiece, Lydia uses 4.5 ounces of decorative stones. If Lydia needs to make 17 centerpieces for the dinner, how many ounces of stones will she need?
    Ⓕ 13.5 ounces
    Ⓖ 21.5 ounces
    Ⓗ 75.5 ounces
    Ⓙ 76.5 ounces

Write each decimal as a mixed number or fraction in simplest form.

32. 1.5   33. 1.125   34. 0.004   35. -6.14

GO for Help

For Exercises	See Lesson
32–35	1-4

Online lesson quiz, PearsonSuccessNet.com

Working Backward

In multiple-choice tests, the correct answer is among the choices. To determine which answer is correct, you can use the problem-solving strategy *Work Backward*.

EXAMPLES

1 A bus can hold 72 passengers. A school uses the equation $b = \frac{n}{72}$ to calculate the number of buses needed to transport n students. What is the greatest number of students 6 buses can hold?

   Ⓐ 288   Ⓑ 360   Ⓒ 432   Ⓓ 504

You can answer the question without solving the equation. Substitute each answer choice for the variable until you find the solution.

Let $n = 288$. Then $\frac{288}{72} = 4$. Since $4 \neq 6$, choice A is wrong.

Let $n = 360$. Then $\frac{360}{72} = 5$. Since $5 \neq 6$, choice B is wrong.

Let $n = 432$. Then $\frac{432}{72} = 6$. Since $6 = 6$, the correct answer is choice C.

You do not need to try choice D.

2 Which expression is equivalent to $12x^2 - 28x$?

   Ⓐ $12x(x - 2)$ Ⓑ $4x(3x - 7)$ Ⓒ $4x^2(3 - 7)$ Ⓓ $6(2x^2 - 4)$

You can multiply each of the answer choices to answer the question.

$12x(x - 2) = 12x^2 - 24x$ This is not equal to $12x^2 - 28x$, so choice A is wrong.

$4x(3x - 7) = 12x^2 - 28x$ Choice B is correct.

You do not need to test the other two choices.

Exercises

Solve each of the following by working backward.

1. The equation $m = 33g$ describes the number of miles m a car can travel on g gallons of gas. For which value of g does $m = 297$?

   Ⓐ 4   Ⓑ 6   Ⓒ 9   Ⓓ 14

2. Jorge wants to run a half-marathon (13.1 miles). About how many miles per hour should he run to complete the half-marathon in 1.5 hours? Use the equation $d = rt$.

   Ⓕ 5.2   Ⓖ 8.7   Ⓗ 9.6   Ⓙ 19.6

Chapter 2 Review

Vocabulary Review

scientific notation (p. 66)

1. Explain when it may be more efficient to use scientific notation.

Skills and Concepts

Lesson 2-1

- To write numbers in standard form and scientific notation

Go Online

For vocabulary quiz
PearsonSuccessNet.com

A number is in **scientific notation** if the first factor is greater than or equal to 1 and less than 10 and the second factor is a power of 10. Multiplying a number by 10^n moves the decimal point n places to the right if n is positive or n places to the left if n is negative. To write a number in scientific notation, determine the first factor. Then write the second factor as a power of 10.

Write each number in standard form.

2. 2.5×10^3 **3.** 8×10^5 **4.** 6.1×10^{-6}

Write each number in scientific notation.

5. 40,000   **6.** 0.0003205   **7.** 93,000,000

8. Probability If you flip a coin 9 times, the probability that the coin will land on "heads" each time is 2^{-9}. How do you represent 2^{-9} as a fraction?

Lesson 2-2

- To multiply powers with the same base

To multiply numbers with the same base, add the exponents.

Write each expression using a single exponent.

9. $8^{10} \cdot 8^9$ **10.** $(-3)^4 \cdot (-3)^9$ **11.** $2.6^{12} \cdot 2.6^{12}$

12. $x \cdot x^2$ **13.** $c \cdot c \cdot c$ **14.** $(-b)^3 \cdot (-b)^8$

Simplify each expression.

15. $7a^4 \cdot a^2$ **16.** $3x^4 \cdot 4x^4$ **17.** $5n^3 \cdot 5n^3$ **18.** $-8x \cdot x^3$

19. $r \cdot r^2 \cdot r^3$ **20.** $-m \cdot 5m^5$ **21.** $\frac{1}{3}x^2 \cdot 12x^3$ **22.** $\frac{1}{2}x \cdot \frac{2}{3}x^2$

23. Meteorology A weather report states that the average rainfall in an area is 2^{-4} in. for the month of July. How do you represent 2^{-4} as a fraction?

Lesson 2-3

- To multiply numbers written in scientific notation and choose units with scientific notation

To multiply numbers written in scientific notation, multiply the first factors. Then multiply the powers of 10 by adding the exponents.

Multiply. Write each product in scientific notation.

24. $(3 \times 10^6)(2 \times 10^{12})$ **25.** $5(1.4 \times 10^6)$ **26.** $(6 \times 10^9)(5 \times 10^4)$

27. $(2.1 \times 10^7)(7 \times 10^{12})$ **28.** $(9.3 \times 10^2)(6 \times 10^{-9})$ **29.** $4(8.4 \times 10^3)$

30. Choose the most reasonable unit to describe the quantity. Then use scientific notation to describe the quantity using the other unit.

A typical cell of the human body is 5×10^{-2} _____. (km, mm)

Lesson 2-4

- To divide powers with the same base and to simplify expressions with negative exponents

To divide nonzero numbers with the same base, subtract the exponents. Any nonzero number with a zero exponent equals 1. For any nonzero number a and integer n, $a^{-n} = \frac{1}{a^n}$.

Write each expression using a single exponent.

31. $\dfrac{5^{10}}{5^7}$ **32.** $\dfrac{(-8)^{12}}{(-8)^2}$ **33.** $\dfrac{76^{11}}{76^5}$ **34.** $\dfrac{1.8^6}{1.8^5}$

Simplify each expression.

35. 8^0 **36.** $(-16)^0$ **37.** $g^0 g^5$ **38.** $(8b)^0 0^2$

39. 5^{-4} **40.** x^{-9} **41.** 9^{-2} **42.** h^{-8}

Lesson 2-5

- To divide and compare numbers written in scientific notation

To divide numbers written in scientific notation, divide the first factor of the first term by the first factor of the second term. Then divide the powers of 10 by subtracting the exponents. You can estimate how many times greater one number in scientific notation is than another by dividing the larger number by the smaller number.

Simplify. Write each quotient in scientific notation.

43. $(8 \times 10^5) \div (4 \times 10^2)$ **44.** $(7 \times 10^8) \div (5 \times 10^5)$

45. $(4 \times 10^{18}) \div (9 \times 10^7)$ **46.** $(6.3 \times 10^8) \div 7.4$

47. $9.1 \div (4.3 \times 10^4)$ **48.** $(3.6 \times 10^9) \div (2.4 \times 10^3)$

49. Order the numbers from greatest to least.

3.7×10^{-4}, 3.6×10^3, 4.1×10^4, 4.0×10^3

Chapter 2 Test

Write each number in standard form.

1. 5×10^4
2. 3.2×10^{-2}
3. 6.0×10^2
4. 1.13×10^3
5. 2.6×10^{-3}
6. 4×10^8
7. 7×10^5
8. 9.32×10^{-1}

Write each number in scientific notation.

9. 0.0405
10. 200,000
11. 100,000
12. 334,000,000
13. 83,000
14. 0.0022
15. 0.37
16. 140,000

Write each expression using a single exponent.

17. $10^7 \cdot 10^6$
18. $3.4^3 \cdot 3.4^6$
19. $6^{-3} \cdot 6^8$
20. $a^0 \cdot a^5$
21. $(-x)^7 \cdot (-x)^6$
22. $2^6 \cdot 2^{-14}$
23. $r^3 \cdot r^4 \cdot r^5$
24. $3.2^{-2} \cdot 3.2^8$

Simplify each expression.

25. 7^0
26. 8^{-4}
27. -9.3^0
28. $(-5.3)^0$
29. -6^{-3}
30. 3^{-4}
31. -36^0
32. 9^{-2}
33. 7^{-2}

34. **Physics** As a person walks away from a light source, the intensity of the light decreases to 2^{-4} the original intensity. How do you write 2^{-4} as a fraction?

Multiply. Write each product in scientific notation.

35. $5(7 \times 10^4)$
36. $11(8 \times 10^2)$
37. $(9 \times 10^{-5})(3 \times 10^{12})$

Choose the most reasonable unit to describe the quantity. Then use scientific notation to describe the quantity using the other unit.

38. A map shows that the distance between two cities is about 15 _____. (cm, km)

39. The Eiffel Tower is about 300 _____ tall. (km, m)

Write each expression using a single exponent.

40. $\dfrac{6^{11}}{6^3}$
41. $\dfrac{c^8}{c^{-6}}$
42. $\dfrac{(-3)^2}{(-3)^4}$
43. $\dfrac{(-n)^4}{(-n)^9}$
44. $\dfrac{2.8^7}{2.8^4}$
45. $\dfrac{1.4^{-9}}{1.4^2}$

Divide. Write each quotient in scientific notation. Round to the nearest tenth if necessary.

46. $(6 \times 10^3) \div (8 \times 10^6)$
47. $(1.4 \times 10^8) \div 2.3$

Estimate how many times greater the first number is than the second number. Round to the nearest hundred.

48. $2.5 \times 10^6, 4.1 \times 10^3$
49. $9 \times 10^6, 5 \times 10^4$

50. **Writing in Math** How would you explain to a classmate why 5^0 is equal to 1?

51. **Biology** The human eye blinks about 4.2×10^6 times each year. About how many times has the eye of a 14-year-old blinked? Write your answer in scientific notation.

52. Order the numbers from greatest to least.
1.09×10^3, 1.9×10^3, 2.0×10^2, 2.0×10^{-2}

53. Order the numbers from least to greatest.
1.43×10^{-3}, 1.24×10^{-6}, 2.14×10^{-3}, 1.44×10^{-2}

Multiple Choice

Choose the correct letter.

1. Which shows the numbers $3, -4, -8, 2,$ and 11 in order from greatest to least?
   - (A) $-4, -8, 2, 3, 11$
   - (C) $11, 2, 3, -8, -4$
   - (B) $11, 3, 2, -4, -8$
   - (D) $-8, -4, 2, 3, 11$

2. What is the sum of $-96 + 187$?
   - (F) 283
   - (H) 91
   - (G) 111
   - (J) -283

3. Myron and Jane are hiking in a valley. When they start their hike, Myron and Jane are 489 feet above the valley floor. After their 3-hour hike, they are at the bottom of the valley. What was the hikers' vertical speed?
   - (A) $1,467$ ft/hour
   - (C) 164 ft/hour
   - (B) 486 ft/hour
   - (D) 163 ft/hour

4. Which is the decimal 0.872 written as a fraction in simplest form?
   - (F) $\frac{109}{125}$
   - (H) $\frac{872}{1000}$
   - (G) $\frac{218}{250}$
   - (J) $\frac{436}{500}$

5. What is the approximate distance between the two points on the number line?

   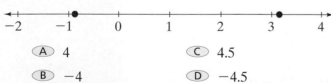

   - (A) 4
   - (C) 4.5
   - (B) -4
   - (D) -4.5

6. Randy owes his personal trainer \$442. He wants to pay over an $8\frac{1}{2}$ month period. How much will Randy pay each month?
   - (F) \$51   (G) \$51.50   (H) \$52   (J) \$52.50

7. There are about 10,550 radio stations in the United States. How do you write 10,550 in scientific notation?
   - (A) 1.055×10^3
   - (C) 10.55×10^3
   - (B) 1.055×10^4
   - (D) 10.55×10^4

8. A cube-shaped jewelry box has a volume of 125 cubic centimeters. What is the length of one side of the cube?

   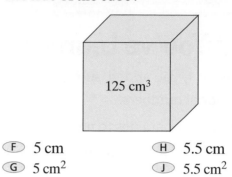

   - (F) 5 cm
   - (H) 5.5 cm
   - (G) 5 cm^2
   - (J) 5.5 cm^2

Gridded Response

9. Over the summer, you mowed lawns around the neighborhood. You counted the money you earned and calculated the number of hours you worked. If you earned \$603.84 for 48 hours of cutting grass, how much did you earn per hour?

Short Response

10. Is the following number sentence true or false? Explain your reasoning.

    $$2.34 \times 10^6 > 2.43 \times 10^5$$

11. Write 3.284 as a mixed number in simplest form.

Extended Response

12. The largest U.S. state in population is California. It has about 3.8×10^7 people. The U.S. state with the smallest population is Wyoming, which has about 5.7×10^5 people. Write a short paragraph describing the steps you would follow to find how many times as great the population of California is than the population of Wyoming.

CHAPTER 3 Equations

What You've Learned

- In Chapter 1, you added, subtracted, multiplied, and divided integers and rational numbers.
- You used number lines to model operations with integers.
- You compared and ordered rational numbers.

 Check Your Readiness

GO for Help

For Exercises	See Lesson
1–6	1-6
7–10	1-3
11–18	1-5

Adding and Subtracting Rational Numbers

Find each sum or difference.

1. $5.304 - 0.89$ **2.** $2.35 + 1.8 - 4.45$

3. $-2.15 - 1\frac{1}{4}$ **4.** $\frac{3}{4} - \frac{7}{8} + \frac{3}{8}$

5. $3.7 + (-1.9)$ **6.** $-1\frac{2}{5} - 2.5$

Multiplying and Dividing Integers

Find each product or quotient.

7. $-12 \cdot 3$ **8.** $-3 \div (-3)$ **9.** $-6 \cdot (-7)$ **10.** $-54 \div 9$

Comparing and Ordering Rational Numbers

Compare each pair of rational numbers. Use <, =, or >.

11. $1\frac{1}{8}$ ■ $-1\frac{3}{8}$ **12.** -5.99 ■ -6 **13.** 5.6 ■ $\frac{52}{3}$

14. $6\frac{1}{3}$ ■ $6.\overline{3}$ **15.** 0.7 ■ $0.\overline{7}$ **16.** $-\frac{11}{15}$ ■ $-\frac{2}{5}$

Order from greatest to least.

17. $-2,\ 2.2,\ \frac{13}{9},\ 3.7,\ 2\frac{3}{4}$ **18.** $5,\ \frac{1}{5},\ -0.5,\ 0.\overline{5},\ 0$

What You'll Learn Next

- In this chapter, you will solve equations by adding, subtracting, multiplying, or dividing.

- You will write and evaluate algebraic expressions.

- You will solve word problems leading to one-step and multi-step equations.

- You will identify whether a linear equation has one solution, no solution, or infinitely many solutions.

- Applying what you learn, you will be able to solve equations to track temperature variation in the Grand Canyon related to changes in elevation.

Key Vocabulary

- Addition Property of Equality (p. 114)
- algebraic expression (p. 103)
- coefficient (p. 108)
- Division Property of Equality (p. 115)
- inverse operations (p. 114)
- like terms (p. 108)
- Multiplication Property of Equality (p. 114)
- Subtraction Property of Equality (p. 114)
- variable (p. 103)

Describing Patterns

You can identify and describe patterns to make predictions.

ACTIVITY

During part of its flight, an airplane rises 12 feet in altitude each second. Use this information to find a pattern.

Time (t)	Distance (ft)
1	12
5	60
10	120
20	■
25	■
50	■
100	■
200	■

1. Look at the table at the right. Explain how to find the distance the plane rises for each amount of time.

2. Copy and complete the table at the right.

3. At t seconds, how many feet has the plane risen?

You can use different scales to measure temperature. The Celsius and Kelvin scales have a special relationship.

Celsius (C)	Kelvin (K)
0	273
1	274
5	278
10	■
20	■
30	■
75	■
100	■

4. Look at the table of temperatures at the right. Explain how to find the temperature in Kelvin for each temperature in degrees Celsius.

5. Copy and complete the table.

6. At c degrees Celsius, what is the temperature in Kelvin?

Exercises

Copy and complete each table. Describe the pattern you find.

1.

A	B
1	8
2	9
5	12
10	■
30	■
50	■
n	■

2.

C	D
1	−4
2	−3
5	0
10	■
25	■
45	■
n	■

3.

E	F
1	40
2	80
5	200
10	■
100	■
500	■
n	■

4. **Reasoning** What does the letter n represent in each table above? How is it used to describe the pattern in the table?

3-1 Evaluating and Writing Algebraic Expressions

© **CONTENT STANDARD**

7.EE.4

Test Prep Tip

You can use diagrams to represent algebraic expressions.

What You'll Learn

To write and evaluate algebraic expressions

New Vocabulary variable, algebraic expression

Why Learn This?

You can use algebraic expressions to help you make predictions based on patterns. If you know how far you can swim in 1 minute, you can estimate how far you can swim in 5 minutes.

A **variable** is a symbol that represents one or more numbers. Variables are usually letters. An **algebraic expression** is a mathematical phrase with at least one variable.

Diagrams and algebraic expressions can represent word phrases.

Word Phrase	Diagram	Algebraic Expression
a temperature of t degrees increased by 5 degrees	t | 5	$t + 5$
five cats fewer than c cats	c / ? | 5	$c - 5$
the product of 5 and n nickels	n n n n n	$5n$
a dinner bill of d dollars divided among five friends	d / $\frac{d}{5}$ $\frac{d}{5}$ $\frac{d}{5}$ $\frac{d}{5}$ $\frac{d}{5}$	$\frac{d}{5}$

EXAMPLE Writing Algebraic Expressions

1 Write an algebraic expression for each word phrase.

a. swimming m meters per minute for 3 minutes → $3m$

b. 12 heartbeats more than x heartbeats → $x + 12$

✓ Quick Check

1. Write an algebraic expression for a price p decreased by 16.

You can use algebraic expressions to represent real-world situations.

EXAMPLE Application: Public Service

2 The Environmental Club is making posters. The materials for each poster cost $4. Write an algebraic expression for the cost of *p* posters.

Words	$4 per poster	times	the number of posters

Expression	4	·	*p*

An algebraic expression for the cost of the posters is 4*p*.

✓ Quick Check

2. Nine students will hang *t* posters each. Write an algebraic expression for the total number of posters the students will hang.

You can translate algebraic expressions into word phrases.

EXAMPLE Writing Word Phrases

3 Write three different word phrases for $x + 2$.

> A number plus two

> A number increased by two

> Two more than a number

✓ Quick Check

3. Write three different word phrases for $c - 50$.

You can substitute for a variable to evaluate an algebraic expression.

EXAMPLE Evaluating Algebraic Expressions

4 Evaluate each expression. Use the values $p = 2$, $n = 3$, and $s = 5$.

a. $2p + 7$ **b.** $p + (n \cdot s)$

$$2p + 7 = 2(2) + 7 \quad \leftarrow \text{Substitute.} \rightarrow \quad p + (n \cdot s) = 2 + (3 \cdot 5)$$
$$= 4 + 7 \quad\quad \leftarrow \text{Multiply.} \rightarrow \quad\quad = 2 + (15)$$
$$= 11 \quad\quad \leftarrow \text{Add.} \rightarrow \quad\quad = 17$$

✓ Quick Check

4. Use the values $n = 3$, $t = 5$, and $y = 7$ to evaluate $(n + t) \cdot y$.

Online active math

For: Expressions Activity
Use: Interactive Textbook, 3-1

1. **Vocabulary** A numerical expression is a mathematical phrase that uses numbers. What is the difference between an *algebraic* expression and a *numerical* expression?

Tell which operation you would use for each word phrase.

2. six goals fewer than g goals

3. p people increased by two

Write a word phrase for each algebraic expression.

4. $w - 3$

5. $5 \cdot w$

6. $12 + w$

7. $\frac{w}{4}$

Evaluate each expression. Use the value $p = 2$.

8. $p + 8$

9. $3 \cdot p$

10. $16 - p$

11. $\frac{12}{p}$

Homework Exercises

For more exercises, see **Extra Skills and Word Problems.**

GO for Help

For Exercises	See Examples
12–16	1–2
17–24	3
25–30	4

Write an algebraic expression for each word phrase. You may find a diagram helpful.

12. four more than s shirts

13. the quotient of p and 5

14. the sum of t TVs and 11 TVs

15. five times your quiz score q

16. Your job pays \$7 per hour. Write an algebraic expression for your pay in dollars for working h hours.

Write a word phrase for each algebraic expression.

17. $d + 2$

18. $\frac{4}{n}$

19. $c - 9.1$

20. $6.5 - h$

21. $1.3 \cdot p$

22. $10 + q$

23. $\frac{w}{10}$

24. $3.5v$

Evaluate each expression. Use the values $p = 4$, $n = 6$, and $s = 2$.

25. $7n$

26. $-6.1p$

27. $5 - s$

28. $\frac{n}{2}$

29. $8s - 6$

30. $1.5(p + n)$

31. **Guided Problem Solving** A student mows one lawn each week day after school and two lawns on Saturday. She earns \$15.75 per lawn. Write an algebraic expression for the amount of money she makes in w weeks.
   • How many lawns does she mow in one week?
   • *Draw a picture* to represent the amount of money she makes in one week.

Write an algebraic expression for the *n*th term of each table.

32.

A	0	1	2	3	5	10	n
B	5	6	7	8	10	15	?

33.

C	0	1	2	3	5	10	n
D	0	10	20	30	50	100	?

34. Write an algebraic expression to find the number of seconds in *n* minutes. Evaluate the expression for $n = 20$.

35. **Birds** The blue-throated hummingbird has a heart rate of about 1,260 beats per minute. Explain how you would calculate the number of times the hummingbird's heart beats in a 24-hour day. Then find the number of beats in a 24-hour day.

36. Describe a situation that the expression $10n$ can model.

37. **Writing in Math** You can write "twelve less than a number" as $n - 12$, but not as $12 - n$. Explain why.

38. **Estimation** This section of a page from a telephone directory shows a column with 11 names in 1 inch. Each page has four 10-inch columns. Write an algebraic expression for the approximate number of names in *p* pages of the directory.

6-4462	**Daalling V** 8 Everett All............
2-3302	**Daavis K** 444 Greeley R.........
4-1775	**Dabady V** 94 Burnside All.......
2-0014	**Dabagh L** 13 Lancaster R......
6-3356	**Dabagh W** Dr 521 Weston All...
4-7322	**Dabar G** 98 River All............
6-1530	**Dabarera F** 34 Roseland All....
2-2279	**Dabas M** 17 Riverside R.......
4-9978	**D'Abate D** 86 Moss Hill Rd All...
2-6745	**D'Abate G** 111 South Central R
4-5456	**Dabbous H** 670 Warren Dr All..
6-3064	**Dabbraccio F** 151 Century All..
6-2257	**Dabby D** 542 Walnut All.........
2-9987	**Dabcovich M G** 219 Green R...
6-5643	**Dabcovich M** 72 Main All........

39. **Challenge** A student baby-sitting for $5 per hour writes the expression $5n$ to represent the money he makes for *n* hours. Another student writes $3n + 15$ to represent the amount in dollars she makes. What is the second student's hourly rate? What does the number 15 represent?

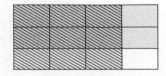
Test Prep and Mixed Review **Practice**

Multiple Choice

40. In ancient Greece, a measurement called a cubit equaled 18.3 inches. Which expression represents the number of inches in *c* cubits?

Ⓐ $c - 18.3$　　Ⓑ $c \div 18.3$　　Ⓒ $18.3 + c$　　Ⓓ $18.3c$

41. Which expression does the model represent?

Ⓕ $\frac{2}{3} \times \frac{3}{4}$　　Ⓗ $\frac{1}{2} \times \frac{2}{3}$

Ⓖ $\frac{1}{3} \times \frac{3}{4}$　　Ⓙ $\frac{1}{2} \times \frac{3}{4}$

Find the value of each expression.

42. $7(1.2) + 7(0.5)$　　**43.** $3(4 + 5) + 2(4 + 5)$　　**44.** $5(0.25 \cdot 40)$

GO for Help

For Exercises	See Skills Handbook
42–44	p. 598

Using Spreadsheets

You can use a computer spreadsheet to keep track of the balance in a checking account. You add deposits and subtract checks. Using the formulas you supply, the spreadsheet computes values in cells.

EXAMPLE **Using Spreadsheets**

Use the spreadsheet. Find the balance after each entry.

	A	B	C	D
1	Date	Deposits	Checks	Balance
2				$350
3	4/29	$100		■
4	4/30		$400	■

Use the formula "= D2 + B3".
← The computer finds 350 + 100 = 450.

← Use the formula "= D3 − C4".
The computer finds 450 − 400 = 50.

● The first balance is $450. The second balance is $50.

Exercises

Use the spreadsheet at the right.

1. Find the account balance after each entry. Write the formulas you used.

2. Which formula can you use to find the balance in cell D9, whether or not a check has been written or a deposit has been made?

   Ⓐ = D8 − B9 + C9   Ⓒ = D8 + B9 + C9

   Ⓑ = D8 − B9 − C9   Ⓓ = D8 + B9 − C9

3. **Reasoning** Suppose the balance in cell D9 is $130.34. Was the amount of a deposit entered into cell B9, or was the amount of a check entered into cell C9? Support your answer.

4. **Writing in Math** Consider your answer to Exercise 2. Explain why the formula you chose works. Give examples.

5. **Reasoning** Suppose the balance in cell D8 is $250 and you do not know the original balance. Explain how you would calculate the original balance in cell D2. Then find the original balance.

	A	B	C	D
1	Date	Deposits	Checks	Balance
2				$250
3	11/3		$25.98	■
4	11/9		$239.40	■
5	11/10	$122.00		■
6	11/13		$54.65	■
7	11/20	$350.00		■
8	11/29		$163.80	■

3-2 | Simplifying Expressions

© **CONTENT STANDARD**
7.EE.1

What You'll Learn

To simplify algebraic expressions using properties of operations

New Vocabulary like terms, coefficient

Why Learn This?

You evaluate algebraic expressions by substituting values for variables. Scientists often substitute data from experiments into formulas with several variables to interpret their results.

Like terms are terms that have the same variable factors. For example, $12x$ and $3x$ are like terms, but $4a$ and $5b$ are not like terms. You can use the properties of operations to order, group, and combine like terms.

A **coefficient** is a numerical factor of a term with a variable. In each of the terms below, the coefficients are highlighted.

Coefficients
$$12x, \quad 5b, \quad 3xy^2, \quad (5 + 2)m$$

EXAMPLE **Using Properties to Add and Subtract**

1. Simplify $5x + 9 + 2x - 4$.

$5x + 9 + 2x - 4$ ← Identify which parts of the expression are like terms.

$= 5x + 2x + 9 - 4$ ← Commutative Property of Addition

$= (5 + 2)x + 9 - 4$ ← Distributive Property

$= 7x + 9 - 4$ ← Simplify the coefficient.

$= 7x + 5$ ← Simplify.

The simplified expression is $7x + 5$.

✓ Quick Check

1. Simplify each expression.

   a. $2x + 8 + 4x - 5$ **b.** $6 + 7.2y - 4.2y + 1$ **c.** $10r - 5 + 3 + r$

Sometimes an expression should be expanded before it is simplified.

EXAMPLE **Expanding Expressions**

② Simplify $\frac{2}{3}(12y + 9) + 4$.

$$\frac{2}{3}(12y + 9) + 4$$
$$= (8y + 6) + 4 \qquad \leftarrow \text{Distributive Property}$$
$$= 8y + (6 + 4) \qquad \leftarrow \text{Associative Property of Addition}$$
$$= 8y + 10 \qquad \leftarrow \text{Simplify}$$

The simplified expression is $8y + 10$.

✓ **Quick Check**

2. Simplify each expression.

   a. $6(2x + 3) - 4$ **b.** $\frac{1}{2}(2 - 8v) + 5$ **c.** $9 - 4(3z + 2)$

You can use the Distributive Property to rewrite an addition expression as a product of two factors. This process is called factoring. Use the greatest common factor (GCF) so the expression is factored completely.

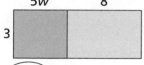
EXAMPLE **Factoring Expressions**

③ **a.** Factor $4x + 14$.

   GCF of 4 and 14 is 2.   ← Identify the GCF.
   $4x + 14 = 2 \cdot 2x + 2 \cdot 7$ ← Factor each term by the GCF.
          $= 2(2x + 7)$ ← Distributive Property

The factored expression is $2(2x + 7)$.

b. Factor $12y - 6$

   GCF of 12 and 6 is 6.   ← Identify the GCF.
   $12y - 6 = 6 \cdot 2y - 6 \cdot 1$ ← Factor each term by the GCF.
          $= 6(2y - 1)$ ← Distributive Property

The factored expression is $6(2y - 1)$.

✓ **Quick Check**

3. Factor each expression completely.
   a. $9x + 15$ **b.** $36 + 24t$ **c.** $8c - 20$

1. **Vocabulary** Terms that have the same variable factors, such as $7y$ and $-3y$, are called __?__ .

Simplify each expression.

2. $15 + 4$

3. $8n - 2n$

4. $30s + 7 + 3s$

5. $6 - 3r - 3$

6. $2y + 4 + 0.5$

7. $2(15 + 5w) - w$

Identify the greatest common factor of the terms in each expression.

8. $4n - 40$

9. $27 + 18v$

10. $15t + 25$

Homework Exercises

For more exercises, see Extra Skills and Word Problems.

GO for Help

For Exercises	See Examples
11–22	1-2
23–28	3

Simplify each expression.

11. $9x + 3 + 2x - 2$

12. $6y + 7 - 3y + 3$

13. $12w - 7 + 1 + 4w$

14. $4 - 6x + 8 + 3x$

15. $3a + 8 + a - 9 - 2a$

16. $4(5x + 2) - 6$

17. $10 + 3(2v - 3)$

18. $4 - 5(3t + 3)$

19. $6(y + 2) - 6 + 5y$

20. $0.9 - 2(3r + 0.2)$

21. $24 - 45m - 11 + 3m$

22. $\frac{2}{3}(6 + 3x) - 7x$

Factor each expression completely.

23. $6x + 10$

24. $30 + 20y$

25. $12x - 28$

26. $12c - 30$

27. $18b + 2$

28. $42 - 14v$

GPS 29. **Guided Problem Solving** Simplify $\frac{6x + 4}{2}$.

- **Make a Plan** Rewrite the quotient as a product. Apply the Distributive Property. Write all fractions in simplest form.
- **Carry Out the Plan**

$$\frac{6x + 4}{2} = \blacksquare(6x + 4) = \blacksquare x + \blacksquare = \blacksquare x + \blacksquare$$

Simplify each expression.

30. $\frac{24x + 16}{8}$

31. $\frac{15 + 36y}{3}$

32. $\frac{96b - 24}{12}$

33. **Writing in Math** The expression $3x - 6 + 2x + 4$ is modeled with algebra tiles as shown.

Explain how to use the model to simplify the expression.

Simplify each expression.

34. $8.4x + 10.2 + 4.3x - 2.9$

35. $5y + 4.7 + 2.08 - 0.6y$

36. $\frac{2}{3}(8x + 12) - \frac{4}{3}$

37. $1 + \frac{1}{2}x - \frac{3}{4}\left(\frac{1}{6} - \frac{2}{9}x\right)$

38. Error Analysis Jane did the work shown. Explain her error.

> $9y - 2 + 4y$
> $9y - 4y + 2$
> $5y + 2$

39. Earning Money You work 40 hours a week and earn d dollars an hour. You get a raise of $3 an hour plus a $13 bonus in the first week. Write and simplify the expression that shows the amount you will earn in the week.

40. Number Sense. Use $>, <,$ or $=$ to make each statement true.

a. $10 + c + 6 \ \bullet \ 2c + 2 \cdot 5 - c$

b. $2b + 2c - 5 \ \bullet \ 12 + 2(b + c) - 7$

c. $3x + 4 - 4x + 2 \ \bullet \ 3(2 - x) + 2x$

41. Challenge Find the perimeter of a rectangle with a length of $4x + 1.5$ and a width of $x - 0.3$. Simplify your answer.

GO Online
Homework Video Tutor
PearsonSuccessNet.com

Test Prep and Mixed Review

Practice

Multiple Choice

42. Simplify $4(3n + 5) - 10n$.

Ⓐ $2n + 5$

Ⓒ $12n + 5$

Ⓑ $2n + 20$

Ⓓ $22n + 20$

43. A decorator buys y square yards of wallpaper at $9.99 per square yard and z square yards of another design for $13.95 a square yard. Which expression represents her change if she pays with a $100 bill?

Ⓕ $100 - 9.99y + 13.95z$

Ⓗ $100 - (9.99y + 13.95z)$

Ⓖ $100 - 23.94yz$

Ⓙ $9.99y + 13.95z - 100$

Find the product or quotient.

44. $8(-12)$

45. $(-3.1)(-10)$

46. $81 \div (-3)$

47. $(9 + 7) \div (-2)$

Write each fraction as a decimal.

48. $\frac{2}{8}$

49. $\frac{1}{3}$

50. $\frac{5}{6}$

51. $\frac{17}{20}$

Write each decimal as a mixed number or fraction in simplest form.

52. 8.75

53. 1.05

54. 0.86

55. 0.33

GO for Help

For Exercises	See Lesson
44–47	1-3
48–55	1-4

Write an algebraic expression for each word phrase.

1. four less than a number
2. three times a number
3. the quotient of 4 and a number
4. nine more than a number

Simplify each expression.

5. $5k + 2 - 2k - 1$
6. $4(2n + 5) - 9n$
7. $7 + 0.6x + 2.4x - 1$
8. $\frac{1}{5}t + 5 + \frac{3}{5}t - 9$

9. **Science** The chemical element aluminum was discovered in 1825 by Hans Christian Oersted. This was 18 years after year y, when Sir Humphry Davy discovered the element sodium. Write an expression for the year aluminum was discovered.

10. Factor $25r - 10$.

MATH GAMES

Evaluating Expressions

What You'll Need

- 24 index cards. Cut them in half so you have 48 smaller cards. On each card, write a different algebraic expression.
- Two number cubes

How to Play

- Deal all the cards. Each player chooses one card from his or her hand and places it face down on the table.
- A player rolls the number cubes. The sum of the numbers is the value of the variable for the first round.
- Each player turns over his or her card, evaluates the expression, and announces its value. Record the value for each player.
- Play continues until all players have rolled the number cubes.
- Find each player's total. The player with the lowest total wins.

Modeling Equations

You can model and solve equations using algebra tiles.

EXAMPLE **Solving Addition Equations**

1 Use algebra tiles to solve $x + 4 = 12$.

$x + 4 = 12$  ← Model the equation. Use yellow tiles for positive integers.

$x + 4 - 4 = 12 - 4$ 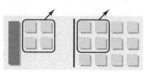 ← Remove 4 tiles from each side.

$x = 8$  ← Simplify.

EXAMPLE **Solving Multiplication Equations**

2 Use algebra tiles to solve $3x = -21$.

$3x = -21$  ← Model the equation. Use red tiles for negative integers.

$\dfrac{3x}{3} = \dfrac{-21}{3}$  ← Divide each side into three equal groups.

$x = -7$  ← Simplify.

Exercises

Use algebra tiles to solve each equation.

1. $x + 12 = 18$ **2.** $x + 3 = 16$ **3.** $x + 8 = 17$ **4.** $x + (-7) = 13$

5. $x + (-2) = -7$ **6.** $x + (-7) = -11$ **7.** $3x = 18$ **8.** $5x = -25$

9. $7x = 21$ **10.** $2x = -18$ **11.** $4x = 28$ **12.** $2x = 24$

3-3 Solving One-Step Equations

What You'll Learn

To solve equations by adding, subtracting, multiplying, or dividing

New Vocabulary Properties of Equality, inverse operations

Why Learn This?

If you can solve equations, you can use known information to find unknown information. To solve an equation, you want to get the variable alone on one side of the equation. You can use **inverse operations**, operations that undo each other, to get the variable alone.

Addition and subtraction are inverse operations. You can use addition to undo subtraction and subtraction to undo addition.

KEY CONCEPTS **Properties of Equality**

Addition Property of Equality

If you add the same value to each side of an equation, the two sides remain equal.

Arithmetic	**Algebra**
$\frac{20}{2} = 10$, so $\frac{20}{2} + 3 = 10 + 3$.	If $a = b$, then $a + c = b + c$.

Subtraction Property of Equality

If you subtract the same value from each side of an equation, the two sides remain equal.

Arithmetic	**Algebra**
$\frac{12}{2} = 6$, so $\frac{12}{2} - 4 = 6 - 4$.	If $a = b$, then $a - c = b - c$.

Multiplication and division are inverse operations. You can use division to undo multiplication and mutiplication to undo division.

KEY CONCEPTS **Multiplication Property of Equality**

If you multiply each side of an equation by the same number, the two sides remain equal.

Arithmetic	**Algebra**
$\frac{12}{2} = 6$, so $\frac{12}{2} \cdot 2 = 6 \cdot 2$.	If $a = b$, then $a \cdot c = b \cdot c$.

KEY CONCEPTS   **Division Property of Equality**

If you divide each side of an equation by the same nonzero number, the two sides remain equal.

Arithmetic	**Algebra**
Since $3(2) = 6, \dfrac{3(2)}{2} = \dfrac{6}{2}$.	If $a = b$, and $c \neq 0$, then $\dfrac{a}{c} = \dfrac{b}{c}$.

EXAMPLE   Solving Equations by Adding

Test Prep Tip

You can represent the equation in Example 1 with this model.

x	
34	−46

1 Solve $x - 34 = -46$.

$$x - 34 = -46$$

$x - 34 + 34 = -46 + 34$ ← Addition Property of Equality: Add 34 to each side.

$\qquad x + 0 = -12$ ← The numbers −34 and 34 are additive inverses.

$\qquad\qquad x = -12$ ← Identity Property of Addition

Check $\;x - 34 = -46$ ← Check the solution in the original equation.

$\qquad -12 - 34 = -46$ ← Substitute −12 for x.

$\qquad\qquad -46 = -46$ ✔   ← Subtract.

✅ Quick Check

1. Solve the equation $x - 104 = 64$.

Just as addition undoes subtraction, subtraction undoes addition.

EXAMPLE   Solving Equations by Subtracting

2 Your friend's mountain bike cost $245 more than his skateboard. His mountain bike cost $290. How much did your friend's skateboard cost?

Words   cost of bike   is $245   more than   cost of skateboard

    Let $\;s\;$ = the cost of the skateboard.

Equation   290   = 245   + s

$$290 = 245 + s$$

$290 - 245 = 245 - 245 + s$ ← Subtract 245 from each side.

$\qquad\quad 45 = s$ ← Simplify.

The skateboard cost $45.

✅ Quick Check

2. A hardcover book costs $19 more than its paperback edition. The hardcover book costs $26.95. How much does the paperback cost?

Solving Equations by Multiplying

3 Solve $\frac{t}{-45} = -5$.

$$\frac{t}{-45} = -5 \qquad \leftarrow \text{Notice that } t \text{ is divided by } -45.$$

$$(-45) \cdot \left(\frac{t}{-45}\right) = (-45) \cdot (-5) \leftarrow \text{Multiply each side by } -45.$$

$$t = 225 \qquad \leftarrow \text{Simplify.}$$

☑ **Quick Check**

● **3.** Solve the equation $\frac{w}{26} = -15$. Check your answer.

EXAMPLE **Solving Equations by Dividing**

GO ●nline

Video Tutor Help
PearsonSuccessNet.com

4 Solve $4p = 22.68$.

$$4p = 22.68 \qquad \leftarrow \text{Notice } p \text{ is being } multiplied \text{ by 4.}$$

$$\frac{4p}{4} = \frac{22.68}{4} \qquad \leftarrow \text{Divide each side by 4 to get } p \text{ alone.}$$

$$p = 5.67 \qquad \leftarrow \text{Simplify.}$$

Check $4p = 22.68 \qquad \leftarrow \text{Check your solution in the original equation.}$

$4(5.67) \stackrel{?}{=} 22.68 \qquad \leftarrow \text{Replace } p \text{ with 5.67.}$

$22.68 = 22.68 \; ✔ \qquad \leftarrow \text{The solution checks.}$

☑ **Quick Check**

● **4.** Solve each equation. Check your answer.
   a. $3x = -21.6$ **b.** $-12y = -108$ **c.** $104x = 312$

☑ **Check Your Understanding**

1. Vocabulary __?__ operations are operations that undo each other.

2. Error Analysis Dylan and Jean tried to solve the equation $x + 4 = -9$. Who solved the equation correctly? Explain.

Dylan
$$x + 4 = -9$$
$$x + 4 + 4 = -9 + 4$$
$$x = -5$$

Jean
$$x + 4 = -9$$
$$x + 4 - 4 = -9 - 4$$
$$x = -13$$

Fill in the missing numbers to solve each equation.

3. $$b + 12 = 39$$
$$b + 12 - ■ = 39 - ■$$

4. $$y - 8 = 35$$
$$y - 8 + ■ = 35 + ■$$

Match each equation with the correct first step of the solution.

5. $-6y = 12$ **A.** Multiply both sides by -6.

6. $12y = -6$ **B.** Divide both sides by -6.

7. $\dfrac{y}{-6} = 12$ **C.** Divide both sides by 12.

Homework Exercises

For more exercises, see **Extra Skills and Word Problems.**

GO for Help

For Exercises	See Examples
8–10	1
11–13	2
14–16	3
17–20	4

Solve each equation. Check your answer. You may find a model helpful.

8. $t - 32.8 = -27$ **9.** $h - 37 = -42$

10. $q - 16 = 40$ **11.** $k + 17 = 29$

12. $d + 261.9 = -48$ **13.** $x + 34 = 212$

14. $\dfrac{z}{8} = -3$ **15.** $\dfrac{n}{3} = 9$

16. $\dfrac{t}{8} = 12.6$ **17.** $-7n = -294$

18. $0.2x = 4$ **19.** $-0.5r = -8$

20. Entertainment A local park rents paddle boats for $5.50 per hour. You have $22 to spend. For how many hours can you rent a boat?

GPS **21. Guided Problem Solving** A runner's heart rate is 133 beats per minute. This is 62 beats per minute more than his resting heart rate. Write and solve an equation to find the runner's resting heart rate.
- Choose a variable to represent the resting heart rate.
- Write an equation that represents the information provided.
- Check your answer. Does it fit the details of the problem?

22. Biology A student collects 12 ladybugs for a science project. This is 9 fewer than the number of ladybugs the student collected yesterday. Write and solve an equation to find the number of ladybugs the student collected yesterday.

23. Money Use the advertisement at the right. Write and solve an equation to find the original price of the sweater.

SALE $21.50
SAVE $8.45

24. Writing in Math A student is saving money for field hockey camp. Her savings are modeled by the equation $135 + d = 250$. Explain what each part of the equation represents.

25. Trees A growing tree absorbs about 26 lb of carbon dioxide each year. How many years will the tree take to absorb 390 lb of carbon dioxide?

26. The world record for playgoing is held by Dr. H. Howard Hughes of Fort Worth, Texas. He saw 6,136 plays in 31 years. How many plays did Dr. Hughes see in an average year?

27. There are a total of 968 students enrolled in the three grades at Middletown Middle School. There are 329 students in the sixth grade, and 328 students in the seventh grade. Write and solve an equation to find how many students are in the eighth grade.

Open-Ended **Write a problem that can be solved using each equation.**

28. $3x = 30$ **29.** $\frac{n}{5} = 2$ **30.** $2.5 + p = 10$

31. Challenge During five baseball games, your team scores 3, 4, 2, 6, and 8 runs. How many more runs must your team score to have a total of 30 runs? Write and solve an equation.

Test Prep and Mixed Review   **Practice**

Multiple Choice

32. The model represents the equation $x - 4 = 2$. What is the value of x?

Ⓐ 2
Ⓑ 4
Ⓒ 3
Ⓓ 6

Key
⊕ = +1
⊖ = −1

33. Which problem situation matches the equation $7.50 + x = 100$?

Ⓕ Roberto bought a box of 100 baseball cards for $7.50. What is x, the price for each baseball card?

Ⓖ Will works 7.5 hours a day. He will get a pay raise when he works 100 hours. What is x, the number of days he works to get a raise?

Ⓗ Mr. Midas bought a case of fruit for $7.50. He paid the cashier with a $100 bill. What is x, the amount of change he received?

Ⓙ Jennifer walks for 7.5 minutes. What is x, the number of miles she can walk in 100 minutes?

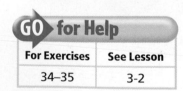
GO for Help

For Exercises	See Lesson
34–35	3-2

Simplify each expression.

34. $3 - 4 + 5 \cdot 6 - (-4)$ **35.** $4 \cdot 5 - 6 + (5 - 2)^2$

Keeping the Balance

You can use a balance-scale model to solve equations. The scales below are balanced. Use them for the activity. Objects that look identical have the same weight. Objects that look different have different weights.

 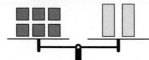

ACTIVITY

1. Decide whether each scale is balanced. Explain your reasoning.

a.    **b.**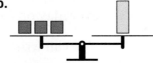

c. 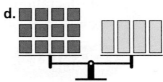   **d.**

Exercises

Tell whether each statement is true or false. Explain.

1. A balanced scale will stay balanced if I add the same amount to each side.

2. A balanced scale will stay balanced if I remove the same amount from each side.

3. A balanced scale will stay balanced if I multiply each side by the same amount.

4. A balanced scale will stay balanced if I divide each side by the same amount.

Decide whether each scale is balanced. Explain your reasoning.

5. 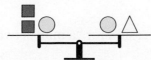   6. 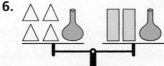   7.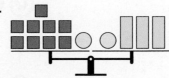

3-4 Exploring Two-Step Equations

Check Skills You'll Need

1. **Vocabulary Review** A(n) ? is a mathematical phrase with at least one variable.

Evaluate each expression. Use the value $a = -4$.

2. $a + 5$ 3. $9 - a$

4. $-6a$ 5. $\frac{a}{2}$

 **for Help**
Lesson 3-1

© CONTENT STANDARD
7.EE.4.a

What You'll Learn

To write and evaluate expressions with two operations and to solve two-step equations using number sense

Why Learn This?

Suppose you are ordering roses online. Roses cost $5 each, and shipping costs $10. Your total cost depends on how many roses you buy. Two-step equations can help you solve everyday problems.

You can write expressions with variables using one operation. Now you will write algebraic expressions with two operations.

EXAMPLES Writing and Evaluating Expressions

1 Define a variable and write an algebraic expression for the phrase "$10 plus $5 times the number of roses ordered."

Let n = the number of roses ordered   ← **Define the variable.**

$10 + 5 \cdot n$ ← **Write an algebraic expression.**

$10 + 5n$ ← **Rewrite 5 · n as 5n.**

2 Evaluate the expression for 12 roses.

$10 + 5n$

$10 + 5 \cdot 12$ ← **Evaluate the expression for 12 roses.**

$10 + 60$ ← **Multiply.**

70 ← **Simplify.**

If you order 12 roses, you will have to pay $70.

Quick Check

1. Define a variable and write an algebraic expression for "a man is two years younger than three times his son's age."

2. Evaluate the expression to find the man's age if his son is 13.

Suppose your grandmother sends you 5 games for your birthday. Each game has the same weight. The box she mails them in weighs 8 ounces. The total weight is 48 ounces. What is the weight of one game?

You can represent this situation with the diagram below.

Let g represent the weight of a game.

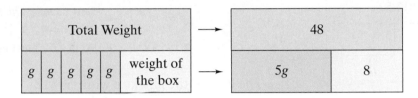

You can solve this problem using the equation $5g + 8 = 48$. Since there is more than one operation in the equation, there will be more than one step in the solution.

EXAMPLE   **Using Number Sense**

3   Solve $5g + 8 = 48$ by using number sense.

$5g + 8 = 48$

$\blacksquare + 8 = 48$ ← **Cover 5g.** *Think*: **What number added to 8 is 48? Answer: 40**

$5g = 40$ ← **So** $\blacksquare$, **or 5g, must equal 40.**

$5 \cdot \blacksquare = 40$ ← **Now cover g.** *Think*: **What number times 5 is 40? Answer: 8**

$g = 8$ ← **So** $\blacksquare$, **or g, must equal 8.**

Check

$5g + 8 = 48$ ← **Check your solution in the original equation.**

$5(8) + 8 \overset{?}{=} 48$ ← **Substitute 8 for g.**

$40 + 8 \overset{?}{=} 48$ ← **Simplify.**

$48 = 48$ ✔ ← **The solution checks.**

✓ Quick Check

3. Solve each equation using number sense.
   a. $3m + 9 = 21$ **b.** $8d + 5 = 45$ **c.** $4y - 11 = 33$

EXAMPLE   Application: Food

4 Suppose you buy a jumbo lemonade for $1.50 and divide the cost of an order of chicken wings with two friends. Your share of the total bill is $5.50. Write and solve an equation to find the cost of the chicken wings.

| **Words** | cost of lemonade | plus | (cost of wings ÷ 3) | is | $5.50 |

Let z = the cost of the chicken wings.

| **Expression** | 1.50 | + | $(z \div 3)$ | = | $5.50 |

$1.50 + \dfrac{z}{3} = 5.50$

$1.50 + \blacksquare = 5.50$ ← *Cover* $\frac{z}{3}$. *Think*: What number added to 1.50 is 5.50? Answer: 4

$\dfrac{z}{3} = 4$ ← So $\blacksquare$, or $\frac{z}{3}$, must equal 4.

$\dfrac{\blacksquare}{3} = 4$ ← Now cover *z*. *Think*: What number divided by 3 is 4? Answer: 12

$z = 12$ ← So $\blacksquare$, or *z*, must equal 12.

The cost of the chicken wings is $12.

Test Prep Tip

You can represent the relationships in the problem with this model.

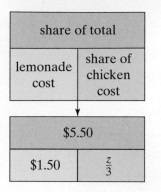

✓ Quick Check

4. Basketball During the first half of a game you scored 8 points. In the second half you made only 3-point baskets. You finished the game with 23 points. Write and solve an equation to find how many 3-point baskets you made.

✓ Check Your Understanding

1. **Vocabulary** What is the difference between a one-step expression and a two-step expression?

2. Write and solve the equation modeled at the left.

Match each phrase with the correct algebraic expression.

3. 10 centimeters less than twice *x*, your hand length

4. 10 people fewer than half *x*, the town's population

5. 10 more than two times a number *x*

A. $\frac{1}{2}x - 10$

B. $2x - 10$

C. $2x + 10$

Using number sense, fill in the missing number.

6. $4b + 5 = 17$
   $4b = \blacksquare$

7. $7c - 20 = 50$
   $7c = \blacksquare$

For more exercises, see Extra Skills and Word Problems.

GO for Help

For Exercises	See Examples
8–12	1
13–20	2
21–27	3–4

Define a variable and write an algebraic expression for each phrase.

8. two points fewer than 3 times the number of points scored before

9. one meter more than 6 times your height in meters

10. seven pages fewer than half the number of pages read last week

11. eight pounds less than five times the weight of a chicken

12. twice the distance in miles flown last year, plus 100 miles

Evaluate each expression for the given value of the variable.

13. $4m - 6.5$; $m = 2$

14. $5 + 2f$; $f = 6.1$

15. $12 - 3b$; $b = 4.3$

16. $6x + 2$; $x = 3$

17. $5y - 5$; $y = 5$

18. $7 + 8c$; $c = 7$

19. $2p + 4.5$; $p = 5.1$

20. $12 - 2.2s$; $s = 4$

Solve each equation using number sense. You may find a model helpful.

21. $2t + 9.4 = 39.8$

22. $4m + 12 = 52$

23. $10h + 14 = 84$

24. $7w + 16 = 37$

25. $3y + 13.6 = 40.6$

26. $5v + 19 = 24$

27. Money A fitness club advertises a special for new members. Each month of membership is $19, with an initial enrollment fee of $75. Write an expression for the total cost. Then evaluate your expression for 8 months of membership.

GPS

28. Guided Problem Solving You want to buy an iguana that costs $49. You already have $13. If you save $9 per week, when will you have enough money to buy the iguana?
 • How much money do you already have?
 • How much more money do you need?

29. 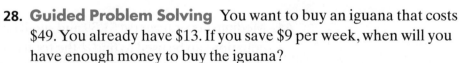 **Writing in Math** In addition to her hourly rate, an electrician charges a fee to come to your house. This can be modeled by $40h + 35 = 115$. Explain what each part of the equation represents. Then solve the equation to find the number of hours she works.

30. You order 3 posters advertised on the Internet. Each poster costs the same amount. The shipping charge is $5. The total cost of the posters plus the shipping charge is $41. Find the cost of one poster.

31. Open-Ended Describe a situation that can be modeled by the equation $\frac{b}{2} + 5 = 51$.

Solve each equation using number sense.

32. $5h + 3 = 18.5$ **33.** $3m - 7.6 = 26.9$ **34.** $8y + 17 = 65$

35. $\frac{x}{3} - 3 = 12$ **36.** $2p - 5 = 15$ **37.** $\frac{t}{4} + 1 = 6$

38. Telephone A cellular telephone company charges $40 per month plus a $35 activation fee. Write an expression for the total cost. Then evaluate your expression for 10 months of service.

39. Food You are helping to prepare food for a large family gathering. You can slice 2 zucchinis per minute. You need 30 sliced zucchinis. How long will it take you to finish, if you have already sliced 12 zucchinis?

40. Your family rented a car for a trip. The car rental cost $35 per day plus $.30/mile. After a one-day rental, the bill was $74. How many miles did your family drive?

41. Reasoning When you solve an equation, you must do the same operation to both sides. Explain why this is true.

42. Challenge You spend 5 minutes jogging as a warmup. Then you run 4 miles and cool down for 5 minutes. The total time you exercise is 54 minutes. What is your average time for running a mile?

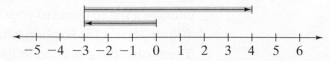
Test Prep and Mixed Review
Practice

Multiple Choice

43. Daniel bought one dozen tennis balls priced at 3 balls for $1.99 and a tennis racquet for $49.99. What is the total amount he spent, not including tax, on tennis balls and a tennis racquet?
   Ⓐ $51.98   Ⓒ $57.95
   Ⓑ $55.96   Ⓓ $73.87

44. Medium beverages cost $1.39 and small beverages cost $0.89. Which equation can be used to find d, the total cost in dollars of 6 medium drinks?
   Ⓕ $6 = 0.89d$ Ⓗ $6 = 1.39d$
   Ⓖ $d = 0.89(6)$ Ⓙ $d = 1.39(6)$

45. Which expression is represented by the model below?

   Ⓐ $-3 + 2$ Ⓑ $-3 + 4$ Ⓒ $-3 + 0$ Ⓓ $-3 + 7$

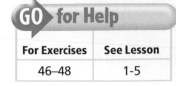

For Exercises	See Lesson
46–48	1-5

Compare each pair of rational numbers. Use <, =, or >.

46. $\frac{7}{9}$ ▇ $\frac{4}{5}$ **47.** $-\frac{9}{27}$ ▇ $\frac{1}{3}$ **48.** $\frac{5}{12}$ ▇ $-\frac{2}{6}$

Modeling Two-Step Equations

You can use algebra tiles to solve two-step equations.

EXAMPLE **Solving Two-Step Equations**

Use algebra tiles to solve $2x + 1 = 7$.

$2x + 1 = 7$  ← Model the equation. Use yellow tiles for positive integers.

$2x + 1 - 1 = 7 - 1$
$2x = 6$  ← Remove 1 yellow tile from each side.

$\dfrac{2x}{2} = \dfrac{6}{2}$  ← Divide each side into 2 equal groups.

$x = 3$  ← Simplify.

Exercises

Write and solve the equation represented by each model.

1.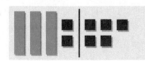

2.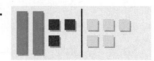

3.

Use algebra tiles to solve each equation.

4. $3x - 4 = 2$ 5. $2x - 1 = 9$ 6. $2x + 4 = 10$

7. $3x + 4 = 7$ 8. $2x + 6 = -8$ 9. $2x - 6 = -18$

10. At a county fair, an admission ticket costs $5, and each ride costs $2. You have $13. Write an algebraic equation for the number of rides you can go on. Use algebra tiles to solve the equation.

11. **Reasoning** Suppose you have 20 green, 20 red, and 20 yellow algebra tiles. Explain how you could use the tiles to model the equation $500x - 200 = 1{,}300$.

3-5 Solving Two-Step Equations

ⓒ **CONTENT STANDARDS**
7.EE.3, 7.EE.4.a

What You'll Learn

To solve two-step equations using inverse operations

Why Learn This?

Detectives often retrace steps to find missing information. Like detectives, you can work step-by-step to find a missing quantity. You can solve a two-step equation by using inverse operations and the properties of equality to get the variable on one side of the equation.

For many equations, you can undo addition or subtraction first. Then you can multiply or divide to get the variable alone.

EXAMPLE   **Undoing Subtraction First**

1 Solve $5n - 18 = -33$.

$$5n - 18 = -33$$

$$5n - 18 + 18 = -33 + 18 \qquad \leftarrow \text{To undo subtraction, add 18 to each side.}$$

$$5n = -15 \qquad \leftarrow \text{Simplify.}$$

$$\frac{5n}{5} = \frac{-15}{5} \qquad \leftarrow \text{To undo multiplication, divide each side by 5.}$$

$$n = -3 \qquad \leftarrow \text{Simplify.}$$

Check $5n - 18 = -33 \qquad \leftarrow$ Check your solution with the original equation.

$5(-3) - 18 \overset{?}{=} -33 \qquad \leftarrow$ Substitute -3 for n.

$-15 - 18 \overset{?}{=} -33 \qquad \leftarrow$ Simplify.

$-33 = -33 \; ✔ \qquad \leftarrow$ The solution checks.

✓ Quick Check

1. Solve the equation $-8y - 28 = -36$. Check your answer.

EXAMPLE **Undoing Addition First**

2 Solve $\frac{x}{3} + 11 = 16$.

$$\frac{x}{3} + 11 = 16$$

$$\frac{x}{3} + 11 - 11 = 16 - 11 \quad \leftarrow \textbf{To undo addition, subtract 11 from each side.}$$

$$\frac{x}{3} = 5 \quad \leftarrow \textbf{Simplify.}$$

$$3\left(\frac{x}{3}\right) = 3(5) \quad \leftarrow \textbf{To undo division, multiply each side by 3.}$$

$$x = 15 \quad \leftarrow \textbf{Simplify.}$$

✓ Quick Check

2. Solve the equation $\frac{x}{5} + 35 = 75$. Check your answer.

You can use two-step equations to solve real-world problems.

EXAMPLE **Solving Two-Step Equations**

3 **Multiple Choice** On weekday afternoons, a local bowling alley offers a special. Each bowling game costs $2.50, and shoe rental is $2.00. You spend $14.50 total. What is the number of games that you bowl?

   Ⓐ 3   Ⓑ 5   Ⓒ 7   Ⓓ 9

Words 2.50 times number of games plus 2.00 is 14.50

Let n = the number of games you bowl.

Equation 2.50 · n + 2.00 = 14.50

$$2.5n + 2 = 14.50$$

$$2.5n + 2 - 2 = 14.50 - 2 \quad \leftarrow \textbf{Subtract 2 from each side.}$$

$$2.5n = 12.50 \quad \leftarrow \textbf{Simplify.}$$

$$\frac{2.5n}{2.5} = \frac{12.50}{2.5} \quad \leftarrow \textbf{Divide each side by 2.5.}$$

$$n = 5 \quad \leftarrow \textbf{Simplify.}$$

You bowled 5 games. The answer is B.

Test Prep Tip

You can eliminate answer choices using number sense. Choice D can be eliminated because it is too high. If you played 9 games, your total cost would be greater than $18.

✓ Quick Check

3. Solomon decided to make posters for the student council election. He bought markers that cost $0.79 each and a poster board that cost $1.25. The total cost was $7.57. Write and solve an equation to find the number of markers that Solomon bought.

More Than One Way

A family expects 88 people to attend its family reunion. There will be 16 children. Picnic tables seat 8 adults per table. The children will eat on blankets. How many picnic tables does the family need?

Sarah's Method

I can use number sense. First, I know that tables are needed only for adults. There are $88 - 16$, or 72, adults. Each table holds 8 adults. Since $72 \div 8 = 9$, the family needs 9 tables.

Ryan's Method

I can write and solve an equation. Let t represent the number of tables. Then $8t$ is the number of adults.

adults + children = 88 people

$8t + 16 = 88$ ← Write the equation.

Each term is divisible by 8. So I will divide first.

$$\frac{8t}{8} + \frac{16}{8} = \frac{88}{8}$$ ← Divide each term by 8.

$$t + 2 = 11$$ ← Simplify.

I can use mental math to solve the equation. I know that 9 plus 2 is equal to 11. So, the family needs 9 tables.

Choose a Method

You had $25 in your savings account six weeks ago. You deposited the same amount of money each week for five weeks. Your balance is now $145. How much money did you deposit each week? Describe your method and explain why you chose it.

Check Your Understanding

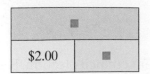

1. Fill in the missing numbers to make the diagram at the left represent the following situation: A taxi charges a flat fee of $2.00 plus $0.50 for each mile. Your fare is $5.00. How many miles did you ride?

Solve each equation. Check your answer.

2. $5p - 2 = 18$ 3. $7n - (-16) = 100$ 4. $\frac{y}{4.25} + 15 = -17$

For more exercises, see Extra Skills and Word Problems.

GO for Help

For Exercises	See Examples
5–16	1
17–29	2-3

Solve each equation. Check your answer. You may find a model helpful.

5. $8r - 8 = -32$

6. $3w - 6 = -1.5$

7. $4g - 4 = 28$

8. $7t - 6 = -104$

9. $12x - 14 = -2$

10. $10m - \frac{2}{5} = 9\frac{3}{5}$

11. $0.5y - 1.1 = 4.9$

12. $-2d - 1.7 = -3.9$

13. $-8a - 1 = -23$

14. $2h - \frac{1}{10} = \frac{5}{8}$

15. $6t - \frac{1}{6} = 9$

16. $5q - 3.75 = 26.25$

17. $\frac{w}{5} + 3 = 6$

18. $\frac{n}{4} + 2 = 4$

19. $\frac{x}{8} + 4 = 13$

20. $\frac{a}{7} + 10 = 17$

21. $\frac{m}{-11} + 1 = -10$

22. $\frac{p}{9} + 14 = 16$

23. $\frac{c}{-7} + 3.2 = -2.2$

24. $\frac{v}{-3} + \frac{3}{4} = -\frac{1}{8}$

25. $\frac{b}{-8} + \frac{5}{7} = \frac{11}{14}$

26. $\frac{c}{2} + 7.3 = 29.3$

27. $\frac{m}{-10} + 12 = 67$

28. $\frac{y}{-6.5} + 2 = -4$

29. Kristine bought a vase that cost $5.99 and roses that cost $1.25 each. The total cost was $20.99. Write and solve an equation to find how many roses Kristine bought.

30. Guided Problem Solving Renting canoes on a lake costs $22 per hour plus a flat fee of $10 for insurance. You have $98. Write and solve an equation to find the number of hours you can rent a canoe.

- insurance plus 22 times number of hours = total paid

Write and solve an equation for each situation.

31. A skating rink rents skates at $3.95 for the first hour plus $1.25 for each additional hour. When you returned your skates, you paid $7.70. How many additional hours did you keep the skates?

32. Jobs You earn $20 per hour landscaping a yard. You pay $1.50 in bus fare each way. How many hours must you work to earn $117?

33. Geometry The sum of the measures of the angles in a triangle is 180 degrees. One angle measures 45 degrees. The measures of the other two angles are equal. What is the measure of each of the other two angles?

34. Olympics The first modern Olympic games were held in Greece in 1896. The 2004 Olympic games in Athens had 202 participating countries. The number of countries in the 2004 Olympic games was 6 more than 14 times the number of countries in the 1896 games. How many countries participated in the 1896 Olympic games?

$2400 plus
$184 per credit

Solve each equation.

35. $\dfrac{x + 4}{5} = 3$

36. $\dfrac{t - 7}{-2} = 11$

37. $\dfrac{y + \frac{1}{3}}{4} = 2\frac{1}{4}$

38. Writing in Math Your class budgets a certain amount of money from the class treasury for a dance. Expenses will include a fixed amount for decorations, plus an hourly wage for the disc jockey. This can be represented by the equation $30x + 65 = 170$. Explain how each number in the equation relates to the problem.

39. College In college, you earn credits for courses taken. For one semester, tuition at a local college is $2,400. You have financial aid that will cover $5,160 for the semester. Refer to the information at the left. How many credits can you take?

40. The student council sponsored a bake sale to raise money. Kim bought a slice of cake for $1.50 and also bought six cupcakes. She spent $4.20 in all. How much did each cupcake cost?

41. Open-Ended Write two different two-step equations that both have a solution of 3.

42. Challenge You buy 1.25 lb of apples and 2.45 lb of bananas. The total cost, after using a 75¢-off coupon, is $2.58. Apples and bananas sell for the same price per pound. Find their price per pound.

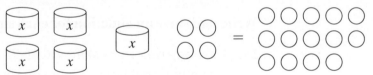

Test Prep and Mixed Review   **Practice**

Multiple Choice

43. The model below represents the equation $5x + 4 = 14$.

What is the value of x?

Ⓐ $x = \dfrac{18}{5}$ Ⓑ $x = 2$ Ⓒ $x = -2$ Ⓓ $x = 5$

44. The Dead Sea is 1,345 feet below sea level. What method can be used to find the altitude of the Dead Sea in yards?
Ⓕ Multiply $-1,345$ by 46.   Ⓗ Divide $-1,345$ by 12.
Ⓖ Multiply $-1,345$ by 3.   Ⓙ Divide $-1,345$ by 3.

45. What is the value of the expression $2(15 - 12)^2 \div 6 + 3$?
Ⓐ 12   Ⓑ 9   Ⓒ 6   Ⓓ 2

GO for Help

For Exercises	See Lesson
46–48	3-3

Describe a problem situation that matches each equation. Then solve.

46. $r + 11 = 2$ **47.** $h - 9 = 5.5$ **48.** $\frac{1}{6}q = 9$

Solve each equation.

1. $g - 5 = -9.4$

2. $y + 10.2 = 12$

3. $-5x = 45.5$

4. $\frac{h}{6} = 8$

5. $t - 3.02 = 2.98$

6. $\frac{r - 8}{4} = \frac{1}{2}$

7. $3x + 4 = 19$

8. $\frac{t}{5} - 2 = 6$

9. $-2y - 5 = -9$

10. $\frac{d}{-3} + 7 = 10$

11. $6g + 6 = -6$

12. $\frac{f}{-1} - 8 = -3$

13. Fingernails grow about 1.5 inches per year. How long would it take to grow nails 37 inches long?

14. A sweater costs \$12 more than twice the cost of a skirt. The sweater costs \$38. Find the cost of the skirt.

MATH AT WORK

Detective

Most people think of a detective as a person in a trench coat, looking for clues. In reality, detectives dress like anyone else. They can work for lawyers, government agencies, and businesses. Detectives may gather information to trace debtors or conduct background investigations.

Detectives use mathematics to locate stolen funds, develop financial profiles, or monitor expense accounts.

Go Online For information about detectives
PearsonSuccessNet.com

Practice Solving Problems

Big Burgers The world's largest hamburger weighed 8,266 lb. If half of the weight was meat, how many regular quarter-pound hamburgers could have been made from that burger?

What You Might Think

> What do I know?
> What am I trying to find out?

> How do I show the main idea?

> How do I estimate the answer?

> How do I solve the problem?

> What is the answer?
> Is it reasonable?

What You Might Write

The burger weighed 8,266 lb and $\frac{1}{2}$ was meat. How many $\frac{1}{4}$ pounds is that?

Draw a diagram.

8,266	
meat	other

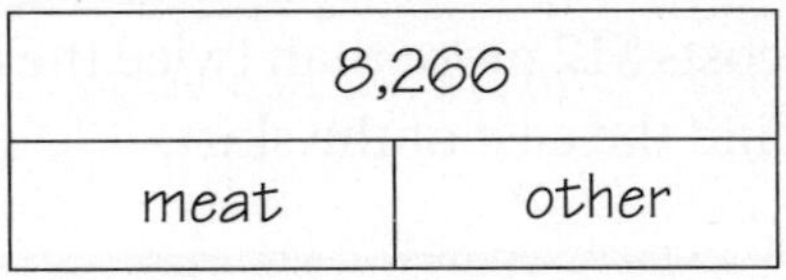

↳ How many $\frac{1}{4}$-lb burgers can be made from the meat?

8,266 lb is about 8,000 lb. Half of that is 4,000 lb. How many $\frac{1}{4}$ pounds are in 4,000 lb? Solve either $\frac{1}{4}x = 4,000$ or $x = 4,000 \div \frac{1}{4}$.

$x = 16,000$

$8,266 \div 2 = 4,133$
Write and solve an equation.
$\frac{1}{4}x = 4,133$

$x = 16,532$

The answer is 16,532 burgers. It's reasonable. The answer is close to the estimate of 16,000.

Think It Through

1. In the diagram, why do *meat* and *other* equally share the space under 8,266?

2. Explain why $\frac{1}{4}x = 4,000$ and $x = 4,000 \div \frac{1}{4}$ are equivalent.

Exercises

Solve. For Exercises 3 and 4, answer the questions first.

3. To celebrate National Hot Dog Month, a beef company made a hot dog that measured 16 feet 1 inch. A regular hot dog is $5\frac{1}{2}$ inches long. How many regular hot dogs would you need to make this hot dog?
   a. What do you know? What do you want to find out?
   b. Explain how the diagram below shows the situation. Write an equation.

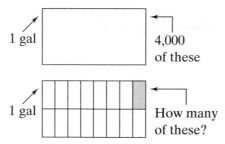

4. The world's largest glass of milk held 4,000 gallons. A gallon holds 16 cups. How many cups were in the world's largest glass of milk?
   a. Explain how the diagram below shows the situation. Write an equation.

5. a. Look at the graph at the right. Estimate how many more calories per day an American consumed in 2000 than in 1980.
   b. Suppose the increase in calories per day was entirely from hamburgers. A quarter-pound hamburger has about 450 calories. About how many more burgers per week did an American eat in 2000 than in 1980?

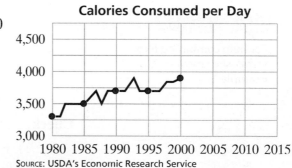

6. Assume the graph at the right keeps climbing at the same rate. Estimate the number of calories an average American consumes each day this year.

7. A 125-pound soccer player burns about 65 calories in 10 minutes. How long would the player need to play to burn up a snack that contains 260 calories?

3-6 Solving Multi-Step Equations

Check Skills You'll Need

1. **Vocabulary Review** Identify the *like terms* in $3x + 2x + 8 - x$.

Simplify.

2. $5 - 3m + 7 - 23m$

3. $4(7 - 3r)$

4. $(q + 1)5 + 3q$

for Help
Lesson 3-2

© **CONTENT STANDARDS**
7.EE.4.a, 8.EE.7, 8.EE.7.b

for Help

For help combining like terms, see Lesson 3-2, Example 1.

What You'll Learn

To write and solve multi-step equations

Why Learn This?

You can model many situations with one- and two-step equations. More complicated situations, such as finding the cost of multiple items, involve multiple steps.

You often need to simplify at least one side of an equation before solving it. To simplify, you combine like terms.

EXAMPLE Simplifying Before Solving an Equation

1 Solve $3n + 9 + 4n = 2$.

$$3n + 9 + 4n = 2$$
$$3n + 4n + 9 = 2 \quad \leftarrow \text{Commutative Property}$$
$$7n + 9 = 2 \quad \leftarrow \text{Combine like terms.}$$
$$7n + 9 - 9 = 2 - 9 \quad \leftarrow \text{Subtract 9 from each side.}$$
$$7n = -7 \quad \leftarrow \text{Simplify.}$$
$$\frac{7n}{7} = \frac{-7}{7} \quad \leftarrow \text{Divide each side by 7.}$$
$$n = -1 \quad \leftarrow \text{Simplify.}$$

Check $3n + 9 + 4n = 2$
$$3(-1) + 9 + 4(-1) \stackrel{?}{=} 2 \quad \leftarrow \text{Substitute } -1 \text{ for } n.$$
$$2 = 2 \ ✔ \quad \leftarrow \text{The solution checks.}$$

✓ Quick Check

1. Solve $-15 = 5b + 12 - 2b + 6$. Check the solution.

You can use the Distributive Property to simplify an equation.

EXAMPLE Using the Distributive Property

2 Multiple Choice Your class hopes to collect 1,200 returnable bottles to raise money for a class trip. During the first week, the 24 students in your class collect an average of 34 bottles each. How many more bottles per student should the class collect?

  Ⓐ 11 bottles   Ⓑ 16 bottles   Ⓒ 49 bottles   Ⓓ 384 bottles

Words   24 students $\cdot$ ($\dfrac{34\text{ bottles}}{\text{per student}}$ + $\dfrac{\text{additional}}{\text{bottles per}}_{\text{student}}$) = 1,200 bottles

Equation   Let r = the number of additional bottles.

$$24 \quad \cdot \quad (34 \quad + \quad r) \quad = \quad 1,200$$

$$24(34 + r) = 1,200$$
$$816 + 24r = 1,200 \quad \leftarrow \textbf{Distributive Property}$$
$$816 - 816 + 24r = 1,200 - 816 \quad \leftarrow \textbf{Subtract 816 from each side.}$$
$$24r = 384 \quad \leftarrow \textbf{Simplify.}$$
$$\frac{24r}{24} = \frac{384}{24} \quad \leftarrow \textbf{Divide each side by 24.}$$
$$r = 16 \quad \leftarrow \textbf{Simplify.}$$

Each student should collect 16 more bottles. The correct answer is choice B.

Check for Reasonableness Round 24 to 20 and 34 to 40. The class collected about $20 \cdot 40$, or 800 bottles. They need to collect 400 more, or 20 bottles per student. 16 is close to 20. The answer is reasonable.

Test Prep Tip Ⓐ Ⓑ Ⓒ Ⓓ

Be sure to answer the question asked. You need to find the number of additional bottles each student should collect, not the total number each should collect.

✓ Quick Check

2. **Class Trips** Your class goes to an amusement park. Admission is $10 for each student and $15 for each chaperone. The total cost is $380. There are 12 girls in your class and 6 chaperones on the trip. How many boys are in your class?

You can also use division to simplify equations. The algebra tiles below model one way to simplify the equation $2(x + 1) = 12$. First, divide each side by 2, grouping the tiles into two equal groups. Then, remove one group from each side. The simplified equation is $x + 1 = 6$.

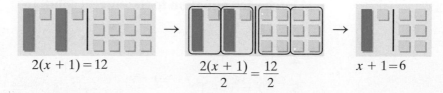

$2(x + 1) = 12$ $\dfrac{2(x + 1)}{2} = \dfrac{12}{2}$ $x + 1 = 6$

More Than One Way

Solve the equation $5(2.9 + k) = 8.3$.

Eric's Method

I'll use the Distributive Property to eliminate the parentheses.

$$5(2.9 + k) = 8.3$$
$$5(2.9) + 5k = 8.3 \quad \leftarrow \text{Distributive Property}$$
$$14.5 + 5k = 8.3 \quad \leftarrow \text{Simplify.}$$
$$14.5 - 14.5 + 5k = 8.3 - 14.5 \quad \leftarrow \text{Subtract 14.5 from each side.}$$
$$5k = -6.2 \quad \leftarrow \text{Simplify.}$$
$$\frac{5k}{5} = \frac{-6.2}{5} \quad \leftarrow \text{Divide each side by 5.}$$
$$k = -1.24 \quad \leftarrow \text{Simplify.}$$

Jasmine's Method

I'll use division to eliminate the parentheses.

$$5(2.9 + k) = 8.3$$
$$\frac{5(2.9 + k)}{5} = \frac{8.3}{5} \quad \leftarrow \text{Divide each side by 5.}$$
$$2.9 + k = 1.66 \quad \leftarrow \text{Simplify.}$$
$$2.9 - 2.9 + k = 1.66 - 2.9 \quad \leftarrow \text{Subtract 2.9 from each side.}$$
$$k = -1.24 \quad \leftarrow \text{Simplify.}$$

Choose a Method

Solve $3(m - 6.5) = 27$. Explain why you chose the method you used.

Check Your Understanding

1. **Vocabulary** When you simplify an expression, you combine   ?   terms.

2. Describe the first step in simplifying the expression $2h - 4(h - 5)$.

Match each equation to the correct solution.

3. $-7 + x = 4$

4. $16 = -2x$

5. $-9 = x - 12$

A. -8

B. 3

C. 11

For more exercises, see Extra Skills and Word Problems.

GO for Help

For Exercises	See Examples
6–13	1
14–20	2

Solve each equation. Check the solution. Write your answer in simplest form.

6. $5h + 2 - h = 22$

7. $-8 = \frac{1}{10}z + \frac{3}{10}z$

8. $3b + b - 8 = 4$

9. $3a + 12 - 6a = -9$

10. $21 = 6 - 2.3x - 2.7x$

11. $2m + 8 - 4m = 28$

12. $-3y + 4 + 5y = -6$

13. $8 = \frac{3}{4}c + 12 - c + 4$

14. $4(m + 3) = -32$

15. $14 = 2(s + 5)$

16. $40 = 1.6(d - 2)$

17. $\frac{8}{9}(z - 1) = 16$

18. $-2(x - 9) = -24$

19. $7(4 - t) = -84$

20. Food You want to buy 4 lb of Cortland apples and some Gala apples. Each variety of apple costs $1.20/lb. You can spend $7.20. How many pounds of Gala apples can you buy?

21. Guided Problem Solving You mailed 3 identical letters weighing more than 1 oz each. Mailing each letter cost $0.37 for the first ounce, plus $0.23 for each additional ounce. Each letter required $1.29 postage. How much did each letter weigh, to the nearest ounce?
- **Make a Plan** Write and solve an equation to solve for *x*, the number of additional ounces.
- **Check the Answer** Be sure you answer the question asked.

22. Jobs An employee earns $7.00 an hour for the first 35 hours worked in a week and $10.50 for any hours over 35. One week's paycheck (before deductions) was for $308.00. How many hours did the employee work?

GO Online
Homework Video Tutor
PearsonSuccessNet.com

Use this information to write an equation for Exercises 23–25.
When you count by ones from any integer, you are counting consecutive integers. Using variables, three consecutive integers are *n*, *n* + 1, and *n* + 2.

23. The sum of two consecutive integers is −45. What are they?

24. The sum of three consecutive integers is 48. What are they?

25. The sum of three consecutive integers is −255. What are they?

26. Writing in Math To solve $5y - 2 - 3y = 8$, can you start by adding 2 to each side? Justify your reasoning.

Solve each equation. Write your answer in simplest form.

27. $15 = -3(c - 1) + 9$

28. $2(1.5n + 4) - 6n = -7$

29. $2(z - 20) + 3z = 10$

30. $\frac{2}{5}s - 2 + 3(s - 11) = 50$

Write an equation for each diagram. Then find the unknown lengths.

31.

21 ft

m m m m 5 ft

32.

1,000 in.

y $2y$ 505 in.

33. **Choose a Method** To make peanut butter and jelly sandwiches for her class, a teacher bought bread for $2.79 per loaf, peanut butter for $3.19 per jar, and jars of jelly. The total cost was $14.56. If the teacher bought two of each item, what was the cost of one jar of jelly? Explain why you chose the method you used.

34. **Challenge** Solve $1.5 - 0.25(a + 4) = 3 + 3(0.05 - 0.5a)$.

Test Prep and Mixed Review

Ⓐ Ⓑ Ⓒ Ⓓ

Practice

Multiple Choice

35. Two classes went to the zoo for $5 per person. The total cost was $200. One class has 19 people. Solve the equation $5(n + 19) = 200$ to find n, the number of people in the other class.

Ⓐ 105　　　　　Ⓒ 21

Ⓑ 36　　　　　Ⓓ 10

36. You are working 20 hours a week over the summer. You earn x dollars per hour. Your boss gives you a bonus of $17 dollars during your first week. Which of these is an expression that shows the amount you will make during your first week at your job?

Ⓕ $20 \times 17 + x$　　　Ⓗ $20x + 17$

Ⓖ $20 + 17x$　　　　Ⓙ $20x \times 17$

37. An online movie club offers a plan that costs $8.50 per month with a $15 registration fee. How much would it cost to join the club for a year and a half?

Ⓐ $27.75　　　　Ⓒ $117

Ⓑ $168　　　　　Ⓓ $170

38. In one evening, customers at a restaurant ordered 72 dinners. Fifty-six customers ordered salad with their dinners. The rest ordered soup. What fraction of the dinners was ordered with soup?

Ⓕ $\dfrac{7}{9}$　　　　Ⓗ $\dfrac{1}{4}$

Ⓖ $\dfrac{2}{8}$　　　　Ⓙ $\dfrac{2}{9}$

Algebra Solve each equation.

39. $\dfrac{n}{4} - 1 = 10$

40. $\dfrac{x}{-5} - 7 = 8$

41. $\dfrac{a}{8} + 12 = -4$

GO for Help

For Exercises	See Lesson
39–41	3-5

Online lesson quiz, PearsonSuccessNet.com

3-7 Solving Equations With Variables on Both Sides

Check Skills You'll Need

1. **Vocabulary Review**
   Operations that undo each other are called __?__.

Simplify.

2. $9(t + 7) - 16$

3. $12 - 6(2r - 8)$

4. $2x - (5x + 7)$.

GO for Help
Lesson 3-2

© CONTENT STANDARDS
8.EE.7, 8.EE.7.b

What You'll Learn

To write and solve equations with variables on both sides

Why Learn This?

Equations can help you calculate your savings from part-time jobs. An equation shows that two expressions are equal. Because expressions can contain variables, some equations have variables on both sides of the equal sign.

To solve an equation with variables on both sides, bring all the variable terms to one side of the equation.

EXAMPLE Variables on Both Sides

① Solve $7 + 3h = -1 - 5h$.

$$7 + 3h = -1 - 5h$$
$$7 + 3h + 5h = -1 - 5h + 5h \quad \leftarrow \text{Add } 5h \text{ to each side.}$$
$$7 + 8h = -1 \quad \leftarrow \text{Combine like terms.}$$
$$7 - 7 + 8h = -1 - 7 \quad \leftarrow \text{Subtract 7 from each side.}$$
$$8h = -8 \quad \leftarrow \text{Simplify.}$$
$$\frac{8h}{8} = \frac{-8}{8} \quad \leftarrow \text{Divide each side by 8.}$$
$$h = -1 \quad \leftarrow \text{Simplify.}$$

Check $7 + 3h = -1 - 5h$
$$7 + 3(-1) \stackrel{?}{=} -1 - 5(-1) \quad \leftarrow \text{Substitute } -1 \text{ for } h.$$
$$4 = 4 \; ✔ \quad \leftarrow \text{The solution checks.}$$

✓ Quick Check

1. Solve $7b - 2 = b + 10$. Check the solution.

EXAMPLE   **Application: Science**

② **Gridded Response** Your science class is doing an experiment. You start with 2 plants. Plant A is 5 cm tall and Plant B is 8 cm tall. Plant A is fertilized and grows 2 cm per day. Plant B is not fertilized and grows 1.5 cm per day. Predict in how many days the plants will be the same height.

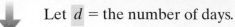

Words 5 + 2 cm · number of days = 8 + 1.5 cm · number of days

Let d = the number of days.

Equation 5 + 2 · d = 8 + 1.5 · d

Test Prep Tip

You can also solve the equation at the right by moving all of the variables to the left side.

$$5 + 2d = 8 + 1.5d$$
$$5 + 2d - 2d = 8 + 1.5d - 2d \quad \leftarrow \text{Subtract } 2d \text{ from each side.}$$
$$5 = 8 - 0.5d \quad \leftarrow \text{Simplify.}$$
$$5 - 8 = 8 - 8 - 0.5d \quad \leftarrow \text{Subtract 8 from each side.}$$
$$-3 = -0.5d \quad \leftarrow \text{Simplify.}$$
$$\frac{-3}{-0.5} = \frac{-0.5d}{-0.5} \quad \leftarrow \text{Divide each side by } -0.5.$$
$$6 = d \quad \leftarrow \text{Simplify.}$$

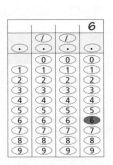

The plants will be the same height in 6 days.

✅ Quick Check

2. One cell phone plan costs $29.94 per month plus $0.10 for each text message sent. Another plan costs $32.99 per month plus $0.05 for each text message sent. For what number of text messages will the monthly bill for both plans be the same?

✓ Check Your Understanding

Identify the like terms in each group of expressions.

1. $-\frac{7}{9}, -2.8, 3, 0$ 2. xy, x, y, yx 3. $11a, -4.1a^2, a, a^2$

4. Is 7 a solution of the equation $3x + 8 - x = 5x - 4$?

5. **Error Analysis** A student solved an equation as shown at the left. Explain the error the student made. Solve the equation correctly.

$$3x + 4 - x = 7 + x$$
$$3x + 4 = 7$$
$$3x = 3$$
$$x = 1$$

6. **Mental Math** Is the solution of $2x = 3x - 12 - 5x$ a positive or a negative integer? Explain.

For more exercises, see Extra Skills and Word Problems.

For Exercises	See Examples
7–15	1–2

Solve each equation. Check the solution.

7. $2 + 14z = -8 + 9z$

8. $-8 - 5y = 12 - 9y$

9. $22 + 2x = 37 + 6 + x$

10. $\frac{2}{3}d + 1 = 16 - d$

11. $-k = 9(k - 10)$

12. $7m = 9(m + 4)$

13. $0.8(4 - a) = 5.6a$

14. $8 - 3(p - 4) = 2p$

15. At Video Shack, movie rentals cost $3.99 each. The cost of renting three movies and one video game is $0.11 less than the cost of renting five video games. How much does renting a video game cost?

16. Guided Problem Solving A croquet ball weighs 460 grams. Together a golf ball and a croquet ball weigh the same as 11 golf balls. How much does one golf ball weigh?
- What quantity will you represent with a variable?
- Write and solve an equation.

17. Efren leaves home at 9 A.M. and walks 4 miles per hour. His brother, Gregory, leaves half an hour later and runs 8.5 miles per hour in the same direction as Efren. Predict the time at which Gregory will catch up to Efren.

GO **Online**

Homework Video Tutor

PearsonSuccessNet.com

18. Writing in Math Explain how to solve an equation with the same variable on both sides.

19. Challenge Solve $0.75 + 2(x - 0.5) = 3x - 0.4$.

Test Prep and Mixed Review

Practice

Gridded Response

20. The side of a square is $2x + 8$ inches long. The perimeter of the square is $20x + 8$ inches. What is the side length of the square in inches?

21. A selection of jigsaw puzzles at one store is priced at $12 each. During a sale, a customer who buys 2 of these puzzles at the regular price may buy additional puzzles at half price. How many puzzles could a customer buy for $42?

GO **for Help**

For Exercises	See Lesson
23–24	3-6

22. A square has an area of 40 square units. To the nearest tenth, how many units long is each side of the square?

Algebra **Solve each equation.**

23. $6q + 3 - 4q = 9$

24. $7(x + 1) - 1 = 34$

Writing Equations

Ticket Prices Mr. and Mrs. Smith have two children, ages 4 and 8. They are trying to decide whether to buy day passes or a yearly membership to an aquarium. After how many single-day visits would it be better for the Smiths to have a yearly membership?

Aquarium Ticket Prices

Single-Day Tickets

Adults $21.95
Children $10.95

Yearly Membership

Unlimited visits for
2 adults and
2 children (3–12) $175

What You Might Think

> What do I know? What do I want to find out?

> What equation can I write?

> When will the cost of single-day tickets equal the cost of a yearly membership?

> Is the answer reasonable?

What You Might Write

I know single-day tickets are $21.95 for adults and $10.95 for children.
Two adult tickets → 2 × $21.95 = $43.90.
Two child tickets → 2 × $10.95 = $21.90.
A yearly membership is $175. I want to find when a yearly membership would be less expensive.

Let d = the number of visits. Then the total cost of d visits is $43.90d + 21.90d$.

$$43.90d + 21.90d = 175$$
$$65.80d = 175$$
$$d \approx 2.66$$

Since you cannot have 2.66 visits, round the answer up to 3. So for three or more visits it would be better to have the yearly membership.

The cost for single-day tickets is about $40 + $20 or $60. 3 × $60 = $180. So 3 visits is a reasonable answer.

Think It Through

1. **Reasoning** Can an answer to this problem be 2 visits? Explain.

2. Can you use the following equation to solve this problem? Explain.
$$21.95d + 21.95d + 10.95d + 10.95d = 175$$

Exercises

Solve each problem. For Exercises 3 and 4, answer parts (a) and (b) first.

3. The cost of a membership at a health club last year was 75% of the cost at the club this year. This year's membership costs $20 more than last year's membership. Find the cost of a membership last year and the cost of a membership this year.
   a. Let x = the cost of last year's membership. What is the cost of this year's membership?
   b. Represent the cost of last year's membership as $0.75(x + 20)$. To find the value of x, solve $x = 0.75(x + 20)$.

4. A camp counselor buys granola bars and juice drinks for the campers. She decides to buy 3 times as many drinks as granola bars. Predict how many of each she can buy on a budget of $24.

   a. Let x = the number of granola bars the counselor buys and let $3x$ = the number of juice drinks she buys. What is the cost of x granola bars? The cost of $3x$ juice drinks?
   b. Use your answers to part (a) to write and solve an equation to find how many of each the camp leader can buy.

5. In a random survey of adults and children, children were found to have 23% more snacks between meals each year than adults. Altogether, the adults and children in this survey had 3,000 snacks between meals in one year. About how many snacks did the children in this survey have in one year? (*Hint:* Let x = the number of between-meal snacks the adults in this survey had in one year.)

Checkpoint Quiz 3

Solve each equation.

1. $-z - (z - 6) = 8$

2. $5a + 4 - 2a = 10$

3. $6(s + 0.3) = 18$

4. $-\frac{2}{3}(7 - w) = -6$

5. $6 + 2m = -3 + 5m$

6. $2.5 - 4f = 10 - 2.5f$

7. $\frac{2}{5}(k + 10) = \frac{2}{3}k$

8. $9 - 2(b + 3) = 4b$

Write and solve an equation to answer each question. Round to the nearest hundredth, if necessary.

9. **Jobs** An employee earns 1.5 times the hourly rate for each hour worked in a week over 40 hours. One week the employee worked 46 hours and earned $588 (before deductions). What is the employee's hourly rate?

10. **Food** A pineapple costs $5.04. Together one banana and one pineapple cost the same as 13 bananas. What does one banana cost?

MATH GAMES

Greatest Solution

What You'll Need

Four players

How to Play

- The first player names two terms containing the same variable, such as $3x$ and $-2x$, and two numbers, such as 4 and 1.

- The other three players write an equation using all the terms the first player named. The terms may be arranged in any order, and any operation signs may be used. Parentheses may also be used.

- The players solve the equations they wrote.

- The number in a player's solution is the number of points that player receives for the round.

- The game continues for 3 more rounds. A different player names the terms for each round.

- The player with greatest total points is the winner.

3-8 Types of Solutions of Linear Equations

✓ Check Skills You'll Need

1. **Vocabulary Review**
   A value of the variable for which an equation is true is a __?__ of the equation.

Solve each equation. Check the solution.

2. $2a + 4 = 4a - 2$

3. $3w - 1 = -2(w + 3)$

4. $3(z - 2) = 5z + 1$

 **for Help**
Lesson 3-7

© CONTENT STANDARDS
8.EE.7, 8.EE.7.a, 8.EE.7.b

What You'll Learn

To identify whether a linear equation in one variable has one, infinitely many, or no solutions

Why Learn This?

Equations with variables on both sides can help you check whether two ways of paying for something, such as swimming lessons, cost the same.

The equations solved in this chapter so far have resulted in a variable equal to a number. Sometimes, solving an equation may result in a number equal to the same number, or a different number. Each of these results indicates how many solutions an equation has. This is summarized in the table below, where x represents the variable and a and b represent different numbers.

KEY CONCEPTS Types of Solutions

Algebraic Form	Number of Solutions	Description
$a = b$	None	There are *no* values of the variable for which the equation is true.
$x = a$	One	The equation is true for *exactly one* value of the variable.
$a = a$	Infinitely many	The equation is true for *all* values of the variable.

EXAMPLE Identifying Types of Solutions

1. Tell whether each equation has one solution, infinitely many solutions, or no solution. Justify your answer.

   a.
   $$2x - 4 = -x - 1$$
   $$2x + 1x - 4 = -x + 1x - 1 \quad \leftarrow \textbf{Add 1}x \textbf{ to each side.}$$
   $$3x - 4 = -1 \quad \leftarrow \textbf{Simplify.}$$
   $$3x - 4 + 4 = -1 + 4 \quad \leftarrow \textbf{Add 4 to each side.}$$
   $$3x = 3 \quad \leftarrow \textbf{Simplify.}$$
   $$x = 1 \quad \leftarrow \textbf{Divide both sides by 3.}$$

   The result is an equation of the form $x = a$. This equation is true for exactly one value. So, the equation has one solution.

b.
$$2x - 4 = 2(x - 2)$$
$$2x - 4 = 2x - 4 \qquad \leftarrow \text{Use the Distributive Property.}$$
$$2x - 4 - 2x = 2x - 4 - 2x \qquad \leftarrow \text{Subtract } 2x \text{ from each side.}$$
$$-4 = -4 \qquad \leftarrow \text{Simplify.}$$

The result is an equation of the form $a = a$. This equation is true for all values of x. So, the equation has infinitely many solutions.

c.
$$2x - 4 = 2(x + 1)$$
$$2x - 4 = 2x + 2 \qquad \leftarrow \text{Use the Distributive Property.}$$
$$2x - 4 - 2x = 2x + 2 - 2x \qquad \leftarrow \text{Subtract } 2x \text{ from each side.}$$
$$-4 = 2 \qquad \leftarrow \text{Simplify.}$$

The result is an equation of the form $a = b$. There are no values of x for which the equation is true. So, the equation has no solution.

✓ Quick Check

1. Tell whether each equation has one solution, infinitely many solutions, or no solution. Justify your answer.
   a. $5x + 8 = 5(x + 3)$ **b.** $9x = 8 + 5x$
   c. $6x + 12 = 6(x + 2)$ **d.** $7x - 11 = 11 - 7x$

EXAMPLE   **Application: Comparing Costs**

2. **Sports** You want to take 10 lessons at a swim club. You can pay a membership fee of $20 plus a fee per lesson. You can also decide not to pay a membership fee. In that case, the fee per lesson is $3 more. Is there any lesson fee for which these two plans cost the same? Justify your answer.

Words $\dfrac{\text{membership}}{\text{fee}} + \boxed{\dfrac{10}{\text{lessons}}} \cdot \boxed{\dfrac{\text{lesson}}{\text{fee}}} = \boxed{\dfrac{10}{\text{lessons}}} \cdot \left(\boxed{\dfrac{\text{lesson}}{\text{fee}}} + \boxed{\$3}\right)$

Equation Let f = lesson fee.

$$20 \quad + \quad 10 \quad \cdot \quad f \quad = \quad 10 \quad \cdot \quad (f + 3)$$
$$20 + 10f = 10(f + 3)$$
$$20 + 10f = 10f + 30 \qquad \leftarrow \text{Use the Distributive Property.}$$
$$20 + 10f - 10f = 10f + 30 - 10f \qquad \leftarrow \text{Subtract } 10f \text{ from each side.}$$
$$20 = 30 \qquad \leftarrow \text{Simplify.}$$

The result is an equation of the form $a = b$. So the equation has no solution. There is no lesson fee for which these two plans cost the same.

✓ Quick Check

2. Admission to the museum is $8 for students and $16 for adults. Yesterday, twice as many students as adults came to the museum. The total admissions paid by students and the total admissions paid by adults were equal. Can you find the number of adults that came to the museum yesterday? Justify your answer.

1. **Vocabulary** When any value can be substituted for the variable in an equation to create a true equation, the equation has __?__ solution(s).

Match each equation to the correct number of solutions.

2. $4x + 8 = 4(x + 4)$ **A.** one

3. $5x = 9 + 2x$ **B.** infinitely many

4. $x + 9 = 7x + 9 - 6x$ **C.** none

5. **Reasoning** What number could you substitute for a in the equation $6x + 9 = a(2x + 3)$ to create an equation with infinitely many solutions? Explain.

Homework Exercises

For more exercises, see **Extra Skills and Word Problems.**

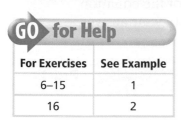

For Exercises	See Example
6–15	1
16	2

Show whether each equation has one solution, infinitely many solutions, or no solution. Justify your answer.

6. $7x = 3x - 12$

7. $3x + 3 = 3(x + 1)$

8. $22y = 11(3 + y)$

9. $-3t + 1 = t + 9 - 4t$

10. $16z - 24 = 8(2z - 3)$

11. $-5w = 7 - 4w + 8$

12. $4(-x - 1.6) = -4x + 6.4$

13. $1 + c + 1.4 = c + 2.4$

14. $\frac{5}{3}s = \frac{15}{3} + \frac{3}{2}s - \frac{1}{4}$

15. $-\frac{2}{9}\left(-n + \frac{3}{9}\right) = \frac{2}{9}n - \frac{5}{9}$

16. A recreation center offers a membership for $75. Members may take classes for $10 each. Nonmembers must pay $15 for these classes. How many classes could a nonmember take and pay the same total amount as a member? Justify your answer.

17. **Guided Problem Solving** Six more than a number equals two times the sum of one-half the number plus three. Is this statement true for only one number, for all numbers, or for no numbers? Explain your reasoning.
    - Write an equation to represent the statement.
    - Simplify the equation until an equivalent equation of the form $x = a, a = a,$ or $a = b$ results.

18. Two more than a number equals three times the sum of one third of the number plus six. Is this statement true for only one number, for all numbers, or for no numbers? Explain your reasoning.

19. **Open Ended** The equation $20y + 4 = 4(3y + 1)$ has exactly one solution. Change one number in the original equation to create a new equation that has infinitely many solutions. Then change one number in the new equation to create another equation that has no solution.

20. **Geometry** Greg is buying fabric from a store. He has the choice of buying fabric that is 2 feet wide or 3 feet wide. The diagrams show how much fabric of each type he can buy for d dollars.

   a. For what value(s) of d is the perimeter of both choices the same?

   b. For what value(s) of d is the area of both choices the same?

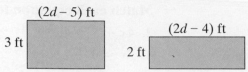

21. **Writing in Math** In the process of simplifying an equation, Marco eliminated all the variables. How many solutions could the original equation have? Explain your reasoning.

22. **Open Ended** Write three equations with the same variable on each side. One equation should have one solution, one equation should have infinitely many solutions, and one equation should have no solutions. Justify your work.

23. **Challenge** Find the number of solutions of the equation $6(0.8 + 2z) - 3.2 = 4(3z - 0.3) + 2.8$. Justify your answer.

Test Prep and Mixed Review
Practice

Multiple Choice

24. Which equation has exactly one solution?

   Ⓐ $3x + 7 = 2x + 14 + x$ Ⓒ $3(x + 7) = 4x + 21 - x$

   Ⓑ $3(x + 7) = 2(x + 7) + x$ Ⓓ $3x + 7 = 5x + 7 - 3x$

25. For a party, you buy 2 dozen cupcakes and 3 quarts of ice cream. Your friend buys 1 dozen cupcakes and 2 quarts of ice cream. Let d = cost of a dozen cupcakes and q = cost of a quart of ice cream. Which expression represents the total cost of the cupcakes and ice cream?

   Ⓕ $2d + 2q$ Ⓗ $3d + 5q$

   Ⓖ $2d + 3q$ Ⓙ $5d + 3q$

26. A cube-shaped storage container can hold 0.125 cubic feet of material. What is the length of one of its edges?

   Ⓐ 5 ft Ⓒ 0.5 ft

   Ⓑ 0.05 ft Ⓓ 0.005 ft

27. Which is an expression that represents the following situation: eight pages more than a third of the pages read last month, m?

   Ⓕ $8 + \frac{1}{3}m$ Ⓗ $\frac{1}{3} \times 8m$

   Ⓖ $8m + \frac{1}{3}$ Ⓙ $8\frac{1}{3}m$

GO for Help

For Exercises	See Lesson
28–30	1-4

Write each fraction as a decimal.

28. $\frac{13}{16}$ 29. $\frac{3}{11}$ 30. $\frac{5}{9}$

Writing Short Responses

Short-response questions are usually worth a maximum of 2 points. To get full credit, you need to give the correct answer, including appropriate units. You may also need to show your work or justify your reasoning.

EXAMPLE

The cost for using a phone card is 45¢ per call plus 5¢ per minute. A recent call cost $2.05. Write and solve an equation to find the length of the call.

To get full credit you must use a variable to set up an equation, solve the equation, and find the length of the call. Below is a scoring guide that shows the number of points awarded for different answers.

Scoring

[2]   The equation and the solution are correct. The call took 32 minutes.

[1]   There is no equation, but there is a method to show that the call took 32 minutes, OR There is an equation and a solution, both of which may contain minor errors.

[0]   There is no response, or the response is completely incorrect.

Three responses are shown below with the points each one received.

2 points	1 point	0 points
Let m represent the number of minutes. $205 = 45 + 5m$ $160 = 5m$ $32 = m$ The call took 32 minutes.	$\dfrac{2.05 - 0.45}{0.05}$ 32 minutes	30 minutes

Exercises

Use the scoring guide above to answer each question.

1. Explain why each response above received the indicated points.

2. Write a 2-point response that includes the equation $0.05n + 0.45 = 2.05$.

Chapter 3 Review

Vocabulary Review

Addition Property of Equality (p. 114)
algebraic expression (p. 103)
coefficient (p. 108)

Division Property of Equality (p. 115)
inverse operations (p. 114)
like terms (p. 108)

Multiplication Property of Equality (p. 114)
Subtraction Property of Equality (p. 114)
variable (p. 103)

Go Online
For vocabulary quiz
PearsonSuccessNet.com

Choose the correct vocabulary term to complete each sentence.

1. A letter that represents a number is called a(n) (coefficient, variable).

2. If you subtract both sides of an equation by the same number so the two sides remain equal, you are using (inverse operations, the Subtraction Property of Equality).

3. A mathematical phrase with at least one variable in it is a(n) (algebraic expression, Addition Property of Equality).

4. Terms that have the same variable factors are (coefficients, like terms).

5. A number placed before another number or variable to indicate multiplication is a(n) (algebraic expression, coefficient).

Skills and Concepts

Lesson 3-1
• To write and evaluate algebraic expressions

A **variable** is a letter that stands for a number. An **algebraic expression** is a mathematical phrase that uses variables, numbers, and operation symbols. To evaluate an expression, substitute a given value for each variable and then simplify.

Evaluate each expression for $n = 3$, $p = 5.5$, and $w = -2$.

6. $3n - 2w$ 7. $\dfrac{4n}{w}$ 8. $p + 4w$ 9. $7w - 2p$

Lesson 3-2
• To simplify algebraic expressions using properties of operations

You can use the properties of operations to order, group, and combine **like terms**. Sometimes an expression needs to be expanded before being simplified.

Simplify each expression.

10. $3x + 14 - x - 15$ 11. $-6.6z + 11 + 1.3 + 2z$

12. $\dfrac{5}{12}n + \dfrac{1}{2}n + \dfrac{1}{2}$ 13. $2(r + 5) - 2$

14. $-3 - 7(r + 0.9)$ 15. $\dfrac{1}{4}n + \dfrac{3}{4}(n + 4) - 1$

Lesson 3-3

- To solve equations by adding, subtracting, multiplying, or dividing

You can use the **Properties of Equality** of Addition, Subtraction, Multiplication, and Division to solve equations. To solve a one-step equation, use **inverse operations.**

Use inverse operations to solve each equation.

16. $y + 14 = 38$ **17.** $p - 12 = 72$ **18.** $\frac{m}{11} = 9$ **19.** $-7b = 84$

Lessons 3-4, 3-5

- To write and evaluate expressions with two operations and to solve two-step equations using number sense
- To solve two-step equations using inverse operations

You can also use inverse operations to solve two-step equations. Undo addition and subtraction; then undo multiplication and division.

Solve each equation.

20. $8r - 6 = 7$ **21.** $\frac{x}{2} - 14 = 66$ **22.** $5b + 0.5 = -4.75$

23. Your plumber charged a fee of $60 and an additional $21.50 per hour for a repair visit. Your bill was $124.50. How long was the plumber's repair visit?

Lessons 3-6, 3-7

- To write and solve multi-step equations
- To write and solve equations with variables on both sides

When solving a multi-step equation, you often need to simplify at least one side first. You can do this by combining like terms.

Solve each equation. Check the solution.

24. $3w - 4 + 5w = 12$ **25.** $-4.8 = 1.2s + 2s + 4$

26. $4a + 3 - a = -7 + 2 + a$ **27.** $\frac{2}{5}b - 8 = -\frac{1}{5}b + 7$

28. A jumbo smoothie costs $4.95. Two jumbo smoothies and one medium smoothie cost $0.15 more than 4 medium smoothies. How much does a medium smoothie cost?

Lesson 3-8

- To identify whether a linear equation has one, infinitely many, or no solutions

By transforming a linear equation into its simplest form, you can tell how many solutions the equation has.

Tell whether each solution has one solution, infinitely many solutions, or no solution. Justify your answer.

29. $2x + 5 = 2(x + 3)$ **30.** $0.5a - 3 = 0.3(2a - 3)$

31. $\frac{1}{2}v + 2 = \frac{1}{4}(2v + 8)$ **32.** $7r - 6 = 7(2r + 3)$

Chapter 3 Test

Go Online For online chapter test PearsonSuccessNet.com

Evaluate each expression for $n = 3$, $p = 10.5$, $t = -2$, and $y = 4$.

1. $3n + 2t$ **2.** $5y - 4n$

3. $2.6p + t$ **4.** $ny - 6 + p$

5. $\dfrac{2ny}{t}$ **6.** $-2t + 6n$

Simplify each expression.

7. $3t + 7 - 5t + 16$ **8.** $6 - 8x + 3x + 4$

9. $-4.9n + 0.9 + 3n$ **10.** $0.7 + 0.2x + 1.1x - 2.7$

11. $4(q + 7) + 2q$ **12.** $\dfrac{3}{10}b - \left(\dfrac{1}{10}b - 10\right)$

13. $14 + 2r + 5(2r - 1)$ **14.** $\dfrac{5}{6}(2g + 1) - g$

Solve each equation.

15. $x + 7 = 12$ **16.** $m - \dfrac{1}{3} = \dfrac{1}{6}$

17. $13 + d = 44$ **18.** $p - 1.8 = 6.2$

19. $5n = 45.5$ **20.** $\dfrac{h}{7} = 8$

21. $-\dfrac{1}{3}t = 24$ **22.** $\dfrac{k}{-4} = -12$

23. $x + 7 = 18 - 2x$ **24.** $2 + \dfrac{4}{5}y = -7 + \dfrac{2}{5}y$

25. $0.6c = 360$ **26.** $2(c + 1) = c - 7$

Write and solve an equation for each problem.

27. Masonry A mason is laying a brick foundation 72 in. wide. Each brick is 6 in. wide. How many bricks will the mason need across the width of the foundation?

28. The music boosters sell 322 music buttons and raise $483 for the music department. How much does each button cost?

29. Your family drives from Austin, Texas, to Tampa, Florida. The trip is about 1,145 mi and lasts four days. How many miles must your family drive each day?

30. A cricket bat weighs 42 oz. Together, two cricket balls and a cricket bat weigh the same as eight cricket balls plus 9 oz. How much does a cricket ball weigh?

31. Open-Ended Write a problem you can represent with $2k - 10 = 6$. Solve the equation. Show your work.

Solve each equation.

32. $14 + 3n = 8$ **33.** $9h - 21 = 24$

34. $\dfrac{w}{5} - 10 = -4$ **35.** $14 + \dfrac{y}{8} = 10$

36. $-5 = 7 + 4x$ **37.** $2r - \dfrac{3}{4} = 1$

38. $11 + 2z = 14.78$ **39.** $20 - 0.4n = 3.2$

Determine whether each equation has no solution, one solution, or infinitely many solutions.

40. $4(z - 1) = 2z - 4$ **41.** $0.5t + 2 = 0.5(t + 4)$

42. $5(2c - 4) = 10c - 9$ **43.** $3r - 8 = 2(r - 4) + r$

44. $1.8d + 3 = 2(0.9d - 1.5)$

45. $\dfrac{2}{3}w = \dfrac{1}{3}(w - 9)$

46. Groceries You buy 12 apples. You also buy a box of cereal that costs $3.35. The bill is $8.75. How much does each apple cost?

47. Six friends split the cost of a party. Each person also spends $65 for a hotel room. Each person spends $160 on the party and a room. What is the cost of the party?

48. The perimeter of a room is 98 feet. If the room is a rectangle with a width of 22 feet, what is the length of the room in yards?

49. Writing in Math Two even integers are represented by $2n$ and $2n + 2$. Explain how you can find the value of those integers if their sum is 14. Name the integers.

Multiple Choice
Read each question. Then write the letter of the correct answer on your paper.

1. Which pair of numbers has a product that is greater than its sum?
   - (A) $-2, -5$
   - (B) $-3, 3$
   - (C) $4, -2$
   - (D) $0, 1$

2. Which of the following shows the expression $-4(2x + 7) + 15$ simplified?
   - (F) $-8x - 13$
   - (G) $-4x - 13$
   - (H) $-4x + 23$
   - (J) $8x + 13$

3. Which shows the value of the expression $7r - \frac{1}{2}t$ for $r = 2$ and $t = 4$?
   - (A) 27
   - (B) 12
   - (C) 10
   - (D) 5

4. A store sells a package of socks for $4.89, a T-shirt for $7.79, and shorts for $14.95. Ellie buys one item and receives $12.21 change from a $20 bill. Which equation can you use to find out what Ellie buys?
   - (F) $20n = 12.21$
   - (G) $20 + n = 12.21$
   - (H) $14.95 - n = 12.21$
   - (J) $20 - n = 12.21$

5. What is the solution of $5y + 11 = 56$?
   - (A) 8
   - (B) 9
   - (C) 13
   - (D) 10

6. Which list is in order from least to greatest?
   - (F) $\frac{1}{3}, \frac{3}{4}, -0.2$
   - (G) $5\frac{1}{8}, 5\frac{1}{4}, 5\frac{2}{3}$
   - (H) $\frac{13}{12}, 0.8, \frac{3}{7}$
   - (J) $\frac{8}{9}, \frac{2}{5}, \frac{1}{2}$

7. The average person drinks about 2.5 quarts of water each day. How many pints is this?
   - (A) 2 pt
   - (B) 3 pt
   - (C) 4 pt
   - (D) 5 pt

8. Which variable expression can be described by the word phrase "r increased by 2"?
   - (F) $2r$
   - (G) $r - 2$
   - (H) $r + 2$
   - (J) $r \cdot 2$

9. Which decimal is closest to $\frac{11}{16}$?
   - (A) 0.687
   - (B) 0.69
   - (C) 0.68
   - (D) 0.7

10. Which is the best estimate of $6\frac{3}{4} \cdot 3\frac{1}{5}$?
    - (F) 18
    - (G) 21
    - (H) 24
    - (J) 27

11. Your friend divided 0.56 by 0.7 and got 8 for an answer. This answer is not correct. Which answer is correct?
    - (A) 0.08
    - (B) 0.008
    - (C) 0.8
    - (D) 80

12. You plan a party and spend $26 on decorations. Each of the tables will have 8 party favors and 8 individual flowers. The flowers cost $2.50 each. Which equation can you use to find the cost of each party favor?
    - (F) $8x + 2.50 = 26$
    - (G) $8(2.50)x = 26$
    - (H) $8(x + 2.50) = 26$
    - (J) $8(x - 2.50) = 26$

Gridded Response
Record your answer in a grid.

13. During the summer, you work 27 hours per week. Each week, you earn $168.75. How many dollars do you earn per hour?

Short Response

14. Define a variable and write an expression to model the word phrase "three less than a number."

15. You and four friends are planning a surprise birthday party. Each of you contributes the same amount of money m for the food.
    a. Write a variable expression for the total amount of money contributed for food.
    b. Evaluate your expression for $m = \$7.75$.

Extended Response

16. Eli collects old vinyl records. He buys 2 vinyl records each month. He started with 18 vinyl records.
    a. Write an expression to model the number of records Eli has after x months.
    b. How many records will Eli have after 22 months? Justify your answer.

What You've Learned

- In Chapter 1, you added, subtracted, multiplied, and divided integers, fractions, and decimals.

- In Chapter 3, you solved equations by adding, subtracting, multiplying, and dividing.

Check Your Readiness

GO for Help

For Exercises	See Lesson
1–4	1-6
5–7	1-7
8–10	1-8
11–16	3-3
17–19	3-5

Adding and Subtracting Rational Numbers

Find each sum or difference. Write your answer in simplest form.

1. $-6.75 + 3.68$ **2.** $\dfrac{7}{12} + \dfrac{11}{12}$

3. $6 - 4.2$ **4.** $\dfrac{5}{8} - \dfrac{3}{4}$

Multiplying Rational Numbers

Find each product. Write your answer in simplest form.

5. $1\dfrac{1}{2} \cdot (-7)$ **6.** $0.4 \cdot 0.6$ **7.** $(-1.8)(-4)$

Dividing Rational Numbers

Find each quotient. Write your answer in simplest form.

8. $-6.4 \div 1.6$ **9.** $-\dfrac{3}{8} \div \dfrac{1}{2}$ **10.** $2.75 \div 0.5$

Solving Equations

Solve each equation. Write your answer in simplest form.

11. $x + 2 = 7$ **12.** $-8.4 + b = -3.1$ **13.** $t + \dfrac{2}{3} = \dfrac{3}{4}$

14. $7.2 = -3h$ **15.** $\dfrac{w}{2} = -10$ **16.** $-\dfrac{3}{4}a = \dfrac{5}{6}$

17. $3 + 4g = 23$ **18.** $1.5k - 2.4 = 2.1$ **19.** $\dfrac{1}{2} + \dfrac{m}{5} = \dfrac{3}{10}$

What You'll Learn Next

- In this chapter, you will write inequalities and graph their solutions on number lines.

- You will solve inequalities by adding, subtracting, multiplying, or dividing.

Key Vocabulary

- Addition Property of Inequality (p. 160)
- Division Property of Inequality (p. 165)
- inequality (p. 156)
- Multiplication Property of Inequality (p. 167)
- solution of an inequality (p. 156)
- Subtraction Property of Inequality (p. 161)

Graphing and Writing Inequalities

 **Check Skills You'll Need**

1. **Vocabulary Review** *Integers* are the set of whole numbers and their __?__.

Compare using <, =, or >.

2. 0 ▦ −2
3. 14 ▦ −14
4. −4 ▦ 5
5. −17 ▦ −18

 **for Help**
Lesson 1-1

© **CONTENT STANDARD**
7.EE.4.b

What You'll Learn

To graph and write algebraic inequalities

New Vocabulary inequality, solution of an inequality

Why Learn This?

When you use an expression such as *at least* or *at most*, you are talking about an inequality. You can use inequalities to represent situations that involve minimum or maximum amounts.

A mathematical sentence that contains <, >, ≤, ≥, or ≠ is an **inequality.** Sometimes an inequality contains a variable, as in $x \geq 2$.

A **solution of an inequality** is any value that makes the inequality true. For example, 6, 8, and 15 are solutions of $x \geq 6$ because $6 \geq 6$, $8 \geq 6$, and $15 \geq 6$.

YOU MUST BE AT LEAST THIS TALL (4FT) TO RIDE!

EXAMPLE **Identifying Solutions of an Inequality**

1 Find whether each number is a solution of $x \leq 2$; −3, 0, 2, 4.5.

Test each value by replacing the variable and evaluating the sentence.

$-3 \leq 2$ ← **−3 is less than or equal to 2: true.** ✔

$0 \leq 2$ ← **0 is less than or equal to 2: true.** ✔

$2 \leq 2$ ← **2 is less than or equal to 2: true.** ✔

$4.5 \leq 2$ ← **4.5 is less than or equal to 2: false.** ✘

The numbers −3, 0, and 2 are solutions of $x \leq 2$. The number 4.5 is not a solution of $x \leq 2$.

Vocabulary Tip

Read > as "is greater than."

Read < as "is less than."

Read ≥ as "is greater than or equal to."

Read ≤ as "is less than or equal to."

✓ Quick Check

1. Which numbers are solutions of the inequality $m \geq -3$; −8, −2, 1.4?

A graph can show all the numbers in a solution. You use closed circles and open circles to show whether numbers are included in the solution.

 **Graphing Inequalities**

2 Graph the solution of each inequality.

a. $n \geq -3$

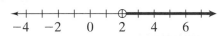 ← Use a closed circle at −3 to show that n can equal −3.

b. $h < 7$

← Use an open circle at 7 to show that h cannot equal 7.

✓ Quick Check

● **2.** Graph the solution of the inequality $w < -3$.

You can write an inequality by analyzing its graph.

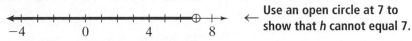 **Writing Inequalities**

3 Write an inequality for the graph.

← Since the circle at 2 is open, 2 is not a solution.

$x > 2$ ← Since the graph shows values greater than 2, use >.

✓ Quick Check

● **3.** Write an inequality for the graph.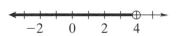

You can write inequalities to describe real-world situations.

 Application: Nutrition

4 To be labeled sugar free, a food product must contain less than 0.5 g of sugar per serving. Write an inequality to describe this requirement.

| Words | amount of sugar | is less than | 0.5 g of sugar |

Let s = the number of grams of sugar in a serving of food.

| Equation | s | < | 0.5 |

The inequality is $s < 0.5$.

✓ Quick Check

4. Write an inequality for "To qualify for the race, your time can be at most 62 seconds."

1. **Vocabulary** What is the name of a mathematical sentence that contains the symbols $<$, $>$, $\leq$, $\geq$, or $\neq$?

2. **Reasoning** Is $-4 \geq 4$? Explain.

3. Which inequality does NOT have 8 as a solution?
   - Ⓐ $-3 < y$
   - Ⓑ $13 \geq y$
   - Ⓒ $y < 8$
   - Ⓓ $y \geq 8$

Which numbers are solutions of each inequality?

4. $x \geq -5; -6, -1, 0$

5. $x \leq -1; -1, 1\frac{1}{2}, 3$

6. $x > 0; -1, 0, 0.1$

Homework Exercises

For more exercises, see Extra Skills and Word Problems.

Which numbers are solutions of each inequality?

GO for Help

For Exercises	See Examples
7–10	1
11–18	2
19–23	3–4

7. $x < 1; -2, 1, 2$

8. $x > -5; -7, -5, -1$

9. $x \leq -9; -12, -4.5, 2$

10. $x < -8; -10, -5\frac{3}{4}, 0$

Graph the solution of each inequality.

11. $x \geq 4$

12. $x \leq -2$

13. $x < 2$

14. $x > -4$

15. $x \leq 0$

16. $h > -5$

17. $t \geq -5$

18. $p < -6$

Write an inequality for each graph.

19.
```
←——+——+——+——+——●——+——→
    0     3     6
```

20.
```
←——+——+——+——⊕——+——+——+——→
   -2    0     2     4     6
```

21.
```
←——+——+——●——+——+——+——+——→
   -2    0     2     4
```

22.
```
←——+——+——+——●——+——+——+——→
  -4   -2    0     2
```

23. Write an inequality for "Every item costs one dollar or less!"

24. **Guided Problem Solving** Write an inequality for "The car ride to the park will take at least 30 minutes."
    - Choose a variable: Let x represent how long the car ride will be.
    - Read for key words: Decide whether to use $<$, $>$, $\leq$, or $\geq$.
    - Write the inequality: x ▇ 30.

Write an inequality for each statement. Graph the solution.

25. To see the movie, you must be at least 17 years old.

26. The temperature is greater than 100°F.

27. A number p is not positive.

28. The speed limit on the highway is at most 65 mi/h.

29. Writing in Math Explain how you know whether to draw an open or closed circle when you graph an inequality.

30. Reasoning Explain why $-17 > -22$.

Use a variable to write an inequality for each situation.

31.

32.

Vocabulary Tip

A *compound inequality* is a number sentence with more than one inequality symbol.

Identify an integer that is a solution for each *compound inequality*.

33. $-3 \le x < 0$ **34.** $-2 < y \le 1$ **35.** $-6 \le p \le -4$

36. Challenge If $a \ge 9$ and $9 \ge b$, then $a \blacksquare b$. Complete the statement using $<$, $>$, $\le$, or $\ge$.

Test Prep and Mixed Review

Practice

Multiple Choice

37. The maximum weight an elevator can hold is 800 pounds. Which inequality describes this situation?
- Ⓐ $w < 800$
- Ⓒ $w \le 800$
- Ⓑ $w > 800$
- Ⓓ $w \ge 800$

38. What is the first step in solving the equation $2x + 5 = 9$?
- Ⓕ Add 5 to each side of the equation.
- Ⓖ Subtract 5 from each side of the equation.
- Ⓗ Divide each side of the equation by 5.
- Ⓙ Subtract 2 from each side of the equation.

39. A recipe calls for 3 pounds of ground turkey. Carmen has one package of ground beef that weighs $1\frac{1}{2}$ pounds, one package of ground turkey that weighs $1\frac{1}{4}$ pounds, and another package of ground turkey that weighs $1\frac{5}{8}$ pounds. Which information is NOT necessary to find how much more ground turkey Carmen needs?
- Ⓐ Total amount of ground turkey needed for the recipe
- Ⓑ Weight of Carmen's smaller package of ground turkey
- Ⓒ Weight of Carmen's package of ground beef
- Ⓓ Weight of Carmen's larger package of ground turkey

GO for Help

For Exercises	See Lesson
40–42	1-1

Order the numbers from least to greatest.

40. $-2, 4, -4, 2, 7, -1$ **41.** $3, -8, -9, 12, -6$ **42.** $10, 0, -5, -2, 7$

4-2 Solving Inequalities by Adding or Subtracting

© **CONTENT STANDARD**
7.EE.4.b

What You'll Learn

To solve inequalities by adding or subtracting

New Vocabulary Addition Property of Inequality, Subtraction Property of Inequality

Why Learn This?

Buildings and buses have limits on the number of people they can hold. You can use inequalities to find how many people can fit safely.

You can solve inequalities using properties similar to those you used solving equations.

If you add 3 to each side of the inequality $-3 < 2$, the resulting inequality, $0 < 5$, is also true.

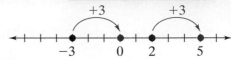

KEY CONCEPTS **Addition Property of Inequality**

You can add the same value to each side of an inequality.

Arithmetic	Algebra
Since $7 > 3$, $7 + 4 > 3 + 4$.	If $a > b$, then $a + c > b + c$.
Since $1 < 3$, $1 + 4 < 3 + 4$.	If $a < b$, then $a + c < b + c$.

EXAMPLE **Solving Inequalities by Adding**

for Help

For help with graphing inequalities, see Lesson 4-1, Example 2.

1 Solve $n - 10 > 14$. Graph the solution.

$$n - 10 > 14$$
$$n - 10 + 10 > 14 + 10 \quad \leftarrow \text{Add 10 to each side.}$$
$$n > 24 \quad \leftarrow \text{Simplify.}$$

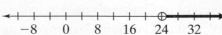

✓ Quick Check

● **1.** Solve $y - 3 < 4$. Graph the solution.

To solve an inequality involving addition, use subtraction.

KEY CONCEPTS **Subtraction Property of Inequality**

You can subtract the same value from each side of an inequality.

Arithmetic	**Algebra**
Since $9 > 6$, $9 - 3 > 6 - 3$.	If $a > b$, then $a - c > b - c$.
Since $15 < 20$, $15 - 4 < 20 - 4$.	If $a < b$, then $a - c < b - c$.

Note: The Properties of Inequality also apply to $\leq$ and $\geq$.

EXAMPLE **Solving Inequalities by Subtracting**

2 Solve $y + 7 \geq 12$. Graph the solution.

$$y + 7 \geq 12$$
$$y + 7 - 7 \geq 12 - 7 \quad \leftarrow \textsf{Subtract 7 from each side.}$$
$$y \geq 5 \quad \leftarrow \textsf{Simplify.}$$

$$-2 \quad 0 \quad 2 \quad 4 \quad 6 \quad 8 \quad 10$$

✓ Quick Check

2. Solve each inequality. Graph the solution.

   a. $x + 9 > 5$ **b.** $y + 3 < 4$ **c.** $w + 4 \leq -5$

EXAMPLE **Application: Transportation**

3 A school bus can safely carry as many as 76 students. If 19 students are already on the bus, how many more can board the bus?

Words	students already on bus	plus	students remaining	is at most	76

Let s = the number of students remaining.

Expression	19	+	s	$\leq$	76

$$19 + s \leq 76$$
$$19 - 19 + s \leq 76 - 19 \quad \leftarrow \textsf{Subtract 19 from each side.}$$
$$s \leq 57 \quad \leftarrow \textsf{Simplify.}$$

At most 57 more students can board the bus.

✓ Quick Check

3. To get an A, you need more than 200 points on a two-part test. You score 109 on the first part. How many more points do you need?

Check Your Understanding

1. **Vocabulary** The _?_ states that you can add the same value to each side of an inequality.

2. **Reasoning** What value is a solution of $y + 7 \geq 12$ but is not a solution of $y + 7 > 12$?

Match each inequality with the graph of its solution.

3. $h - 4 < 5$

4. $h + 4 \geq 5$

5. $h - 4 \leq -5$

6. $h + 4 < -5$

A. ![number line from -12 to 9, open circle at -6, shaded left]

B. ![number line from -3 to 4, closed circle at -1, shaded left]

C. ![number line from -9 to 12, open circle at 9, shaded left]

D. ![number line from -3 to 4, closed circle at 1, shaded right]

Homework Exercises

For more exercises, see Extra Skills and Word Problems.

Solve each inequality by adding. Graph the solution.

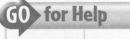

For Exercises	See Examples
7–15	1
16–25	2-3

7. $g - 2 \leq -8$ 8. $m - 3 > -24$ 9. $y - 5 \geq 11$

10. $x - 7 > -11$ 11. $n - 10 \leq 17$ 12. $p - 9 < -9$

13. $y - 5 \geq 12$ 14. $q - 2 < 4$ 15. $b - 4 > -6$

Solve each inequality by subtracting. Graph the solution.

16. $h + 8 < -13$ 17. $n + 3 \geq 4$ 18. $r + 9 > 4$

19. $p + 10 \leq 6$ 20. $b + 22 > -1$ 21. $f + 5 \geq 0$

22. $m + 3 > 4$ 23. $x + 10 < 11$ 24. $k + 4 \leq -7$

 25. **Guided Problem Solving** The weight of a loaded dump truck is less than 75,000 lb. When empty, the truck weighs 32,000 lb. Write and solve an inequality to find how much the load can weigh.

words: empty truck plus _?_ is less than 75,000 lb

inequality: 32,000 + ■ < 75,000

26. **Science** Water boils when the temperature is at least 212°F. A pot of water has a temperature of 109°F. How many degrees must the temperature rise for the water to boil?

27. **Consumer Issues** Your parents give you $35 for a scooter that costs at least $100. How much money do you have to save to buy the scooter?

Solve each inequality by adding or subtracting.

28. $h - 9 < 1.3$ **29.** $-\frac{3}{4} < w - \frac{1}{4}$ **30.** $98 \le x + 5$

31. $j + 6.2 \ge 1.2$ **32.** $k + 42 \ge 36$ **33.** $3\frac{7}{10} > a - 1\frac{4}{5}$

34. Write an inequality for the sentence "Ten is less than 15 plus a number." Solve the inequality.

35. Reasoning Are the solutions of the inequalities $x + 5 \le -2$ and $-2 \le x + 5$ the same? Explain.

36. Sports To win the long jump, you need to jump a distance greater than 2.25 m. Your personal best jump is 2.1 m. Write and solve an inequality to find how much farther you need to jump to win.

37. Writing in Math The basketball team needs to score at least 420 points this season in order to set a new school record. It has already scored 82 points. Four players argue about which inequality represents the number of points yet to be scored: $p \ge 338$, $338 \ge p$, $p > 338$, or $338 > p$. Which is correct? Explain.

38. A *compound inequality* is a number sentence with more than one inequality symbol. Solve the compound inequality $-3 \le x + 4 < 9$.

39. Challenge You want to eat no more than 3,000 calories in a day. You consume 710 calories for breakfast and have two bowls of soup for lunch. Each bowl contains 535 calories. How many calories can you consume at dinner?

Test Prep and Mixed Review   **Practice**

Gridded Response

40. A baby who weighed 7.2 pounds at birth gained about 1.4 pounds each month. How many pounds did the baby weigh when it was 6 months old?

41. Two of the driest cities in the United States are Yuma, Arizona, and Las Vegas, Nevada. Yuma averages 3.01 inches of rain each year and Las Vegas averages 4.49 inches each year. How many more inches of rain does Las Vegas receive each year than Yuma?

42. The table shows record weights of 3 types of sunfish. In decimal form, how many pounds did the redbreast sunfish weigh? Round to the nearest hundredth.

Fish	Weight (lb)
Green sunfish	$\frac{17}{8}$
Redbreast sunfish	$\frac{33}{16}$
Redear sunfish	$\frac{87}{16}$

GO for Help

For Exercises	See Lesson
43–45	1-3

Simplify each expression.

43. $-9(6)$ **44.** $-8(-4)$ **45.** $7(-7)$

Write an inequality for each graph.

1.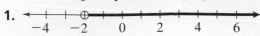

2.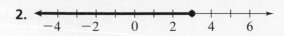

Graph the solution of each inequality.

3. $x \geq 3$

4. $p \leq -4$

5. $b + 7 < -1$

6. $h - 2 \geq -4$

7. The driver of a car puts money in a meter to pay for 45 min of parking. The driver can walk from the car to the store and back again in 8 min. Write and solve an inequality to find how many minutes the driver can be inside the store.

8. After serving 6 ears for dinner, you want to have at least 3 ears left to make corn salsa. Write and solve an inequality to find how many ears of corn you should buy.

4-2b Activity Lab

Data Analysis

Inequalities in Bar Graphs

A class conducted a survey on free time. The standard bar graph shows the average number of hours per week students spend on various activities. The floating bar graph shows the minimum and maximum number of hours students spend on each activity.

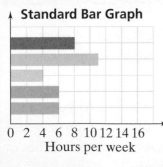

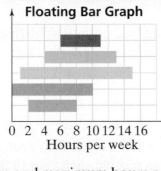

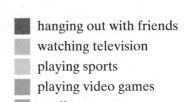

hanging out with friends
watching television
playing sports
playing video games
reading

1. What are the minimum and maximum hours per week that students in the survey spend hanging out with friends?

2. Which activity is not done by all students? Which activity shows the least variety in how students responded to the survey? Explain.

3. Let x represent the number of hours per week spent on an activity. Which activity in the floating bar graph is represented by the inequality $2 \leq x \leq 8$? Write inequalities to represent each activity on the floating bar graph.

4-3 Solving Inequalities by Multiplying or Dividing

Check Skills You'll Need

1. **Vocabulary Review** How is the *Addition Property of Equality* similar to the *Addition Property of Inequality*?

Solve each inequality.

2. $x + 3 \le 5$

3. $p - 9 > -2$

4. $8 \ge d + 5$

5. $r - 2 < -8$

 **for Help**
Lesson 4-2

© CONTENT STANDARD
7.EE.4.b

What You'll Learn

To solve inequalities by multiplying or dividing

New Vocabulary Division Property of Inequality, Multiplication Property of Inequality

Why Learn This?

Inequalities can help you plan. You can solve inequalities to make sure you have enough ingredients when you are cooking.

Look at the pattern when you divide each side of an inequality by an integer.

$18 > 12$

$\dfrac{18}{6} > \dfrac{12}{6}$

$\dfrac{18}{3} > \dfrac{12}{3}$

← When the integer is positive, the direction of the inequality symbol stays the same.

$\dfrac{18}{-2} < \dfrac{12}{-2}$

$\dfrac{18}{-6} < \dfrac{12}{-6}$

← When the integer is negative, the direction of the inequality symbol is reversed.

KEY CONCEPTS   **Division Property of Inequality**

If you divide each side of an inequality by the same positive number, the direction of the inequality symbol remains unchanged.

Arithmetic	**Algebra**
$9 > 6$, so $\dfrac{9}{3} > \dfrac{6}{3}$	If $a > b$, and c is positive, then $\dfrac{a}{c} > \dfrac{b}{c}$.
$15 < 20$, so $\dfrac{15}{5} < \dfrac{20}{5}$	If $a < b$, and c is positive, then $\dfrac{a}{c} < \dfrac{b}{c}$.

If you divide each side of an inequality by the same negative number, the direction of the inequality symbol is reversed.

Arithmetic	**Algebra**
$16 > 12$, so $\dfrac{16}{-4} < \dfrac{12}{-4}$	If $a > b$, and c is negative, then $\dfrac{a}{c} < \dfrac{b}{c}$.
$10 < 18$, so $\dfrac{10}{-2} > \dfrac{18}{-2}$	If $a < b$, and c is negative, then $\dfrac{a}{c} > \dfrac{b}{c}$.

Solving Inequalities by Dividing

1 Solve $-3y \le -27$. Graph the solution.

$$-3y \le -27$$
$$\frac{-3y}{-3} \ge \frac{-27}{-3} \qquad \leftarrow \text{ Divide each side by } -3. \text{ Reverse the direction of the symbol.}$$
$$y \ge 9 \qquad \leftarrow \text{ Simplify.}$$

$$\begin{array}{c|c|c|c|c|c|c|c}
\hline
-12 & -6 & 0 & 6 & 12 & 18 \\
\end{array}$$

✓ Quick Check

1. Solve each inequality. Graph the solution.

   a. $-4p < 36$ **b.** $-1.8m \ge -5.4$ **c.** $\frac{2}{3}n > -2$

You can solve an inequality that involves multiplication by dividing each side of the inequality by the same number.

EXAMPLE **Application: Planning**

2 Your class is taking a trip to a museum that is 190 miles away. The bus can travel at 55 miles per hour. At least how many hours should your class plan for the trip to the museum?

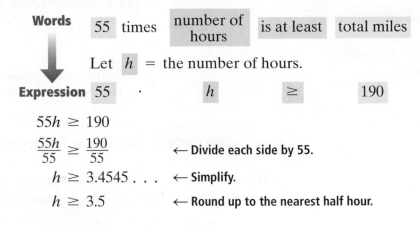

Words | 55 | times | number of hours | is at least | total miles

Let h = the number of hours.

Expression | 55 | · | h | $\ge$ | 190

$$55h \ge 190$$
$$\frac{55h}{55} \ge \frac{190}{55} \qquad \leftarrow \text{ Divide each side by 55.}$$
$$h \ge 3.4545 \ldots \qquad \leftarrow \text{ Simplify.}$$
$$h \ge 3.5 \qquad \leftarrow \text{ Round up to the nearest half hour.}$$

Your class should plan for at least 3 hours and 30 minutes.

✓ Quick Check

2. A long-distance telephone company is offering a special rate of $.06 per minute. Your budget for long-distance telephone calls is $25 for the month. At most how many minutes of long distance can you use for the month with this rate?

The properties of inequality apply to multiplication as well.

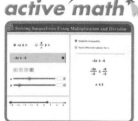

KEY CONCEPTS **Multiplication Property of Inequality**

If you multiply each side of an inequality by the same positive number, the direction of the inequality symbol remains unchanged.

Arithmetic	**Algebra**
$12 > 8$, so $12 \cdot 2 > 8 \cdot 2$	If $a > b$, and c is positive, then $a \cdot c > b \cdot c$.
$3 < 6$, so $3 \cdot 4 < 6 \cdot 4$	If $a < b$, and c is positive, then $a \cdot c < b \cdot c$.

If you multiply each side of an inequality by the same negative number, the direction of the inequality symbol is reversed.

Arithmetic	**Algebra**
$6 > 2$, so $6(-3) < 2(-3)$	If $a > b$, and c is negative, then $a \cdot c < b \cdot c$.
$3 < 5$, so $3(-2) > 5(-2)$	If $a < b$, and c is negative, then $a \cdot c > b \cdot c$.

EXAMPLE **Solving Inequalities by Multiplying**

3 Solve $\dfrac{y}{-8} \geq 2$.

$$\frac{y}{-8} \geq 2$$

$$-8 \cdot \frac{y}{-8} \leq -8 \cdot 2 \quad \leftarrow \begin{array}{l}\textbf{Multiply each side by } -8.\\ \textbf{Reverse the direction of the symbol.}\end{array}$$

$$y \leq -16 \quad \leftarrow \textbf{Simplify.}$$

Online active math

For: Inequalities Activity
Use: Interactive Textbook, 4-3

✓ **Quick Check**

● **3.** Solve $\dfrac{k}{-5} < -4$. Graph the solution.

EXAMPLE **Solving Inequalities by Multiplying by the Reciprocal**

4 Solve $-\dfrac{2}{3}h < -6$.

$$-\frac{2}{3}h < -6$$

$$-\frac{3}{2} \cdot \left(-\frac{2}{3}h > -\frac{3}{2} \cdot (-6)\right) \leftarrow \begin{array}{l}\textbf{Multiply each side by } -\dfrac{3}{2}\textbf{, the reciprocal of}\\ -\dfrac{2}{3}\textbf{. Reverse the direction of the symbol.}\end{array}$$

$$h > 9 \qquad \leftarrow \textbf{Simplify.}$$

✓ **Quick Check**

● **4.** Solve $-\dfrac{3}{4}w \geq 12$. Graph the solution.

1. **Vocabulary** What happens when you multiply each side of an inequality by a negative number?

2. If $x > y$, which statement is NOT always true?
   Ⓐ $y < x$ Ⓒ $x - z > y - z$
   Ⓑ $x + z > y + z$ Ⓓ $xz > yz$

Fill in the missing inequality symbol.

3. $3m > 99$
   $$\frac{3m}{3} \ \blacksquare \ \frac{99}{3}$$

4. $-1.6z \le 80$
   $$\frac{-1.6z}{-1.6} \ \blacksquare \ \frac{80}{-1.6}$$

5. $\frac{d}{-3} < 12$
   $$\frac{d}{-3} \cdot (-3) \ \blacksquare \ 12 \cdot (-3)$$

Homework Exercises

For more exercises, see Extra Skills and Word Problems.

Solve each inequality by dividing. Graph the solution.

GO for Help

For Exercises	See Examples
6–12	1-2
13–21	3-4

6. $6x < -48$ 7. $-8b \ge -24$ 8. $-5w \le 30$

9. $-4.5p \le 22.5$ 10. $7y < -42.7$ 11. $8.3w \ge 53.95$

12. A photo album page can hold six photographs. You have 296 photographs. How many pages do you need?

Solve each inequality by multiplying. Graph the solution.

13. $\frac{y}{7} > -8$ 14. $\frac{n}{-2} > -5$ 15. $\frac{m}{-6} \le 5$

16. $\frac{g}{1.2} \ge -7$ 17. $\frac{p}{-8} < 2.1$ 18. $\frac{f}{5} \le -5.5$

19. $\frac{4}{5}t > -8$ 20. $-\frac{5}{6}a \le \frac{1}{3}$ 21. $-\frac{7}{8}s \ge -\frac{3}{4}$

GPS 22. **Guided Problem Solving** A forklift can safely carry as much as 6,000 lb. A case of paint weighs 70 lb. At most how many cases of paint can the forklift safely carry at one time?
   • Use number sense: How much do 100 cases weigh?
   • Try the strategy *Systematic Guess and Check*: How much do 90 cases weigh? 80 cases?

23. **Rides** A roller coaster can carry 36 people per run. At least how many times does the roller coaster have to run to allow 10,000 people to ride?

24. **Baking** A recipe for an apple pie calls for 6 apples per pie. You have 27 apples. At most how many apple pies can you make?

Write an inequality for each sentence. Solve the inequality.

25. 12 is less than the product of −3 and a number.

26. A number multiplied by 4.4 is at most −44.

27. 10 is greater than a number divided by −9.

28. The quotient of a number and 5 is at least −8.

29. The product of $\frac{2}{5}$ and a number is less than −10.

30. **Writing in Math** Explain how solving $-5x < 25$ is different from solving $5x < 25$.

Use the drawing at the left for Exercises 31–33. You have $15.

31. At most how many hot dogs can you buy?

32. At most how many bags of peanuts can you buy?

33. You buy two hot dogs. How many bags of peanuts can you buy? How much money do you have left?

PEANUTS $1.25   HOT DOGS $4.75

34. **Error Analysis** A student solves the inequality $5n > -25$. He says the solution is $n < -5$. Explain the student's error.

35. **Reasoning** Solve and graph $-18 \geq -2y$ and $-2y < -18$. Are the solutions the same? Explain.

36. **Challenge** Ten more than −3 times a number is greater than 19. Write and solve an inequality. Graph the solution.

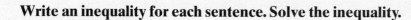

ⒶⒷⒸⒹ **Test Prep and Mixed Review** **Practice**

Multiple Choice

37. A 1-ton truck can haul 2,000 lb. A refrigerator weighs 312 lb. How many refrigerators can the truck carry?
Ⓐ at least 6 Ⓒ 6 at most
Ⓑ at least 7 Ⓓ 7 at most

38. Arnold had a collection of baseball cards that he divided evenly among 5 friends. Each friend received 17 baseball cards. Which equation can be used to find y, the number of baseball cards Arnold had?
Ⓕ $5y = 17$ Ⓗ $17y = 5$
Ⓖ $\frac{y}{5} = 17$ Ⓙ $\frac{y}{5} - 5 = 17$

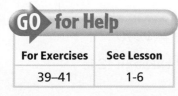
GO for Help

For Exercises	See Lesson
39–41	1-6

Simplify each expression.

39. $2\frac{1}{2} + 3\frac{5}{8}$ **40.** $-1\frac{2}{3} + 2\frac{1}{4}$ **41.** $1\frac{5}{6} + \left(-3\frac{7}{8}\right)$

Writing Inequalities

Cap Prices The drama club at one middle school wants to order caps with the name of the play they are performing stitched on the caps. After checking the price of the caps, one club member stated that the club could buy enough caps for all the cast members for less than $200. How many cast members could there be?

Solid Color Caps adjustable to fit all size heads. Washable. May be customized with machine-sewn letters.
Cap...........................$9.50
Customization.............$6.75

Place in Shopping Cart

What You Might Think

> What do I know?
> What do I want to find out?

> What inequality can I write?

> For what number of caps will the cost be less than $200?

> Is the answer reasonable?

What You Might Write

I know that one cap costs $9.50 and that it costs $6.75 to stitch the name of the play on it.

Cost of one customized cap → $9.50 + $6.75

The total cost of the caps will be less than $200. There will be one cap for each cast member, so the number of caps and the number of cast members will be the same. I want to find how many caps the club plans on buying because that will tell me the number of cast members.

Let c = the number of caps. Then the total cost of c caps is $c(9.50 + 6.75)$.
So, $c(9.50 + 6.75) < 200$.

$$c(9.50 + 6.75) < 200$$
$$c(16.25) < 200$$
$$c < 12.307\ldots$$

Since the number of caps must be a whole number, the number of caps must be a whole number less than approximately 12.3. So, the number of cast members could be any whole number from 1 through 12.

The cost for one customized cap is about $10 + $10, or $20. 12 × $20 = $240

So, any whole number from 1 through 12 is a reasonable answer.

Think It Through

1. **Reasoning** Can a solution to this problem be 0? Explain.

2. Can you use the following inequality to solve this problem? Explain.
   $9.50c + 6.75c < 200$

Exercises

Solve each problem. For Exercises 3 and 4, answer parts (a) and (b) first.

3. A family has budgeted $15 for popcorn and water at one movie theater.

$3.50 $2.00

   How many popcorn and water combos could the family buy?
   a. Let c = the number of popcorn and water combos. A popcorn and water combo costs $3.50 + $2.00. What is the cost of c popcorn and water combos?
   b. Use your answer to part (a) to write and solve an inequality to find how many popcorn and water combos the family could buy.

4. On a trip from Chicago to Dallas, a family wants to drive at least 300 miles each day. Overall, their usual average driving speed is 55 miles per hour. Because they have to pass through some road construction, they think that their average speed will be reduced by 10 miles per hour. How many hours should this family plan to drive each day?
   a. Let h = the number of hours. How many miles can the family drive in h hours?
   b. Use your answer to part (a) to write and solve an inequality to find how many hours the family should plan to drive each day.

5. You are shopping at a store that sells shorts for $18 and t-shirts for $10. For each set of shorts and a t-shirt that shoppers buy, the store offers $5 off. If your budget is $75, how many sets of shorts and a t-shirt could you buy?

4-4 Solving Two-Step Inequalities

Check Skills You'll Need

1. **Vocabulary Review** How is a *two-step equation* different from a *one-step equation*?

Solve each equation.

2. $3d + 5 = 11$

3. $\frac{v}{4} - 6 = -4$

4. $2c - 1.5 = -2.3$

5. $-\frac{a}{6} + 0.2 = -0.3$

GO for Help
Lesson 3-5

ⓒ **CONTENT STANDARD**
7.EE.4.b

What You'll Learn

To solve two-step inequalities using inverse operations

Why Learn This?

When you lose something, you often undo or trace your steps in reverse order to find it.

You can solve a two-step inequality by using inverse operations and the properties of inequality to get the variable alone on one side of the inequality.

For many inequalities, you undo the addition or subtraction first. Then you undo the multiplication or division. These are the same steps you followed when solving a two-step equation.

EXAMPLE Undoing Addition First

1 Solve $\frac{a}{4} + 3 \le -2$. Graph the solution.

$$\frac{a}{4} + 3 \le -2$$

$$\frac{a}{4} + 3 - 3 \le -2 - 3 \quad \leftarrow \text{Subtract 3 from each side.}$$

$$\frac{a}{4} \le -5 \quad \leftarrow \text{Simplify.}$$

$$4 \cdot \frac{a}{4} \le 4 \cdot (-5) \quad \leftarrow \text{Multiply each side by 4.}$$

$$a \le -20 \quad \leftarrow \text{Simplify.}$$

$\xleftarrow{\hspace{1cm}}$ −26 −24 −22 −20 −18 −16 $\xrightarrow{\hspace{1cm}}$

Vocabulary Tip

According to the order of operations, you multiply and divide before you add and subtract. Reverse this order to solve a two-step inequality.

Quick Check

1. Solve the inequality $-5 + \frac{c}{3} > -1$. Graph the solution.

EXAMPLE Undoing Subtraction First

GO for Help

For help with when to reverse the direction of an inequality sign, see Lesson 4-3, Examples 1 and 3.

2 Solve $-3.5x - 6 > -1.8$. Graph the solution.

$-3.5x - 6 > -1.8$

$-3.5x - 6 + 6 > -1.8 + 6$ ← **Add 6 to each side.**

$-3.5x > 4.2$ ← **Simplify.**

$\dfrac{-3.5x}{-3.5} < \dfrac{4.2}{-3.5}$ ← **Divide each side by −3.5.**

$x < -1.2$ ← **Simplify.**

✓ **Quick Check**

2. Solve $\dfrac{1}{5} \geq -\dfrac{1}{3}a + \dfrac{1}{2}$. Graph the solution on a number line.

EXAMPLE Application: Music Downloads

3 **Multiple Choice** A music club charges $0.75 per song download plus a membership fee of $5.70. Diego can spend at most $15. What is the greatest number of songs that Diego can download?

Ⓐ 14 Ⓑ 13 Ⓒ 12 Ⓓ 11

Words $0.75 times   number of songs   plus   monthly fee   is at most $15

Let s = the number of songs

Expression $0.75 \cdot s + 5.7 \leq 15$

$0.75s + 5.7 \leq 15$

$0.75s + 5.7 - 5.7 \leq 15 - 5.7$ ← **Subtract 5.7 from each side.**

$0.75s \leq 9.3$ ← **Simplify.**

$\dfrac{0.75s}{0.75} \leq \dfrac{9.3}{0.75}$ ← **Divide each side by 0.75.**

$s \leq 12.4$ ← **Simplify.**

Only whole-number solutions are reasonable in this context, so Diego can download at least 0 songs and no more than 12 songs. The correct answer is choice C.

Test Prep Tip

Reverse the direction of the inequality symbol when you multiply or divide each side of an inequality by a negative number.

✓ **Quick Check**

3. A phone plan charges $0.20 per text message plus a monthly fee of $42.50. Lin can spend at most $50. Write an inequality for the number of text messages Lin can send. Describe the solution.

More Than One Way

You want to buy a new tablet that costs at least $450. You have already saved $130. You want to save the same amount each month for the next 4 months to have enough money for the tablet. What is the least amount of money you need to save each month?

Lee's Method

I'll use number sense. I know that I have saved $130 already. Since a tablet costs at least $450, I still need at least $450 − $130, or at least $320. I will save the same amount for 4 months. So, each month I must save at least $320 ÷ 4, or at least $80.

Olivia's Method

I'll write and solve an inequality. Let s = amount of money I still need to save each month. Then $4s$ is the total amount I still need to save.

savings needed + savings on hand ≥ cost of tablet
$$4s \quad + \quad 130 \quad \geq \quad 450$$

I'll work backward through the order of operations.

$$4s + 130 - 130 \geq 450 - 130 \quad \leftarrow \text{Subtract 130 from each side.}$$

$$4s \geq 320 \quad \leftarrow \text{Simplify.}$$

$$\frac{4s}{4} \geq \frac{320}{4} \quad \leftarrow \text{Divide each side by 4.}$$

$$s \geq 80 \quad \leftarrow \text{Simplify.}$$

I need to save at least $80 each week.

Choose a Method

You want to buy some T-shirts and a pair of shorts. At one store, T-shirts cost $10 each and shorts cost $20 each. You do not want to spend more than $85. How many T-shirts can you buy?

Check Your Understanding

Describe the first step in solving each inequality.

1. $-3t + 7 > 1$ **2.** $-3.4 - 1.5h \leq 2.6$ **3.** $\frac{7}{10}s + \frac{1}{5} \geq \frac{3}{10}$

Solve each inequality. Graph the solution. Write your answer in simplest form.

4. $2z \leq -10$ **5.** $\frac{a}{3} > \frac{1}{2}$ **6.** $-4 < -0.8k$

For more exercises, see Extra Skills and Word Problems.

GO for Help

For Exercises	See Examples
7–15	1
16–25	2-3

Solve each inequality. Graph the solution. Write your answer in simplest form.

7. $-2 + 4v > -14$

8. $-3r - 4 > 26$

9. $2 > \dfrac{e}{6} - 1$

10. $-5.6c - 7.2 < -15.6$

11. $-7.1 + 2.4w < 8.5$

12. $-1.7 - \dfrac{s}{1.5} > 4.9$

13. $\dfrac{5}{7} - \dfrac{6}{7}z < -\dfrac{2}{7}$

14. $\dfrac{1}{8} > -\dfrac{3}{4}y - \dfrac{3}{8}$

15. $\dfrac{d}{3} - \dfrac{1}{6} \geq \dfrac{1}{12}$

16. $3 + 6t < 15$

17. $\dfrac{b}{-4} + 7 \leq 4$

18. $-16 \leq 3g + 2$

19. $5 - 1.6x > 7.4$

20. $2.8 + 3.7y \geq 25$

21. $\dfrac{z}{-1.2} + 7.1 > 1.1$

22. $\dfrac{1}{4} + -\dfrac{5}{8}u \leq \dfrac{1}{16}$

23. $\dfrac{1}{2} > \dfrac{2}{3}m + \dfrac{1}{3}$

24. $\dfrac{1}{2} + \dfrac{x}{5} \geq \dfrac{1}{10}$

25. Tricia receives a $5 allowance every week. She also earns $6.50 for every hour that she baby-sits. Next week she wants to earn at least $21.25 to buy a present. Write and solve an inequality to find the number of hours she needs to baby-sit.

GPS

26. Guided Problem Solving Kate sells bracelets at a craft fair and earns $9.60 per bracelet. She pays a rental fee of $35.20 for her booth. She wants to earn at least $200. Write an inequality to find the number of bracelets Kate needs to sell. Graph and describe the solutions.

- **Make a Plan** Complete the chart below:

  Words ___ times [number of bracelets] minus [rental fee] [is at least] ___

  Let b = the number of bracelets

  Expression ___ · ___ − ___ ▮ ___

- **Carry Out the Plan** Solve the inequality. Graph and describe the solutions.

27. Event Planning A play is being presented in a school gymnasium that can hold a maximum of 600 people. One hundred twenty people can sit on the bleachers. Chairs will be set up in 15 equal rows. Describe the number of chairs that can be in each row.

28. Error Analysis A student solves the inequality $4n + 8 \leq 24$. She says the solution is $n \leq -2$ because $n + 8 \leq 6$. Explain the student's error.

29. Darrell wants to make a pennant with the pattern shown. He has 4 feet of gold trim. Write an inequality for the value of x so that there is enough gold trim to go around all three edges of the pennant. Graph and describe the solutions.

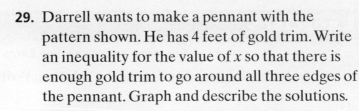

30. **Writing in Math** Randy wants a snack with no more than 200 calories. He includes some cherries that have 5 calories each and a banana that has 121 calories. Randy writes the inequality $5c + 121 \le 200$ to describe the number of cherries c he can eat. Describe the steps Randy must take to determine the value of c.

31. **Challenge** Two less than -5 times the sum of a number and 4 is greater than -37. Write and solve the inequality.

Test Prep and Mixed Review **Practice**

Multiple Choice

32. Raul has 50 ft of fencing that he can use to enclose a rectangular garden. The garden will be 6 ft long. Which statement about the garden's width must be true?

6 ft [ ] w

  (A) It will be 19 ft long at most.   (C) It will be 38 ft long at most.
  (B) It will be 22 ft long at most.   (D) It will be 44 ft long at most.

33. Which problem situation matches the equation below?

$$2x + 3 = 21$$

  (F) Janice is 3 years more than twice as old as Rashon. Janice is 21 years old. How old is Rashon?
  (G) Felicity has scored 2 points more than 3 times as many points as Kendra. Kendra has scored 21 points. How many points has Felicity scored?
  (H) Drew paid $2 more than Adam for tickets to a play. Richard's tickets cost him 3 times as much as Drew's tickets. Richard paid $21. How much did Adam pay for his tickets?
  (J) Nate worked 2 hours more than 3 times as many hours as Chad. Nate worked 21 hours. How many hours did Chad work?

34. Two of the driest cities in the United States are Yuma, Arizona, and Las Vegas, Nevada. Yuma averages 3.01 inches of rain each year and Las Vegas averages 4.49 inches each year. How many more inches of rain does Las Vegas receive each year than Yuma?

  (A) 0.37   (B) 1.00   (C) 1.48   (D) 7.50

Simplify each expression. Write your answer in simplest form.

35. $\dfrac{3}{8} \div \dfrac{5}{6}$ **36.** $\dfrac{1}{2} \div 2\dfrac{1}{4}$ **37.** $1\dfrac{5}{6} \div \dfrac{2}{5}$

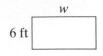

GO for Help

For Exercises	See Lesson
35–37	1-8

Reading for Understanding

Reading-comprehension questions are based on a passage that gives you facts and information. First read the question carefully. Make sure you understand what is being asked. Then read the passage. Look for the information you need to answer the question.

EXAMPLE

Recycling Math The United States produces more than 4 pounds of trash per person each day, and recycles slightly more than one third of it. Canada produces more than $3\frac{1}{2}$ pounds of trash per person each day, and recycles about one tenth of it. Japan produces less than $2\frac{1}{2}$ pounds of trash per person each day, and recycles about one fifth of it.

In one week, a family living in the United States produced 112 pounds of trash. About how many pounds of the trash were recycled?

What is being asked? How many pounds of trash were recycled?

Identify the information you need. The United States recycles slightly more than one third of the trash it produces.

Solve the problem. Pounds of recycled trash $> \frac{1}{3} \cdot 112$, or $37\frac{1}{3}$. More than 37 pounds of the American family's trash were recycled.

Exercises

Use the passage in the example to complete Exercises 1–4.

1. **a.** About how many pounds of trash will a Canadian family of four produce in one week?

   b. About how many pounds of the trash will be recycled?

2. In one week, a family living in Japan produces 85 pounds of trash. About how many pounds of the trash will be recycled?

3. Suppose your family recycles one half of its trash. How much more trash does your family recycle than an average U.S. family?

4. In one month, a school recycled two fifths of its paper and produced more than 25 pounds of paper. How many pounds were *not* recycled?

Chapter 4 Review

Vocabulary Review

Choose the correct property used to solve each inequality.

1. $\frac{z}{4} < 6$

$4 \cdot \frac{z}{4} < 6 \cdot 4$

$z < 24$

A. Addition Property of Inequality

B. Subtraction Property of Inequality

C. Multiplication Property of Inequality

D. Division Property of Inequality

Go Online

For vocabulary quiz
PearsonSuccessNet.com

2. $a + 4 \geq -2$

$a + 4 - 4 \geq -2 - 4$

$a \geq -6$

3. $-2.5n > -8$

$\frac{-2.5n}{-2.5} > \frac{-8}{-2.5}$

$n < 3.2$

4. $15 \leq x - 3$

$15 + 3 \leq x - 3 + 3$

$18 \leq x$

Skills and Concepts

Lesson 4-1

- To graph and write inequalities

A mathematical sentence that contains $<, >, \leq, \geq,$ or $\neq$ is called an **inequality**. A **solution of an inequality** is any number that makes an inequality true. When graphing, use an open circle for $>$ and $<$, and use a closed circle for $\geq$ and $\leq$.

Which of the given numbers are solutions of each inequality?

5. $x \geq -3; -5.2, -3, -1$

6. $x < 4; \frac{1}{6}, 4, 6\frac{1}{2}$

Graph the solution of each inequality.

7. $a > -5$

8. $4.7 \geq b$

9. $c < \frac{7}{8}$

Write an inequality for each statement. Then graph the inequality.

10. The ticket is at most $10.

11. The race is less than 5 miles.

12. You swim more than 45 min.

13. Lunch costs at least $4.75.

Lessons 4-2, 4-3

- To solve inequalities by adding or subtracting
- To solve inequalities by multiplying or dividing

You solve inequalities involving addition or subtraction just as you solve equations. You use inverse operations, and whatever you do to one side of the inequality, you do to the other side of the inequality.

When you multiply or divide each side of an inequality by the same positive number, the direction of the inequality symbol remains unchanged. When you multiply or divide each side of any inequality by the same negative number, the direction of the inequality symbol is reversed.

Solve each inequality. Then graph the inequality.

14. $7 + h < -15$

15. $-\dfrac{1}{2} + w < \dfrac{1}{6}$

16. $7.8 \geq z - 2.4$

17. $-3 \leq \dfrac{p}{5}$

18. $-30 < 5k$

19. $1.5 \leq -\dfrac{c}{3.2}$

20. A movie theater can seat 200 people. For one show, 85 people are in the theater already. Write and solve an inequality to find how many more people can attend this show.

21. A farmer has at least 60 lb of seed. This is enough to plant 3 crops of the same size. Write and solve an inequality to find how much seed the farmer needs for each crop.

Lesson 4-4

- To solve two-step inequalities using inverse operations

You can also use inverse operations to solve two-step inequalities. First you add or subtract the same number from each side. Then you multiply or divide each side by the same number.

Solve each inequality. Then graph the inequality.

22. $-4q + 3 > -5$

23. $2.6 + \dfrac{x}{1.8} \leq 4$

24. $-7 - \dfrac{r}{5} < 6$

25. $-2\dfrac{3}{4} \leq \dfrac{3}{4}t - \dfrac{1}{2}$

26. $\dfrac{2}{3} + \dfrac{-2}{3}w < 1$

27. $1.4 < \dfrac{b}{0.6} - 2$

28. You budget $20 for a pizza. A cheese pizza costs $12.95, and each additional topping costs $1.50. How many toppings can you order?

29. The difference of a number divided by 7 and 6 is at least -2. What could the number be?

Which numbers are solutions of each inequality?

1. $a > -2; 0, 1, -3$

2. $k \geq \frac{7}{8}; \frac{3}{8}, 1, -2\frac{1}{8}$

3. $2.4 \geq w;$
   $2.6, 2.4, 3.4$

4. $h < 0; -\frac{1}{2}, -3, 2$

5. $1\frac{3}{4} \leq e;$
   $1\frac{3}{4}, \frac{3}{4}, 2\frac{1}{4}$

6. $0.9 > b;$
   $0.9, 0.12, -0.4$

Define a variable and write an inequality for each statement.

7. The game's duration is at most 3 hours.

8. To rent a car, you must be at least 25 years old.

9. The truck can haul more than 20,000 lb.

10. There are fewer than 10 tickets available for the concert tonight.

Solve each inequality. Graph your solution.

11. $12 + n \geq 15$

12. $10 < y - 14$

13. $m - 8 \leq -17$

14. $3.7 + h < 4.9$

15. $b + \frac{1}{8} > -\frac{3}{8}$

16. $-\frac{1}{2} + z \leq 4$

17. $12x < -48$

18. $0.8h \geq 40$

19. $6 < \frac{v}{-8}$

20. $\frac{p}{1.1} \leq -6$

21. $-\frac{7}{12}k \leq -84$

22. $-4 > \frac{x}{-15}$

23. $4q + 3 > 11$

24. $-5 + -3c \leq 13$

25. $\frac{w}{0.5} - 1.2 \geq 7.8$

26. $\frac{5}{6} > \frac{a}{6} + \frac{1}{3}$

27. $-\frac{2}{5}k - \frac{1}{2} > \frac{4}{5}$

28. $2.3 + 1.8u \leq 6.8$

Define a variable. Then write and solve an inequality for each problem.

29. **Transportation** A ferry can safely transport at most 220 people. There are already 143 people aboard. How many more people can the ferry take aboard?

30. **Money** A sports drink costs $1.49 per bottle. At most how many bottles can you buy if you have $12?

31. **Shopping** Alex and his mother spent at least $130 while shopping for new clothes. Alex spent $52. How much money did his mother spend?

32. **Admission** After spending $42 for admission to a museum, a family estimates that they will have at least $50 left to spend on their day's visit to the city. How much money in all does this family have to spend on their visit?

33. **Groceries** You have $7 and want to buy 8 containers of yogurt. What is the greatest cost of 1 container so that you can purchase 8 containers?

34. **Savings** If you save $35 more, you will have more than enough to buy a computer monitor that costs $229. How much have you already saved?

35. **Music** You practice piano at least 60 min each day. You spend 20 min working on a performance piece and the rest of the time working on technique. How much time do you work on technique each day?

36. **Shipping** You are sending gifts to your grandparents in a carton that can hold a maximum of 25 lb. You place 3 same-size books in the box. The remaining items weigh 18.4 lb. How much does each book weigh?

37. The difference of $\frac{3}{4}$ of a number and 6 is more than 10. What could the number be?

38. Three tenths more than the product of -4 and a number is less than 11.98. What could the number be?

39. **Open-Ended** Write a problem you can represent with $2x - 6 > 8$. Solve the inequality. Show your work.

40. **Writing in Math** Describe the similarities and differences between solving inequalities and equations. Include examples.

Multiple Choice

Read each question. Then write the letter of the correct answer on your paper.

1. Which numbers are all solutions of the inequality $-3x > 15$?
   - Ⓐ $-5, -10, -8$
   - Ⓑ $0, -3, 4$
   - Ⓒ $-20, -7, -10$
   - Ⓓ $10, 6, 9$

2. Which graph shows the solution of $d + 10 \le 19$?

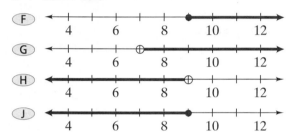

3. Which shows the integers in order from greatest to least?
   - Ⓐ $5, -1, -6$
   - Ⓑ $-6, 5, -1$
   - Ⓒ $-6, -1, 5$
   - Ⓓ $-1, 5, -6$

4. Your math class lasts for $\frac{5}{6}$ hr. Which shows the same amount of time?
   - Ⓕ 0.83 hr
   - Ⓖ $0.8\overline{3}$ hr
   - Ⓗ $0.\overline{83}$ hr
   - Ⓙ 0.84 hr

5. What can the expression $n - 4$ represent?
   - Ⓐ the time you are in 4 classes that are each n minutes long
   - Ⓑ the cost of each egg roll in a serving of 4 egg rolls that costs n dollars
   - Ⓒ your age if you are 4 years older than your cousin who is n years old
   - Ⓓ the hours you must still travel 4 hours after you start a trip of n hours

6. You trim 4.8 cm from a board that is 95 cm long. How much of the board is left?
   - Ⓕ 99.8 cm
   - Ⓖ 91.8 cm
   - Ⓗ 90.2 cm
   - Ⓙ 4.7 cm

7. Which expression is NOT equivalent to $12a$?
   - Ⓐ $2(-6a)$
   - Ⓑ $2(2a) + 8a$
   - Ⓒ $-3(-4a)$
   - Ⓓ $3(-2a) + 18a$

8. What is the solution of $4(x - 5) = 20$?
   - Ⓕ $x = 0$
   - Ⓖ $x = 5$
   - Ⓗ $x = 10$
   - Ⓙ $x = 25$

Gridded Response

Record your answer in a grid.

9. You have $40 to spend on DVDs. Each DVD costs $13.99. What is the greatest number of DVDs you can buy?

Short Response

10. During the summer, you work 27 hours per week. Each week, you earn $168.75. How many dollars do you earn per hour?

11. The sum of -2 times a number and 6 is less than 4.
    a. After you write the inequality, what is the first step you will take to solve it?
    b. What is the second step?

Extended Response

12. You save the same amount of money each month for 3 months. Your grandparents give you $25 for your birthday.
    a. Write an inequality to show that you have more than you need to buy an MP3 player that costs $130.
    b. How much money did you save each month? Justify your answer.

What You've Learned

- In Chapter 1, you compared and ordered rational numbers.
- You converted between fractions and decimals.
- You used addition, subtraction, multiplication, and division to solve problems involving rational numbers.

 Check Your Readiness

Multiplying and Dividing Rational Numbers

Find each product or quotient.

1. $(3.6)(4)$
2. $\left(\dfrac{1}{8}\right)\left(\dfrac{3}{5}\right)$
3. $\left(1\dfrac{1}{2}\right)\left(\dfrac{7}{8}\right)$

4. $52.6 \div 5$
5. $\dfrac{1}{2} \div \dfrac{3}{4}$
6. $2\dfrac{1}{4} \div \dfrac{1}{8}$

Solving One-Step Equations

(**Algebra**) **Solve.**

7. $4n = -32$
8. $\dfrac{a}{6} = 10$
9. $18 = -9z$
10. $-15 = \dfrac{p}{-5}$

Comparing and Ordering Fractions

Compare. Use <, =, or >.

11. $\dfrac{8}{9} \ \blacksquare\ \dfrac{3}{4}$
12. $\dfrac{7}{12} \ \blacksquare\ \dfrac{4}{5}$
13. $\dfrac{6}{3} \ \blacksquare\ \dfrac{24}{12}$
14. $\dfrac{1}{6} \ \blacksquare\ \dfrac{1}{7}$

Simplifying Fractions

Write each fraction in simplest form.

15. $\dfrac{12}{16}$
16. $\dfrac{15}{30}$
17. $\dfrac{27}{72}$
18. $\dfrac{19}{57}$
19. $\dfrac{16}{56}$

GO for Help

For Exercises	See Lesson
1–3	1-7
4–6	1-8
7–10	3-3
11–14	1-5
15–19	1-4

What You'll Learn Next

- In this chapter, you will write ratios and unit rates.
- You will write and solve proportions.
- You will use rates and proportions to solve problems involving similar figures, maps, and scale models.
- You will decide whether two quantities are in a proportional relationship and, if so, determine the constant of proportionality.

Key Vocabulary

- constant of proportionality (p. 222)
- cross products (p. 194)
- equivalent ratios (p. 185)
- indirect measurement (p. 208)
- polygon (p. 207)
- proportion (p. 193)
- rate (p. 188)
- ratio (p. 184)
- scale (p. 213)
- scale drawing (p. 213)
- similar polygons (p. 207)
- unit cost (p. 189)
- unit rate (p. 188)

Check Skills You'll Need

1. **Vocabulary Review**
   What is a *terminating decimal*?

   Write each fraction as a decimal.

2. $\frac{1}{2}$ 3. $\frac{3}{4}$

4. $\frac{3}{8}$ 5. $\frac{1}{3}$

GO for Help
Lesson 1-4

CONTENT STANDARD
Prepares for 7.RP.1

What You'll Learn

To write ratios and use them to compare quantities

New Vocabulary ratio, equivalent ratios

Why Learn This?

The keys on a music keyboard have a repeating pattern of five black keys and seven white keys. You can use ratios to describe patterns.

The ratio of black keys to white keys in the pattern is 5 to 7. What is the ratio of black keys to all keys in the pattern?

5	7
12	

KEY CONCEPTS Ratio

A **ratio** is a comparison of two quantities by division. You can write a ratio in three ways.

Arithmetic	**Algebra**
5 to 7 5 : 7 $\frac{5}{7}$	a to b $a : b$ $\frac{a}{b}$
	where $b \neq 0$

Video Tutor Help
PearsonSuccessNet.com

GO online

EXAMPLE Writing Ratios

1 **Music** Using the pattern shown above, write the ratio of black keys to all keys in three ways.

black keys → 5 to 12 ← all keys

black keys → 5 : 12 ← all keys

$\frac{5}{12}$ ← black keys
← all keys

Quick Check

1. Write each ratio in three ways. Use the pattern of keys shown above.
   a. white keys to all keys
   b. white keys to black keys

Two ratios that name the same number are **equivalent ratios.** In a previous course, you learned to write equivalent fractions. You can find equivalent ratios by writing a ratio as a fraction and finding an equivalent fraction.

EXAMPLES **Writing Equivalent Ratios**

2 Find a ratio equivalent to $\frac{4}{5}$.

$$\frac{4 \times 2}{5 \times 2} = \frac{8}{10} \quad \leftarrow \text{ Multiply the numerator and denominator by 2.}$$

3 Write the ratio 2 yd to 20 ft as a fraction in simplest form.

$$\frac{2 \text{ yd}}{20 \text{ ft}} = \frac{2 \times 3 \text{ ft}}{20 \text{ ft}} \quad \leftarrow \text{ There are 3 ft in each yard.}$$

$$= \frac{6 \text{ ft}}{20 \text{ ft}} \quad \leftarrow \text{ Multiply.}$$

$$= \frac{6 \text{ ft} \div 2}{20 \text{ ft} \div 2} \quad \leftarrow \text{ Divide by the GCF, 2.}$$

$$= \frac{3}{10} \quad \leftarrow \text{ Simplify.}$$

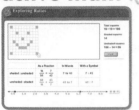

For: Ratios Activity
Use: Interactive
Textbook, 5-1

✓ Quick Check

2. Find a ratio equivalent to $\frac{7}{9}$.

3. Write the ratio 3 gal to 10 qt as a fraction in simplest form.

You can use decimals to express and compare ratios.

EXAMPLE **Comparing Ratios**

4 **Social Studies** An official U.S. flag has a length-to-width ratio of 19 : 10. The largest U.S. flag measures 505 ft by 255 ft. Is this an official U.S. flag?

official flag   largest flag
      ↓   ↓

$\frac{19}{10}$ $\leftarrow$ length $\rightarrow$ $\frac{505}{255}$
             $\leftarrow$ width $\rightarrow$

$\frac{19}{10} = 1.9$ $\leftarrow$ Write as a decimal. Round if necessary. $\rightarrow$ $\frac{505}{255} \approx 1.98$

Since 1.98 is not equal to 1.9, the largest flag is *not* an official U.S. flag.

For help writing fractions as decimals, go to Lesson 1-4.

✓ Quick Check

4. Tell whether the ratios are *equivalent* or *not equivalent*.

    a. 7 : 3, 128 : 54   **b.** $\frac{180}{240}, \frac{25}{34}$ **c.** 6.1 to 7, 30.5 to 35

1. **Vocabulary** How are equivalent ratios like equivalent fractions?

2. **Number Sense** Do all ratios compare a part to a whole? Explain.

Find an equivalent ratio for each ratio.

3. $\frac{1}{8}$ 4. 2 to 7   5. 10 : 9

Write each ratio as a fraction in simplest form.

6. 2 gal to 14 qt   7. 34 in. to 4 ft   8. $\frac{4 \text{ min}}{90 \text{ s}}$

Tell whether the ratios are *equivalent* or *not equivalent*.

9. $\frac{12}{24}, \frac{50}{100}$ 10. 1 to 3, 2 to 9   11. 2 : 3, 24 : 36

Homework Exercises

For more exercises, see Extra Skills and Word Problems.

GO for Help

For Exercises	See Example
12–13	1
14–16	2
17–22	3
23–25	4

Write a ratio in three ways, comparing the first quantity to the second.

12. A week has five school days and two weekend days.

13. About 21 out of 25 Texans live in an urban area.

Find an equivalent ratio for each ratio.

14. $\frac{14}{28}$ 15. 6 to 7   16. 4 : 5

Write each ratio as a fraction in simplest form.

17. $\frac{4 \text{ ft}}{8 \text{ ft}}$ 18. 10 s : 1 min   19. $\frac{30 \text{ mL}}{2 \text{ L}}$

20. 12 oz : 3 lb   21. 2 ft to 30 in.   22. $\frac{1 \text{ m}}{300 \text{ cm}}$

Tell whether the ratios are *equivalent* or *not equivalent*.

23. $\frac{18}{24}, \frac{3}{4}$ 24. 6 : 7, 30 : 36   25. 16 to 3, 27 to 5

26. **Guided Problem Solving** The students in Room 101 and Room 104 have one class together. Write the ratio of girls to boys for the combined class.

	Room 101	Room 104
Girls	12	9
Boys	16	20

   • **Make a Plan** First find the total numbers of girls and boys. Then find the ratio of girls to boys for the combined class.

27. **Cooking** To make pancakes, you need 2 cups of water for every 3 cups of flour. Write an equivalent ratio to find how much water you will need with 9 cups of flour.

28. Error Analysis Your math class includes 15 girls and 10 boys. Two new students, a girl and a boy, join the class. Your friend says the ratio of girls to boys is the same as before. Explain your friend's error.

29. 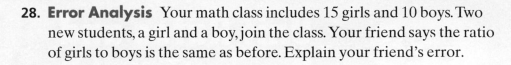 **Writing in Math** How can you tell when a ratio is in simplest form?

30. Chemistry A chemical formula shows the ratio of atoms in a substance. The formula for carbon dioxide, CO_2, tells you that there is 1 atom of carbon (C) for every 2 atoms of oxygen (O). Write the ratio of hydrogen (H) atoms to oxygen atoms in water, H_2O.

31. Antifreeze protects a car's radiator from freezing. In extremely cold weather, you must mix at least 2 parts antifreeze with every 1 part water.
  a. List all of the ratios in the table that provide the necessary protection.
  b. Reasoning How much antifreeze and how much water should you use to protect a 15-qt radiator?

Mixing Antifreeze	
Antifreeze (qt)	Water (qt)
8	4
7.5	3
12	8
3.5	1
9	18

32. Challenge A bag contains colored marbles. The ratio of red marbles to blue marbles is 1 : 4. The ratio of blue marbles to yellow marbles is 2 : 5. What is the ratio of red marbles to yellow marbles?

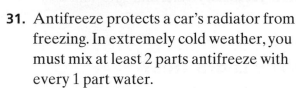 **Test Prep and Mixed Review** **Practice**

Multiple Choice

33. Maria tossed a coin 20 times and got 12 heads. What is the first step to find the ratio of the number of tails to the total number of tosses?
  Ⓐ Divide 12 by 20.   Ⓒ Multiply 12 by 20.
  Ⓑ Subtract 12 from 20. Ⓓ Add 12 to 20.

34. The model represents the equation $3x - 2 = -8$. What is the value of x?
  Ⓕ $x = -6$
  Ⓖ $x = -3$
  Ⓗ $x = -\frac{10}{3}$
  Ⓙ $x = -2$

Key
⊖ = −1

35. Emily ran $4\frac{1}{8}$ miles at track practice one day and 3.75 miles the next day. How many miles did she run in those two days?
  Ⓐ $7\frac{1}{2}$ miles   Ⓑ $7\frac{3}{4}$ miles   Ⓒ $7\frac{7}{8}$ miles   Ⓓ $8\frac{1}{8}$ miles

Algebra Solve each equation.

36. $72 = 8k$ **37.** $\frac{y}{3} = 15$ **38.** $-5 = \frac{q}{7}$

Unit Rates and Proportional Reasoning

ⓒ CONTENT STANDARD
7.RP.1

What You'll Learn

To find unit rates and unit costs using proportional reasoning
New Vocabulary rate, unit rate, unit cost

Why Learn This?

You make decisions about the foods you eat every day. Looking at rates such as grams of fat per serving can help you stay healthy.

A **rate** is a ratio that compares two quantities measured in different units. There are 15 grams of fat in 5 servings of canned soup. The rate of grams of fat per serving is $\frac{15 \text{ grams of fat}}{5 \text{ servings}}$.

The rate for one unit of a given quantity is the **unit rate.** To find a unit rate, divide the first quantity by the second quantity. For a rate of $\frac{15 \text{ grams of fat}}{5 \text{ servings}}$, the unit rate is 3 grams of fat per serving.

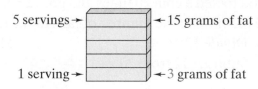

5 servings → 15 grams of fat

1 serving → 3 grams of fat

The model shows that

$$\text{total fat} \div \frac{\text{number of}}{\text{servings}} = \frac{\text{fat per}}{\text{serving}}$$

EXAMPLE **Finding a Unit Rate Using Whole Numbers**

1 A package of cheddar cheese contains 15 servings and has a total of 147 grams of fat. Find the unit rate of grams of fat per serving.

$$\begin{array}{l} \text{grams} \rightarrow \\ \text{servings} \rightarrow \end{array} \frac{147}{15} = 9.8 \quad \leftarrow \textbf{Divide the first quantity by the second quantity.}$$

The unit rate is $\frac{9.8 \text{ grams}}{1 \text{ serving}}$, or 9.8 grams of fat per serving.

✓ Quick Check

1. Find the unit rate for 210 heartbeats in 3 minutes.

You can also find unit rates from data expressed as fractions or decimals.

EXAMPLE **Finding a Unit Rate Using Fractions**

 Cindy walks $\frac{6}{10}$ mile in $\frac{1}{4}$ hour. What is her speed in miles per hour?

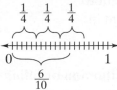

$$\text{miles to hours} = \frac{6}{10} \text{ to } \frac{1}{4} \quad \rightarrow \quad \textbf{Write the ratio.}$$

$$\text{miles} \div \text{hours} = \frac{6}{10} \div \frac{1}{4} \quad \rightarrow \quad \textbf{Divide the first quantity by the second quantity.}$$

$$= \frac{24}{10} = \frac{12}{5} \quad \rightarrow \quad \textbf{Simplify.}$$

$$= 2\frac{2}{5} \quad \rightarrow \quad \textbf{Write as a mixed number.}$$

Cindy walks $2\frac{2}{5}$ miles per hour.

For help dividing by a rational number, go to Lesson 1-8.

✓ Quick Check

2. Find the unit rate for $\frac{3}{10}$ mile in $\frac{3}{4}$ hour.

A unit rate that gives the cost per unit is a **unit cost**. To find the unit cost of an item, divide the total cost of the item by the number of units in the item.

EXAMPLE **Using Unit Cost to Compare**

The "better buy" is the item that has the lower unit cost.

3 **Smart Shopping** Two sizes of shampoo bottles are shown. Which size is the better buy? Round to the nearest cent.

Divide to find the unit cost of each size.

$$\begin{array}{l} \text{cost} \rightarrow \\ \text{size} \rightarrow \end{array} \frac{\$3.99}{13.5 \text{ fl oz}} \approx \$.30/\text{fl oz}$$

$$\begin{array}{l} \text{cost} \rightarrow \\ \text{size} \rightarrow \end{array} \frac{\$6.19}{16 \text{ fl oz}} \approx \$.39/\text{fl oz}$$

Since $\$.30 < \$.39$, the 13.5-fl-oz bottle is the better buy.

✓ Quick Check

3. Which bottle of apple juice is the better buy: 48 fl oz for $3.05 or 64 fl oz for $3.59?

1. **Vocabulary** What makes a unit rate a unit cost?

2. Use the model at the right to find the total grams of fat in 4 servings.

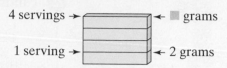

4 servings → ■ grams

1 serving → ← 2 grams

Find the unit rate for each situation by filling in the blanks.

3. skating 1,000 m in 200 s: $\frac{\text{meters}}{\text{seconds}} \rightarrow \frac{1,000}{■} = 5$ meters per second

4. drinking $\frac{7}{8}$ container of juice in $\frac{1}{2}$ min:
   containers to minutes → ■ to $\frac{1}{2}$ = ■ container(s) per minute

5. spending $89.50 in 5 h: $\frac{\text{dollars}}{\text{hours}} \rightarrow \frac{89.5}{■} = ■$ dollars per hour

Homework Exercises

For more exercises, see Extra Skills and Word Problems.

GO for Help

For Exercises	See Examples
6–9	1
10–13	2
14–18	3

Find the unit rate for each situation. Round to the nearest hundredth, if necessary.

6. traveling 1,200 mi in 4 h

7. scoring 96 points in 6 games

8. reading 53 pages in 2 h

9. 592 students in 17 classrooms

Find each unit rate.

10. $\frac{1}{2}$ dozen pencils in $\frac{1}{3}$ box

11. $\frac{4}{5}$ chapter in $\frac{1}{4}$ hour

12. $\frac{3}{5}$ page in $\frac{3}{4}$ minute

13. $\frac{7}{12}$ liter in $\frac{3}{10}$ kilometer

Find each unit cost. Round to the nearest hundredth, if necessary.

14. $12 for 4 yd^2

15. $3.45 for 3.7 oz

16. $9 for 5 L

Test Prep Tip

Drawing a model can help you find unit rates.

Which size is the better buy?

17. detergent: 32 fl oz for $1.99
    50 fl oz for $2.49

18. crackers: 12 oz for $2.69
    16 oz for $3.19

19. **Guided Problem Solving** A school has 945 students and 35 teachers. If the numbers of teachers and students both increase by 5, does the unit rate remain the same? Explain.

   • Find unit rates. $\frac{\text{students}}{\text{teachers}} \rightarrow \frac{■}{■} = ■$ students per teacher

20. **Biking** You bike 18.25 km in 1 h 45 min. What is the unit rate in kilometers per minute? In meters per minute?

21. **Crafts** The costs for three different types of ribbon are $.79 for 1 yd, $1.95 for 3 yd, and $2.94 for 6 yd. Which is the best buy?

Find each unit rate.

22. $2\frac{1}{2}$ miles in $11\frac{1}{2}$ minutes

23. $2\frac{1}{5}$ sandwiches in $4\frac{2}{5}$ minutes

24. **Landscaping** A landscaper used $\frac{1}{10}$ pound of fertilizer in the soil for every $22\frac{1}{3}$ square feet of lawn. What is the unit rate in pounds per square foot?

25. **Open-Ended** Write a scenario and find the unit rate: $1\frac{2}{3}$ liter in $\frac{1}{6}$ square meter.

26. The world record for the women's 3,000-m steeplechase is 9 min 1.59 s. Find the runner's speed in meters per second. Round your answer to the nearest hundredth.

27. **Geography** Population density is the number of people per unit of area.
   a. Alaska has the lowest population density of any state in the United States. It has 626,932 people in 570,374 mi². What is its population density? Round to the nearest person per square mile.
   b. **Reasoning** New Jersey has 1,134.5 people/mi². Can you conclude that 1,134.5 people live in every square mile in New Jersey? Explain.

28. **Writing in Math** Explain the difference between a rate and a unit rate.

29. **Challenge** A human heart beats an average of 2,956,575,000 times in 75 years. About how many times does a heart beat in one year? In one day? In one minute?

Test Prep and Mixed Review
Practice

Multiple Choice

30. A grocery store sells apple juice in these sizes: 64 ounces for $2.48, 128 ounces for $4.48, and 48 ounces for $1.92. Which size has the lowest unit cost?
   Ⓐ 48-oz only
   Ⓒ 128-oz only
   Ⓑ 64-oz only
   Ⓓ 128-oz and 64-oz

31. The table shows some of Aaron's quiz scores. Which algebraic expression represents his score when he answers n questions correctly?

Questions Answered Correctly	6	7	10	n
Score	24	28	40	?

   Ⓕ $n + 30$
   Ⓖ $\frac{n}{4}$
   Ⓗ $n - 6$
   Ⓙ $4n$

32. Kim makes a mix of $\frac{5}{8}$ lb of peanuts and 0.7 lb of cashews. Then she places an equal amount of mix in each of 10 bags for a party. To the nearest hundredth, how much does she place in each bag?
   Ⓐ 0.13 lb
   Ⓑ 0.23 lb
   Ⓒ 1.33 lb
   Ⓓ 13.25 lb

Solve each inequality. Graph the solution.

33. $m + 3 > 7$

34. $t - 7 \le 0$

35. $h + 0.6 < -2.8$

GO for Help

For Exercises	See Lesson
33–35	4-2

Conversion Factors

In Lesson 5-2, you learned how to write rates. A conversion factor is a rate that equals 1. For example, since 1 in. and 2.54 cm are equivalent measures, you can write $\frac{1 \text{ in.}}{2.5 \text{ cm}}$ and $\frac{2.5 \text{ cm}}{1 \text{ in.}}$ as conversion factors because they equal 1. You can use conversion factors to convert between the metric system and the customary system.

Equivalent Measures

Length
1 in. = 2.54 cm
1 km ≈ 0.62 mi

Capacity
1 L ≈ 1.06 qt

Weight and Mass
1 oz ≈ 28 g
1 kg ≈ 2.2 lb

EXAMPLE **Converting to the Customary System**

The mass of a western diamondback rattlesnake is about 6.7 kg. How many pounds does the snake weigh? Round to the nearest tenth.

Step 1 Find a pair of equivalent measures in the table that have the same units named in the problem.
$1 \text{ kg} \approx 2.2 \text{ lb}$

Step 2 Use the measures to write conversion factors.
$\frac{1 \text{ kg}}{2.2 \text{ lb}}$ and $\frac{2.2 \text{ lb}}{1 \text{ kg}}$

Step 3 Write an equation that you can simplify, leaving the unit you are converting to.

$6.7 \text{ kg} = \frac{6.7 \text{ k\!g}}{1} \cdot \frac{2.2 \text{ lb}}{1 \text{ k\!g}}$ ← Use $\frac{2.2 \text{ lb}}{1 \text{ kg}}$ since conversion is to pounds.

Step 4 Simplify and round to the nearest tenth.

$= (6.7)(2.2) \text{ lb}$ ← Simplify.

$= 14.74 \text{ lb}$ ← Multiply.

$\approx 14.7 \text{ lb}$ ← Round to the nearest tenth.

The snake weighs about 14.7 lb.

Exercises

Write a conversion factor you can use to convert each measure.

1. kilometers to miles   2. liters to quarts   3. ounces to grams

Use a conversion factor to convert each measure. Round to the nearest tenth.

4. 22 in. ≈ ■ cm   5. 26.4 lb ≈ ■ kg   6. 20.5 oz ≈ ■ g

7. 500 g ≈ ■ oz   8. 5 km ≈ ■ mi   9. 20 L ≈ ■ qt

5-3 Proportions

What You'll Learn

To test whether ratios form a proportion by using equivalent ratios and cross products

New Vocabulary proportion, cross products

Why Learn This?

Pollsters conduct surveys. They ask different groups of people the same questions. You can use proportions to compare the answers from the different groups.

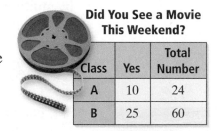

Did You See a Movie This Weekend?

Class	Yes	Total Number
A	10	24
B	25	60

A **proportion** is an equation stating that two ratios are equal. One method of testing whether ratios form a proportion is to write both ratios in simplest form. Then see if they are equal.

EXAMPLE Writing Ratios in Simplest Form

1 Surveys Refer to the table above. For each class, write the ratio of the number of students who saw a movie to the total number of students. Do the ratios form a proportion?

Class A: $\frac{10}{24} = \frac{10 \div 2}{24 \div 2} = \frac{5}{12}$ ← Divide 10 and 24 by their GCF, which is 2.

Class B: $\frac{25}{60} = \frac{25 \div 5}{60 \div 5} = \frac{5}{12}$ ← Divide 25 and 60 by their GCF, which is 5.

Since both ratios are equal to $\frac{5}{12}$, the ratios are proportional.

✓ Quick Check

1. Do $\frac{10}{12}$ and $\frac{40}{56}$ form a proportion?

KEY CONCEPTS **Proportion**

Ratios that are equal form a proportion.

Arithmetic
$\frac{6}{8} = \frac{9}{12}$

Algebra
$\frac{a}{b} = \frac{c}{d}, b \neq 0, d \neq 0$

Video Tutor Help
PearsonSuccessNet.com

You can use the properties of equality to discover another way to determine whether ratios form a proportion.

$$\frac{6}{8} = \frac{9}{12}$$ ← Use the ratios from the beginning of the lesson.

$$\frac{6}{8}\left(\frac{8}{1} \cdot \frac{12}{1}\right) = \frac{9}{12}\left(\frac{8}{1} \cdot \frac{12}{1}\right)$$ ← **Use the Multiplication Property of Equality.** Multiply each side by both denominators.

$$\frac{6}{\cancel{8}_1}\left(\frac{\cancel{8}^1}{1} \cdot \frac{12}{1}\right) = \frac{9}{\cancel{12}_1}\left(\frac{8}{1} \cdot \frac{\cancel{12}^1}{1}\right)$$ ← **Divide numerators and denominators by their GCF.**

$$6 \cdot 12 = 9 \cdot 8$$

The products $6 \cdot 12$ and $9 \cdot 8$ are called cross products. For two ratios, the **cross products** are the two products found by multiplying the denominator of each ratio by the numerator of the other ratio.

$6 \cdot 12$ $\dfrac{6}{8} \bowtie \dfrac{9}{12}$ $8 \cdot 9$

KEY CONCEPTS   **Cross-Products Property**

If two ratios form a proportion, the cross products are equal. If two ratios have equal cross products, they form a proportion.

Arithmetic	Algebra
$\dfrac{6}{8} = \dfrac{9}{12}$	$\dfrac{a}{b} = \dfrac{c}{d}$
$6 \cdot 12 = 8 \cdot 9$	$ad = bc$, where $b \neq 0$ and $d \neq 0$

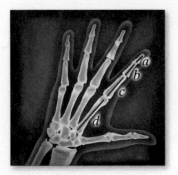

The lengths of the bones in your hands form a proportion.

Source: *Fascinating Fibonaccis*

You can use the Cross-Products Property to determine whether ratios form a proportion.

EXAMPLE   **Using Cross Products**

2   Do the ratios in each pair form a proportion?

a. $\dfrac{5}{9}, \dfrac{30}{54}$ b. $\dfrac{7}{8}, \dfrac{55}{65}$

$\dfrac{5}{9} \stackrel{?}{=} \dfrac{30}{54}$ ← Test each pair of ratios. → $\dfrac{7}{8} \stackrel{?}{=} \dfrac{55}{65}$

$5 \cdot 54 \stackrel{?}{=} 9 \cdot 30$ ← Write cross products. → $7 \cdot 65 \stackrel{?}{=} 8 \cdot 55$

$270 = 270$ ← Simplify. → $455 \neq 440$

Yes, $\dfrac{5}{9}$ and $\dfrac{30}{54}$ form a proportion.   No, $\dfrac{7}{8}$ and $\dfrac{55}{65}$ do *not* form a proportion.

✓ **Quick Check**

2. Determine whether the ratios form a proportion.

a. $\dfrac{3}{8}, \dfrac{6}{16}$ b. $\dfrac{6}{9}, \dfrac{4}{6}$ c. $\dfrac{4}{8}, \dfrac{5}{9}$

1. **Vocabulary** A proportion states that two __?__ are equal.

2. **Number Sense** Without writing $\frac{3}{5}$ and $\frac{9}{15}$ in simplest form or using the Cross-Products Property, how can you tell whether the ratios form a proportion?

Fill in the blank so that each pair of ratios forms a proportion.

3. $\frac{1}{2}$, $\frac{4}{\blacksquare}$

4. $\frac{3}{3}$, $\frac{9}{\blacksquare}$

5. $\frac{3}{4}$, $\frac{\blacksquare}{12}$

6. $\frac{4}{7}$, $\frac{8}{\blacksquare}$

7. $\frac{2}{3}$, $\frac{\blacksquare}{18}$

8. $\frac{\blacksquare}{5}$, $\frac{6}{10}$

9. **Error Analysis** A student used the Cross-Products Property to determine that $\frac{3}{4}$ and $\frac{12}{16}$ do not form a proportion. His work is shown at the right. Is he correct? Explain.

$$\frac{3}{4} \stackrel{?}{=} \frac{12}{16}$$
$$3 \cdot 12 \stackrel{?}{=} 4 \cdot 16$$
$$36 \neq 64$$

Homework Exercises

For more exercises, see Extra Skills and Word Problems.

For Exercises	See Examples
10–18	1
19–27	2

Determine whether the ratios can form a proportion.

10. $\frac{1}{2}$, $\frac{14}{28}$

11. $\frac{6}{8}$, $\frac{4}{3}$

12. $\frac{8}{18}$, $\frac{20}{45}$

13. $\frac{21}{24}$, $\frac{56}{64}$

14. $\frac{15}{45}$, $\frac{3}{15}$

15. $\frac{45}{9}$, $\frac{10}{2}$

16. $\frac{19}{76}$, $\frac{5}{20}$

17. $\frac{17}{34}$, $\frac{2}{3}$

18. $\frac{40}{12}$, $\frac{160}{3}$

19. $\frac{6}{10}$, $\frac{9}{15}$

20. $\frac{4}{5}$, $\frac{10}{13}$

21. $\frac{7}{8}$, $\frac{15}{18}$

22. $\frac{6}{14}$, $\frac{3}{7}$

23. $\frac{7}{22}$, $\frac{28}{77}$

24. $\frac{12}{15}$, $\frac{20}{25}$

25. $\frac{6}{10}$, $\frac{24}{42}$

26. $\frac{5}{9}$, $\frac{15}{27}$

27. $\frac{3}{10}$, $\frac{15}{25}$

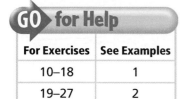

28. **Guided Problem Solving** Your boat engine needs 5 fl oz of oil mixed with every 2 gal of gas. A gas container has 12 gal of gas mixed with 34 fl oz of oil. Is this the correct mixture? Explain.
   - **Make a Plan** Write the ratio of oil to gas for the boat and for the gas container. Determine whether the ratios form a proportion.
   - **Carry Out the Plan** The ratios of oil to gas are $\frac{\blacksquare \text{ fl oz}}{2 \text{ gal}}$ and $\frac{\blacksquare \text{ fl oz}}{12 \text{ gal}}$.

29. **Decorating** A certain shade of green paint requires 4 parts blue to 5 parts yellow. If you mix 16 quarts of blue paint with 25 quarts of yellow paint, will you get the desired shade of green? Explain.

Do the ratios in each pair form a proportion?

30. $\frac{18}{12}, \frac{4.8}{3.6}$

31. $\frac{20}{1.5}, \frac{60}{4.5}$

32. $\frac{3.5}{35}, \frac{2.04}{204}$

33. $\frac{1}{3} : 3, \frac{1}{4} : 4$

34. $\frac{2}{3} : \frac{2}{9}, \frac{1}{4} : \frac{1}{12}$

35. $\frac{4}{5} : \frac{1}{2}, \frac{2}{3} : \frac{1}{4}$

36. **Writing in Math** Explain why $\frac{a}{b}$ and $\frac{a+b}{b}$ can *never* form a proportion.

37. **Space** An astronaut who weighs 174 lb on Earth weighs 29 lb on the moon. If you weigh 102 lb on Earth, would you weigh 17 lb on the moon? Explain.

38. **Geometry** Is the ratio of b to h the same in both triangles? Explain your reasoning.

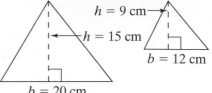

39. **Physical Science** Eighteen-karat gold contains 18 parts gold and 6 parts other metals. A ring contains 12 parts gold and 3 parts other metals. Is the ring eighteen-karat gold? Explain.

Careers Astronauts pilot spacecraft or work on science projects in space.

40. **Challenge** Determine whether $\frac{4n}{3}$ and $\frac{12n}{9}$ *always*, *sometimes*, or *never* form a proportion. Explain.

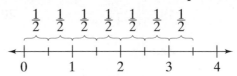
Test Prep and Mixed Review **Practice**

Multiple Choice

41. Which ratio does NOT form a proportion with $\frac{5}{8}$?

Ⓐ $\frac{20}{32}$ Ⓑ $\frac{100}{160}$ Ⓒ $\frac{45}{56}$ Ⓓ $\frac{10}{16}$

42. Which expression does the model below represent?

$$\frac{1}{2} \quad \frac{1}{2} \quad \frac{1}{2} \quad \frac{1}{2} \quad \frac{1}{2} \quad \frac{1}{2} \quad \frac{1}{2}$$

```
+--+--+--+--+--+--+--+--+
0     1     2     3     4
```

Ⓕ $3\frac{1}{2} - \frac{1}{2}$ Ⓖ $\frac{1}{2} \div 3\frac{1}{2}$ Ⓗ $3\frac{1}{2} \div \frac{1}{2}$ Ⓙ $\frac{1}{2} \times 3\frac{1}{2}$

43. Carrie buys T-shirts for $6.25 each. After paying to have her school mascot printed on the shirts, she sells each one for $9.50. Carrie plans to sell 12 T-shirts at a basketball game. What missing information is needed to find how much profit per shirt she will make?

Ⓐ Cost to print the mascot   Ⓒ Sizes of the T-shirts
Ⓑ Number of fans at the game   Ⓓ Price of each T-shirt

GO for Help

For Exercises	See Lesson
44–46	3-3

Algebra Solve each equation.

44. $y - 37 = 68$ **45.** $m + 59 = -348$ **46.** $b + 175 = 102$

Write each ratio in simplest form.

1. $\frac{4}{6}$

2. 24 to 14

3. 18 : 27

Write a unit rate for each situation.

4. typing 126 words in 3 min

5. $\frac{3}{8}$ cup in $\frac{1}{2}$ serving

Find each unit cost. Which is the better buy?

6. 3 for \$.79, 4 for \$.99

7. 5 for \$39, 7 for \$46

Determine whether the ratios form a proportion.

8. $\frac{5}{8}$, $\frac{12}{20}$

9. $\frac{4}{10}$, $\frac{2}{5}$

10. $\frac{24}{15}$, $\frac{4}{3}$

MATH AT WORK

Automotive Engineer

Automotive engineers design, develop, and test all kinds of vehicles. They also test and evaluate a design's cost, reliability, and safety.

Engineers have many opportunities to use math skills. They use problem-solving skills to find out why cars break down.

Computer-aided design systems help automotive engineers plan the cars of the future. Computer simulations allow them to test for quality and to predict how their designs will work in the real world.

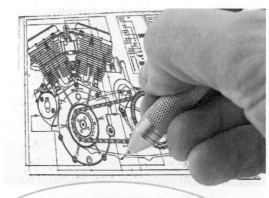

Go **Online** For information on automotive engineer PearsonSuccessNet.com

197

Using Proportions With Data

You can use proportions to estimate the number of times your heart beats in one minute, which is called your heart rate.

ACTIVITY

Copy and complete the table below. Use your data from Steps 1–4.

My Heart Rate Data

Ratio: $\dfrac{\text{counted beats}}{10 \text{ seconds}}$	■
Resting Heart Rate	■
Minimum Target Value	■
Maximum Target Value	■
Exercising Heart Rate	■

Step 1 Count the number of times your heart beats in 10 seconds. Write this value as a ratio.

Step 2 Let x = your heart rate. Use your data to write a proportion.

$$\frac{\text{counted beats}}{10 \text{ seconds}} = \frac{x \text{ beats}}{60 \text{ seconds}}$$

Use mental math to find x. This is your resting heart rate.

Step 3 When you exercise, your heart rate should fall within a target zone. Calculate the values for your target zone.

Minimum value $= 0.6(220 - \text{your age})$
Maximum value $= 0.8(220 - \text{your age})$

Step 4 Jog in place for one minute. Repeat Steps 1 and 2 to estimate your exercising heart rate.

Exercises

1. Compare your exercising rate with your target zone.

2. Explain why counting your heartbeats for 10 seconds, rather than for a full minute, gives you a more accurate estimate of your exercising heart rate.

3. Express your resting heart rate as a unit rate and estimate the number of times your heart beats in 24 hours.

5-4 Solving Proportions

✓ Check Skills You'll Need

1. **Vocabulary Review** When is a ratio a *unit rate*?

Write the unit rate for each situation.

2. 192 km in 24 d

3. 24.8 mi in 4 h

4. 50 push-ups in 2 min

5. $3.75 for 3 songs

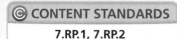
for Help
Lesson 5-2

© **CONTENT STANDARDS**
7.RP.1, 7.RP.2

What You'll Learn

To solve proportions using unit rates, mental math, and cross products

Why Learn This?

You know the price of six oranges, but you want to buy eight. You can solve a proportion to find the total cost of the quantity that you want to buy.

You can use unit rates to solve a proportion. First find the unit rate. Then multiply to solve the problem.

6 for $2.34

EXAMPLE Using Unit Rates

1 **Shopping** Use the information above to find the cost in dollars of 8 oranges.

Solve the proportion $\frac{2.34 \text{ dollars}}{6 \text{ oranges}} = \frac{x \text{ dollars}}{8 \text{ oranges}}$.

Step 1 Find the unit price.

$\frac{2.34 \text{ dollars}}{6 \text{ oranges}}$

$\$2.34 \div 6 \text{ oranges}$ ← Divide to find the unit price.

$\$.39/\text{orange}$

Step 2 You know the cost of one orange. Multiply to find the cost of 8 oranges.

$\$.39 \cdot 8 = \$3.12$ ← Multiply the unit rate by the number of oranges.

The cost of 8 oranges is $3.12.

✓ Quick Check

1. **a.** Postcards cost $2.45 for 5 cards. How much will 13 cards cost?
   b. Swimming goggles cost $84.36 for 12. At this rate, how much will new goggles for 17 members of a swim team cost?

You can use mental math to solve some proportions. When a proportion involves a variable, you solve the proportion by finding the value of the variable.

EXAMPLE Solving Using Mental Math

2 (Algebra) Solve each proportion using mental math.

a. $\frac{z}{12} = \frac{21}{36}$

$$\overset{\times 3}{\frac{z}{12} = \frac{21}{36}}_{\times 3}$$ ← Since 12 × 3 = 36, the common multiplier is 3.

$z = 7$ ← Use mental math to find what number times 3 equals 21.

b. $\frac{8}{10} = \frac{n}{40}$

$$\overset{\times 4}{\frac{8}{10} = \frac{n}{40}}_{\times 4}$$ ← Since 10 × 4 = 40, 8 × 4 = n.

$n = 32$ ← Use mental math.

✓ Quick Check

2. Solve each proportion using mental math.

a. $\frac{3}{8} = \frac{b}{24}$ b. $\frac{m}{5} = \frac{16}{40}$ c. $\frac{15}{30} = \frac{5}{p}$

Many proportions cannot easily be solved with mental math. In these situations, you can use cross products to solve a proportion.

EXAMPLE Solving Using Cross Products

Test Prep Tip

Before you use cross products to solve a proportion, check whether you can use mental math.

3 **Gridded Response** Solve $\frac{25}{38} = \frac{15}{x}$ using cross products.

$\frac{25}{38} = \frac{15}{x}$

$25x = 38(15)$ ← Write the cross products.

$25x = 570$ ← Simplify.

$\frac{25x}{25} = \frac{570}{25}$ ← Divide each side by 25.

$x = 22.8$ ← Simplify.

2	2	.	8
	⊘	⊘	
⊙	⊙	●	⊙
	⓪	⓪	⓪
①	①	①	①
❷	❷	②	②
③	③	③	③
④	④	④	④
⑤	⑤	⑤	⑤
⑥	⑥	⑥	⑥
⑦	⑦	⑦	⑦
⑧	⑧	⑧	❽
⑨	⑨	⑨	⑨

✓ Quick Check

3. Solve each proportion using cross products.

a. $\frac{12}{15} = \frac{x}{21}$ b. $\frac{16}{30} = \frac{d}{51}$ c. $\frac{20}{35} = \frac{110}{m}$

More Than One Way

Nature An oyster bed covers 36 m². Your class studies 4 m² of the oyster bed. In those 4 m² you count 96 oysters. Predict the number of oysters in the entire bed.

Carlos's Method

I will let x represent the number of oysters in the 36-m² bed.

$$\text{oysters} \rightarrow \frac{96}{4} = \frac{x}{36} \leftarrow \text{oysters}$$
$$\text{area} \rightarrow \qquad \qquad \leftarrow \text{area}$$

← Write a proportion.

$$96(36) = 4x$$ ← Write the cross products.

$$3{,}456 = 4x$$ ← Simplify.

$$\frac{3{,}456}{4} = \frac{4x}{4}$$ ← Divide each side by 4.

$$864 = x$$ ← Simplify.

There are about 864 oysters in the oyster bed.

Brianna's Method

Since $9 \cdot 4 \text{ m}^2 = 36 \text{ m}^2$, the entire bed is 9 times as large as the portion studied. So I know there should be about $9 \cdot 96$, or 864, oysters in the oyster bed.

Choose a Method
You buy a bag of 400 marbles. In a handful of 20 marbles, you find 8 red marbles. About how many red marbles are in the bag? Explain why you chose the method you used.

Check Your Understanding

1.  **Writing in Math** How does a unit rate help you solve a proportion?

2. **Number Sense** Does the proportion $\frac{3}{7} = \frac{x}{21}$ have the same solution as $\frac{7}{3} = \frac{21}{x}$? Explain.

Solve each proportion using mental math.

3. $\frac{2}{5} = \frac{m}{10}$

$$\overset{\times 2}{\frac{2}{5} = \frac{m}{10}}_{\times 2}$$

$$m = \blacksquare$$

4. $\frac{1}{6} = \frac{4}{y}$

$$\overset{\times 4}{\frac{1}{6} = \frac{4}{y}}_{\times 4}$$

$$y = \blacksquare$$

5. $\frac{7}{3} = \frac{28}{b}$

$$\overset{\times 4}{\frac{7}{3} = \frac{28}{b}}_{\times 4}$$

$$b = \blacksquare$$

For more exercises, see Extra Skills and Word Problems.

GO for Help

For Exercises	See Examples
6–10	1
11–16	2
17–25	3

Solve each problem by finding a unit rate and multiplying.

6. If 5 goldfish cost $6.45, what is the cost of 8 goldfish?

7. If 12 roses cost $18.96, what is the cost of 5 roses?

8. If 3 onions weigh 0.75 lb, how much do 10 onions weigh?

9. If 13 key chains cost $38.35, what is the cost of 20 key chains?

10. At a telethon, a volunteer can take 48 calls over a 4-hour shift. At this rate, how many calls can 12 volunteers take in a 4-hour shift?

Solve each proportion using mental math.

11. $\frac{2}{7} = \frac{x}{21}$

12. $\frac{18}{32} = \frac{m}{16}$

13. $\frac{c}{10} = \frac{36}{60}$

14. $\frac{c}{35} = \frac{4}{7}$

15. $\frac{16}{38} = \frac{b}{19}$

16. $\frac{9}{w} = \frac{36}{20}$

Solve each proportion using cross products.

17. $\frac{8}{12} = \frac{y}{30}$

18. $\frac{15}{33} = \frac{m}{22}$

19. $\frac{c}{28} = \frac{49}{16}$

20. $\frac{y}{18} = \frac{21}{63}$

21. $\frac{14}{34} = \frac{x}{51}$

22. $\frac{9}{30} = \frac{p}{16}$

23. $\frac{20}{w} = \frac{12}{3}$

24. $\frac{27}{20} = \frac{36}{v}$

25. $\frac{19}{r} = \frac{152}{4}$

26. **Guided Problem Solving** You received $57.04 for working 8 h. At that rate, how much would you receive for working 11 h?

$$\text{hours} \rightarrow \frac{8}{\blacksquare} = \frac{\blacksquare}{x} \quad \leftarrow \text{You would receive } x \text{ dollars for } \blacksquare \text{ hours.}$$
$$\text{pay} \rightarrow$$

27. **History** Franklin D. Roosevelt was elected president in 1932 with about 22,800,000 votes. The ratio of the number of votes he received to the number of votes the other candidates received was about 4 : 3. About how many votes did the other candidates receive?

28. There are 450 students and 15 teachers in a school. The school hires 2 new teachers. To keep the student-to-teacher ratio the same, how many students in all should attend the school?

29. **Reasoning** Brian solved the proportion $\frac{18}{45} = \frac{a}{20}$ at the right. His first step was to simplify the ratio $\frac{18}{45}$. Is his answer correct? Explain.

$$\frac{2\,18}{5\,45} = \frac{a}{20}$$
$$\overset{\times 4}{\frac{2}{5} = \frac{a}{20}}$$
$$\times 4$$
$$a = 8$$

30. A jet takes $5\frac{3}{4}$ h to fly 2,475 mi from New York City to Los Angeles. About how many hours will a jet flying at the same average rate take to fly 5,452 mi from Los Angeles to Tokyo?

Solve each proportion using cross products. Round to the nearest tenth, if necessary.

31. $\frac{1.7}{2.5} = \frac{3.4}{d}$ **32.** $\frac{y}{9.3} = \frac{12.6}{5.4}$ **33.** $\frac{33.1}{x} = \frac{6.2}{1.3}$ **34.** $\frac{16.9}{13.5} = \frac{t}{7.4}$

35. Error Analysis A videocassette recorder uses 2 m of tape in 3 min when set on extended play. To determine how many minutes a tape that is 240 m long can record on extended play, one student wrote the proportion $\frac{2}{3} = \frac{n}{240}$. Explain why this proportion is incorrect. Then write a correct proportion.

36. Health Your heart rate is the number of heartbeats per minute.
  a. What is your heart rate if you count 18 beats in 15 seconds?
  b. Choose a Method How many beats do you count in 15 seconds if your heart rate is 96 beats/min? Explain the method you chose.

37. Writing in Math You estimate you will take 75 min to bike 15 mi to a state park. After 30 min, you have traveled 5 mi. Are you on schedule? Explain.

38. Challenge A recipe for fruit salad serves 4 people. It calls for $2\frac{1}{2}$ oranges and 16 grapes. You want to serve 11 people. How many oranges and how many grapes will you need?

Test Prep and Mixed Review   **Practice**

Gridded Response

39. An antelope ran 237 ft in 3 seconds. If the antelope continued to run at the same rate, how many seconds would it take him to run 790 ft?

40. The table below shows the leaders in punt returns for the National Football Conference during one season.

Punt Return Leaders

Name	Number of Returns	Yards
Brian Westbrook	20	306
Allen Rossum	39	545
Reggie Swinton	23	318
R. W. McQuarters	37	452

What was the unit rate of yards per return for Reggie Swinton? Round to the nearest hundredth.

41. A restaurant bill for four people is $37.80. How much money, in dollars, should each person contribute to share the cost evenly?

Order the numbers from least to greatest.

42. 16, −12, 10, −3   **43.** −6, −3, 8, −2, 1   **44.** 5, 0, −1, 2, −5

GO for Help

For Exercises	See Lesson
42–44	1-1

Proportions and Equations

Often you can translate a proportion problem into an equation.
You can then use the equation to solve similar problems.

Muscles For each 5 pounds of body weight, about 2 pounds is
muscle. How much of a 125-pound student is muscle?

What You Might Think

What do I know?

What am I trying to find out?

How do I solve the problem?

What is the answer?

What You Might Write

Each 5 lb of weight includes 2 lb of muscle.

How many pounds of muscle are in 125 lb of body weight?

I can write an equation to find the muscle weight for any student weight. A proportion that represents the situation is

$$\frac{x}{125} = \frac{2}{5}.$$

To solve for x, I can multiply each side by 125.

$$x = \frac{2}{5}(125)$$

125 represents the student's weight. So if a student's weight is w, then the equation

$x = \frac{2}{5}w$ gives the amount of muscle for any weight w.

$$x = \frac{2}{5}(125)$$
$$= 250 \div 5$$
$$= 50$$

The 125-lb student has about 50 lb of muscle.

Think It Through

1. Show how solving the equation $\frac{2}{5} = \frac{x}{w}$ for x gives the equation $x = \frac{2}{5}w$.

2. Explain why you can use the equation $x = \frac{2}{5}w$ as a shortcut for finding the amount of muscle for any student.

Exercises

Solve each problem. For Exercises 3 and 4, answer the questions first.

3. During one season, a basketball player made 353 of 765 free throws. At that rate, how many free throws would the player make in another 600 attempts?
   a. What do you know? What do you want to find out?
   b. Can you write an equation to predict the number of free throws x the player will make for any number of shots s?

4. Jess wants to sell fruit punch on a hot day. The punch is 2 parts grape juice to 3 parts apple juice. Jess has 5 quarts of apple juice. How many quarts of grape juice does she need?
   a. What do you know? What do you want to find out?
   b. Can you write an equation to find the number of quarts of grape juice g needed for a quarts of apple juice?

5. Jess makes the graph below so that she does not have to keep calculating amounts of juice. Use the graph to find how much grape juice is needed for 15 quarts of apple juice. Then find how much apple juice is needed for 12 quarts of grape juice.

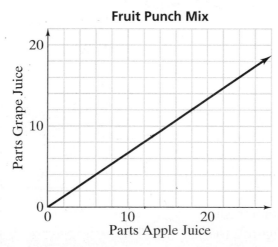

Fruit Punch Mix

6. A concession stand needs 3 hot dogs for every 7 people who attend a football game. If 1,400 fans are expected to attend the game, how many hot dogs are needed?

7. Earth is about 25,000 mi around at the equator. If you are sitting on the equator, about how fast are you traveling? (*Hint:* Earth makes one rotation in 24 hours.)

Exploring Similar Figures

In everyday language, two items are similar if they are the same in some, but not necessarily all, ways. In math, similarity has a related meaning. Complete the activity to find out what makes two figures mathematically similar.

ACTIVITY

Figures 1 and 2 below are similar. Figures 3 and 4 are similar, too. You can test whether two figures are similar by measuring their angles and side lengths.

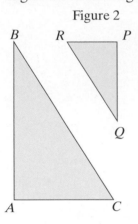

Figure 1

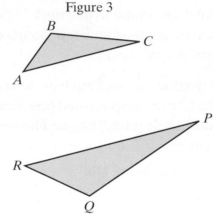

Figure 4

1. Copy the table at the right. Use a protractor to measure each angle of Figure 1 and Figure 2 above. Fill in the missing information in the table. What do you notice about the angle measures in each row of your table?

2. Copy the table at the right. Use a centimeter ruler to measure each side of Figure 1 and Figure 2 to the nearest tenth of a centimeter. Fill in the missing information in the table. What pattern do you notice in the length of the sides in each row of the table?

3. Repeat Steps 1 and 2 for Figures 3 and 4.

4. Make a conjecture about the angle measures and side lengths of similar figures.

Fig. 1	Angle Measure	Fig. 2	Angle Measure
∠A	■	∠P	■
∠B	■	∠Q	■
∠C	■	∠R	■

Fig. 1	Side Length (cm)	Fig. 2	Side Length (cm)
AB	■	PQ	■
BC	■	QR	■
CA	■	RP	■

Check Skills You'll Need

1. Vocabulary Review
An equation stating that two ratios are equal is a __?__.

Solve each proportion.

2. $\frac{x}{4} = \frac{12}{8}$ **3.** $\frac{4}{b} = \frac{16}{48}$

4. $\frac{84}{12} = \frac{g}{6}$ **5.** $\frac{6}{3} = \frac{19}{m}$

 **for Help**
Lesson 5-4

CONTENT STANDARDS
7.RP.1, 7.RP.2, 7.G.1

Test Prep Tip

When solving problems involving similar figures, make sure you are working with corresponding angles and sides.

What You'll Learn

To use proportions to find missing lengths in similar figures

New Vocabulary polygon, similar polygons, indirect measurement

Why Learn This?

The heights of objects such as totem poles may be difficult to measure directly. You can measure indirectly by using figures that have the same shape. When two figures have the same shape, but not necessarily the same size, they are similar.

In the similar triangles below, corresponding angles have the same measure. Since $\frac{40}{60} = \frac{50}{75} = \frac{34}{51}$, the corresponding sides are proportional. You write $\triangle ABC \sim \triangle FGH$. The symbol $\sim$ means "is similar to."

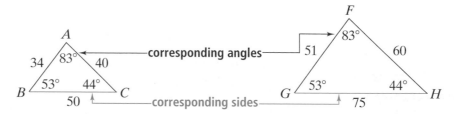

A **polygon** is a closed plane figure formed by three or more line segments that do not cross.

KEY CONCEPTS **Similar Polygons**

Two polygons are **similar polygons** if
- corresponding angles have the same measure, and
- the lengths of the corresponding sides form equivalent ratios.

You can use proportions to find missing side lengths in similar polygons.

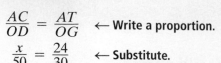

EXAMPLE Finding a Missing Measure

1 **Algebra** △ACT and △ODG are similar. Find the value of x.

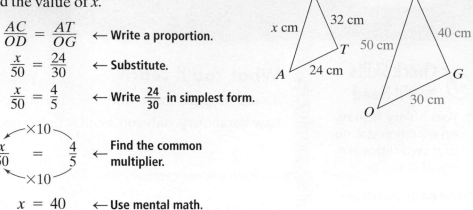

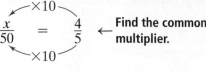

$\frac{AC}{OD} = \frac{AT}{OG}$ ← **Write a proportion.**

$\frac{x}{50} = \frac{24}{30}$ ← **Substitute.**

$\frac{x}{50} = \frac{4}{5}$ ← **Write $\frac{24}{30}$ in simplest form.**

$\underset{\times 10}{\overset{\times 10}{\frac{x}{50} = \frac{4}{5}}}$ ← **Find the common multiplier.**

$x = 40$ ← **Use mental math.**

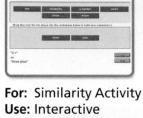
✓ Quick Check

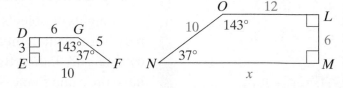

1. The trapezoids are similar. Find x.

You can use **indirect measurement** to measure distances that are difficult to measure directly. You do this by using proportions and similar figures.

EXAMPLE Application: Indirect Measurement

2 **Multiple Choice** A 6-ft-tall person standing near a flagpole casts a shadow 4.5 ft long. The flagpole casts a shadow 15 ft long. What is the height of the flagpole?

    Ⓐ 11.25 ft   Ⓑ 18 ft   Ⓒ 20 ft   Ⓓ 360 ft

Draw a picture and let x represent the height of the flagpole.

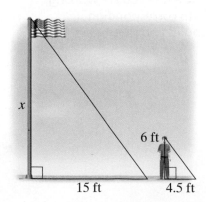

$\frac{x}{6} = \frac{15}{4.5}$ ← **Write a proportion.**

$4.5x = 6 \cdot 15$ ← **Write the cross products.**

$\frac{4.5x}{4.5} = \frac{6 \cdot 15}{4.5}$ ← **Divide each side by 4.5.**

$x = 20$ ← **Simplify.**

The height of the flagpole is 20 ft. The answer is C.

Test Prep Tip

Drawing a picture can help you see what quantities you know and what quantities you are looking for.

✓ Quick Check

2. A 6-ft person has a shadow 5 ft long. A nearby tree has a shadow 30 ft long. What is the height of the tree?

1. **Vocabulary** What must be true about the corresponding angles and the corresponding sides for two polygons to be similar?

△*ABC* is similar to △*RST*. Complete each statement.

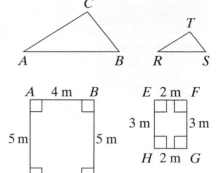

2. ∠*B* corresponds to ___?___.

3. $\overline{RS}$ corresponds to ___?___.

4. **Geometry** Are the rectangles similar? Explain.

5. **Open-Ended** Think of a distance that is difficult to measure directly. How would you find it indirectly?

Homework Exercises

For more exercises, see Extra Skills and Word Problems.

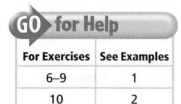

For Exercises	See Examples
6–9	1
10	2

(Algebra) △*ABC* is similar to △*PQR*. Find each measure.

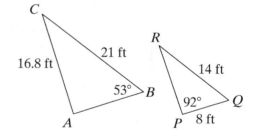

6. length of $\overline{AB}$

7. length of $\overline{RP}$

8. measure of ∠*A*

9. measure of ∠*Q*

10. A woman is 5 ft tall and her shadow is 4 ft long. A nearby tree has a shadow 30 ft long. How tall is the tree?

11. **Guided Problem Solving** An image is 16 in. by 20 in. You want to make a copy that is similar. Its longer side will be 38 in. The copy costs $.60 per square inch. Estimate the copy's total cost.
    • What is the approximate length of the shorter side of the copy?
    • What is the approximate area of the copy?

12. **Social Studies** You want to enlarge a copy of the flag of the Philippines that is 4 in. by 8 in. The two flags will be similar. How long should you make the shorter side if the long side is 6 ft?

GO Online
Homework Video Tutor
PearsonSuccessNet.com

13. **Geometry** A rectangle with an area of 32 in.² has one side measuring 4 in. A similar rectangle has an area of 288 in.². How long is the longer side in the larger rectangle?

Each pair of figures below is similar. Find the value of each variable.

14.
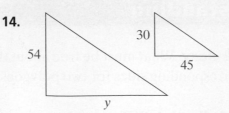

15.
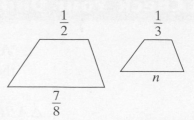

16. A burro is standing near a cactus. The burro is 59 in. tall. His shadow is 4 ft long. The shadow of the cactus is 7 ft long. Estimate the height of the cactus.

17. Surveying Surveyors know that △PQR and △STR are similar. They cannot measure the distance d across the lake directly. Find the distance across the lake.

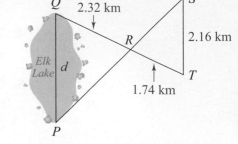

18. **Writing in Math** Give three examples of real-world objects that are similar. Explain why they are similar.

19. Challenge The ratio of the corresponding sides of two similar triangles is 4 : 9. The sides of the smaller triangle are 10 cm, 16 cm, and 18 cm. Find the perimeter of the larger triangle.

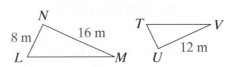
Test Prep and Mixed Review   **Practice**

Multiple Choice

20. In the figure, △LMN ~ △TVU. What is the length of $\overline{UT}$?

N
8 m   16 m
L ———— M

T ———— V
U   12 m

    (A) 6 m   (B) 8 m   (C) 16 m   (D) 24 m

21. The cost of two pounds of pears is $1.78. How much will five pounds of pears cost?

    (F) $0.71   (G) $2.67   (H) $4.45   (J) $8.90

22. Which algebraic expression represents five inches less than twice last year's rainfall f in inches?

    (A) $5 - 2f$ (B) $2f - 5$ (C) $2 - 5f$ (D) $5f - 2$

GO for Help

For Exercises	See Lesson
23–25	3-5

Algebra Solve each equation.

23. $3x + 2 = 17$ **24.** $\frac{x}{5} + 5 = 21$ **25.** $2a - 4 = 8$

Drawing Similar Figures

Using a computer is an excellent way to explore similar figures. For this activity you need geometry software.

ACTIVITY

Follow these steps to draw two similar triangles like those at the right.

Step 1 Draw a triangle and label it ABC.

Step 2 Draw a point D not on the triangle.

Step 3 Draw a triangle similar to $\triangle ABC$ using the dilation command. To use this command, you will need to enter a scale factor and name one point as the center of the dilation. Use 2 as a scale factor and name point D as the center.

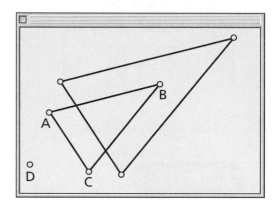

Exercises

1. Change the shape of $\triangle ABC$ by dragging point A, B, or C. What happens to the larger triangle each time?

2. Drag point D to different locations. Describe what happens in each case below.
   a. D is inside $\triangle ABC$.
   b. D is on $\overline{AB}$.
   c. D is on top of point C.

3. Use the software to draw $\overleftrightarrow{AD}$ (line AD), $\overleftrightarrow{BD}$, and $\overleftrightarrow{CD}$.
   a. What do you notice about the lines and the larger triangle?
   b. Why do you think that point D is called the center of the dilation?

4. Draw a third triangle similar to $\triangle ABC$. This time use 0.5 as the scale factor. Keep D as the center. What do you notice about the new triangle?

5. **a. Open-Ended** Draw more triangles similar to $\triangle ABC$ by choosing other scale factors. Again keep D as the center.
   b. **Writing in Math** Explain how your choice of scale factor affects the final figure.
   c. Use what you have learned to write a definition for scale factor.

Scale Drawings and Models

The sketches below show the measurements of Jackie's bedroom. You can use these sketches to make a model of Jackie's bedroom.

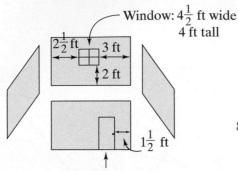

Window: $4\frac{1}{2}$ ft wide
4 ft tall

$2\frac{1}{2}$ ft

3 ft

2 ft

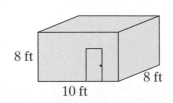

8 ft

10 ft

8 ft

$1\frac{1}{2}$ ft

Door: $3\frac{1}{3}$ ft wide, $6\frac{1}{2}$ ft tall

ACTIVITY

Step 1 Make a drawing on graph paper of the floor and walls of Jackie's room as shown. Let one unit on the graph paper represent one foot. Include the windows and doors.

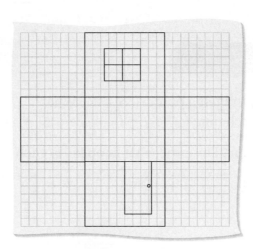

Step 2 Cut around your drawing and tape up the walls to make your model.

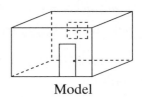

Model

Exercises

1. Jackie's bedroom bureau is shown at the right. Use the same steps as above to make a drawing and a model of the bureau.

2. Measure the heights and lengths of the walls of your classroom. Use graph paper to make an accurate drawing of the floor and walls.

3. Cut around your drawing and make a model of your classroom.

4. Explain how you can use ratios and proportions to find the dimensions of your model.

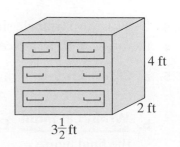

4 ft

2 ft

$3\frac{1}{2}$ ft

✓ Check Skills You'll Need

1. **Vocabulary Review** What are *cross products*?

Solve each proportion.

2. $\frac{2}{3} = \frac{x}{12}$ 3. $\frac{9}{5} = \frac{27}{y}$

4. $\frac{5}{m} = \frac{25}{5}$ 5. $\frac{t}{21} = \frac{6}{18}$

GO for Help
Lesson 5-4

© CONTENT STANDARDS
7.G.1, 7.RP.1

Vocabulary Tip

On a scale drawing, the equal sign in 1 in. = 15 ft does not mean that the two quantities are equal, as it would in an equation.

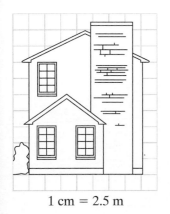

1 cm = 2.5 m

What You'll Learn

To use proportions to solve problems involving scale
New Vocabulary scale drawing, scale

Why Learn This?

When you know how scales work, you can see them in everything from maps to giant sculptures.

A **scale drawing** is an enlarged or reduced drawing of an object that is similar to the actual object.

A **scale** is the ratio that compares a length in a drawing or model to the corresponding length in the actual object. If a 15-foot boat is 1 inch long on a drawing, you can write the scale of the drawing in these three ways.

1 in. : 15 ft $\frac{1 \text{ in.}}{15 \text{ ft}}$ 1 in. = 15 ft
↑   ↑
drawing actual

EXAMPLE   Using a Scale Drawing

1 **Algebra** The length of the side of a house is 3 cm on a scale drawing. What is the actual length of the side of the house?

You can write the scale of the drawing as $\frac{1 \text{ cm}}{2.5 \text{ m}}$. Then write a proportion. Let *n* represent the actual length of the house.

drawing (cm) → $\frac{1}{2.5}$ = $\frac{3}{n}$ ← drawing (cm)
actual (m) →   ← actual (m)

$1n = 2.5(3)$ ← Write the cross products.

$n = 7.5$ ← Simplify.

The actual length is 7.5 m.

✓ Quick Check

1. The chimney of the house is 4 cm tall on the drawing. How tall is the chimney of the actual house?

You can use the GCF to find the scale of a drawing or a model.

EXAMPLE Finding the Scale of a Model

2 **Models** Refer to the model boxcar shown at the right. The actual length of a boxcar is 609 in. What is the scale of the model?

$$\begin{array}{c} \text{scale length} \rightarrow \\ \text{actual length} \rightarrow \end{array} \dfrac{7}{609} = \dfrac{7 \div 7}{609 \div 7} = \dfrac{1}{87} \quad \leftarrow \textbf{Write the ratio in simplest form.}$$

The scale is 1 in. : 87 in.

✅ **Quick Check**

2. The length of a room in an architectural drawing is 10 in. Its actual length is 160 in. What is the scale of the drawing?

EXAMPLE Application: Models

3 **Multiple Choice** You want to make a scale model of a sailboat that is 51 ft long and 48 ft tall. You plan to make the model 17 in. long. Which equation can you use to find x, the height of the model?

Ⓐ $\dfrac{48}{51} = \dfrac{17}{x}$ Ⓑ $\dfrac{17}{51} = \dfrac{x}{48}$ Ⓒ $\dfrac{48}{17} = \dfrac{x}{51}$ Ⓓ $\dfrac{x}{17} = \dfrac{51}{48}$

$$\begin{array}{c} \text{model (in.)} \rightarrow \\ \text{actual (ft)} \rightarrow \end{array} \dfrac{17}{51} = \dfrac{\blacksquare}{\blacksquare} \begin{array}{l} \leftarrow \text{model (in.)} \\ \leftarrow \text{actual (ft)} \end{array} \quad \leftarrow \textbf{Write a proportion.}$$

$$\dfrac{17}{51} = \dfrac{x}{48} \quad \leftarrow \begin{array}{l} \textbf{Fill in the information you know.} \\ \textbf{Use } x \textbf{ for the information you do not know.} \end{array}$$

The correct answer is choice B.

You can solve the proportion to find the height of the model. You can simplify $\frac{17}{51}$ to make calculating easier.

$$\dfrac{\overset{1}{\cancel{17}}}{\underset{3}{\cancel{51}}} = \dfrac{x}{48} \quad \leftarrow \textbf{Simplify } \tfrac{17}{51} \textbf{ by dividing by the GCF, 17.}$$

$$\dfrac{1}{3} = \dfrac{x}{48}$$

$$\overset{\times 16}{\dfrac{1}{3} = \dfrac{x}{48}} \underset{\times 16}{} \quad \leftarrow \textbf{Find the common multiplier, 16.}$$

$$x = 16 \quad \leftarrow \textbf{Use mental math.}$$

The height of the model is 16 inches.

✅ **Quick Check**

3. If the sailboat is 15 ft wide, how wide should the model be?

Test Prep Tip

When writing a proportion, make sure each ratio compares the same types of quantities in the same order.

GO for Help

For help with simplifying ratios, go to Lesson 5-3, Example 1.

You can also use cross products to find a scale.

EXAMPLE **Finding the Scale of a Map**

④ The map key shows that a map distance of $\frac{1}{4}$ in. represents an actual distance of $\frac{5}{8}$ mi. Find the actual distance represented by 1 in. to write the scale of the map.

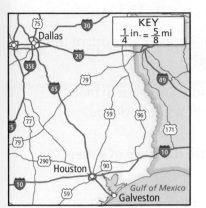

map distance → $\dfrac{\frac{1}{4}}{\frac{5}{8}} = \dfrac{1}{d}$ ← **Write a proportion.**
actual distance →

$\frac{1}{4}d = \left(\frac{5}{8}\right)1$ ← **Write the cross products.**

$\dfrac{d}{4} = \dfrac{5}{8}$ ← **Simplify.**

$4\left(\dfrac{d}{4}\right) = 4\left(\dfrac{5}{8}\right)$ ← **Multiply each side by 4.**

$d = 2\dfrac{1}{2}$ ← **Simplify.**

The actual distance represented by 1 in. on the map is $2\frac{1}{2}$ mi. So, the scale is 1 in. : $2\frac{1}{2}$ mi.

✓ Quick Check

4. Find the actual distance represented by 1 in. to write the scale of a map with the key $\frac{1}{4}$ in. $= \frac{2}{5}$ mi.

✓ Check Your Understanding

1. **Vocabulary** A scale is a __?__ that compares a length in a drawing to the corresponding __?__ in the actual object.

2. **Reasoning** The scale of a drawing is 5 cm : 1 mm. Is the scale drawing larger or smaller than the actual figure? Explain.

3. **Error Analysis** A student wants to write the scale of a statue of President Kennedy, who was 6 ft tall. The statue is 8 ft tall. The student writes the scale as 6 ft : 8 ft. Is the student correct? Explain.

4. Find the actual distance represented by 1 cm to write the scale of a map with the key $\frac{7}{10}$ cm $= \frac{5}{6}$ km.

The scale of a map is 1 inch : 5 miles. Find each distance.

5. A road is 3 in. long on the map. Find the actual length of the road.

6. A lake is 35 miles long. Find the length of the lake on the map.

For more exercises, see Extra Skills and Word Problems.

GO for Help

For Exercises	See Examples
7–9	1
10–11	2-3
12–14	4

(Algebra) A scale drawing has a scale of 1 in. : 11 ft. Find the actual length for each drawing length.

7. 21 in.

8. 45 in.

9. 13.5 in.

10. In a scale drawing, the width of a sofa is 15 cm. The actual width of the sofa is 150 cm. What is the scale of the drawing?

11. A certain car is about 100 in. long and 60 in. wide. You plan to make a model of this car that is 9 in. wide. How long will your model be?

Find the actual distance represented by 1 in. to write the scale of a map with each key.

12. $\frac{1}{4}$ in. $= \frac{3}{4}$ mi

13. $\frac{3}{8}$ in. $= \frac{3}{4}$ mi

14. $\frac{3}{10}$ cm $= \frac{2}{5}$ km

15. Guided Problem Solving The height of a building on a blueprint is 10 in. Its actual height is 150 ft. What is the scale of the drawing?
- What ratio can you use to find the scale?
- How can finding the GCF help you to simplify your answer?

16. Architecture The blueprint below is a scale drawing of an apartment. The scale is $\frac{1}{4}$ in. : 4 ft. Sketch a copy of the floor plan. Write the actual dimensions in place of the scale dimensions.

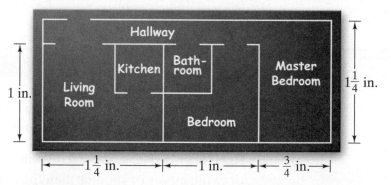

Use a centimeter ruler to measure the length of the segment shown in each figure below. Find the scale of each drawing.

17. Peach Aphid

|← 2 mm →|

18. Killer Whale

|← 8 m →|

GO Online
Homework Video Tutor
PearsonSuccessNet.com

Geography Find the actual distance between each pair of cities. Use a ruler to measure. Round to the nearest mile.

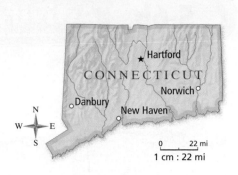

19. Hartford and Danbury

20. Norwich and Hartford

21. New Haven and Norwich

22. New Haven and Danbury

23. **Writing in Math** You are making a scale drawing with a scale of 2 in. = 17 ft. Explain how you find the length of the drawing of an object that has an actual length of 51 ft.

24. **Special Effects** A special-effects artist has made a scale model of a dragon for a movie. In the movie, the dragon will appear to be 16 ft tall. The model is 4 in. tall.
    a. What scale has the artist used?
    b. The same scale is used for a model of a baby dragon, which will appear to be 2 ft tall. What is the height of the model?

25. **Challenge** A building is drawn with a scale of 1 in. : 3 ft. The height of the drawing is 1 ft 2 in. After a design change, the scale is modified to be 1 in. : 4 ft. What is the height of the new drawing?

Test Prep and Mixed Review

Practice

Multiple Choice

26. Doug drew a map with a scale of 1 inch : 5 miles. What distance on Doug's map should represent 4.5 miles?
    Ⓐ 0.45 in.   Ⓑ 0.9 in.   Ⓒ 0.95 in.   Ⓓ 4.5 in.

27. In the figure at the right, $ABCD \sim STUV$. Which of the following statements is NOT true?
    Ⓕ $\overline{UV}$ corresponds to $\overline{CD}$.
    Ⓖ $\overline{AD}$ corresponds to $\overline{SV}$.
    Ⓗ $\angle A$ corresponds to $\angle S$.
    Ⓙ $\angle D$ corresponds to $\angle U$.

28. A cycling route is 56 miles long. There is a water station every $3\frac{3}{4}$ mi. Which equation represents the total number of water stations w?
    Ⓐ $56w = 3\frac{3}{4}$ Ⓒ $3\frac{3}{4} - w = 56$
    Ⓑ $3\frac{3}{4}w = 56$ Ⓓ $w + 3\frac{3}{4} = 56$

GO for Help

For Exercise	See Lesson
29	5-5

29. Find the values of x and y in the similar triangles at the right.

Plan a Trip

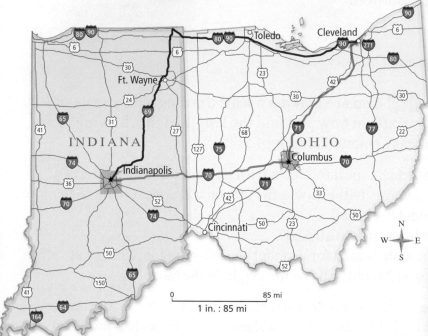

Located on the shore of Lake Erie, the 150,000-square-foot Rock and Roll Hall of Fame and Museum is a landmark for the city of Cleveland, Ohio.

ACTIVITY

Use the map above to plan a trip from Indianapolis to Cleveland.

1. Measure the distances on Routes 69 and 90 from Indianapolis to Fort Wayne, Fort Wayne to Toledo, and Toledo to Cleveland. Add them to get the total map distance.

2. Locate the scale on the map. Use the scale to convert the map distance into the actual distance for your trip.

3. Use an average speed of 50 mi/h. Find the time it will take to drive the total actual distance. If you plan to drive no more than 4 hours per day, how many days will your trip take?

4. Suppose you want to make the same trip, but you want to visit a friend in Columbus. Plan your trip from Indianapolis to Cleveland to pass through Columbus. Compare the two trips.

5. **Research** Now suppose that you are planning a cross-country road trip from Trenton, New Jersey, to San Francisco, California. Locate a map of the United States and plan your trip. Decide which cities you would like to visit along the way. How long will your trip take you?

Solve each proportion.

1. $\dfrac{18}{32} = \dfrac{h}{16}$

2. $\dfrac{35}{z} = \dfrac{20}{4}$

3. Five hamburgers cost $5.25. At this rate, what is the cost of 8 hamburgers?

4. Seven movie tickets cost $57.75. What is the cost of 2 movie tickets?

$\triangle ABC$ **is similar to** $\triangle WXY$. **Find each measure.**

5. $\angle X$

6. $\angle C$

7. length of $\overline{AB}$

8. length of $\overline{WY}$

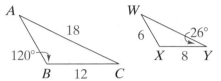

9. The length of a model ship is 8 in. Its actual length is 100 ft. What is the scale of the model?

10. Find the actual distance represented by 1 cm to write the scale of a map with the key $\dfrac{2}{5}$ cm = 8 km.

Vocabulary Builder

Learning Vocabulary

You can make your own dictionary of new math vocabulary terms.

EXAMPLE

Write an entry for your dictionary for the term *ratio*.

Term	Definition	Example
Ratio	Comparison of two different quantities by division	$\dfrac{20 \text{ people}}{5 \text{ people}}$

← Make a table with 3 columns. Label the columns "Term," "Definition," and "Example."

← Write the vocabulary term and its definition. Then give an example of the term.

Exercises

Write an entry for your dictionary for each term.

1. rate

2. proportion

3. similar figures

4. cross products

Graphs and Proportional Relationships

Two quantities have a proportional relationship if the ratio of the two quantities is always the same. Complete the activity to find out how you can use tables and graphs to determine if two quantities have a proportional relationship.

ACTIVITY

The tables below show a person's earnings at the end of each year at two different banks on a deposit of $100 over a five-year period. For each bank, earnings include simple interest paid annually at the same rate each year. In addition, Bank B gives depositors a $5 bonus when an account is first opened.

Bank A

Years	1	2	3	4	5
Earnings	$2	$4	$6	$8	$10

Bank B

Years	1	2	3	4	5
Earnings	$7	$9	$11	$13	$15

1. For each bank, find the ratio comparing years to earnings for all pairs of values in the table. What do you notice about the ratios?

2. Make a graph for each bank, plotting all the values in each table on a coordinate grid.

3. Extend the lines. What are the earnings at each bank for year 0?

4. How are the graphs different?

5. For each bank, determine if years and earnings are proportional. Explain your answer using the tables and the graphs from Step 2.

6. Repeat Steps 1 through 5 for Banks C and D.

Bank C

Years	1	2	3	4	5
Earnings	$3	$6	$9	$12	$15

Bank D

Years	1	2	3	4	5
Earnings	$7	$10	$13	$16	$19

7. Look for patterns between the tables for all four banks. Give a general rule for using a table to decide if two quantities are proportional.

8. Look for patterns between the graphs for all four banks. Give a general rule for using a graph to decide if two quantities are proportional.

5-7 Proportional Relationships

© **CONTENT STANDARDS**

7.RP.2.a, 7.RP.2.b, 7.RP.2.c, 7.RP.2.d

Keisha

Hours	0	2	4	5	7
Miles	0	13	26	32.5	45.5

What You'll Learn

To identify proportional relationships and find constants of proportionality

New Vocabulary constant of proportionality

Why Learn This?

You know the total distances a cyclist traveled at different times during a bike-a-thon.

You can display the times and distances in a table or graph. Then you can determine if the times and distances have a proportional relationship. If they do, you can use the data to find the average speed at which the cyclist rode.

EXAMPLE ▸ **Using a Table to Determine a Proportional Relationship**

① **Interpreting Data** The table at the left shows the distances Keisha traveled during a bike-a-thon. Is there a proportional relationship between time and distance?

Compare the ratios of distance and time.

$$\begin{array}{l}\text{distance} \to \\ \text{time} \to\end{array} \frac{13}{2} = \frac{26}{4} = \frac{32.5}{5} = \frac{45.5}{7}$$

The ratios are equivalent, so there is a proportional relationship between time and distance.

✓ Quick Check

1. The table shows the distances Dave rode in a bike-a-thon. Is there a proportional relationship? Explain.

Dave

Hours	0	3	6	8	9
Miles	0	18.6	35.2	49.6	56.8

The graph of a proportional relationship is a straight line through the origin $(0,0)$. The point $(1, r)$ on the graph of any proportional relationship represents the unit rate.

Using a Graph to Find a Unit Rate

② The graph at the right displays the data given in Example 1. What is Keisha's speed in miles per hour?

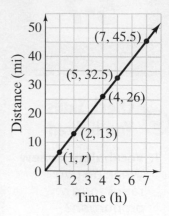

Keisha's speed is a unit rate. Find the value of r in the ordered pair $(1, r)$.

The line passes through $(0,0)$ and $(2, 13)$. So, it must also pass through $(1, 6.5)$. Since $r = 6.5$, the unit rate is 6.5 mi/h. Keisha's speed is 6.5 mi/h.

✓ Quick Check

2. Use the graph at the left. What is Damon's reading speed in pages per day?

The value of the ratio of quantities in a proportional relationship is called the **constant of proportionality**. This value is also equivalent to the unit rate.

Using a Ratio to Identify a Unit Rate

③ The table at the left shows a proportional relationship between the number of minutes and the amount the customer pays for cell phone service. Identify the constant of proportionality.

Minutes, m	Price, p (dollars)
100	$10
500	$50
1,000	$100
1,500	$150

Step 1 Use one data point to find the constant of proportionality c.

$$\frac{\text{price}}{\text{minutes}} = \frac{10}{100} \leftarrow \text{Find the price per minute by dividing the price by the number of minutes.}$$
$$= 0.1 \leftarrow \text{Simplify.}$$

Step 2 Check by multiplying c times the first quantity.

$$100 \times 0.1 = 10 \checkmark \qquad 500 \times 0.1 = 50 \checkmark$$
$$1,000 \times 0.1 = 100 \checkmark \qquad 1,500 \times 0.1 = 150 \checkmark$$

The constant of proportionality is 0.1. The unit rate is $.10 per minute.

Now that you know the unit rate, you can write an equation that represents the proportional relationship. (Think cost per minute!)

Step 3 Use the constant of proportionality to write an equation to find the price p for m minutes. $\qquad p = 0.1\,m$

a.

Yards (y)	16	32	40
Blankets (b)	8	16	20

b.

Hours (h)	2	10	16
Pay (p)	$11	$55	$88

✓ Quick Check

3. Find the constant of proportionality for each table at the left.
   a. yards of cloth per blanket   **b.** pay per hour

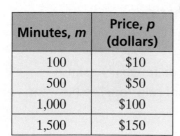

1. **Vocabulary** How is a constant of proportionality like a unit rate?

2. **Number Sense** The graph of a proportional relationship passes through the point (2, 8). What is the constant of proportionality for this relationship?

Answer each question about the data in the table.

3. Is there a proportional relationship between bags and pounds of dog food? Explain your reasoning.

Bags	3	8	11
Dog Food (lb)	7.5	20	27.5

4. What is the constant of proportionality?

5. Using the constant of proportionality, what equation relates p pounds of dog food to b bags?

Homework Exercises

For more exercises, see Extra Skills and Word Problems.

GO for Help

For Exercises	See Examples
6–7	1
8–9	2
10–13	3

Determine whether each table represents a proportional relationship. Explain your reasoning.

6.

x	1	2	4	7	9
y	5	9	17	29	37

7.

x	1	3	5	7	9
y	$\frac{7}{2}$	$\frac{21}{2}$	$\frac{35}{2}$	$\frac{49}{2}$	$\frac{63}{2}$

For Exercises 8–9, explain what the point with x-coordinate 3 represents. Then find the unit rate, r.

8. **Walking**

9. **Hot Air Balloon**

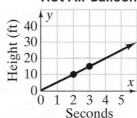

Find the constant of proportionality for each table of values.

10. profit per shirt sold

Shirts	5	10	15
Profit	$7.50	$15.00	$22.50

11. price per pound

Apples (lb)	4	5	6
Price	$7.96	$9.95	$11.94

Pecks per Bushel

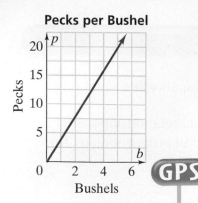

Write an equation using the constant of proportionality to describe the relationship.

12. The graph at left shows the relationship between bushels and pecks. Find the number of pecks p in b bushels.

13. A horse that is 16 hands tall is 64 inches tall. Find the number of hands h in n inches.

14. **Guided Problem Solving** Distance traveled d is proportional to the travel time t at a constant rate r. Write an equation that describes the relationship between d and t.

● What is r in terms of d and t?
● What equation tells how to find d given r and t?

Orange Prices

$	$8	$10	$20
lbs	4	6	10

15. **Error Analysis** A salesperson showed the table at the left while explaining that oranges are the same price per pound, no matter what size bag they come in. Why is the salesperson wrong?

Art Sales

Use the graph for questions 16–18.

16. What is the constant of proportionality, dollars per day?

17. Make a table of values to show the data in the graph.

18. Write an equation to find the amount for any number of days.

19. <u>Writing in Math</u> Explain how to identify the constant of proportionality from a graph of any proportional relationship.

20. **Challenge** Jasmine baby sat for $3\frac{1}{2}$ h one day and 4 h 20 min the next day. She earned $47. Write an equation using the constant of proportionality to describe the relationship between e earnings and h hours worked.

GO Online
Homework Video Tutor
PearsonSuccessNet.com

Test Prep and Mixed Review   **Practice**

Multiple Choice

21. One day, 16 U.S. dollars was worth 10 British pounds. Which equation uses the constant of proportionality to describe the relationship between the number of dollars d in p pounds?

Ⓐ $d = 0.625p$ Ⓑ $d = 1.6p$ Ⓒ $p = 0.625d$ Ⓓ $p = 1.6d$

22. The length of a house on a blueprint is $3\frac{3}{4}$ in. The actual length of the house is 45 ft. What is the scale of the drawing?

Ⓕ 1 in. : 12 ft
Ⓖ 1 in. : 168.75 ft
Ⓗ 1 ft : 12 in.
Ⓙ 1 ft : 168.75 in.

GO for Help

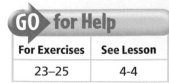

For Exercises	See Lesson
23–25	4-4

Algebra Solve each inequality. Graph the solution.

23. $4 + 3w > 10$ **24.** $7 - 5a \le 22$ **25.** $-4 + \frac{k}{2} \ge -6$

Using a Variable

You can solve many problems by using a variable to represent an unknown quantity.

EXAMPLE

Purple is a mixture of the primary colors red and blue. A certain shade of purple paint requires 6 parts red paint to 7 parts blue paint. If you have 16 quarts of red paint, how many quarts of blue paint do you need to make the desired shade of purple? How many quart cans of blue paint do you need to buy?

The problem is asking for the amount of blue paint needed to make a shade of purple. You can write and solve a proportion.

Let b represent the number of quarts of blue paint you need.

$$\text{red paint} \rightarrow \frac{6}{7} = \frac{16}{b} \leftarrow \text{red paint} \quad \leftarrow \text{Write a proportion.}$$
$$\text{blue paint} \rightarrow \qquad \qquad \leftarrow \text{blue paint}$$
$$6b = 112 \qquad \leftarrow \text{Write the cross products and simplify.}$$
$$\frac{6b}{6} = \frac{112}{6} \qquad \leftarrow \text{Divide each side by 6.}$$
$$b = 18\frac{2}{3} \qquad \leftarrow \text{Simplify.}$$

You need $18\frac{2}{3}$ quarts of blue paint. You should buy 19 cans.

Exercises

Use a variable to write and solve an equation.

1. To serve 16 people, 96 pieces of fruit are needed. How many pieces of fruit are needed to serve 22 people?
   - Ⓐ $18\frac{2}{3}$
   - Ⓑ 11
   - Ⓒ 132
   - Ⓓ 144

2. A paper distributor is shipping mailing tubes to an art gallery. The distributor has previously shipped 560 tubes in 16 boxes. At this rate, how many boxes would the distributor need to ship 112 tubes?
   - Ⓕ 4
   - Ⓖ 5
   - Ⓗ 12
   - Ⓙ 35

3. A class of 37 students is making origami boxes. Each box requires 8 pieces of origami paper. The class will split into groups of at most 3 students per group. If each group is going to make one box, what is the least number of pieces of paper needed by the class?
   - Ⓐ 24
   - Ⓑ 96
   - Ⓒ 104
   - Ⓓ 296

Vocabulary Review

constant of proportionality
(p. 222)
cross products (p. 194)
equivalent ratios (p. 208)
indirect measurement (p. 208)

polygon (p. 207)
proportion (p. 193)
rate (p. 188)
ratio (p. 184)
scale (p. 213)

scale drawing (p. 213)
similar polygons (p. 207)
unit cost (p. 189)
unit rate (p. 188)

Go Online

For vocabulary quiz
PearsonSuccessNet.com

Choose the correct term to complete each sentence.

1. Knowing a(n) (indirect measurement, unit cost) is helpful for getting the best buy when you shop.

2. A speed limit of 40 mi/h is an example of a (rate, proportion).

3. A ratio that compares a length in a drawing to the actual length of an object is a (scale, proportion).

4. When two polygons have corresponding angles with equal measures and corresponding sides with proportional lengths, the polygons are (cross products, similar).

5. The ratio of a pair of values in a proportional relationship is equal to the (unit cost, constant of proportionality).

Skills and Concepts

Lesson 5-1

• To write ratios and use them to compare quantities

A **ratio** is a comparison of two quantities by division. You can write the same ratio in three ways. To find equal ratios, multiply or divide the numerator and denominator by the same nonzero number.

Write each ratio in simplest form.

6. $\frac{9}{30}$ 7. $\frac{64}{20}$ 8. 99 : 33   9. 75 : 20   10. $\frac{45}{180}$

Lessons 5-2, 5-3

• To find unit rates and unit costs using proportional reasoning

• To test whether ratios form a proportion by using equivalent ratios and cross products

A **rate** is a ratio that compares two quantities measured in different units. A **unit rate** has a denominator of 1. Find a **unit cost** by dividing the price of an item by the number of units in the item.

Write the unit rate for each situation.

11. 282 passengers in 47 cars   12. 600 calories in 8 servings

13. **Shopping** A 10-oz box of cereal costs $2.79. A 13-oz box of the same brand of cereal costs $3.99. Find the unit cost for each item and determine which is the better buy.

Lesson 5-4

- To solve proportions using unit rates, mental math, and cross products

A proportion is an equation stating that two ratios are equal. If two ratios form a proportion, the **cross products** are equal.

Solve each proportion.

14. $\frac{3}{7} = \frac{n}{28}$ **15.** $\frac{3}{5} = \frac{15}{x}$ **16.** $\frac{a}{18} = \frac{12}{72}$ **17.** $\frac{32}{c} = \frac{4}{17}$

18. The ratio of the width of a rectangle to its length is $5 : 8$. What is the width in feet if the length is 12 ft?

Lesson 5-5

- To use proportions to find missing lengths in similar figures

Two polygons are **similar polygons** if corresponding angles have equal measures and the lengths of corresponding sides form equivalent ratios.

19. A fire hydrant is 30 in. tall and casts a shadow 8 in. long. How tall is a nearby tree that casts a shadow 4 ft long?

Each pair of figures is similar. Find each missing value.

20.

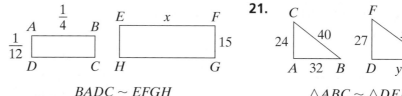

$BADC \sim EFGH$

21.

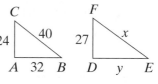

$\triangle ABC \sim \triangle DEF$

Lesson 5-6

- To use proportions to solve problems involving scale

A **scale drawing** is an enlarged or reduced drawing of an object that is similar to the actual object. A **scale** is a ratio that compares a length in a drawing to the corresponding length in an actual object.

22. Maps The scale on a map is 1 in. : 525 mi. The map distance from Chicago to Tokyo is 12 in. Find the actual distance between the cities.

23. Architecture A drawing's scale is 0.5 in. : 10 ft. A room is 15 ft long. How long is the room on the drawing?

Lesson 5-7

- To identify proportional relationships and find constants of proportionality

The value of the ratio of two quantities in a proportional relationship is the **constant of proportionality** for that relationship.

Determine whether each represents a proportional relationship. If so, find the constant of proportionality.

24.

Weeks	2	4	5
Savings ($)	10	20	30

25.

Hours	2	3	5
Miles	80	120	200

26. One day you download 4 songs for $5. Write an equation that uses the constant of proportionality to describe the relationships between s songs and the cost in d dollars.

Chapter 5 Test

Go Online For online chapter test
PearsonSuccessNet.com

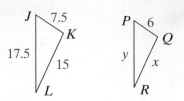

1. Write a ratio for the following information in three ways: In the United States, 98 million out of 99.6 million homes have at least one television.

Write each ratio in two other ways.

2. $\frac{9}{7}$

3. 48 : 100

4. 33 to 9

5. Write the unit rate for the following situation: walking $\frac{2}{3}$ mi in $\frac{1}{4}$ h.

6. **Writing in Math** You need to buy 10 lb of rice. A 2-lb bag costs $1.29. A 10-lb bag costs $6.99. You want to buy a 10-lb bag. Your friend thinks buying five 2-lb bags is a better deal because the unit rate is lower. Is your friend correct? Explain.

Solve each proportion.

7. $\frac{14}{36} = \frac{7}{x}$

8. $\frac{40}{16} = \frac{x}{2}$

9. $\frac{4}{9} = \frac{12}{x}$

10. $\frac{6}{5} = \frac{n}{7}$

11. $\frac{3.5}{d} = \frac{14}{15}$

12. $\frac{1}{2} : \frac{5}{6} = f : \frac{3}{4}$

13. The ratio of teachers to students in a middle school is 2 to 25. There are 350 students in the school. Find the number of teachers.

Determine whether each table represents a proportional relationship. Explain.

14.

Gallon	2	4	5	7
Miles	42	82	105	147

15.

Songs	3	4	6	8
Minutes	12	16	24	32

16. **Maps** A map with a scale of 1 in. : 160 mi shows two cities $2\frac{3}{4}$ in. apart. How many miles apart are the cities?

17. In the figure below, $\triangle JKL \sim \triangle PQR$. Find x and y.

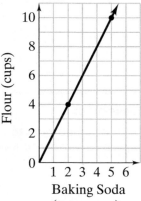

18. **Utilities** Last month, your electric bill was $25.32 for 450 kilowatt-hours of electricity. At that rate, what would be the bill for 240 kilowatt-hours?

19. A person who is 60 in. tall casts a shadow that is 15 in. long. How tall is a nearby tree that casts a shadow that is 40 in. long?

20. **Cooking** The graph at the right shows the amount of baking soda and flour needed to make different size batches of banana muffins. What is the rate of baking soda per cup of flour?

21. Suppose you are making a scale drawing of a giraffe that is 5.5 m tall. The drawing is 7 cm tall. Find the scale of the drawing.

22. **Ballooning** A hot-air balloon 2,100 ft above the ground can descend at the rate of 1.5 ft/s. The balloon is scheduled to land at 3:30 P.M. When should the balloonist start descending?

23. **Science** A 380-cubic-centimeter sample of titanium has a mass of 1,170 g. Write an equation that uses the constant of proportionality to describe the relationship between v cubic centimeters of volume and m grams of mass. Round the constant to the nearest hundredth.

Reading Comprehension

Read each passage and answer the questions that follow.

Europe Goes Euro Until recently, you needed different types of money (francs, marks, punts, etc.) to travel through Europe. Now all you need to get by in most European countries is the new European currency, the euro. One U.S. dollar buys about 0.81 euros. One French franc was worth about 0.15 euros, and an Irish punt was worth about 1.27 euros.

1. About how many euros were 20 French francs worth?
   - Ⓐ 0.15 euros
   - Ⓑ 3.00 euros
   - Ⓒ 20.00 euros
   - Ⓓ 150.00 euros

2. Hsio came home from a trip with currency worth 20 U.S. dollars. She had 10 euros and the rest in U.S. currency. About how many dollars did she have?
   - Ⓕ $12.35
   - Ⓖ $11.90
   - Ⓗ $8.10
   - Ⓙ $7.65

3. About how many U.S. dollars would you get if you exchanged 15 euros?
   - Ⓐ $12.15
   - Ⓑ $18.52
   - Ⓒ $22.50
   - Ⓓ $27.28

4. Which expression shows how many French francs you could get for one Irish punt?
   - Ⓕ 0.15×1.27
   - Ⓖ $\dfrac{0.15}{1.27}$
   - Ⓗ $0.15 + 1.27$
   - Ⓙ $\dfrac{1.27}{0.15}$

More Money Notes In the United States, paper money is all the same size: 2.61 inches wide by 6.14 inches long and 0.0043 inch thick. But did you know that American banknotes used to be bigger? Until 1929, they were 3.125 inches wide by 7.4218 inches long. By the way, it costs about 4.2 cents to produce one paper note.

5. What is the current ratio of length to width for U.S. paper money?
   - Ⓐ 0.43 : 1
   - Ⓑ 2.35 : 1
   - Ⓒ 2.61 : 1
   - Ⓓ 6.14 : 1

6. Suppose you make a stack of one thousand $100 bills. How tall is the stack?
   - Ⓕ 0.043 in.
   - Ⓖ 0.43 in.
   - Ⓗ 4.3 in.
   - Ⓙ 43 in.

7. What is the best approximation of the ratio of the current length of U.S. notes to the length before 1929?
   - Ⓐ 1 : 2
   - Ⓑ 3 : 4
   - Ⓒ 5 : 6
   - Ⓓ 9 : 10

8. The government prints about 12 billion paper notes each year. What is the best estimate of how much this costs?
   - Ⓕ $.5 million
   - Ⓖ $5 million
   - Ⓗ $50 million
   - Ⓙ $500 million

What You've Learned

- In Chapter 1, you compared, ordered, and converted between fractions and decimals.
- In Chapter 3, you solved equations.
- In Chapter 5, you solved proportions.

Check Your Readiness

GO for Help

For Exercises	See Lesson
1–9	1-4
10–13	3-3
14–16	5-4

Fractions and Decimals

Write each fraction as a decimal.

1. $\frac{3}{5}$

2. $\frac{3}{4}$

3. $\frac{3}{8}$

4. $\frac{3}{12}$

Write each decimal as a fraction in simplest form.

5. 0.85 **6.** 0.4 **7.** 0.68 **8.** 1.25 **9.** 0.01

Solving Equations by Multiplying or Dividing

(**Algebra**) **Solve each equation.**

10. $0.8t = 24$ **11.** $0.35w = 280$ **12.** $\frac{n}{0.6} = 14$ **13.** $\frac{z}{0.25} = 12$

Using Proportional Reasoning

Solve each proportion.

14. $\frac{4}{5} = \frac{n}{100}$

15. $\frac{x}{8} = \frac{27}{100}$

16. $\frac{6}{a} = \frac{3}{100}$

What You'll Learn Next

- In this chapter, you will compare, order, and convert between fractions, decimals, and percents.

- You will solve percent problems using equations and proportions.

- You will use percent to solve real-world problems.

Key Vocabulary

- commission (p. 249)
- discount (p. 259)
- markup (p. 259)
- percent (p. 232)
- percent of change (p. 258)
- percent error (p. 250)
- principal (p. 254)
- simple interest (p. 254)

6-1 Percents, Fractions, and Decimals

Check Skills You'll Need

1. **Vocabulary Review** What is a *repeating decimal*?

Write each fraction as a decimal.

2. $\frac{5}{16}$ 3. $\frac{11}{40}$

4. $\frac{4}{9}$ 5. $\frac{2}{15}$

for Help
Lesson 1-4

Ⓒ **CONTENT STANDARD**
7.EE.3

What You'll Learn

To convert between fractions, decimals, and percents

New Vocabulary percent

Why Learn This?

The labels below use a different form of $\frac{1}{2}$. Any rational number can be written as a fraction, a decimal, or a percent. A **percent** is a rate per 100.

50% of the minimum daily amount

Same taste $\frac{1}{2}$ the sugar

This product has 0.5g of fat.

KEY CONCEPTS **Fractions, Decimals, and Percents**

You can write 21 out of 100 as a fraction, a decimal, or a percent.

Fraction	Decimal	Percent
$\frac{21}{100}$	0.21	21%

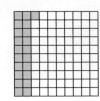

To write a decimal as a percent, you can multiply the decimal by 100.

Test Prep Tip

When you multiply a decimal by 100, the decimal point moves 2 places to the right.

EXAMPLE **Writing Decimals as Percents**

1 Write 0.759, 0.003, and 5.187 as percents.

$$\begin{array}{c|c|c}
0.759 & 0.003 & 5.187 \\
= \dfrac{759}{1000} & = \dfrac{3}{1000} & = \dfrac{5{,}187}{1000} \quad \leftarrow \text{Write as a fraction.} \\
= \dfrac{75.9}{100} & = \dfrac{0.3}{100} & = \dfrac{518.7}{100} \quad \leftarrow \begin{array}{l}\text{Write an equivalent fraction with} \\ \text{100 as the denominator.}\end{array} \\
= 75.9\% & = 0.3\% & = 518.7\% \quad \leftarrow \text{Write as a percent.}
\end{array}$$

✓ Quick Check

1. Write 0.607, 0.005, and 9.283 as percents.

To write a percent as a decimal, you can divide it by 100, or move the decimal point two places to the left.

For: Rational Number Activity
Use: Interactive Textbook, 6-1

EXAMPLE Writing Percents as Decimals

❷ Write 47.5%, 0.06%, and 2500% as decimals.

47.5%	0.06%	2500%	
$= \dfrac{47.5}{100}$	$= \dfrac{0.06}{100}$	$= \dfrac{2500}{100}$	← **Write as a fraction.**
$= 0.475$	$= 0.0006$	$= 25$	← **Divide.**

✓ Quick Check

2. Write each percent as a decimal.
    a. 3500%   **b.** 12.5%   **c.** 0.78%

When the denominator of a fraction is a factor of 100, you can easily use equivalent ratios to convert the fraction to a percent. For fractions with other denominators, you can use a calculator to convert the fraction into a decimal, and then rewrite the decimal as a percent.

EXAMPLE Writing Fractions as Percents

❸ **Nutrition** In a slice of cheese pizza, 45 Calories are from fat. The total number of Calories in each slice is 158. About what percent of the Calories are *not* from fat? Round to the nearest tenth of a percent.

Step 1 Find the number of Calories that are not from fat.

$$158 - 45 = 113$$

Step 2 Estimate.

$\dfrac{113}{158} \approx \dfrac{120}{160}$, which is $\dfrac{3}{4}$, or 75%.

Step 3 Write the ratio.

$\dfrac{113}{158}$ ← **Calories from fat**
       ← **total Calories**

$113 \div 158 = 0.71518987$ ← **Use a calculator.**

$ = 71.518987\%$ ← **Write as a percent.**

$ \approx 71.5\%$ ← **Round to the nearest tenth of a percent.**

About 71.5% of the Calories are not from fat.

Check for Reasonableness Since 71.5% is close to the estimate 75%, the answer is reasonable.

✓ Quick Check

3. Write $\dfrac{21}{40}$ as a percent. Round to the nearest tenth of a percent.

You can write a percent as a fraction. First write the percent as a fraction with a denominator of 100. Then simplify the fraction.

EXAMPLE Writing Percents as Fractions

4 **Science** Behavioral scientists observed an elephant that slept about 12.5% of each day. What fraction of each day did the elephant sleep?

$$12.5\% = \frac{12.5}{100}$$ ← **Write 12.5% as a fraction with a denominator of 100.**

$$= \frac{12.5 \times 10}{100 \times 10}$$ ← **Multiply the numerator and denominator by 10.**

$$= \frac{125 \div 125}{1{,}000 \div 125}$$ ← **Divide both numerator and denominator by the GCF, 125.**

$$= \frac{1}{8}$$ ← **Simplify the fraction.**

The elephant slept about $\frac{1}{8}$ of each day.

Quick Check

4. An elephant eats about 6% of its body weight in vegetation each day. Write this as a fraction in simplest form.

To compare rational numbers in different forms, you can write all the numbers in the same form. Then graph each number on a number line.

EXAMPLE Ordering Rational Numbers

5 Order 0.52, 37%, 0.19, and $\frac{1}{400}$ from least to greatest.

Write all the numbers as decimals. Then graph them.

0.52 ← **This number is already in decimal form.**

$37\% = 0.37$ ← **Move the decimal point two places to the left.**

0.19 ← **This number is already in decimal form.**

$\frac{1}{400} = 0.0025$ ← **Divide the numerator by the denominator.**

GO for Help

For help converting a fraction to a decimal, go to Lesson 1-4.

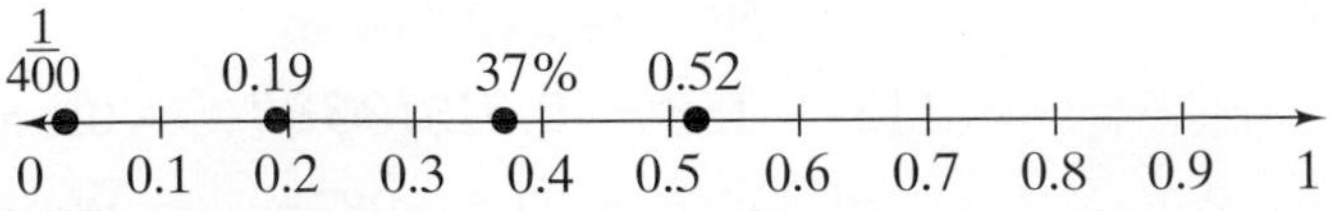

From least to greatest, the numbers are $\frac{1}{400}$, 0.19, 37%, and 0.52.

Quick Check

5. Order from least to greatest.

a. $\frac{3}{10}$, 0.74, 29%, $\frac{11}{25}$

b. 15%, $\frac{7}{20}$, 0.08, 500%

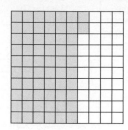

1. Write the shaded part of the model at the left as a percent, a fraction, and a decimal.

2. In each set, find the number that does *not* equal the other two.
   a. 9.9%, $\frac{99}{100}$, 0.99   b. 64%, $\frac{16}{50}$, 0.64   c. 12%, $\frac{3}{25}$, 1.2

3. **Mental Math** Order 0.54, 55%, and $\frac{1}{2}$ from least to greatest.

4. **Reasoning** When you write a percent as a decimal, why do you move the decimal point 2 units to the left?

Homework Exercises

For more exercises, see Extra Skills and Word Problems.

GO for Help

For Exercises	See Examples
5–9	1
10–14	2
15–20	3
21–26	4
27–29	5

Write each decimal as a percent.

5. 0.57   6. 0.375   7. 0.009   8. 0.155   9. 0.6

Write each percent as a decimal.

10. 32%   11. 88%   12. 19.1%   13. 333%   14. 1.25%

Write each fraction as a percent to the nearest tenth of a percent.

15. $\frac{45}{50}$ 16. $\frac{7}{800}$ 17. $\frac{1}{12}$ 18. $\frac{41}{450}$ 19. $\frac{3}{11}$

20. Out of 49 fish, 31 are goldfish. About what percent are goldfish?

Write each percent as a fraction in simplest form.

21. 15%   22. 6%   23. 240%   24. 37.5%   25. 17%

26. **Computers** A computer screen shows the print on a page at 78% of its actual size. Write 78% as a fraction in simplest form.

Order from least to greatest.

27. $\frac{1}{2}$, 120%, 0.25   28. 0.68%, 0.37, $\frac{3}{10}$ 29. 0.81, $\frac{4}{5}$, 90%

30. **Guided Problem Solving** In your class, 9 of the 26 students are in the chorus. What percent of your class is in the chorus? Round to the nearest tenth of a percent.
    • What ratio can help to find the percent of students in the chorus?
    • Should you multiply or divide by 100 to find the percent?

31. **Writing in Math** Does 0.4 equal 0.4%? Explain.

32. Compare 0.32 and 3.2%. Use <, =, or >.

33. **Math in the Media** Use the cartoon below to complete the table.

Topping	With Olives	Plain	With Onions and Green Peppers
Percent of the Pizza	■	■	■
Number of Slices	■	■	■

Macaroni & Cheese

Nutrition	
Fat	33 g
Carbohydrates	40 g
Protein	17 g

Spaghetti & Meat Sauce

Nutrition	
Fat	12 g
Carbohydrates	39 g
Protein	19 g

34. **Nutrition** The tables at the left give data on two different foods. A gram of fat has 9 Calories. A gram of carbohydrates and a gram of protein each have 4 Calories. What percent of the Calories in each food are from carbohydrates? Round to the nearest percent.

35. Your teacher uses different methods of grading quizzes. Your quiz grades are 85%, $\frac{9}{10}$, $\frac{16}{20}$, 92%, $\frac{21}{25}$, and 79%.
    a. Write your quiz grades in order from least to greatest.
    b. Find the average percent grade of your quizzes.

36. **Challenge** Write 0.0375% as a fraction in simplest form.

Test Prep and Mixed Review
Practice

Multiple Choice

37. Nathan runs m miles each weekday and $3\frac{1}{4}$ times farther on Saturday. He runs $6\frac{1}{2}$ miles on Saturday. Which equation can be used to find the number of miles Nathan runs each weekday?

    (A) $3\frac{1}{4}m = 6\frac{1}{2}$ (C) $m + 3\frac{1}{4} = 6\frac{1}{2}$

    (B) $6\frac{1}{2}m = 3\frac{1}{4}$ (D) $m \div 3\frac{1}{4} = 6\frac{1}{2}$

38. The prices of 3 different bags of onions are given in the table below. Which size bag has the lowest price per pound?
    (F) The 5-lb bag only
    (G) The 5-lb bag and the 15-lb bag
    (H) The 10-lb bag only
    (J) The 15-lb bag only

Bag (lb)	Price
5	$3.49
10	$6.70
15	$10.33

GO for Help

For Exercises	See Lesson
39–41	4-3

Solve each inequality.

39. $6.3 \geq -7x$ 40. $-12 < \frac{m}{2}$ 41. $-10.2 \leq -0.2y$

Solving Percent Problems Using Proportions

6-2

Check Skills You'll Need

1. **Vocabulary Review**
A *proportion* is an equation stating that two __?__ are equal.

Solve each proportion.

2. $\frac{n}{32} = \frac{1}{4}$

3. $\frac{6}{n} = \frac{2}{5}$

4. $\frac{7}{8} = \frac{n}{100}$

GO for Help
Lesson 5-4

ⓒ **CONTENT STANDARD**
7.RP.3

Online
active math

For: Percents Activity
Use: Interactive
Textbook, 6-2

What You'll Learn

To use proportions to solve problems involving percent

Why Learn This?

Survey and poll results are often reported using percents.

In a survey of 2,000 people in the United States, 204 said they are left-handed. You can use this information to find the percent of people who are left-handed.

You can use a model to help find this percent.

```
                        part            whole
                         ↓               ↓
Number    0    204                      2,000

Percent   0%   n%                       100%
```

$$\frac{204}{2,000} = \frac{n}{100}$$ ← The part, 204, corresponds to *n* in the model.
← The whole, 2,000, corresponds to 100.

EXAMPLE   Finding a Percent

① What percent of 2,000 is 204?

Using the model above, you can write and solve a proportion.

$$\frac{204}{2,000} = \frac{n}{100}$$ ← Write a proportion.

$$2000n = 204(100)$$ ← Write cross products.

$$\frac{2,000n}{2,000} = \frac{204(100)}{2,000}$$ ← Divide each side by 2,000.

$$n = 10.2$$ ← Simplify.

204 is 10.2% of 2,000.

✓ Quick Check

1. What percent of 92 is 23?

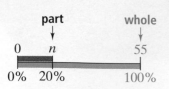

EXAMPLES Finding a Part and the Whole

2 20% of 55 is what number?

part → n, whole → 55

0   n   55
0%   20%   100%

$\frac{n}{55} = \frac{20}{100}$ ← Write a proportion.

$\frac{n}{55} = \frac{1}{5}$ ← Simplify the fraction.

$\frac{n}{55} = \frac{1}{5}$ ×11 ← Use the common multiplier, 11.

$n = 11$ ← Simplify.

11 is 20% of 55.

3 Budgets Suppose your entertainment budget is 30% of your weekly wages from a job. You plan to spend $10.50 on a movie night. How much will you need to earn at your job in order to stay within your budget?

part
0   $10.50   n
0%   30%   100%

$\frac{10.50}{n} = \frac{30}{100}$ ← Write a proportion.

$30n = 10.50(100)$ ← Write cross products.

$\frac{30n}{30} = \frac{10.50(100)}{30}$ ← Divide.

$n = 35$ ← Simplify.

You need to earn $35 to stay within your budget.

✓ Quick Check

2. 85% of 20 is what number?

3. Your math teacher assigns 25 problems for homework. You have done 60% of them. How many problems have you done?

KEY CONCEPTS Percents and Proportions

Finding a Percent
What percent of 25 is 5?

0   5   25
0%   n%   100%

$\frac{5}{25} = \frac{n}{100}$
$n = 20$

5 is 20% of 25.

Finding a Part
What is 20% of 25?

0   n   25
0%   20%   100%

$\frac{n}{25} = \frac{20}{100}$
$n = 5$

5 is 20% of 25.

Finding a Whole
20% of what is 5?

0   5   n
0%   20%   100%

$\frac{5}{n} = \frac{20}{100}$
$n = 25$

20% of 25 is 5.

Number Sense Tell whether the answer to the question is a *percent*, a *part*, or a *whole*. Then answer the question.

1. What percent of 200 is 50?   **2.** 12 is 80% of what?

3. 50% of what number is 8?   **4.** What is 30% of 90?

Match each question with the proportion you could use to answer it.

5. What is 40% of 15?

6. 15 is what percent of 40?

7. 40% of what number is 15?

A. $\dfrac{15}{40} = \dfrac{n}{100}$

B. $\dfrac{15}{n} = \dfrac{40}{100}$

C. $\dfrac{n}{15} = \dfrac{40}{100}$

Homework Exercises

For more exercises, see Extra Skills and Word Problems.

GO for Help

For Exercises	See Examples
8–13	1
14–19	2
20–24	3

Test Prep Tip ⊙⊙⊙⊙

You can use a model to help you solve percent problems.

Use a proportion to find the percent.

8. 24 is what percent of 32?   **9.** What percent of 230 is 23?

10. What percent of 25 is 23?   **11.** 8 is what percent of 400?

12. What percent of 600 is 84?   **13.** 21 is what percent of 168?

Use a proportion to find the part.

14. What is 4% of 350?   **15.** 1% of 500 is what number?

16. What number is 62% of 50?   **17.** 15% of 15 is what number?

18. 40% of 25 is what number?   **19.** What is 37.5% of 8?

Use a proportion to find the whole.

20. 36 is 72% of what number?   **21.** 80% of what number is 15?

22. 21 is 84% of what number?   **23.** 28 is 35% of what number?

24. A sweater is on sale for $33. This is 75% of the original price. Find the original price.

25. Guided Problem Solving In a market, 44 of the 80 types of vegetables are grown locally. What percent of the vegetables are grown locally?
  • Identify the part. Identify the whole.
  • Complete and solve the proportion: $\dfrac{\blacksquare}{\blacksquare} = \dfrac{\blacksquare}{100}$.

26. A school holds classes from 8:00 A.M. to 2:00 P.M. For what percent of a 24-hour day does this school hold classes?

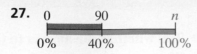
Write a proportion for each model. Solve for *n*.

27.

0   90   *n*
0%   40%   100%

28.

0   *n*   80
0%   70%   100%

29.

0   54   144
0%   *n*% 100%

30.

0   139.1   *n*
0%   65%   100%

31. Music In a school band of 24 students, 9 students play brass instruments. What percent of the members play brass instruments?

32. You purchase a telescope in a state with a 5% sales tax. You pay $14.85 in tax. Estimate the price of the telescope.

33. Open-Ended Write a percent problem that compares the number of boys to the number of girls in your class.

34. At the library, you find 9 books on a certain topic. The librarian tells you that 55% of the books on this topic have been signed out. How many books does the library have on the topic?

35. Writing in Math A proportion that models a percent problem has four numbers. One of the numbers is always the same. Explain why.

36. Challenge A car dealer advertises "All cars 19% off sticker price!" A buyer pays $15,930.95 for a car. Estimate the sticker price.

Ⓐ Ⓑ Ⓒ Ⓓ **Test Prep and Mixed Review** （ **Practice** ）

Multiple Choice

37. Out of 45 students, 29 go on a field trip. Which best represents the percent of the students who do NOT go on the trip?

　Ⓐ 16%　　Ⓑ 36%　　Ⓒ 64%　　Ⓓ 84%

38. In 2001, 56.5% of households in the United States had a computer. Which expression provides the best estimate for the number of households with computers in a survey of 621 households in 2001?

　Ⓕ 60% of 650　　　　　　Ⓗ 60% of 600
　Ⓖ 50% of 600　　　　　　Ⓙ 50% of 650

39. The model below represents $4n + 6 = 18$. What is the value of *n*?

| *n* | *n* | *n* | *n* |　○○○　=　○○○○○○
　　　　　　　　　　　　　　○○○　　○○○○○○
　　　　　　　　　　　　　　　　　　○○○○○○

　Ⓐ $n = 24$　　Ⓑ $n = 6$　　Ⓒ $n = 3$　　Ⓓ $n = -3$

Write each fraction as a decimal.

40. $\frac{8}{10}$　　　**41.** $\frac{48}{12}$　　　**42.** $\frac{5}{100}$　　　**43.** $\frac{6}{24}$

GO for Help

For Exercises	See Lesson
40–43	6-1

6-3 Solving Percent Problems Using Equations

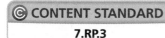

Video Tutor Help

PearsonSuccessNet.com

What You'll Learn

To use equations to solve problems involving percent

Why Learn This?

Suppose a ski resort reports that 60% of its trails are open. If you know how many trails are open, you can solve an equation to find the total number of trails in the park.

You can translate percent problems into equations to find parts, wholes, or percents.

EXAMPLE Finding a Whole

① **Multiple Choice** A ski resort in New Hampshire begins the season with 60% of its trails open. There are 27 trails open. How many trails does the ski resort have?

    Ⓐ 5   Ⓑ 16   Ⓒ 22   Ⓓ 45

Words   60% of the number of trails is 27

Let x = the number of trails at this ski resort.

Equation   0.60 · x = 27

$$0.60x = 27 \quad \leftarrow \text{Write the equation.}$$

$$\frac{0.60x}{0.60} = \frac{27}{0.60} \quad \leftarrow \text{Divide each side by 0.60.}$$

$$x = 45 \quad \leftarrow \text{Simplify.}$$

The ski resort has 45 trails. The correct answer is choice D.

✓ Quick Check

1. A plane flies with 54% of its seats empty. If 81 seats are empty, what is the total number of seats on the plane?

You can use an equation to find a whole, a part, or a percent.

EXAMPLE   **Finding a Part**

2   What number is 39% of 377?

 Words   A number is 39% of 377

   Let n = the number.

 Equation n $= 0.39 \cdot 377$

   $n = 0.39 \cdot 377 = 147.03$ ← Simplify.

✓ Quick Check

 ●   **2.** 27% of 60 is what number?

EXAMPLE   **Finding a Percent**

3   **Recreation** Of 3,072 teens surveyed, 2,212 say they read for fun. What percent of the teens surveyed say they read for fun?

Estimate About 2,000 of 3,000 teens read for fun.

$$\frac{2{,}000}{3{,}000} = \frac{2}{3} \approx 0.67 = 67\%$$

  $3{,}072p = 2{,}212$ ← Write an equation. Let p = the percent of teens who read for fun.

  $\dfrac{3{,}072p}{3{,}072} = \dfrac{2{,}212}{3{,}072}$ ← Divide each side by 3,072.

   $p \approx 0.7200520833$ ← Use a calculator.

   $p \approx 72\%$ ← Write the decimal as a percent.

About 72% of the teens surveyed say they read for fun.

Check for Reasonableness 72% is close to the estimate 67%.

✓ Quick Check

 ●   **3.** It rained 75 days last year. About what percent of the year was rainy?

KEY CONCEPTS   **Percents and Equations**

Finding a Percent	**Finding a Part**	**Finding a Whole**
What percent of 25 is 5?	What is 20% of 25?	20% of what is 5?
$n \cdot 25 = 5$	$n = 0.2 \cdot 25$	$0.2 \cdot n = 5$
$n = 0.2$	$n = 5$	$n = 25$
5 is 20% of 25.	5 is 20% of 25.	20% of 25 is 5.

1. **Number Sense** Do the following questions mean the same thing? Explain. *What is 20% of 40? 20 is what percent of 40? 20 is 40% of what number?*

Reasoning Match each question with the equation you could use to answer it.

2. What is 16% of 200?

3. 16 is what percent of 200?

4. 16% of what number is 200?

A. $0.16n = 200$
B. $n = 0.16(200)$
C. $16 = 200n$

Write an equation for each question. Then answer the question.

5. What percent of 625 is 500?

6. What number is 5% of 520?

Homework Exercises

For more exercises, see **Extra Skills and Word Problems.**

GO for Help

For Exercises	See Examples
7–11	1
12–15	2
16–20	3

Use an equation to find the whole.

7. 96% of what number is 24?

8. 40% of what number is 30?

9. 50.4 is 36% of what number?

10. 12.8 is 32% of what number?

11. You answered 22 questions correctly and scored 88% on a test. How many questions were on the test?

Use an equation to find a part.

12. 18% of 90 is what number?

13. What number is 41% of 800?

14. What number is 56% of 48?

15. 70% of 279 is what number?

Use an equation to find the percent.

16. What percent of 496 is 124?

17. 18 is what percent of 48?

18. 39 is what percent of 260?

19. What percent of 620 is 372?

20. A sports team has won 21 out of the 40 games it has played. About what percent of the games has the team won?

21. **Guided Problem Solving** Suppose 24% of a 1,500-Calorie diet is from protein. How many Calories are *not* from protein?
   • **Make a Plan** Find the number of Calories that are from protein. Subtract that number from the daily total number of Calories.
   • **Carry Out the Plan** 24% of 1,500 is ■. Subtract ■ from 1,500.

22. A water tank containing 496 gallons is 62% full. How many more gallons are needed to fill the tank?

Use the table at the right. Find the percent of days in a 365-day year that are school days in each country. Round to the nearest percent.

23. China   **24.** Israel   **25.** Russia

26. Scotland   **27.** United States

Length of School Year

Country	Days
China	251
Israel	215
Russia	210
Scotland	200
United States	180

SOURCE: *The Top 10 of Everything*

28. Food You make 72 cookies for a bake sale. This is 20% of the cookies at the bake sale. How many cookies are at the bake sale?

29. The attendance at the school play on Friday was 95% of the attendance on Saturday night. If 203 people attended on Saturday night, estimate how many attended on Friday night.

30. Writing in Math If 25% of a number is 45, is the number greater than or less than 45? If 150% of a number is 45, is the number greater than or less than 45? Explain how you can tell.

31. Of the 60 members of a choir, 30% sing alto and 45% sing soprano. How many members of the choir sing alto or soprano?

32. Challenge You plant 40 pots with seedlings. Eight of the pots contain tomato plants. What percent of your seedlings are *not* tomato plants?

Test Prep and Mixed Review

Practice

Multiple Choice

33. About 12% of an iceberg's mass is above water. If the mass above water is 9,000,000 kg, what is the mass of the entire iceberg?

Ⓐ 108,000 kg   Ⓒ 75,000,000 kg

Ⓑ 1,080,000 kg   Ⓓ 120,000,000 kg

34. On average, a group of 25 college students contains 14 females. Which equation can be used to find x, the percent of females in a typical group of college students?

Ⓕ $\frac{x}{100} = \frac{14}{25}$ Ⓖ $\frac{x}{25} = \frac{14}{100}$ Ⓗ $\frac{x}{25} = \frac{14}{39}$ Ⓙ $\frac{x}{14} = \frac{25}{100}$

35. The model at the right represents which expression?

Ⓐ $\frac{1}{5} \times \frac{3}{5}$ Ⓒ $\frac{1}{2} \times \frac{3}{5}$

Ⓑ $\frac{1}{3} \times \frac{3}{5}$ Ⓓ $\frac{2}{3} \times \frac{7}{10}$

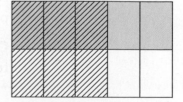

GO for Help

For Exercises	See Lesson
36–39	5-3

Determine whether the ratios in each pair can form a proportion.

36. $\frac{4}{12}, \frac{140}{360}$ **37.** $\frac{7}{9}, \frac{35}{45}$ **38.** $\frac{12}{28}, \frac{3}{7}$ **39.** $\frac{45}{60}, \frac{3}{4}$

Write each percent as a decimal and as a fraction in simplest form.

1. 45%   **2.** 135%   **3.** 0.98%

4. Write $\frac{14}{25}$ as a percent.

5. Order 0.245, $\frac{1}{6}$, 20%, and $\frac{1}{4}$ from least to greatest.

Find each answer using a proportion.

6. 35 is what percent of 60?   **7.** 14.4 is 90% of what number?   **8.** What percent of 75 is 63?

Find each answer using an equation.

9. What percent of 120 is 54?   **10.** What is 72% of 95?   **11.** What is 120% of 185?

12. One hour is what percent of one week? Round to the nearest tenth of a percent.

13. A club has 100 members. Five of the members are officers. Each officer gets six other members to help them decorate for a club party. What percent of the club members help decorate?

14. You walked to school on 135 days out of 180 days. What percent of the days did you walk? Round to the nearest tenth of a percent.

MATH GAMES

Order, Please!

What You'll Need

- 30 pieces of construction paper, each with a fraction, decimal, or a percent written on it. Include mixed numbers or the equivalent decimals and percents.

How To Play

- Select two teams of five players. Each player receives one piece of construction paper.
- When play begins, team members must order their numbers from the least to the greatest number.
- The first team to order their numbers correctly is the winner.

Solving Percent Problems

Braces are cool! A recent survey of 406 mothers by the American Association of Orthodontists reported that 69% felt that wearing braces makes their children feel cool. If each mother had only one child with braces, how many children would that be?

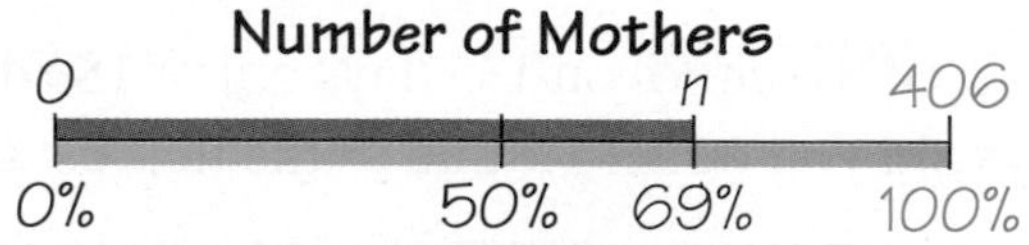

What You Might Think

What You Might Write

What do I know?

69% of 406 mothers said wearing braces made their children feel cool. Each mother had 1 child, so that's 69% of 406 children.

What am I trying to find out?

The number of children who felt cool wearing braces.

How do I show the main idea?

Make a diagram.

Number of Mothers

```
0                        n        406
├──────────────┼────┼────┤
0%             50%  69%  100%
```

How can I estimate the answer?

69% is close to 75%, which is $\frac{3}{4}$.

406 is close to 400.

$\frac{3}{4}$ and 400 are compatible; $\frac{3}{4}$ of 400 is 300.

How do I solve the problem?

69% is 0.69.

$0.69 \times 406 = n$

$280.14 = n$

280.14 can be rounded to 280.

Is the answer reasonable?

280 is close to the estimate of 300. The answer is reasonable.

Think It Through

1. What percent of 406 mothers did not say their children felt cool wearing braces? How many children is that?

2. How does the diagram above help show the main idea?

Exercises

For Exercises 3 and 4, answer the questions first, and then solve the problem.

3. A solo guitarist received a royalty payment of 9% based on the sales of her CD. If she received a check for $5,238, what were the total sales of her CD?
   a. What do you know?
   b. What do you want to find out?
   c. How can the diagram below help you write an equation?

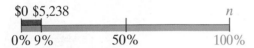

4. The human body is about 67% water. A student weighs 130 pounds. About how much of his weight is water?
   a. What do you know?
   b. What do you want to find out?
   c. What diagram would help you show the main idea?

5. Teenagers were asked how many hours per week they worked. The data are shown below. Assume they were paid $6.50 per hour. About how much per week would the largest category of students make? The second-largest?

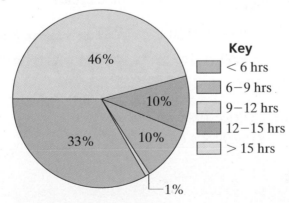

Key
- < 6 hrs
- $6-9$ hrs
- $9-12$ hrs
- $12-15$ hrs
- > 15 hrs

6. When water freezes, its volume increases by 9%. If you freeze one gallon of water to make ice for a party, how many cubic inches of ice will you have? (*Hint*: 1 gallon $= 231$ in.^{3})

7. Research says that humans learn through listening 11% of the time and through observing 83% of the time. In a 50-minute math class, how much time would you spend learning by listening? By observing?

6-4 Applications of Percent

 CONTENT STANDARD
7.RP.3

What You'll Learn

To find and estimate solutions to application problems involving percent and to use different ways to represent a situation

New Vocabulary commission, percent error

Why Learn This?

You use percents to calculate taxes, tips, commissions fees, and percent error.

In many states, you must pay a sales tax on items you buy. The sales tax is a percent of the purchase price. A tax percent is also called a tax rate.

To find sales tax, you can use the formula *sales tax = tax rate · purchase price.*

EXAMPLE Finding Sales Tax

1. **Shopping** The price of a bicycle you plan to buy is $159.99. The sales tax rate is 6%. How much will you pay for the bicycle?

Method 1 $0.06 \cdot 159.99 \approx 9.60$ ← **Find the sales tax. Round to the nearest cent.**

$159.99 + 9.60 = 169.59$ ← **Add the sales tax to the purchase price.**

You will pay $169.59 for the bicycle.

Method 2 Price + (Price)(0.06) = Price × 1.06
$159.99 × 1.06 = $169.59

✓ Quick Check

1. Find the total cost for a purchase of $185 if the sales tax rate is 5.5%.

You can use estimation and mental math to find a 15% tip.

Round the bill to the nearest dollar. Find 10% of the bill by moving the decimal point one place to the left. Find 5% of the bill by taking one half of the result of Step 2. Add the amounts of Step 2 and Step 3 together to find 15%.

EXAMPLE **Estimating a Tip**

2 Your family takes a taxi to the train station. The taxi fare is $17.85. Estimate a 15% tip to give the driver.

$17.85 \approx 18$ ← **Round to the nearest dollar.**

$0.1 \cdot 18 = 1.8$ ← **Find 10% of the bill.**

$\frac{1}{2} \cdot 1.8 = 0.9$ ← **Find 5% of the bill. 5% is $\frac{1}{2}$ of the 10% amount.**

$1.8 + 0.9 = 2.7$ ← **Add the 10% and 5% amounts to get 15%.**

For a $17.85 taxi fare, a 15% tip is about $2.70.

✓ Quick Check

2. Estimate a 15% tip for each amount.
   a. $58.20   **b.** $61.80   **c.** $49.75

Some sales jobs pay you a **commission**, a percent of the amount of your sales. To find a commission, use *commission = commission rate · sales.*

EXAMPLES **Finding a Commission**

3 Find the commission on a $500 sale with a commission rate of 12.5%.

$0.125 \cdot 500 = 62.5$ ← **Write 12.5% as 0.125 and multiply.**

The commission on the sale is $62.50.

4 A sales agent earns a weekly salary of $650, plus a commission of 4% on all sales. His sales this week are $1,250. How much does he earn?

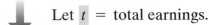

Words   total earnings = salary + commission

Let t = total earnings.

Equation t =   650   +   0.04 · 1,250

$t = 650 + 0.04 \cdot 1,250$ ← **Write the equation.**

$= 650 + 50$ ← **Multiply.**

$= 700$ ← **Simplify.**

The sales agent earns $700 this week.

✓ Quick Check

3. Find the commission on a $3,200 sale with a commission rate of 6%.

4. Suppose you earn a weekly salary of $800 plus a commission of 3.5% on all sales. Find your earnings for a week with total sales of $1,400.

GO **nline**

Video Tutor Help
PearsonSuccessNet.com

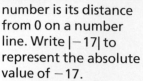
Quality control supervisors use percent error to assure that products meet their specifications. The formula for **percent error** uses the absolute value of the difference between the measured value and the actual or desired value.

$$\text{Percent Error} = \frac{|\text{Actual Value} - \text{Measured Value}|}{\text{Actual Value}} \times 100$$

EXAMPLE   **Application: Percent Error in Manufacturing**

⑤ The supervisor at a shoelace factory checks the length of 1 shoelace out of every 500 made. If shoelaces are not within 0.5% of the specified length, they will be rejected. A 36-inch shoelace she just checked was $35\frac{7}{8}$ in. long. Does she reject this shoelace?

$$\text{Percent Error} = \frac{|36 - 35.875|}{36} \times 100 \quad \leftarrow \textbf{Use decimals in the formula.}$$

$$= \frac{0.125}{36} \times 100 \quad \leftarrow \textbf{Find the absolute value.}$$

$$= 0.003472 \times 100 \quad \leftarrow \textbf{Simplify the fraction.}$$

$$= 0.3472 \quad \leftarrow \textbf{Multiply.}$$

To Skills Handbook, page 599.

The percent error is 0.35% rounded to the nearest hundredth, so the shoelace is not rejected.

✓ Quick Check

5. At a sporting goods factory, a quality control technician checking the weights of baseball bats measures a bat that should weigh 26 oz at $26\frac{1}{4}$ oz. If a bat is not within 0.6% of its specified weight, it is rejected. Why does this bat pass or fail this test?

Almost all states charge fees for various services. Some fees are flat fees, such as paying $15 for a fishing license. But other fees are percentages of some value.

EXAMPLE   **Finding a Registration Fee**

⑥ In one state the fee to register a medium weight truck is 1.5% of its assessed value. What is the fee to register a truck with an assessed value of $14,500?

$$0.015 \cdot 14{,}500 = 217.5 \quad \leftarrow \textbf{Write 1.5\% as 0.015 and multiply.}$$

The fee is $217.50.

✓ Quick Check

6. All states charge a fee for using cell phones. In one state, the fee is 1.14% of the bill. What is the monthly fee for a $39.00 bill?

1. **Vocabulary** What does it mean to earn an 8% commission?

2. **Number Sense** Is 4% sales tax on a $250 item *greater than, less than,* or *equal to* 4% commission on a $250 sale?

3. **Mental Math** Calculate a 15% tip on a restaurant bill of $24.

Find the sales tax for each item. The tax rate is 6%.

4. a CD priced at $12.99

5. a $450 TV

Find each commission, given the sale.

6. 5% on a $900 sale

7. 2% on a $35.50 sale

Homework Exercises

For more exercises, see Extra Skills and Word Problems.

Find the total cost.

8. $35.99 with a 5% sales tax

9. $72.75 with a 6% sales tax

Estimate a 15% tip for each amount.

10. $68.50

11. $30.80

12. $9.89

13. $27.59

Find each commission, given the sale and the commission rate.

14. $800, 12%

15. $2,500, 8%

16. $2,000, 7.5%

17. $600, 4.5%

GO for Help

For Exercises	See Examples
8–9	1
10–13	2
14–17	3-4
18	5
19	6

18. John measures the mass of a 250-gram standard mass with a balance. John's measure is 249.7 grams. What is the percent error of his balance? If he now measures a 1,000-gram mass, what will the reading on the balance be?

19. Rental agents often charge a fee for finding apartments. Liza's agent charges 5% of the monthly rent. What fee will Liza pay for an apartment with a monthly rent of $950?

20. **Guided Problem Solving** Your lunch bill is $19.75. A 5% sales tax will be added, and you want to give a tip of about 20% of $19.75. Estimate how much you will pay for lunch.
    • To what number should you round the bill?
    • About how much tip should you give?

21. Your neighbor pays $40 to have her lawn mowed and always adds a 15% tip. You and your friend decide to mow the lawn together and split the earnings evenly. How much will each of you make?

GO Online
Homework Video Tutor
PearsonSuccessNet.com

22. **Writing in Math** Explain how you can use mental math to find the percent error when the weight of a bar of zinc that should weigh 100 lb measures only 99 lb.

23. A purchase costs $25.79 with a tax of $1.29. Find the sales tax rate.

24. **Art** For a craft project, you select the four packages of modeling clay and the set of tools shown at the right. If there is a 6% sales tax, what is the total cost?

$2.79 ea.
plus tax

CLAY

$1.79
plus tax

25. A real estate agent earns a weekly salary of $200. This week, the agent sold a home for $120,000 and was paid a 5.5% commission. Find the agent's earnings for the week.

26. **Sales** A store pays a 6% commission on the first $500 in sales and 8% on sales over $500. Find the commission on an $800 sale.

27. **Reasoning** Daniel makes two measurements and analyzes his results.
    a. A 10-g mass measures 9.5 g. What is the percent error?
    b. A 500-g mass measures 499.5 g. What is the percent error?
    c. If the measurements of a heavy object and a light object are each off by 0.5 grams, which measurement has the greater percent error? Explain.

28. **Challenge** Find the commission rate if the total earnings are $970, including a salary of $350 and a commission on sales of $12,400.

Test Prep and Mixed Review

Practice

Multiple Choice

29. Laundry workers can expect a tip between 15% and 20%. Which is closest to the amount Diane should offer in order to give the minimum tip for a laundry service of $11.50?
    Ⓐ $4.00　　Ⓑ $2.50　　Ⓒ $2.00　　Ⓓ $1.75

30. A rental agency charges a fee of 6% of a month's rent for finding an apartment. Nikolai is looking at apartments with monthly rents of $880, $960 and $1050. What is the lowest fee he might pay?
    Ⓕ $63.00　　Ⓖ $57.60　　Ⓗ $52.80　　Ⓙ $51.00

31. Raul bought 3 posters for $2.59 each and 2 posters for $1.98 each. He paid 59 cents tax. What other information is necessary to find Raul's correct change?
    Ⓐ The amount of money Raul gave the cashier
    Ⓑ Whether the posters were on sale
    Ⓒ The total amount of money Raul spent
    Ⓓ How Raul got to the store

For Exercises	See Lesson
32–33	5-2

Write each unit rate.

32. 408 mi on 12 gal of gasoline

33. $16.45 for 7 lb of fish

x=?

Algebra Thinking

Percent Equations

When you have a multiple-choice question with an equation using percent, you can quickly eliminate some of the choices. Use benchmark numbers for percents to help you. Here are some benchmarks:

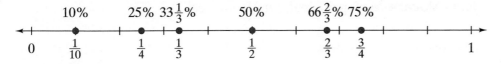

EXAMPLE

Which statement is true for $49\% \times x = 30$? Explain.

Ⓐ $x \approx 30$ Ⓑ x is negative.   Ⓒ $x < 60$ Ⓓ $x > 30$

Choice A is not true.   ← 49% is about $\frac{1}{2}$ and $\frac{1}{2}$ of 30 is 15. So $x \approx 30$ isn't close.

Choice B is not true.   ← That would make the left side a negative number.

Choice C is not true.   ← 49% is a little less than $\frac{1}{2}$, and $\frac{1}{2}$ of 60 is 30.

Choice D is true.   ← x must be big enough that half of it is 30.
                      x must be about twice 30.

● The correct answer is choice D.

Exercises

Reasoning Which choice is true for the equation? Use benchmark numbers to explain. Check each answer choice. Do not compute.

1. $31\% \times x = 23.1$

Ⓐ $x < 23.1$ Ⓑ $x < 100$ Ⓒ $x \approx 90$ Ⓓ $x \approx \frac{2}{3}$

2. $90 \times x\% = 8.9$

Ⓕ $x \approx 10$ Ⓖ $x > 30$ Ⓗ $x \approx 50$ Ⓙ $x > 10$

3. $251 \div 500 = x\%$

Ⓐ $x < 0$ Ⓑ $x \approx 50$ Ⓒ $x \approx 2$ Ⓓ $x < 45$

Write three statements about the variable for each equation. Make some statements true and some false. Circle the ones that are true.

4. $26\% \times x = 101$ **5.** $500 \div 1007 = x\%$ **6.** $20 \times x\% = 10.5$

Check Skills You'll Need

1. **Vocabulary Review** What is a *percent*?

Change each percent to a decimal.

2. 4%   3. 9%

4. 2.0%   5. 6.5%

GO for Help
Lesson 6-1

© **CONTENT STANDARD**
7.RP.3

What You'll Learn

To find simple interest

New Vocabulary principal, simple interest

Why Learn This?

Money may not grow on trees, but it can grow in a bank. When you deposit money, you earn money called interest. When you borrow money, you pay interest on your loan.

The original amount you deposit or borrow is the **principal**. Interest earned only on the principal is **simple interest**.

You can use a formula to calculate simple interest.

KEY CONCEPTS   Simple Interest Formula

$$I = prt$$

I is the interest earned, *p* is the principal, *r* is the interest rate per year, and *t* is the time in years.

GO Online

Video Tutor Help
PearsonSuccessNet.com

EXAMPLE   Finding Simple Interest

1 **Gridded Response** You borrow $300 for 5 years at an annual interest rate of 4%. What is the simple interest you pay in dollars?

$I = prt$ ← Write the formula.

$I = (300)(0.04)(5) = 60$ ← Substitute. Use 0.04 for 4%.

The interest is $60.

Quick Check

1. Find the simple interest you pay on a $220 loan at a 5% annual interest rate for 4 years.

A graph can show the increase in interest earned over time.

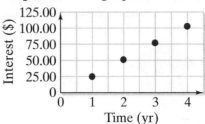
EXAMPLE Graphing Simple Interest

2 You have $500 in an account that earns an annual rate of 5.1%. At the end of each year, you withdraw the interest you have earned. Graph the total interest you earn after 1, 2, 3, and 4 years.

Step 1 Make a table.

Time (yr)	Interest ($)
1	25.50
2	51.00
3	76.50
4	102.00

Step 2 Draw a graph.

✓ Quick Check

2. Graph the simple interest earned on $950 at an annual rate of 4.2%.

EXAMPLE Comparing Loans

3 **Banking** You need to borrow $1,000. You can borrow it for 3 years at 8% simple interest or for 2 years at 11% simple interest. Which loan will cost more?

3 Year Loan	2 Year Loan	
$I = prt$	$I = prt$	← **Write the formula.**
$I = 1000(0.08)(3)$	$I = 1000(0.11)(2)$	← **Substitute.**
$I = 240$	$I = 220$	← **Simplify.**
$240 > 220$		← **Compare.**

The 3-year loan will cost more.

✓ Quick Check

3. Barbara wants to borrow $2000. She can get a loan of $2000 at 7% simple interest for 3 years or at 11% simple interest for 2 years. Which loan will cost her more?

✓ Check Your Understanding

1. **Vocabulary** The original amount, p, is the _____.

2. Find the simple interest earned on $2000 at 10% for 6 years.

3. **Number Sense** If you draw a line through the points on a simple interest graph, is the line straight or curved?

4. True or False: Doubling the principal will double the balance.

For more exercises, see Extra Skills and Word Problems.

Find the simple interest on a $340 loan at each rate.

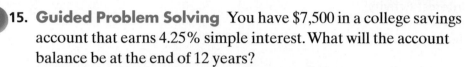
GO for Help

For Exercises	See Examples
5–8	1
9–14	2

5. 7% annual interest, 3 years

6. 12% annual interest, 5 years

7. 15% annual interest, 1 year

8. 4.6% annual interest, 6 years

Graph the total simple interest earned for each amount over 4 years.

9. $500 at 4.5%

10. $1,200 at 6.5%

11. $375 at 5.75%

12. $200 at 5.0%

13. $2,000 at 10%

14. $2,000 at 0.5%

GPS **15. Guided Problem Solving** You have $7,500 in a college savings account that earns 4.25% simple interest. What will the account balance be at the end of 12 years?
- What is 4.25% expressed as a decimal?
- What value do you substitute for each variable in the formula $I = prt$?

16. You borrow $500 at 18% simple annual interest. You make no payments for 6 months. How much do you owe after 6 months?

17. Suppose you invest $2,000 for 5 years at 4% simple interest. Which would increase your balance in 5 years the most?
- Ⓐ Increasing the starting amount from $2,000 to $3,000
- Ⓑ Increasing the interest rate to 5% annual interest
- Ⓒ Increasing the time from 5 years to 6 years

18. Writing in Math Which earns more interest: $2,000 at 6% interest for 5 years or $2,000 at 5% interest for 6 years? Explain.

19. Challenge You invest $2,000 in a simple interest account. The balance after 8 years is $2,720. What is the interest rate?

Multiple Choice

20. When a principal p has a simple interest rate r for t years, the balance B is given by $B = p(1 + rt)$. Which expression represents the balance for $200 invested for 6 years at a 5% simple interest rate?
- Ⓐ $200(1 + 0.05 + 6)$
- Ⓒ $200(1 + (0.05)(6))$
- Ⓑ $200(1)(0.05 + 6)$
- Ⓓ $200(0.05)(6)$

21. The names of six of the 48 contiguous states of the U.S. begin with M. Which proportion can you use to find the percent of contiguous states with names beginning with M?
- Ⓕ $\frac{x}{6} = \frac{48}{100}$
- Ⓖ $\frac{6}{x} = \frac{100}{48}$
- Ⓗ $\frac{6}{48} = \frac{x}{100}$
- Ⓙ $\frac{48}{6} = \frac{x}{100}$

GO for Help

For Exercises	See Lesson
22–23	6-3

Use an equation.

22. 32% of what number is 20?

23. 45% of 80 is what number?

Online lesson quiz, PearsonSuccessNet.com

Find the total cost.

1. $56.80 with a 5% sales tax

2. $35.99 with a 5% sales tax

Find the commission or fee, given the amount and rate.

3. $5,500, 4.5% commission

4. $345.50, 2% commission

5. $975, 5% fee

Find the simple interest on a $750 loan at each rate.

6. 6% annual interest, 4 years

7. 12% annual interest, 2 years

8. Science A chemist measures the boiling point of a sample of benzene as 79.8°C. The actual boiling point is 80.1°C. Rounded to the nearest hundredth of a percent, what is the percent error in the boiling point for the sample?

6-6a Activity Lab

Data Analysis

Exploring Percent of Change

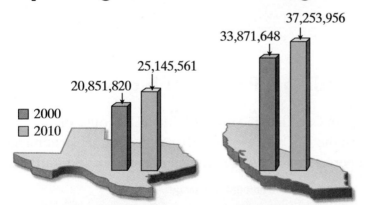

Texas Population   **California Population**

Use the graph above to complete the following exercises.

1. Find the population change from 2000 to 2010 for each state.

2. Which state had the greater change in population?

3. For each state, write the ratio $\frac{\text{change in population}}{\text{2000 population}}$. Write each as a percent.

4. Which state had the greater population change in terms of percent?

5. Reasoning Compare your answers to 1 and 3.

6-6 Finding Percent of Change

Check Skills You'll Need

1. **Vocabulary Review** What are the *cross products* in the proportion $\frac{5}{16} = \frac{n}{100}$?

Solve each proportion.

2. $\frac{2}{20} = \frac{n}{100}$

3. $\frac{1}{8} = \frac{n}{100}$

4. $\frac{6.5}{13} = \frac{n}{100}$

 **for Help**
Lesson 5-4

© CONTENT STANDARDS
7.RP.3, 7.EE.2

What You'll Learn

To find percents of increase and percents of decrease

New Vocabulary percent of change, markup, discount

Why Learn This?

You can use percent of change to describe how much an amount increases or decreases over time. For example, every 10 years, the number of U.S. representatives for a state may change, based on the change in the state's population.

A **percent of change** is the percent a quantity increases or decreases from its original amount. Use a proportion to find a percent of change.

$$\frac{\text{amount of change}}{\text{original amount}} = \frac{\text{percent of change}}{100}$$

EXAMPLE Finding a Percent of Increase

1 **Government** South Carolina had 6 seats in the U.S. House of Representatives in the 2000s. After the 2010 census, South Carolina had 7 seats. Find the percent of increase in the number of representatives.

$7 - 6 = 1$ ← **Find the amount of change.**

$\frac{1}{6} = \frac{n}{100}$ ← **Write a proportion. Let n = percent of change.**

$100 \cdot \frac{1}{6} = \frac{n}{100} \cdot 100$ ← **Multiply each side by 100.**

$\frac{100}{6} = n$ ← **Simplify.**

$16.7 \approx n$ ← **Divide.**

The number of South Carolina representatives increased by about 17%.

✓ Quick Check

1. In 2010, Georgia went from 13 to 14 representatives. Find the percent of increase in the number of representatives.

To make a profit, stores charge more for items than they pay for them. The difference between the selling price and the store's cost of an item is called the **markup.** The percent of markup is a percent of increase.

$$\frac{\text{amount of markup}}{\text{original cost}} = \frac{\text{percent of markup}}{100}$$

EXAMPLE **Finding a Percent of Markup**

2 An electronics store orders sets of walkie-talkies for $14.85 each. The store sells each set for $19.90. What is the percent of markup?

$19.90 - 14.85 = 5.05$ ← **Find the amount of markup.**

$\dfrac{5.05}{14.85} = \dfrac{n}{100}$ ← **Write a proportion. Let *n* be the percent of markup.**

$14.85n = 5.05(100)$ ← **Write cross products.**

$\dfrac{14.85n}{14.85} = \dfrac{5.05(100)}{14.85}$ ← **Divide each side by 14.85.**

$n \approx 34$ ← **Simplify.**

The percent of markup is about 34%.

✓ Quick Check

2. Find the percent of markup for a $17.95 headset marked up to $35.79.

The difference between the original price and the sale price of an item is called a **discount.** The percent of discount is a percent of decrease.

$$\frac{\text{amount of discount}}{\text{original cost}} = \frac{\text{percent of discount}}{100}$$

EXAMPLE **Finding a Percent of Discount**

Test Prep Tip

Before you find the percent of change, decide whether the change is an increase or a decrease.

3 **Music** During a clearance sale, a keyboard that normally sells for $49.99 is discounted to $34.99. What is the percent of discount?

$49.99 - 34.99 = 15.00$ ← **Find the amount of discount.**

$\dfrac{15}{49.99} = \dfrac{n}{100}$ ← **Write a proportion. Let *n* be the percent of discount.**

$49.99n = 15(100)$ ← **Write cross products.**

$\dfrac{49.99n}{49.99} = \dfrac{15(100)}{49.99}$ ← **Divide each side by 49.99.**

$n \approx 30$ ← **Simplify.**

The percent of discount for the keyboard is about 30%.

✓ Quick Check

3. Find the percent of discount of a $24.95 novel on sale for $14.97.

More Than One Way

A jacket goes on sale with a discount of 40% off the original price. The original price of the jacket is $42.95. What is the sale price of the jacket?

Anna's Method

I can find the amount of the discount by multiplying $42.95 by 40%. Then I will subtract the discount from the original price.

$42.95 \cdot 0.40 = 17.18$ ← **Find the amount of the discount.**

$42.95 - 17.18 = 25.77$ ← **Subtract the discount from the original price.**

The sale price of the jacket is $25.77.

Chris's Method

The jacket is discounted by 40%, so I will pay 60% of the original price. I can multiply the original price of $42.95 by the percent I need to pay.

$42.95 \cdot 0.60 = 25.77$ ← **Find the discounted price.**

The sale price of the jacket is $25.77.

Choose a Method

You get a discount of 20% on a $27.50 ticket. How much will your ticket cost? Describe your method and explain why it is appropriate.

Check Your Understanding

1. **Vocabulary** How are percent of markup and percent of discount similar? How are they different?

2. **Number Sense** Is it possible for a markup to be 200%? Give an example and explain.

Write the proportion to find percent of change.

3. $35 to $50

4. 98 to 72

5. 748 to 374

Matching Match each situation with the correct percent of change.

6. Boots first priced at $110 go on sale for $88.

7. A radio costs a store $88 but sells for $110.

A. 25% markup

B. 20% discount

For more exercises, see Extra Skills and Word Problems.

GO for Help

For Exercises	See Examples
8–16	1
17–21	2
22–26	3

Find each percent of increase. Round to the nearest percent.

8. 60 to 75　　**9.** 88 to 99　　**10.** 135 to 200　　**11.** 12 to 18

12. 2 to 7　　**13.** 12 to 63　　**14.** 120 to 240　　**15.** 15 to 35

16. Business A worker earning $5.15/h receives a raise. She now earns $6/h. Find the percent of increase in her hourly rate of pay.

Find each percent of markup. Round to the nearest percent.

17. $22 marked up to $33　　**18.** $15 marked up to $60

19. $13.50 marked up to $25　　**20.** $40 marked up to $59.75

21. Clothing Find the percent of markup for a shirt that a store buys for $3.25 and sells for $7.50.

Find each percent of discount. Round to the nearest percent.

22. $70 discounted to $63　　**23.** $9 discounted to $4

24. $10 discounted to $7　　**25.** $480 discounted to $300

26. Crafts A package of poster board usually sells for $8.40. This week the package is on sale for $6.30. What is the percent of discount?

27. Guided Problem Solving The annual precipitation for a city dropped from 65 cm to 47 cm over the course of 5 years. What is the average percent of change in the amount of precipitation for 1 year?
- What was the amount of change in the precipitation over 5 years?
- What was the percent of change over 5 years?

28. A scientist earning an annual salary of $49,839 gets a 4% raise. Estimate the new annual salary for this scientist.

29. Sports A football player gained 1,200 yd last season and 900 yd this season. Find the percent of change. State whether the change is an increase or a decrease.

30. Error Analysis The number of students enrolled in a school has increased from 1,938 to 2,128. A student calculates the percent of increase. His work is shown at right. Explain the student's mistake.

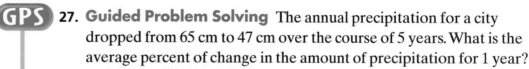

$$2,128 - 1,938 = 190$$
$$190 \div 2,128 \approx 0.089$$
$$0.089 = 8.9\%$$

Careers Scientists develop vaccines and treatments.

31. Writing in Math Describe how you can find the percent of change in the number of students in your school from last year to this year.

Find the price of each item.

32. originally $35.75; 65% markup   **33.** originally $82; 35% discount

34. originally $19.50; 43% markup   **35.** originally $299; 15% discount

36. Choose a Method A TV goes on sale with a discount of 28%. The original price of the TV is $942. What is the sale price of the TV?

37. Business A toy store opened five years ago. The owner uses a computer to track sales. She uses a program that prints @@@ in some cells instead of numbers. Copy and complete the spreadsheet.

	A	B	C	D	
1	Year	Sales ($)	Change From Last Year ($)	Change From Last Year (%)	
2	1	200,000	(not open last year)	(not open last year)	
3	2	240,000	40,000	@@@	
4	3	300,000	@@@	@@@	
5	4	330,000	@@@	@@@	

38. Challenge A storeowner buys a case of 144 pens for $28.80. Tax and shipping cost an additional $8.64. He sells the pens for $.59 each. What is the markup per pen? What is the percent of markup?

Test Prep and Mixed Review   **Practice**

Gridded Response

39. A store orders 200 copies of a DVD at $4.50 a copy. The store puts a selling price of $13.50 on the DVDs. What is the percent markup?

40. Five students in Ms. Power's class ran for charity. The distances they ran were as follows: 5.8 mi, $4\frac{1}{2}$ mi, 2.4 mi, $3\frac{9}{10}$ mi, and 7 mi. What was the distance, in miles, the students ran altogether?

41. Today Louise plans to run $2\frac{4}{5}$ times the distance she ran yesterday. What percent change is that?

42. Mr. Chun earns a salary of $150 a week plus 8% commission on all sales. How much will he earn in dollars if his sales in one week are $2,990?

Algebra Find each payment.

43. $218 with a 6.25% sales tax   **44.** $451 with a 4.5% sales tax

Working Backward

A useful problem solving strategy for answering multiple-choice questions is to *Work Backward*. Check to see which choice results in a correct answer by substituting the answers into the problem.

EXAMPLE

In a pile of dimes and quarters, the number of quarters is 50% of the number of dimes. The total value of the coins is $9.45. How many quarters are in the pile?

  (A) 11   (B) 18   (C) 21   (D) 24

For each quarter there are 2 dimes. Check each answer to see whether it works.

Choice A 11 quarters: 2.75   22 dimes: 2.20   2.75 + 2.20 = 4.95 ✗
Choice B 18 quarters: 4.50   36 dimes: 3.60   4.50 + 3.60 = 8.10 ✗
Choice C 21 quarters: 5.25   42 dimes: 4.20   5.25 + 4.20 = 9.45 ✔
Choice D 24 quarters: 6.00   48 dimes: 4.80   6.00 + 4.80 = 10.80 ✗

The correct answer is choice C.

Exercises

Solve each problem by working backward.

1. What is the greatest number of movie tickets you can buy if you have $33.48 and each movie ticket costs $6.75?
  (A) 3   (B) 4   (C) 5   (D) 6

2. A rental agent's fee is 5% of the monthly rent. For one apartment, the agent received $41.50. What is the monthly rent for that apartment?
  (F) $43.58   (G) $207.50   (H) $830   (J) $2075

3. If you start with a number, add 5, and then multiply by 7, the result is 133. What is the number?
  (A) 12   (B) 14   (C) 15   (D) 21

4. For your birthday, you receive $48 and a $15 gift certificate to a department store. The store is having a sale that takes 40% off the price of all items. What is the total value of the merchandise you can buy and still have $7.50 left for lunch?
  (F) $70.50   (G) $88.20   (H) $92.50   (J) $100

Vocabulary Review

commission (p. 249)
discount (p. 259)
markup (p. 259)

percent (p. 232)
percent of change (p. 258)
percent error (p. 250)

principal (p. 254)
simple interest (p. 254)

Choose the vocabulary term from the column on the right that completes the sentence.

1. The difference between the selling price and a store's cost is the __?__.

2. A __?__ can be an increase or a decrease.

3. A __?__ is a ratio that compares a number to 100.

4. The difference between the original price and the sale price is the __?__.

5. A __?__ is a percent of the sales made by a salesperson.

6. A __?__ shows the difference between a measured value and the desired value.

A. commission
B. discount
C. markup
D. percent
E. percent error
F. percent of change

Go Online

For vocabulary quiz
PearsonSuccessNet.com

Skills and Concepts

Lesson 6-1

• To convert between fractions, decimals, and percents

A **percent** is a rate per 100.

To write a decimal as a percent, multiply the decimal by 100, or move the decimal point two places to the right. To write a percent as a decimal, divide by 100, or move the decimal point two places to the left.

To write a fraction as a percent, first convert the fraction into a decimal.

Write each percent as a decimal.

7. 65%   8. 2%   9. 1.8%   10. $62\frac{1}{2}\%$

11. Write $\frac{3}{8}$ as a percent.   12. Write 0.16 as a percent.

Lessons 6-2, 6-3

• To use proportions to solve problems involving percent

• To use equations to solve problems involving percent

Percent problems are solved by using a proportion or an equation.

Use a proportion or an equation to solve.

13. What percent of 40 is 28?   14. 38 is 80% of what number?

15. What is 60% of 420?   16. 80% of 15 is what number?

17.

18.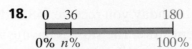

19. **Technology** The price of a new version of a computer game is 120% of the price of the original version. The original version cost $48. What is the cost of the new version?

Lesson 6-4

- To find and estimate solutions to application problems involving percent

A sales tax is a percent of a purchase price.

A tip is a percent of a bill that you give to the person providing a service. A **commission** is a percent of a sale.

Percent error shows the difference between a measured value and an actual value.

Find the sales tax for each item. The sales tax rate is 4%.

20. a book for $14.95   **21.** a used car for $2,990

22. A gardener adds 3.5 oz of plant food to 2 gallons of water. The amount that he was supposed to add is 4 oz. What is the percent error in mixing the plant food?

23. You go to a restaurant with four other people. The total for the food is $43.85. You need to add 5% for tax and 15% for tip. If you decide to split the bill evenly, estimate how much you will pay?

24. Diamonds Find the commission on a diamond that is sold for $6,700 when the commission paid is 4%.

Find each commission, given the sale and the commission rate.

25. $700, 9%   **26.** $3,600, 6%   **27.** $5,000, 5.5%

28. Insurance An insurance company pays its agents 40% commission on the first year's premium and 5% on the second year's premium for life insurance policies. If the premiums are $500 per year, what is the total commission that will be paid during the two years?

Lessons 6-5, 6-6

- To find simple interest
- To find percents of increase and percents of decrease

Use the formula $I = prt$ to find simple interest.

29. You deposit $1,500 in an account that earns 6% simple interest. How much interest do you earn in five years?

A **percent of change** is the percent a quantity increases or decreases from its original amount. Use the proportion $\frac{\text{amount of change}}{\text{original amount}} = \frac{\text{percent change}}{100}$.

Markup is an example of a percent of increase. **Discount** is an example of a percent of decrease.

Find each percent of change. Tell whether it is an increase or a decrease.

30. $90 to $75   **31.** 3.5 ft to 4.2 ft   **32.** 120 lb to 138 lb

33. Shopping The sale price of a game is $24.95. Its original price was $36.00. Find the percent of change. Round to the nearest percent.

Go Online For online chapter test
PearsonSuccessNet.com

Write each decimal as a percent and write each percent as a decimal.

1. 5%   2. 0.3   3. 125%

4. 0.0045   5. 0.39%   6. 3.4

Write each fraction as a percent.

7. $\frac{7}{8}$ 8. $\frac{3}{4}$ 9. $\frac{6}{5}$

10. You work 20 hours per week at a grocery store during the summer. Sixty percent of your job is restocking the shelves. How many hours per week do you spend restocking the shelves?

Write an equation for each question. Then solve the equation.

11. What percent of 82 is 10.25?

12. 108% of 47 is what number?

13. 99 is 72% of what number?

14. 12 is what percent of 1,920?

15. What is 62% of 128?

16. 168% of what number is 714?

17. In a grade of 250 students, there are 6 sets of twins. What percent of the students in this grade have a twin?

Write a proportion for each model. Solve for *n*.

18.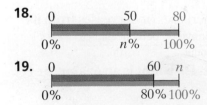

19.

20. **Shopping** You buy a sweater for $18.75, which is 25% off the original price. What was the original price?

21. To prepare for competitions, your coach required you to swim 8 lengths in the pool. You swam 10 lengths. What percent of the required practice did you swim?

Find the sales tax for each item. The sales tax rate is 6%.

22. a lawnmower for $149.50

23. a skateboard for $79.99

24. Pure platinum has a melting point of 3,216°C. A sample said to be platinum melts at 2,814°F. What is the percent error in melting point?

25. You deposit $2,500 in an account that earns 4% simple interest. How much interest do you earn in eight years?

Find each percent of change. Round to the nearest tenth of a percent. State whether the change is an increase or a decrease.

26. 4.15 to 4.55   27. 379 to 302   28. 72 to 102

29. **Jobs** According to the U.S. Department of Labor, total employment is expected to increase from 143 million in 2010 to 164 million in 2020. Find the percent of increase.

30. A salesperson receives a salary of $300 per week and a 6% commission on all sales. How much does this salesperson earn in a week with $2,540 in sales?

31. A bicycle store pays $29.62 for a helmet. The store sells the helmet for $39.99. Find the percent of markup.

32. **Writing in Math** How do you determine whether you are finding a percent of increase or a percent of decrease between two values? Explain.

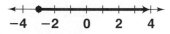

Multiple Choice

Read each question. Then write the letter of the correct answer on your paper.

1. KI, potassium iodide, has one potassium ion, K^+, with a charge of $+1$, for every iodide ion, I^-, with a charge of -1. What is KI's charge?
   - Ⓐ 0
   - Ⓑ 1
   - Ⓒ 2
   - Ⓓ 11

2. Which equation is NOT equivalent to $2x - 3 = 5$?
   - Ⓕ $2x = 8$
   - Ⓗ $2x - 4 = 4$
   - Ⓖ $4x - 3 = 10$
   - Ⓙ $x - 1.5 = 2.5$

3. What are the factors of $18 + 27q$?
   - Ⓐ $(2 + 3)q$
   - Ⓒ $9(5)q$
   - Ⓑ $9(2 + 3)q$
   - Ⓓ $9(2 + 3q)$

4. What inequality is shown on the number line?

   -4 -2 0 2 4
   - Ⓕ $x \geq -3$
   - Ⓗ $x \leq -3$
   - Ⓖ $x > -3$
   - Ⓙ $x < -3$

5. Which ratio is NOT equivalent to $\frac{5}{7}$?
   - Ⓐ $\frac{10}{14}$
   - Ⓑ $\frac{15}{28}$
   - Ⓒ $\frac{25}{35}$
   - Ⓓ $\frac{30}{42}$

6. Which fraction is closest in value to 0.46?
   - Ⓕ $\frac{19}{50}$
   - Ⓖ $\frac{22}{50}$
   - Ⓗ $\frac{25}{50}$
   - Ⓙ $\frac{28}{50}$

7. How many digits repeat when $\frac{3}{11}$ is converted to a decimal?
   - Ⓐ 4
   - Ⓑ 3
   - Ⓒ 2
   - Ⓓ 1

8. Which statement is NOT true?
   - Ⓕ $\frac{12}{16} = \frac{9}{12}$
   - Ⓗ $\frac{12}{9} = \frac{16}{12}$
   - Ⓖ $\frac{12 + 16}{16} = \frac{9 + 12}{12}$
   - Ⓙ $\frac{12 + 1}{16} = \frac{9 + 1}{12}$

9. What is $\frac{5}{8}$ written as a percent?
   - Ⓐ 625%
   - Ⓑ 160%
   - Ⓒ $62\frac{1}{2}\%$
   - Ⓓ 16%

10. You want to use 3 yd of fabric for a pair of pants and you want at least 2 more yards for a shirt. Which inequality shows how much fabric you need to buy?
    - Ⓕ $x \geq 5$
    - Ⓖ $x > 5$
    - Ⓗ $x \leq 5$
    - Ⓙ $x < 5$

11. What is the value of $\frac{2m}{m + 2n}$ when $m = -4$ and $n = 3$?
    - Ⓐ -8
    - Ⓑ -4
    - Ⓒ 0
    - Ⓓ 4

12. An agent charges a fee of 6% of the monthly rent. What fee will Ruth pay for an apartment with a monthly rent of $960?
    - Ⓕ $4.80
    - Ⓖ $5.76
    - Ⓗ $57.60
    - Ⓙ $966

13. Which expression has the greatest value?
    - Ⓐ $32 - (-12)$
    - Ⓒ $-32 - (-12)$
    - Ⓑ $32 - |-12|$
    - Ⓓ $|-32 - (-12)|$

14. Find the value of $7 + 3z$ when $z = 5.1$.
    - Ⓕ 22.3
    - Ⓖ 15.5
    - Ⓗ 15.1
    - Ⓙ 12.1

Gridded Response

Record your answer in a grid.

15. Aaron earns $66.24 for working 9 hours. At that rate, how much will he earn for working 14 hours?

16. Meg owes Ruth $68.40. She wants to use part of her allowance to pay Ruth back over the next $7\frac{1}{2}$ weeks. By what amount in dollars will her allowance change for each of the first 7 weeks?

Short Response

17. Eighteen students in a class of 25 students plan to go on a hiking trip. What percent of the students plan to go on the trip? Show your work.

18. A blue shark swims about 2.26 mi in 10 min. What is the speed of the shark in miles per minute and in miles per hour?

Extended Response

19. A movie theater charges $9 for admission and $4.50 for a bucket of popcorn. Write an expression for the total cost for a group of friends to see a movie and split one bucket of popcorn. Then evaluate your expression for five friends.

CHAPTER 7 Introduction to Functions

What You've Learned

- In a previous course, you worked with points on the coordinate plane.

- In Chapter 3, you substituted numbers for variables.

- You evaluated expressions after substitution to check solutions.

Check Your Readiness

GO for Help

For Exercises	See Lessons
6–11	3-3
12–13	Skills Handbook p. 607

Graphing in the Coordinate Plane

Graph each point on the same coordinate plane.

1. $(0, 3)$ **2.** $(-1, 5)$ **3.** $(6, -8)$

4. Which vertex of the figure at the right is in the second quadrant?

5. What are the coordinates of point S?

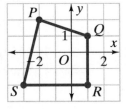

Evaluating Expressions

Verify that the given value is the solution to the equation.

6. $x = 6$ for $2x - 4 = 8$

7. $x = 2$ for $1 = 3x - 5$

8. $x = 4$ for $5x + 9 = 29$

9. $x = 5$ for $12 = 4x - 8$

10. $x = 4$ for $41 = 8x + 9$

11. $x = 3$ for $7x - 8 = 13$

Making Graphs

Draw a line graph for the data below.

12.

HEIGHT OF TREE					
Year	0	1	2	3	4	5
Height (ft)	0	1	3	7.5	8	8.5

13.

MONTHLY AVERAGE HIGH TEMPERATURE Centerville											
Month	J	F	M	A	M	J	J	A	S	O	N	D
Temp (°F)	26	29	38	51	65	73	78	76	67	55	42	30

What You'll Learn Next

- In this chapter, you will use graphs to help identify increasing and decreasing data.

- You will identify proportional relationships.

- You will find the slope of a line given ordered pairs on that line.

- You will identify, describe, and graph linear functions.

Key Vocabulary

- continuous data (p. 288)
- discrete data (p. 288)
- function (p. 275)
- function rule (p. 275)
- linear (p. 270)
- linear function (p. 287)
- nonlinear (p. 270)
- proportional relationship (p. 270)
- slope (p. 293)
- slope of a line (p. 293)
- slope-intercept form (p. 299)
- *y*-intercept (p. 299)

© **CONTENT STANDARD**
Prepares for 8.EE.5

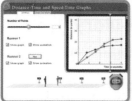

For: Graph Activity
Use: Interactive Textbook, 7-1

What You'll Learn

To interpret and sketch graphs that represent real-world situations

New Vocabulary linear, nonlinear

Why Learn This?

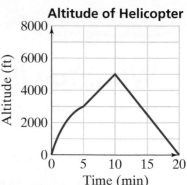

Newspapers, books, and magazines often use graphs to display data. A graph shows complex relationships between variables in a simple, visual way.

Drawing a graph makes it easier to analyze data. You can use a line graph to see if data is increasing or decreasing and if change in data is linear or nonlinear. Change in data is **linear** if it forms a straight line when graphed. If data does *not* form a straight line when graphed, then its change is **nonlinear**.

EXAMPLE **Interpreting a Graph**

Altitude of Helicopter

1. **Transportation** The graph to the right shows the altitude of a helicopter during a flight.

   a. When is the altitude increasing?

   Altitude is increasing from 0 min to 10 min.

   b. When is the altitude decreasing?

   Altitude is decreasing from 10 min to 20 min.

   c. When is the change in altitude linear?

   Altitude change is linear from 5 min to 10 min and from 10 min to 20 min.

   d. When is the change in altitude nonlinear?

   Altitude change is nonlinear from 0 min to 5 min.

✓ Quick Check

1. Between which two times did the speed of the helicopter increase the most?

When you draw a graph without actual data, you are making a sketch.

EXAMPLE Sketching a Graph

② **Fitness** Kim measured her pulse rate occasionally during a 45-min workout. The workout included a 10-min warmup period and a 10-min cool-down period. Sketch and label a graph showing her pulse rate during her workout.

The graph below shows that as Kim warmed up, her pulse rate increased. While she was in the middle of her workout, her pulse rate was high, but stable. The cool-down brought her pulse rate down again.

Test Prep Tip

After you sketch a graph, check to be sure it makes sense in relation to the problem.

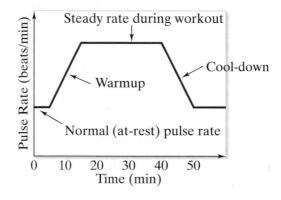

Quick Check

2. You walk to your friend's house. For the first 10 min, you walk from home to a park. For the next 5 min, you watch a ball game in the park. For the last 5 min, you run to your friend's house. Sketch and label a graph showing your distance from home during your trip.

Check Your Understanding

Use the following information for Exercises 1–5. A student wants to sketch a graph that shows the distance of a bus from the transit center during the morning commute. The trip includes three stops where people get on and a highway where the bus travels at 50 mi/h.

1. **Vocabulary** Why should the student use a line graph?

2. What label should the student put on the horizontal scale? What label should be on the vertical scale?

3. When is the line on the graph parallel to the horizontal axis?

4. When is the line farthest away from the horizontal axis?

5. **Reasoning** Which section of the graph should be steeper, the section for the bus on the highway or the section for the bus in the city? Explain.

For more exercises, see Extra Skills and Word Problems.

Science Use the graph below for Exercises 6–9.

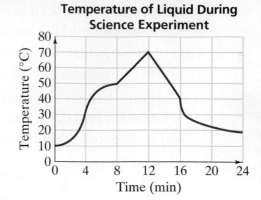

Temperature of Liquid During Science Experiment

6. When during the experiment is the temperature of the liquid increasing?

7. When during the experiment is the temperature of the liquid decreasing?

8. When during the experiment is the change in temperature linear?

9. When during the experiment is the change in temperature nonlinear?

10. **Temperature** In general, air temperature rises during the day and drops during the night. Sketch and label a graph showing the temperature during a 24-hour period.

11. **Pets** Haley took her dog to the park. She walked slowly to the park and then sat with a friend. Haley and her dog ran home together. Sketch a graph showing their distance from home throughout the trip.

12. **Guided Problem Solving** Abel, Ben, and Cam left the computer lab at 2:30 P.M. Cam walked the fastest and Abel the slowest. At the same time, Dan and Erin were walking toward the lab. Erin was walking faster than Dan but slower than Cam. Sketch a graph of each student's distance from the computer lab over time.
    • For which students does distance from the lab increase with time?
    • Which student is represented by the steepest line in the graph?

Use the graph at the right for Exercises 13–16.

13. Who started the race later?

14. Who finished the race first?

15. Who stopped to tie his shoe?

16. **Writing in Math** Describe the outcome of the race.

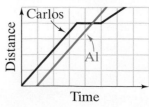

17. **Chemistry** Water is poured at a constant rate into the container at the left. Sketch a graph of the water level as the container is filled.

18. A boat travels at low speed for 3 min while leaving a harbor. Then it travels at a constant cruising speed for 15 min. Finally, it travels at low speed for 5 min while entering another harbor. Sketch a graph that shows the boat's speed during the trip.

19. **Geometry** As the length of the side of a square increases, the area of the square increases. Sketch a graph that shows the area of the square as the side length changes.

20. **Challenge** You throw a ball into the air. It lands four seconds later. Sketch and label a graph showing the ball's height during this time.

Test Prep and Mixed Review

Practice

Multiple Choice

21. Maritza walks home from school, stopping at a friend's house on the way. Which graph could describe the total distance she walked?

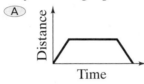

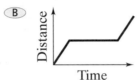

22. A store pays a 5% commission on the first $300 of a sale. If the sale is greater than $300, the store pays a 9% commission on the amount above $300. Which is the commission on a $900 sale?

  F $68   H $70

  G $69   J $71

23. At the movies, you buy a ticket for $7.50. You also split the cost of a large popcorn with two friends. Your total cost is $12.75. Which equation can you use to find the cost of the large popcorn?

  A $7.50 + p = 12.75$ C $7.50 + \dfrac{p}{3} = 12.75$

  B $7.50 + \dfrac{p}{2} = 12.75$ D $\dfrac{7.50 + p}{3} = 12.75$

Simplify each expression.

24. $6x + x + 3x$ 25. $12y - 7y + 2y$

26. $3a + 2b - 2a + 11b$ 27. $4(k - 3) - 8k$

GO for Help

For Exercises	See Lesson
24–27	3-2

Changing Graphs

Graphs that show relationships of an event can change if you use different variables.

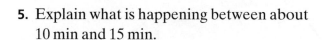
ACTIVITY

1. Two graphs of the same school bus trip are shown. What is the difference between the two graphs?

2. When is speed increasing and when is it decreasing?

3. When is distance increasing and when is it decreasing?

4. Do the graphs increase and decrease during the exact same times? Explain.

5. Explain what is happening between about 10 min and 15 min.

6. Explain what is happening between about 16 min and 30 min.

7. Suppose you are riding in a car for 30 min. Assume the car slowly accelerates to 50 mi per hr during the first 5 min of the ride.

   • Toss a coin 5 times and record results. Each toss represents a 5-min period of time after the first 5 min of your car ride. Heads represents an increase in speed and tails represents a decrease in speed.
   • Decide if the changes in speed are constant or gradual.
   • Then sketch a graph relating time and speed and a graph relating time and distance.

8. Write a paragraph summarizing both graphs.

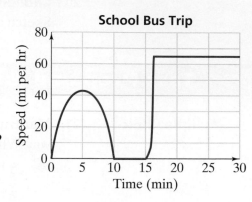

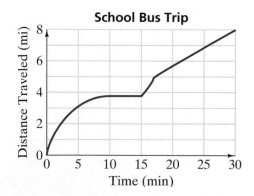

7-2 Functions

Check Skills You'll Need

1. **Vocabulary Review** What is the *variable* in the expression $3a + 7$?

Evaluate each expression for $v = 7$.

2. $2(v - 3)$

3. $7v + 4$

4. $3v - 12$

5. $-5(15 - 2v)$

GO for Help
Lesson 3-2

What You'll Learn

To evaluate functions and complete input-output tables

New Vocabulary function, function rule

Why Learn This?

The time it takes you to get to your destination is a function of how fast you travel. Your speed affects how long the trip will take.

A **function** is a rule that assigns to each input value exactly one output value. A **function rule** is an equation that describes a function.

You can use a function rule to evaluate a function. Functions have input variables and output variables. Examples of function rules appear below.

Buffalo	34
Albany	312
New York	460

input variables

$$y = 4x + 4 \qquad d = 30t \qquad F = \frac{9}{5}C + 32$$

output variables

© CONTENT STANDARD
Prepares for 8.EE.5

EXAMPLE Evaluating Functions

Test Prep Tip

To evaluate a function rule, substitute the input value for the variable inside the parentheses.

1 Juan begins his exercise walk from his friend's house which is 50 m from his own house. The function $d = 3t + 50$ gives the distance d in meters after t seconds that Juan is from his own house while walking. Find the output d for the input $t = 10$.

$d = 3t + 50$	← Write the function.
$d = 3(10) + 50$	← Substitute 10 for t.
$d = 30 + 50$	← Simplify.
$d = 80$	

The output d for the input $t = 10$ is 80. So, after 10 minutes of walking, Juan is 80 meters from his house.

Quick Check

1. The function $F = \frac{9}{5}C + 32$ converts temperatures in degrees Celsius, C to degrees Fahrenheit, F. Evaluate the function for $C = 20$.

An input-output table is useful to evaluate multiple values for a function. It also helps you organize data when the function represents a real-world situation.

EXAMPLE **Input-Output Tables**

2 The function $t = \frac{1}{2}m - 12$ gives the temperature t in a container in degrees Celsius m minutes before, at the start, and during an experiment. Use the function to make an input-output table for $m = -2, -1, 0, 1,$ and 2.

Input m (mins)	Output t (temp)	
−2	−13	← $\frac{1}{2}(-2) - 12 = -13$
−1	$-12\frac{1}{2}$	← $\frac{1}{2}(-1) - 12 = -12\frac{1}{2}$
0	−12	← $\frac{1}{2}(0) - 12 = -12$
1	$-11\frac{1}{2}$	← $\frac{1}{2}(1) - 12 = -11\frac{1}{2}$
2	−11	← $\frac{1}{2}(2) - 12 = -11$

✓ Quick Check

2. Use the function $m = \frac{1}{3}n + 1$ to make an input-output table for $n = -1, 0, 1,$ and 2.

To encourage recycling, some states require a five-cent deposit on drink containers. The total deposit you pay depends on how many containers you buy. You can describe this relationship with a function rule.

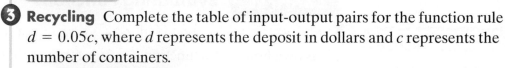

$d = 0.05c \leftarrow$ input variable c = number of containers

↑

output variable d = deposit

EXAMPLE **Application: Recycling**

3 **Recycling** Complete the table of input-output pairs for the function rule $d = 0.05c$, where d represents the deposit in dollars and c represents the number of containers.

Input c (number of containers)	Output d (dollars)	
6	■	← 0.05 × 6 = 0.30
12	■	← 0.05 × 12 = 0.60
24	■	← 0.05 × 24 = 1.20

✓ Quick Check

3. The deposit on a drink container is $.10 in the state of Michigan. Use the function rule $d = 0.1c$. Make a table of input-output pairs to show the total deposits on 5, 10, and 15 containers.

1. **Vocabulary** How are a function and a function rule related?

2. Explain how to evaluate a function for a given input value.

3. **Number Sense** If the input value is negative, is the output value of $f = -4z + 12$ always positive or always negative? Explain.

4. Complete the input-output table for the function $f = 3 + n$.

Input n	0	1	2	3
Output f	3	■	■	■

Homework Exercises

For more exercises, see **Extra Skills and Word Problems.**

GO for Help

For Exercises	See Examples
5–10	1
11–12	2-3

Use the function rule $z = 2x + 3$. Find each output.

5. $x = 0$

6. $x = -2$

7. $x = 2$

8. $x = 10$

9. $x = -16.7$

10. **Energy** The function rule $E = 0.4h$ gives the total energy E in kilowatts the stereo uses during h hours. How much energy is used during 3 hr?

11. **Hockey** Copy and complete the table of input-output pairs for the function rule $t = \frac{n}{11}$. The variable t represents the number of teams formed in a hockey league. The variable n represents the number of people signed up for the league.

Input n (number of people)	Output t (number of teams)
44	■
132	■
165	■

12. The function rule $p = 1.5 + 2m$ represents the taxi fare p in dollars for a ride that is m miles long. Make a table of input-output pairs to show the fare for rides of 2, 6, and 13 miles.

13. **Guided Problem Solving** Paint brushes cost $1.79 each. The function rule $c = 1.79p$ gives the cost c in dollars for p paintbrushes. Jackson has $75.00 and must buy 27 paintbrushes and 2 gallons of paint which costs $13.29 per gallon. How much change will he receive?
   - How much is the cost of the paintbrushes?
   - How much does the paint cost?

GO Online
Homework Video Tutor
PearsonSuccessNet.com

14. **Reasoning** For what values of a and b will the function $I = at + b$ give the input-output table below?

Input, t	1	2	3	4
Output, I	5	7	9	11

15. **Water Use** The function $w = 40\ell$ describes the number w of gallons of water used to wash ℓ loads of laundry in a washing machine.
   a. Find the value of w when $\ell = 6$. What does this represent?
   b. The *domain* of a function is all possible input values. The *range* of a function is all possible output values. Which variable, w or ℓ, represents the domain in part (a)? Explain.
   c. The input variable is also called the *independent variable*. The output variable is the *dependent variable*, because it depends on the input variable. Which is the dependent variable, w or ℓ?

16. **Writing in Math** Find several solutions of the equation $y = 3x - 2$. Explain how these solutions are related to input-output pairs for $y = 3x - 2$.

Copy and complete the table of input-output pairs for each function.

17. $y = 4x$

Input x	Output y
5	■
7	■
9	■
11	■

18. $d = 50t$

Input t	Output d
1	■
2	■
3	■
■	200

19. Fruit smoothies cost $1.50 each plus $0.50 for each fruit mixed into the smoothie. The function $c = 1.5 + 0.5f$ gives the cost c of a smoothie with f fruits. Find the cost of a smoothie with 4 different fruits mixed in.

20. **Challenge** A furniture store charges a fee of $30 to deliver furniture, plus $2 per mile that it has to travel for the delivery. Write a function that describes this relationship where c represents total cost and m represents miles.

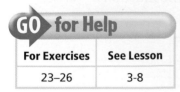

Test Prep and Mixed Review **Practice**

Gridded Response

21. An ad in the newspaper costs $52 plus $2.50 for each line of the ad. What is the cost in dollars of placing a 7-line ad?

22. Using variables, three consecutive even integers can be represented by $n, n + 2,$ and $n + 4$. The sum of three consecutive even integers is -198. What is the middle integer?

For Exercises	See Lesson
23–26	3-8

Find the number of solutions of the equation.

23. $-3(x - 2) + 1 = 2(4 - x) - 1 - x$

24. $3x + 7 = 2(x - 3)$

25. $6x - 5 - 5x + 3 = 4\left(1 + \dfrac{1}{4}x\right)$

26. $x + 3.5(x - 1) = 8x$

Use the function rule $y = -3x - 2$. Find each output for the given input.

1. $x = -1$ **2.** $x = 5$ **3.** $x = 0$ **4.** $x = -10$

5. Suppose potatoes cost \$.99 per pound. Complete the function rule $C = \underline{\ ?\ }$ to describe the relationship between the total cost C and the number of pounds of potatoes p you buy.

Use the graph at the right for Exercises 6–10.

6. How fast was Naomi driving during the first hour of her trip?

7. How many miles did she travel at this speed?

8. When did Naomi's speed first increase?

9. To what speed did it increase?

10. What was Naomi's final speed at the end of the 4 hours?

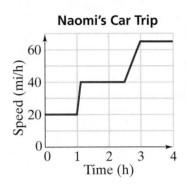

Naomi's Car Trip

MATH GAMES

What's My Output?

How To Play

- Player 1 writes a function rule on paper and shows it to the other players.
- Make a table like the one at the right. Player 1 writes an input in the table for the other players to see.
- In turn, each of the other players guesses the corresponding output.
- If a player guesses the output correctly, the player gets a point.
- Player 1 gets one point each time a player makes an incorrect guess at the function.
- After each player guesses the output, a new round of play starts.
- The player with the most points wins.

What's My Output?

Input	Output
▣	▣
▣	▣
▣	▣
▣	▣

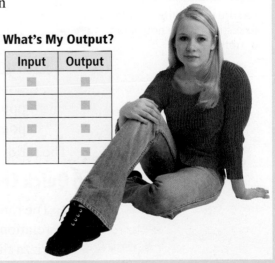

© CONTENT STANDARD
8.EE.5

Test Prep Tip

Be sure to simplify each ratio to see if they are equivalent or not.

What You'll Learn

To determine if relationships are proportional

New Vocabulary proportional relationship

Why Learn This?

Proportional relationships are used for many things like cooking, chemical mixtures, medicines, and shopping.

A **proportional relationship** is a relationship between inputs and outputs in which the ratio of inputs and outputs is always the same. If a relationship is in a table, write the ratio of each input to its corresponding output. If the ratios are the same, then the relationship is proportional.

EXAMPLES Proportional Relationships in Tables

1 Distance-Time Relationships Determine if the relationship is proportional.

Mario's Car Trip	
Time *t* (hr)	Distance *d* (mi)
1	50
2	100
3	150
4	240

$1/50$
$2/100 = 1/50$
$3/150 = 1/50$ ← Write the ratio of each input to its corresponding output. Then simplify.
$4/240 = 1/60$

The ratios are *not* all the same so the relationship is not proportional.

2 Comparison Shopping Determine if the relationship is proportional.

Tomato Prices

2 pounds for $3 $2/\$3$
4 pounds for $6 $4/\$6 = 2/\$3$ ← The number of pounds is the input and the cost is the output.
6 pounds for $9 $6/\$9 = 2/\$3$

The ratios are the same so the relationship is proportional.

✓ Quick Check

1. The ratios of all the inputs to the outputs in a table are $\frac{1}{4}$. Is the relationship proportional?

2. Pizza slices are selling as follows: 1 for $2, 2 for $3, or 4 for $5. Is this relationship proportional? Explain.

You can graph a function with a proportional relationship by making an input-output table.

EXAMPLE   Input-Output Tables and Graphs

3 **Jewelry** Jenna earns $12.00 per hour making bracelets. She uses the function $e = 12h$ to track her earnings where e represents earnings and h represents number of hours. Make an input-output table and graph your results. Does the function have a proportional relationship? Explain.

Step 1 Make an input-output table. Choose values for h and solve for e.

Number of Hours h	Earnings e (in dollars)	
1	12	← 12 × 1 = 12
2	24	← 12 × 2 = 24
3	36	← 12 × 3 = 36
4	48	← 12 × 4 = 48

This can be shown to be a proportional relationship by checking that the ratios are the same and are equal to $\frac{1}{12}$.

Step 2 Sketch a graph. Label the axes using h and e and with titles. Plot the points and draw a line through them.

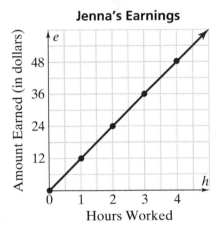

Jenna's Earnings

✓ Quick Check

3. The function $t = 4m$ gives the temperature t in degrees Celsius after m minutes of a liquid during a science experiment. Determine if the function has a proportional relationship.

✓ Check Your Understanding

1. **Vocabulary** How can you determine if a relationship in a table is a proportional relationship?

2. The ordered pairs $(2, 4)$ and $(5, x)$ are a part of the same proportional relationship. Find the value of x.

3. **Reasoning** A baker sells 3 rolls for $5 and 6 rolls for $8. Is the relationship between the price of selling 3 rolls and 6 rolls proportional? Explain.

4. Make an input-output table for the function $y = 4x$ and graph the function.

For more exercises, see **Extra Skills and Word Problems.**

GO for Help

For Exercises	See Examples
5–8	1
9–12	2
13	3

Determine if the relationship is proportional.

5.

x	y
−2	−10
−4	−20
6	30
8	40

6.

d	r
30	40
45	60
60	90
75	100

7.

m	n
−12	6
−14	7
−18	8
−20	9

8.

h	t
150	50
270	90
360	120
600	200

9.
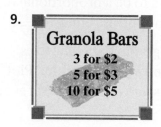

Granola Bars
3 for $2
5 for $3
10 for $5

10.

Bike Rentals
1 hr for $8
2 hr for $16
3 hr for $24
4 hr for $32

11.

Oranges for Sale
2 for $1
5 for $2
8 for $3
12 for $4

12.

Ski Equipment Rentals
4 hr for $10
6 hr for $15
12 hr for $30
1 day for $60

Train A

13. **Landscaping** Tamika earns $15.00 per hour working for a landscape company plus $10 for lunch. She uses the function $e = 15h + 10$ to track her daily earnings where e represents earnings and h represents number of hours. Make an input-output table, graph your results, and determine if the function has a proportional relationship. Explain.

14. **Guided Problem Solving** The graph shows the relationship between time and distance of a train from the Central Train Station. Reynaldo is traveling to his hometown 360 miles away from the station on the train. Based on the graph, estimate how long it will take the train to arrive at Reynaldo's hometown.
   - See if the graph for train A passes through a distance that is a factor of 360.
   - Use the corresponding time to estimate your answer.

Kudzu

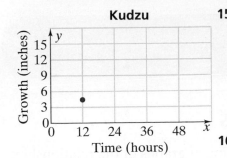

15. Data Analysis The graph at the right shows the relationship between time and total snowfall for a December blizzard. Based on the graph, estimate how long it will take for the amount of snow to total 18 inches.

Blizzard Snowfall

16. Reasoning A scientist measures the growth rate of Kudzu at 4.5 in. every 12 hr. Sketch the graph at the top left on your paper. Use the scientist's information to complete the graph.

Basketball

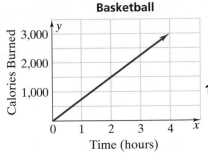

17. Challenge Jake burns calories when cross-country skiing at the rate of 11 calories per minute. The graph at the left shows the calories he burns while playing basketball. Which activity burns calories at a faster rate? Explain.

Test Prep and Mixed Review

Practice

Multiple Choice

18. Which relationship is proportional?

A

d	t
8	4
12	6
20	10
24	11
26	13

C

Pizza Slices
1 for $1.50
2 for $2.25
3 for $3.75
4 for $4.00

B

Paint Sprayer Rental
2 hr for $20
4 hr for $40
12 hr for $50
24 hr for $75

D

x	y
−20	−15
−60	−45
−120	−90
−240	−180
−400	−300

19. Which is the solution to the equation $x^3 = -64$?
  F $x = -8$ G $x = -4$ H $x = 4$ J $x = 8$

20. The area of a square is 11.56 square centimeters. Which is the side length of the square?
  A 2.89 cm   C 3.4 cm
  B 2.89 cm^2 D 3.4 cm^2

GO for Help

For Exercise	See Lesson
20	1-9

Proportional Relationships in Graphs

You can determine if relationships are proportional from looking at graphs of the relationships.

ACTIVITY

Copy and complete the table of ordered pairs for each graph.

Function A

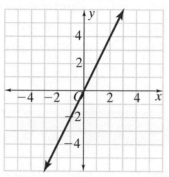

x	−2	−1	1	2
y				

Function B

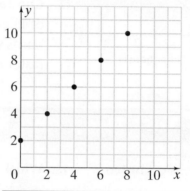

x	8	6	4	2
y				

Function C

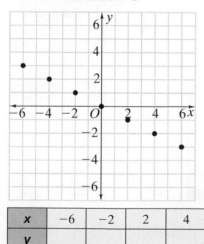

x	−6	−2	2	4
y				

Function D

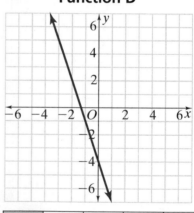

x	−3	−2	−1	1
y				

1. Which functions have proportional relationships? Explain.

2. Look at the graphs of the functions that have proportional relationships. What do they have in common?

3. Look at the graphs of the functions that do *not* have proportional relationships. What do they have in common?

4. How can you determine if a function is proportional by looking at its graph?

Using Data and Graphs

You can use data and graphs to help solve problems.

The table below shows data for the time it takes to make copies on a new photocopy machine. Graph the data, and determine if it has a proportional relationship. Use the data and graph to help find about how long it would take to copy 9,000 pages.

Time (minutes)	0	25	50	75	100	125
Number of Pages	0	875	1,750	2,625	3,500	4,375

What You Might Think

What do I know? What do I want to find out?

How can I find about how long it takes to copy 9,000 pages?

How can I determine if the relationship is proportional?

About how long does it take to copy 9,000 pages?

What You Might Write

I know how long it takes to copy certain numbers of pages. I want to find the amount of time it would take to copy 9,000 pages.

Make ordered pairs from the data and plot them on a graph.

(0,0),
(25, 875),
(50, 1,750),
(75, 2,625),
(100, 3,500),
(125, 4,375)

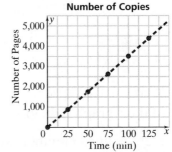

Number of Copies

Look to see if the graph passes through the origin.

Draw a line through the points until it reaches 9,000 copies. Then find the corresponding time.

It takes about 260 minutes to copy 9,000 pages.

Think It Through

1. **Number Sense** How do you know if 260 minutes is reasonable? (*Hint*: Compare it to 4,375 copies in the chart.)

2. Can you use another method for the situation above? Explain.

3. About how long would it take you to copy 5,000 pages? 6,000 pages?

Exercises

4. **Air Travel** A certain airplane can climb 3,000 feet for every mile it travels horizontally. This relationship is represented by the function $A = 3000m$ where A represents altitude in feet and m represents horizontal miles. What will be the plane's altitude after it travels 5 horizontal miles?
   a. What is the input variable?
   b. Substitute 5 for the input variable and evaluate to find the altitude.

5. **Sanitation** The table shows how many tons of trash the county landfill is gaining per month. About how many months will it take for the landfill to have gained 6,000 tons of trash?

Month	1	2	3	4	5
Trash (tons)	650	1,300	1,950	2,600	3,250

   a. Write ordered pairs.
   b. Make a graph to help solve the problem.

6. Student council members are raising funds by selling hats. They take a survey to see how many students will buy the hats at different prices. The results are below.

Price (dollars)	2	4	6	8	10	12
Number of Buyers	400	325	250	175	100	25

   Graph the data. Use the graph to estimate the number of hats that will be sold at $5.

7. **Money** For every dollar that Katie earns, she saves $0.40. Make and complete an input-output table for the function rule $s = 0.4d$ where s represents the amount Katie saves in dollars and d represents dollars. How much will Katie save if she earns $500?

Linear Functions

1. Vocabulary Review
What is the *output variable* in the function $b = 4a - 12$?

Use the function $m = 4n$ to complete the input-output table.

	n	m
2.	1	■
3.	2	■
4.	3	■
5.	4	■

for Help
Lesson 7-2

© CONTENT STANDARD
Prepares for 8.EE.6

What You'll Learn

To recognize linear functions and use tables and equations to graph them

New Vocabulary linear function, discrete data, continuous data

Why Learn This?

When you turn on a faucet or hose, the rate that the water comes out can be modeled with a linear function.

People fill things with liquid every day like gas tanks, watering cans, and swimming pools. If the liquid enters the container at a constant rate, then there is a linear function that relates time and the amount of liquid in the container.

A **linear function** is a function whose points lie on a straight line when the function is graphed. There are many ways to determine if a function is linear. One way is to use a table. If the ratios between the changes in variables in a table are the same, then the function is linear.

EXAMPLE **Linear Functions in Tables**

① Determine which function represented by a table is linear.

Function 1

$+1$ $+1$ $+1$

x	1	2	3	4
y	6	8	10	14

$+2$ $+2$ $+4$

The ratios between the changes in variables are $\frac{1}{2}$, $\frac{1}{2}$, and $\frac{1}{4}$. The ratios are *not* the same so the function is *not* linear.

Function 2

-1 -2 -3

x	2	1	-1	-4
y	-6	-3	3	12

$+3$ $+6$ $+9$

The ratios between the changes in variables are all $-\frac{1}{3}$, $-\frac{2}{6}$, and $-\frac{3}{9}$ which all simplify to $-\frac{1}{3}$. The ratios are the same so the function is linear.

Function 2 is linear since the ratios between the changes in variables are the same.

✓ Quick Check

x	5	9	17	21
y	-12	-13	-15	-16

1. Determine if the function represented in the table is linear. Explain.

Discrete data are data that involve a count of items, such as numbers of people or cars. For discrete data, plot the data points and connect them with a dashed line. **Continuous data** are data where numbers between any two data values have meaning. Use a solid line to indicate continuous data.

EXAMPLE Graphing Discrete Data

Vocabulary Tip

A dashed line in a graph means that not every point on the graph satisfies the conditions of the problem.

2 Groceries A gallon of milk costs $2.59. The total cost of g gallons of milk is a function of the price of one gallon. Make a table and graph the function.

Step 1 Determine whether the data are discrete or continuous. You cannot buy part of a gallon container, so the data are discrete.

Step 2 Make a table. Connect the points with a dashed line.

Number of Gallons	Total Cost (dollars)
1	$2.59
2	$5.18
3	$7.77
4	$10.36

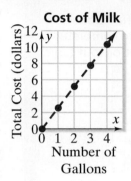

Cost of Milk

✓ **Quick Check**

2. **Tickets** The function $c = 15t$ represents the cost (in dollars) of t adult tickets to a museum. Make a table and graph the function.

EXAMPLE Graphing Continuous Data

3 Fitness Xin lifted weights and burned 100 calories. Then she walked and burned 257 calories per hour. The function $c = 257h + 100$ gives the total calories Xin burned where c represents calories and h represents hours walking. Use the equation to make a table and graph the function.

Xin can walk for part of an hour, so the data is continuous. Plot the data and connect the data points with a solid line.

Calories Burned

Time (hours)	Number of Calories
0	100
1	357
2	614
3	871

✓ **Quick Check**

3. **Flying** The function $a = 4,000 - 600m$ gives the altitude a of a plane in feet after m minutes. Make a table and graph the function.

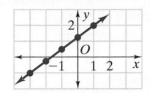

1. **Vocabulary** Explain how you can use a table that represents a function to determine if the function is linear.

2. Does the graph at the left show discrete or continuous data?

3. Make a table for the function $d = 3t$ which gives the distance traveled at the rate of 3 mi per hr. Then graph the function.

Homework Exercises

For more exercises, see **Extra Skills and Word Problems.**

Determine if the function represented by the table is linear. Explain.

GO for Help

For Exercises	See Examples
4–7	1
8–10	2-3

4.

x	−10	−14	−18	−24
y	6	10	16	24

5.

x	−12	−2	6	18
y	−3	−8	−11	−17

Determine whether the data for each function are *discrete* or *continuous*. Then make a table and graph for the function.

6. The function $d = 40 - 15x$ represents the amount of money d (in dollars) you have left after buying x CDs.

7. **Scuba Diving** The deeper a scuba diver descends, the more pressure the diver feels. The function $p = 1 + 0.03x$ represents the approximate pressure p (in atmospheres) at x feet below sea level.

8. The function $y = 1.8x + 32$ represents the equivalent temperature y in degrees Fahrenheit for a temperature of x degrees Celsius.

GPS

9. **Guided Problem Solving** A woman rents a table at a jewelry show. The function $m = 20.25n - 10$ represents the money m in dollars a woman makes for the number of necklaces n she sells. Graph the function. What is the cost of renting the table?
   - What is the input variable? What is the output variable?
   - Choose input values, find the outputs, and graph the function.

10. **Writing in Math** Describe a relation in your daily life that is a function. Explain why it is a function and define the input and the output.

GO Online
Homework Video Tutor
PearsonSuccessNet.com

11. **Science** The height of a burning candle depends on how long the candle has been burning. For one type of candle, the function $h = 8 - \frac{1}{2}t$ gives the candle's height h (in centimeters) as a function of the time t the candle has burned (in hours).
   a. Graph the function.
   b. What was the original height of the candle?
   c. What is the greatest amount of time the candle can burn?

12. Graph the functions $y = 2x + 1$ and $y = 2x - 1$ on the same coordinate grid. What do you notice about the two lines?

13. **Challenge** Plaza Pizza charges $8 for a small pizza plus $2 per topping. Royal Pizza charges $12 for a small pizza and $1 per topping. Write functions for both pizza places using c for cost and t for toppings. Graph the functions on the same axes. For how many toppings will the small pizzas cost the same?

Test Prep and Mixed Review

Practice

Multiple Choice

14. **Which of the following tables is best represented by discrete data?**

A

Temperature	
Time	Temp (°F)
8:00 a.m.	61
9:00 a.m.	62
10:00 a.m.	64
11:00 a.m.	67

C

Points Scored	
Game	Points
1	20
2	32
3	14
4	8

B

Brian's Weight	
Date	Weight (lb)
May 1	98
June 1	102
July 1	101
August 1	100

D

Altitude of Hiker	
Time (min)	Altitude (ft)
30	672
60	783
90	815
120	899

15. The function $d = 45t$ gives the distance d Juan traveled in miles after t hours. The function $d = 30t$ gives the distance d Kelly traveled in miles after t hours. If Juan and Kelly start at the same point and travel in opposite directions, how far apart will they be after 5 hr?

   F 375 mi   G 225 mi   H 150 mi   J 75 mi

16. Which is the best estimate of the perimeter of the square?

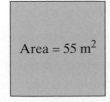

Area = 55 m²

   A 7.4 m   B 29.6 m   C 31.6 m   D 52 m

GO for Help

For Exercises	See Lesson
17–19	3-7

Solve for x.

17. $2x + 7 = 3x - 3$ 18. $5x - 8 = 2x + 10$ 19. $12x + 8 = 8x - 24$

Making Word Cards

You can learn new vocabulary words by making word cards.

- Write the term on one side of the card, and then write the definition on the other.
- Include any math symbols related to the term.
- Give an example and "non-example" of the term.

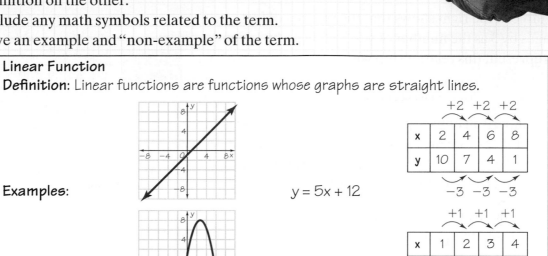

Linear Function

Definition: Linear functions are functions whose graphs are straight lines.

Examples:
$y = 5x + 12$

x	2	4	6	8
y	10	7	4	1

$+2 \; +2 \; +2$ / $-3 \; -3 \; -3$

Non-examples:
$y = 2x^3 - 7$

x	1	2	3	4
y	1	8	27	64

$+1 \; +1 \; +1$ / $+7 \; +19 \; +37$

Make word cards for the vocabulary terms introduced in Chapter 7.

✓ Checkpoint Quiz 2

Lessons 7-3 through 7-4

Determine if the relationship is proportional.

1.

x	y
1	1
3	3
5	5
7	7

2.

x	y
−2	−20
−4	−24
−6	−28
−8	−36

3.

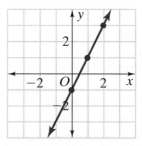

Determine if the function represented is linear.

4.

x	y
3	11
6	15
9	19
12	23

5.

x	y
−7	6
−14	16
−21	28
−28	38

6.

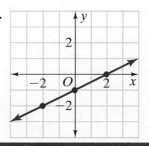

Rate of Change

You know that in 1 yard, there are 3 feet. In 2 yards, there are 6 feet.

The table at the right shows that the number of feet changes by 3 as the number of yards changes by 1. You can represent this relationship with a ratio:

$$\frac{\text{change in number of feet}}{\text{change in number of yards}} = \frac{3}{1}$$

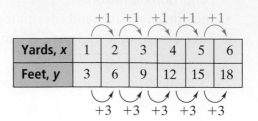

This comparison of two quantities that are changing is called a **rate of change.** As the value of one quantity changes, the value of the other quantity also changes. The rate of change of feet to yards is $\frac{3}{1}$, or 3.

You can find the rate of change from a graph such as the one at the right. Notice that rate of change is the ratio of the vertical change to the horizontal change.

$$\text{rate of change} = \frac{\text{vertical change}}{\text{horizontal change}} = \frac{3}{1}$$

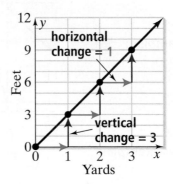

Exercises

Find the rate of change from each table or graph. Explain what the rate of change means in each problem situation.

1.

Age (yr)	8	9	10	11	12
Height (in.)	51	53	55	57	59

2.

Time (h)	1	2	3	4	5
Rainfall (mm)	3	6	9	12	15

3.

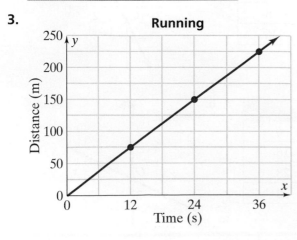

4.

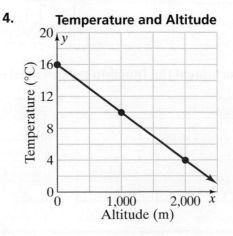

7-5 Understanding Slope

✓ Check Skills You'll Need

1. **Vocabulary Review** Do the *negative integers* include zero?

Simplify each expression.

2. $-3 - 1$

3. $10 - (-4)$

4. $1 - 7$

5. $-8 - (-6)$

GO for Help
Lesson 3-2

What You'll Learn

To find the slope of a line from a graph or table
New Vocabulary slope, slope of a line

Why Learn This?

You can use slope to describe the steepness of an incline or hill. The steepness of a ramp is the ratio of the vertical change to the horizontal change. In math, slope is a number that describes the steepness of a line.

You can also use slope to describe rate of change of a quantity.

$$\text{slope} = \frac{\text{vertical change}}{\text{horizontal change}} \quad \begin{array}{l} \leftarrow \text{rise} \\ \leftarrow \text{run} \end{array}$$

Slope describes the steepness of lines in the coordinate plane. You can find the slope of a line by subtracting the coordinates of any two points on the line.

KEY CONCEPTS **Slope of a Line**

$$\text{slope of a line} = \frac{\text{change in } y\text{-coordinates}}{\text{change in } x\text{-coordinates}} \quad \begin{array}{l} \leftarrow \text{rise} \\ \leftarrow \text{run} \end{array}$$

The direction of the slant of a line indicates a positive or a negative slope.

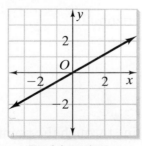
Positive slope

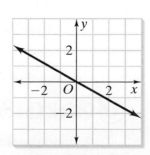
Negative slope

When you find the slope of a line, the first y-coordinate you use for the rise must belong to the same point as the first x-coordinate you use for the run.

EXAMPLE **Finding the Slope of a Line**

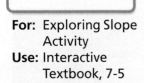

For: Exploring Slope
Activity
Use: Interactive
Textbook, 7-5

① Find the slope of the line in the graph below.

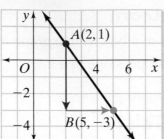

$$\text{slope} = \frac{\text{change in } y\text{-coordinates}}{\text{change in } x\text{-coordinates}}$$

$$= \frac{-3 - 1}{5 - 2} \quad \leftarrow \begin{array}{l}\textbf{Subtract coordinates of}\\ \textbf{\textit{A} from coordinates of \textit{B}.}\end{array}$$

$$= \frac{-4}{3} \text{ or } -\frac{4}{3} \quad \leftarrow \textbf{Simplify.}$$

✓ **Quick Check**

1. Find the slope of each line.

a. 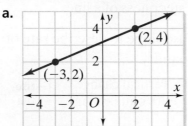   b.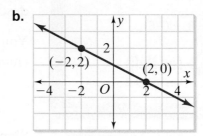

Some lines have slopes that are neither positive nor negative.

EXAMPLE **Slopes of Horizontal and Vertical Lines**

Vocabulary Tip

Do not confuse the terms *zero* and *undefined*. The slope of a horizontal line is zero. The slope of a vertical line is undefined.

② Find the slope of each line. State whether the slope is zero or undefined.

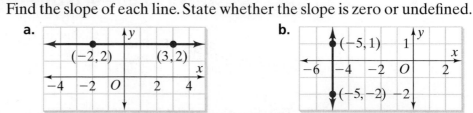

a.

$$\text{slope} = \frac{2 - 2}{3 - (-2)} = \frac{0}{5} = 0$$

The slope of a horizontal line is zero.

b.

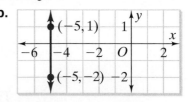

$$\text{slope} = \frac{1 - (-2)}{-5 - (-5)} = \frac{3}{0}$$

Division by zero is undefined. So, the slope of a vertical line is undefined.

✓ **Quick Check**

2. Find the slope of a line through the points $(3, 1)$ and $(3, -2)$. State whether the slope is zero or undefined.

When you graph some data, all the points lie on a line. For such data, you can find slope, or rate of change, using a table.

Finding Slope From a Table

Miles Traveled	Fuel Used (gallons)
80	4
120	6
160	8
200	10

3 Graph the fuel-usage data at the left. Connect the points with a line. Then find the rate of change.

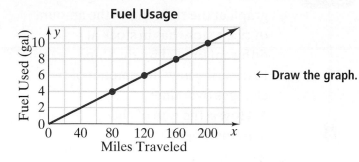

Fuel Usage

← Draw the graph.

$$\text{rate of change} = \text{slope} = \frac{\text{change in } y}{\text{change in } x} = \frac{10 - 4}{200 - 80} \quad \leftarrow \text{Use coordinates of two points.}$$

$$= \frac{6}{120} = \frac{1}{20} \quad \leftarrow \text{Subtract and simplify.}$$

The amount of fuel used is 1 gallon for every 20 miles traveled.

✓ Quick Check

3. Graph the data in the table and connect the points with a line. Then find the slope.

x	−1	0	1	2
y	2	0	−2	−4

✓ Check Your Understanding

1. Vocabulary The slope of a line is the rise over the __?__.

2. Draw one line for each slope: 0, undefined, +1, and −1.

Find the slope of the line that passes through each pair of points.

3. (0, 3) and (6, 1)

4. (2, 2) and (6, −1)

Homework Exercises

For more exercises, see Extra Skills and Word Problems.

GO for Help

For Exercises	See Examples
5–7	1-2
8–9	3

Find the slope of each line.

5.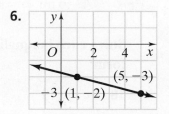

6.

7.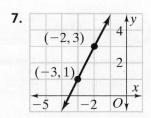

Graph the data in each table and connect the points with a line. Then find the slope of the line.

8.

x	4	5	6	7
y	−2	0	2	4

9.

x	−2	−1	0	1
y	3	2	1	0

GPS 10. **Guided Problem Solving** The graph at the right shows the amount of rice a store has in stock at different times. Use the slope to describe how the amount of rice changes over time.
- How is the rate of change related to the slope?

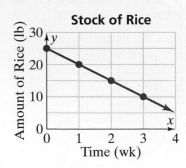

Stock of Rice

11. **Error Analysis** Your classmate said that the slope of a line through (1, 3) and (7, 5) is 3. What error did your classmate make?

12. Which roof is steeper: a roof with a rise of 12 and a run of 7 or a roof with a rise of 8 and a run of 4?

13. **Writing in Math** Point $A(-2, 3)$ lies on a line with a slope of 2. Describe how to find two points on the line on either side of A.

14. **Challenge** Determine whether this statement is *true* or *false*. If the statement is false, rewrite it to make it true. If two lines have the same slope, their equations describe the same line.

GO Online
Homework Video Tutor
PearsonSuccessNet.com

Test Prep and Mixed Review
Practice

Multiple Choice

15. The slope of the line passing through the points (2, 3) and (4, y) is $\frac{3}{2}$. Which is the value of y?
- Ⓐ 9
- Ⓑ 6
- Ⓒ −6
- Ⓓ −9

16. The height of a melting ice sculpture is given by the function $h = 54 - \frac{1}{3}t$ where h is its height in inches and t is time in minutes. How long will it take the ice sculpture to completely melt?
- Ⓕ 162 min
- Ⓖ 81 min
- Ⓗ 54 min
- Ⓙ 18 min

17. A farmer has 35 square miles of land in the shape of a square. Which is closest to the measure of each side of the farm?
- Ⓐ 6 mi
- Ⓑ 9 mi
- Ⓒ 18 mi
- Ⓓ 36 mi

GO for Help

For Exercises	See Lesson
18–20	4-4

Solve each inequality. Graph each solution. Write your answer in simplest form.

18. $3x \leq -9$

19. $\frac{4}{9} > \frac{y}{18}$

20. $-5 \geq -0.25z$

Parallel and Perpendicular Lines

The slopes of parallel and perpendicular lines have special properties

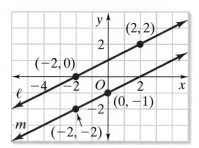

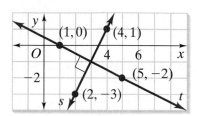

slope of $\ell = \dfrac{2-0}{2-(-2)} = \dfrac{2}{4} = \dfrac{1}{2}$

slope of $m = \dfrac{-1-(-2)}{0-(-2)} = \dfrac{1}{2}$

Parallel lines have the same slope.

slope of $s = \dfrac{1-(-3)}{4-2} = \dfrac{4}{2} = \dfrac{2}{1}$

slope of $t = \dfrac{-2-0}{5-1} = \dfrac{-2}{4} = -\dfrac{1}{2}$

product of slopes $= \dfrac{2}{1} \cdot \left(-\dfrac{1}{2}\right) = -1$

The product of the slopes of perpendicular lines is -1.

EXAMPLE

Line AB has slope $\frac{1}{3}$. Find the slope of a line that is parallel to $\overleftrightarrow{AB}$ and the slope of a line that is perpendicular to $\overleftrightarrow{AB}$.

A line parallel to $\overleftrightarrow{AB}$ has a slope of $\frac{1}{3}$.

Let m represent the slope of a line perpendicular to $\overleftrightarrow{AB}$.

$\frac{1}{3} \cdot m = -1$ ← **The product of the slopes of perpendicular lines is −1.**

$m = -3$ ← **Multiply each side by 3.**

A line perpendicular to $\overleftrightarrow{AB}$ has a slope of -3.

Exercises

Are lines with the given slopes *parallel, perpendicular,* or *neither*?

1. $\dfrac{2}{3}, -\dfrac{3}{2}$

2. $5, -5$

3. $\dfrac{3}{4}, \dfrac{4}{3}$

4. $\dfrac{1}{12}, -12$

5. $\dfrac{3}{9}, \dfrac{1}{3}$

6. $\dfrac{2}{7}, \dfrac{12}{42}$

Find the slope of a line parallel to $\overleftrightarrow{PQ}$ and a line perpendicular to $\overleftrightarrow{PQ}$.

7. $P(1, 2), Q(3, 4)$

8. $P(-5, 1), Q(-1, 2)$

9. $P(3, -2), Q(-2, 1)$

Graphing Equations

You can use a graphing calculator to graph equations
and to find solutions.

EXAMPLE

Graph $y = \frac{1}{2}x + 1$. Make a table of solutions for values of x from
-3 to 3.

Step 1 Press Y=

Enter $\frac{1}{2}x + 1$.

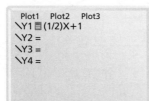

```
Plot1   Plot2   Plot3
\Y1 ■ (1/2)X+1
\Y2 =
\Y3 =
\Y4 =
```

Step 2 Press ZOOM 6
to graph your equation
with the standard
viewing window.

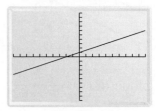

Step 3 Use the
TBLSET feature.
Set TblStart $= -3$
and $\triangle$Tbl $= 1$. The
x-values start at -3
and increase by
increments of 1.

```
TABLE SETUP
 TblStart = -3
 △Tbl = 1
Indpnt: Auto Ask
Depend: Auto Ask
```

Step 4 Use the TABLE
feature to see solutions.

```
 X    | Y1
 -3   | -.5
 -2   | 0
 -1   | .5
 0    | 1
 1    | 1.5
 2    | 2
 3    | 2.5
X=-3
```

Step 5 Sketch the graph and copy the table
of solutions.

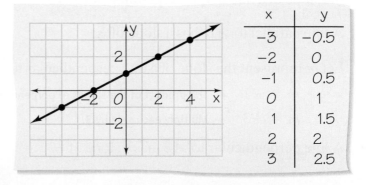

x	y
-3	-0.5
-2	0
-1	0.5
0	1
1	1.5
2	2
3	2.5

Exercises

**Graph each equation using a graphing calculator. Sketch the graph and
make a table of solutions for values of x from -3 to 3.**

1. $y = 2x - 3$
2. $y = 2x + 3$
3. $y = -\frac{2}{3}x - 2$
4. $y = 5x - 2$

5. Compare the graphs of Exercises 1 and 2. What do you notice?

6. Explain how the graphs of Exercises 3 and 4 are different.

7-6 Graphing Linear Functions

Check Skills You'll Need

1. Vocabulary Review
Explain how to find the *slope* of a line.

Find the slope of the line that passes through each pair of points.

2. (2, 4), (−5, 10)

3. (0, 0), (6, 0)

4. (2, 1), (1, 2)

 **for Help**
Lesson 7-5

© **CONTENT STANDARDS**
8.EE.6

GO **Online**

Video Tutor Help
PearsonSuccessNet.com

What You'll Learn

To use tables and equations to graph linear functions

New Vocabulary *y*-intercept, slope-intercept form

Why Learn This?

The graph of a function is the set of ordered pairs consisting of an input and the corresponding output. These ordered pairs are the solutions of the equation. A graph of a line may include solutions that do not appear in a table of values of the equation.

The **y-intercept** is the point where the graph crosses the *y*-axis.

$$y = -\frac{3}{4}x + 5$$

$\uparrow$ $\uparrow$

slope   *y*-intercept

Below is the graph of $y = -\frac{3}{4}x + 5$.

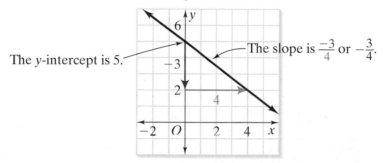

The *y*-intercept is 5.

The slope is $\frac{-3}{4}$ or $-\frac{3}{4}$.

Notice that the slope and *y*-intercept may be part of the equation of a line.

An equation written in the form $y = mx + b$ is in **slope-intercept form.** The graph is a line with slope *m* and *y*-intercept *b*.

A linear function is a function with points that lie on a line. You can write a linear function in the form $y = mx + b$. Then you can use the slope and *y*-intercept to graph the function.

Finding Slope and _y_-intercept

1 Find the slope and _y_-intercept of the graph of the function.

a. $y = 2x + 4$

$y = mx + b$ ← _m_ represents slope
_b_ represents the
_y_-intercept

The slope is 2 and the
_y_-intercept is 4.

b. $y = -\dfrac{5}{6}x - 7$

$y = mx + b$ ← _m_ represents slope
_b_ represents the
_y_-intercept

The slope is $-\dfrac{5}{6}$ and the
_y_-intercept is -7.

✓ Quick Check

1. Find the slope and _y_-intercept of the graph of $y = x - 3$.

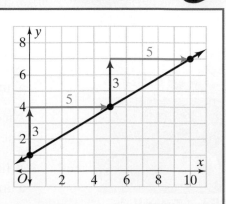

More Than One Way

Graph the function $y = \dfrac{3}{5}x + 1$.

Kevin's Method

First I will make a table. Then I will graph the points.

x	0	1	2	3	4	5
y	1	1.6	2.2	2.8	3.4	4

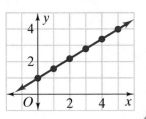

Michelle's Method

I can use slope-intercept form
to graph the equation.

The _y_-intercept is 1 and the slope is $\dfrac{3}{5}$.

Choose a Method

Graph the function $y = -\dfrac{2}{3}x - 2$. Explain why you
chose the method you used.

Below is the graph of $y = 2x$.

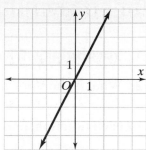

Notice that the slope of the line is $\frac{2}{1}$, or 2. Since the graph passes through the origin, the y-intercept is 0. So the equation of the line in slope-intercept form is $y = 2x + 0$, or $y = 2x$.

KEY CONCEPTS **Slope-Intercept Form of a Linear Equation**

- The slope-intercept form of a line that intersects the y-axis at b is $y = mx + b$.
- The slope-intercept form of a line that intersects the y-axis at the origin is $y = mx$.

EXAMPLE **Graphing Functions of the Form $y = mx$**

2. **Science** The temperature of a substance in degrees Celsius before and during an experiment is given by the function $y = -\frac{4}{5}x$ where y represents temperature and x represents time in minutes. Graph $y = -\frac{4}{5}x$.

Step 1 The y-intercept is 0, so plot a point at $(0, 0)$.

Step 2 The slope is $-\frac{4}{5}$. Move down 4 units and right 5 units. Plot another point. Repeat to find another point on the line.

Step 3 Draw a line through the three points.

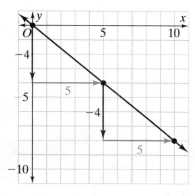

✓ Quick Check

2. Graph the function $y = \frac{1}{5}x$.

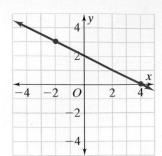

1. **Vocabulary** What is the *y*-intercept of the graph of a line?

2. What is the slope and *y*-intercept of the graph at the left?

For each function, find the slope and the *y*-intercept.

3. $y = 4x - 1$ 4. $y = x + 4$

5. Make a table for the function $y = 3x$. Then graph the function.

Homework Exercises

For more exercises, see Extra Skills and Word Problems.

Find the slope and *y*-intercept of the graph of the function.

For Exercises	See Examples
6–16	1
17–19	2

6. $y = 3x - 4$ 7. $y = 8x + 2$ 8. $y = \frac{1}{4}x - 5$

9. $y = -\frac{2}{5}x + 7$ 10. $y = 12x$ 11. $y = x$

Graph each linear function.

12. $y = -2x + 5$ 13. $y = \frac{2}{3}x - 1$ 14. $y = -\frac{3}{5}x - 2$

15. $y = 3x - 7$ 16. $y = -6x - 1$ 17. $y = x + 4$

18. $y = 5x$ 19. $y = -6x$ 20. $y = \frac{1}{3}x$

GPS 21. **Guided Problem Solving** A woman makes necklaces and sells them at a jewelry show. She pays $10.00 to have a table at the show and makes $20.25 for each necklace she sells. Write a function for the money she earns and graph the function.
   • What is the input variable? What is the output variable?
   • What is the slope of this function? What is the *y*-intercept?

22. **Writing in Math** Describe a relation in your daily life that is a function. Explain why it is a function and define the input and the output.

23. **Nutrition** The label at the right shows the nutrition facts for a package of crackers. Find how many Calories are in one cracker. The number of Calories consumed is a function of the number of crackers eaten. Make a table and a graph for the function.

Nutrition Facts
Serving Size: 8 crackers (31g)
Servings Per Container: about 15

Amount Per Serving

Calories 140   Calories from Fat 35

                           % Daily Value

Total Fat 4g   6%

Saturated Fat 1g   5%

Monounsaturated Fat 1.5g

24. Aman is 3.5 years older than his sister Dalia. Make a table and graph the function relating Aman's age to Dalia's age.

25. Internet Company A charges a fee of $5.00 per month plus $2.00 for each hour of Internet use. Company B charges $10.00 per month plus $1.00 for each hour of Internet use. Graph two functions to show how the total cost each month depends on the hours of usage for each company.

26. Challenge Suppose gasoline costs $2.30 per gallon at one gas station and $2.35 at another. Graph two functions showing how the cost to fill a car's gas tank depends on the number of gallons of gas it needs. For how many gallons of gasoline is there a price difference of $0.30 between the two functions?

Test Prep and Mixed Review   **Practice**

Multiple Choice

27. Which of the following is a graph of the equation $y = 2x - 1$?

F.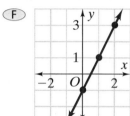

H.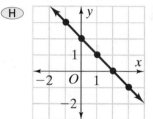

G.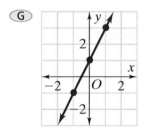

J.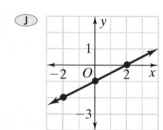

28. Which of the following inequalities is true?
Ⓐ $\sqrt{2} > \pi$ Ⓑ $\pi > \sqrt{5}$ Ⓒ $\sqrt{5} > \pi$ Ⓓ $\pi^2 < \sqrt{7}$

29. Which table represents a linear function?

F.

x	1	3	5	7
y	4	9	14	19

H.

x	−5	−3	−1	1
y	−3	−1	0	3

G.

x	2	4	6	8
y	4	6	9	15

J.

x	0	2	5	9
y	1	3	5	7

GO for Help

For Exercise	See Lesson
30	5-7

30. Sophia earns $12.00 per hour working in an office plus $5 for parking fees. She uses the function $e = 12h + 5$ to represent her daily earnings, where e represents her earnings and h represents the number of hours she works. Explain whether or not the function has a proportional relationship.

Comparing Functions

What You'll Learn

To compare properties of two functions represented in different ways

Why Learn This?

Functions can be represented using words, graphs, tables, or equations. Learning the relationships among these representations can help you compare the properties of two functions each represented in a different way.

The slope of a line describes the rate of change of that line. You can compare slopes of lines represented in different ways.

EXAMPLE **Comparing Rates of Change of Linear Functions**

1 Which function has the greater rate of change?

x	1	2	3	4
y	5	8	11	14

$y = 4x + 2$

Step 1 Find slope from a table.

Use $(1, 5)$ and $(4, 14)$.

$$\text{slope} = \frac{14 - 5}{4 - 1} = \frac{9}{3} = 3$$

Step 2 Find the slope of an equation using $y = mx + b$.

$y = mx + b$

$y = 4x + 2$

The slope, m, is 4.

Since $4 > 3$, the function $y = 4x + 2$ has the greater rate of change.

✓ Quick Check

1. Which function has the greater rate of change? Explain.

x	1	3	4	6
y	5	13	17	25

$y = 2x + 1$

Comparing Initial Values of Linear Functions

2 **Athletics** Aki is trying to decide what baseball camp to attend. For each camp, the relationship between number of days and total cost is linear. Which camp has the greater initial cost?

Bright Future Baseball Camp	Home Run Baseball Camp
• $18 per day • $89 registration fee	• 2 days cost $121. • 7 days cost $236.

Bright Future Baseball Camp
According to the data in the table, there is a registration fee of $89. This is the initial cost.

Home Run Baseball Camp
Write the data in the table as ordered pairs: (2, 121) and (7, 236). The y-intercept of the line through these two points represents the initial cost. Use the ordered pairs to write an equation in slope-intercept form.

$$m = \frac{236 - 121}{7 - 2} = \frac{115}{5} = 23 \qquad \leftarrow \textbf{Find the slope.}$$

$$\begin{aligned} y &= mx + b & \leftarrow \textbf{Use slope-intercept form.}\\ 121 &= 23(2) + b & \leftarrow \textbf{Substitute 23 for } \boldsymbol{m}, \textbf{2 for } \boldsymbol{x}, \textbf{and 121}\\ 121 &= 46 + b & \textbf{for } \boldsymbol{y}. \textbf{ Simplify.}\\ 75 &= b & \leftarrow \textbf{Solve for } \boldsymbol{b}. \end{aligned}$$

The y-intercept is 75, so the initial cost is $75.

Since $89 > $75, the Bright Future Baseball Camp has the greater initial cost.

✓ Quick Check

2. Steve's Scooter Rentals charges $17 per hour plus a $29 rental fee. Scooter World charges $48 for 1 hour and $108 for 4 hours. Both relationships are linear. Which company has the greatest initial cost?

To compare functions, find where the functions increase or decrease; whether they are continuous; and the highest and lowest values.

EXAMPLE **Comparing Nonlinear Functions**

3 Jack and Manny each have a savings account. The graph at the left represents Jack's account. Manny deposited $500 and withdrew $20 each even-numbered day for 30 days. Compare the functions.

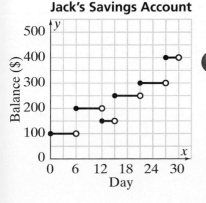

Jack's Savings Account

Jack's Account	Manny's Account
increases and decreases	decreases
not continuous	not continuous
maximum $400; minimum $100	maximum $500; minimum $200

✓ Quick Check

3. Vikram opened a savings account with $150. He deposits $150 every two weeks. Compare Vikram's account to Jack's account.

EXAMPLE **Comparing Proportional Functions**

④ **Bicycle Racing** Arama and Francisco train for bicycle races. The graph at the left represents the distance Arama traveled during today's training session. Francisco's distance is given by the function $d = 18.5t$, where d represents distance in miles and t represents time in hours. Who traveled at the faster rate?

The rate is equal to the slope of the graph of the function.

Arama
Find the slope. Use the two points $(0.5, 10)$ and $(2.5, 50)$.
$$m = \frac{50 - 10}{2.5 - 0.5} = \frac{40}{2} = 20$$
Arama traveled 20 miles per hour.

Francisco
The equation $d = 18.5t$ is in slope-intercept form. The slope is 18.5. Francisco traveled 18.5 miles per hour.

$20 > 18.5$, so Arama traveled at the faster rate.

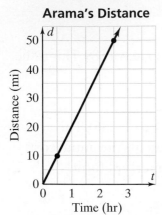

Arama's Distance

✓ Quick Check

4. Jala and Caleb are having a card-house building competition. The functions below represent the number of levels each person built. Who built at the faster rate?

Jala's Card House

Caleb's Card House

Time (min)	Number of Levels
2	3
6	9
10	15
12	18

1. **Reasoning** How can you find the rate of change from the graph of a linear function?

Match each linear function with its rate of change.

2.

x	2	5	6	10
y	6	15	18	30

3. $y = 2x - 5$

4. $(5, 6), (12, 34)$

5. John earns $25 plus $1 for every magazine subscription he sells.

A. 1

B. 2

C. 3

D. 4

Homework Exercises

For more exercises, see Extra Skills and Word Problems.

GO for Help

For Exercises	See Examples
6–7	1
8–9	2
10	3
11	4

Determine which function has the greater rate of change.

6. $y = 3x - 4$;

x	1	2	3	4
y	8	10	12	14

7. $y = 1.5x + 2$;

x	0	3	6	9
y	1	5	9	13

8. Twin Lakes Pool has a membership fee of $150 and charges $7 per visit. Duck Pond pool charges $260 for 15 visits and $316 for 22 visits. Which pool has the greater initial cost?

9. The graph at the right models the distance Reggie jogs over time. Linda jogs 2.5 miles in 25 minutes and 4 miles in 40 minutes. Who jogs faster?

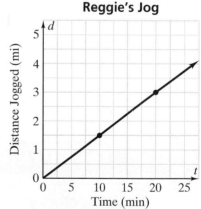

Reggie's Jog

Compare the functions with the graph at the left.

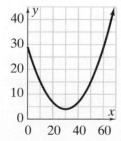

10. When the value of x is 0, the value of y is 15. Each time the value of x increases by 1, the value of y increases by 3.

11. When the value of x is 0, the value of y is 640. Each time the value of x increases by 1, the value of y is halved.

A: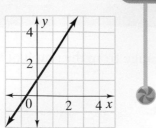

GPS **12. Guided Problem Solving** Order linear functions A, B, C, and D from least to greatest rate of change.
- Find the slope of each function.

B: $y = 0.5x - 0.25$

C:

x	−2	0	2	4
y	7	9	11	13

D: As x increases by 3 units, y increases by 2 units.

G: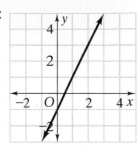

13. Order linear functions G, T, E, and W from least to greatest slope.

T:

x	−4	0	4	8
y	2	3	4	5

E: $y = \dfrac{5}{3}x + 2$

W: As x increases by 3 units, y increases by 1 unit.

14. Order the stocks from greatest to least rate of price increase.

Alpha, Inc.

Week	0	1	2	3	4
Price($)	16	19	22	25	28

Delta Corp.

Week	0	1	2	3	4
Price($)	21	16.5	12	7.5	3

Beta Co.
A starting price of $54 decreases weekly by $2.50.

Gamma, Inc.
$d = 3.5w - 27$
(w is weeks, d is dollars)

Luxury:

d	2	3	7	14
C	100	130	250	460

15. Writing in Math The functions below represent pricing plans for car rentals, where d is number of days and C is cost. Which plan is least expensive for a long-term rental? Explain your reasoning.

Subcompact: Total cost is $30 plus $25 per day.

Compact: $C = 28d + 10$

GO Online
Homework Video Tutor
PearsonSuccessNet.com

16. Challenge Which of the following functions has the greatest rate of change? Explain your reasoning.

K: $2x + 3y = 9$ L: $3x + 2y = 4$ M: $x + y = 11$

Ⓐ Ⓑ Ⓒ Ⓓ **Test Prep and Mixed Review** **Practice**

Multiple Choice

17. Which of the linear functions has the greatest rate of change?

Ⓐ The line that passes through (2, 7) and (5, 22)

Ⓑ

x	5	8	12	13
y	12	18	26	28

Ⓒ $y = 6x - 4$

Ⓓ The function that models Kayla's daily income. Kayla earns $30 plus $8 for every pet she walks.

GO for Help

For Exercises	See Lesson
18–19	3-2

Simplify each expression.

18. $5x + 3y - 18 + 2.5x - 4.8y$

19. $3(x - 4) + 8x + 3.5(x + 17)$

Using a Variable

You can solve many problems by using a variable to represent an unknown quantity. Use the variable to write a function.

EXAMPLE

Mitchell earns $15.00 per hour mowing lawns. Make a table of input-output pairs to show Mitchell's earnings for 5, 10, and 15 hours of work.

The problem asks you to make a table to show how much Mitchell earns for working 5, 10, and 15 hours. First, write a function to represent the amount he earns for working a given number of hours. Let e = earnings and h = hours.

$e = 15h$

Then use the function to create an input-output table.

Number of Hours h	Earnings e (in dollars)
0	0
5	75
10	150
15	225

Mitchell earns $75 for 5 hours work, $150 for 10 hours work, and $225 for 15 hours work.

Exercises

1. A family is on a road trip. They are driving at a rate of 55 miles per hour. Make an input-output table to show how many miles they will have driven in 2 hours, 4 hours, and 7 hours.

2. A local tax rate is six cents for every dollar spent. The total tax you pay depends on the amount you spend. Make an input-output table to find how much tax you must pay for spending $6, $15, and $25.

3. A basketball team practices for 5.5 hours per week. Make an input-output table to find how many hours they will have practiced in 4 weeks, 5 weeks, and 6 weeks.

Vocabulary Review

continifous data (p. 288)
discrete data (p. 288)
function (p. 275)
function rule (p. 275)

linear (p. 270)
linear function (p. 287)
nonlinear (p. 270)
proportional relationship (p. 270)

slope (p. 293)
slope of a line (p. 293)
slope-intercept form (p. 299)
y-intercept (p. 299)

Choose the correct vocabulary term to complete each sentence.

Go Online

For vocabulary quiz
PearsonSuccessNet.com

1. A _?_ is a rule that assigns to each input value exactly one output value.

2. A relationship between inputs and outputs in which the ratio of inputs and outputs is always the same is a _?_ .

Skills and Concepts

Lessons 7-1, 7-2
• To interpret and sketch graphs that represent real-world situations
• To evaluate functions and complete input-output tables

Drawing a graph makes it easier to analyze data. A **function** is a rule that assigns to each input value exactly one output value.

Use the graph at right for Exercises 3–5.

3. When during the hike is Rick's altitude increasing?

4. When during the hike is Rick's altitude decreasing?

5. When during the hike does Rick's altitude appear linear? Nonlinear?

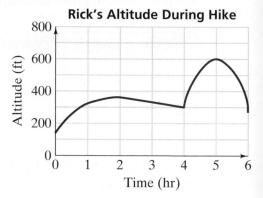

Rick's Altitude During Hike

Use the function rule $d = 3t - 1$. Find each output.

6. $t = 2$ 7. $t = 8$ 8. $t = -4$ 9. $t = 20$ 10. $t = -5$

Lesson 7-3
• To determine if relationships are proportional

A **proportional relationship** is a relationship between inputs and outputs in which the ratio of inputs and outputs is always the same.

Determine if the graph represents a function with a proportional relationship.

11.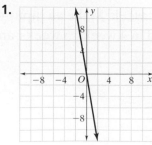

12.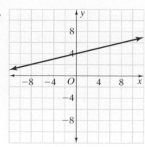

Lesson 7-4
- To recognize linear functions and use tables and equations to graph them

A **linear function** is a function whose points lie on a straight line when the function is graphed. **Nonlinear functions** are functions whose graphs are not straight lines.

Determine if the function represented by the table or graph is linear or nonlinear.

13.

x	1	2	3	4
y	1	8	27	64

14.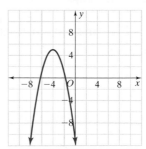

Lessons 7-5, 7-6
- To find the slope of a line from a graph or table
- To use tables and equations to graph linear functions

The **slope of a line** is the steepness of the line. When a linear function is written in the form $y = mx + b$, it is said to be in **slope-intercept form.** The graph is a line with slope m and y-intercept b. The **y-intercept** is the point where the graph crosses the y-axis.

Graph the data in each table and connect the points with a line. Then find the slope of the line.

15.

x	−2	0	2	4
y	−6	0	6	12

16.

x	3	5	7	9
y	11	19	27	35

Find the slope and y-intercept of the graph of each function.

17. $y = 3x + 5$ **18.** $y = -\dfrac{1}{2}x - 4$ **19.** $y = x + 7$ **20.** $y = \dfrac{2}{3}x$

Lesson 7-7
- To compare properties of two functions represented in different ways

You can compare two linear functions by comparing their slopes or their y-intercepts.

Determine which function has the greater rate of change.

21. $y = 7x + 9$

x	0	5	7
y	3	18	24

22. $y = 1.8x - 12$

x	12	14	18
y	7	11	19

Go Online For online chapter test
PearsonSuccessNet.com

1. **Exercise** Gem left her house and started exercising by walking slowly. Then she jogged and then sprinted to the park. She rested at the park and then jogged home. Sketch a graph showing Gem's distance from home throughout the trip.

For Exercises 2–5, find each output for the function $y = x^2 - 4$.

2. $x = 3$ 3. $x = 0$ 4. $x = -4$ 5. $x = 0.5$

Copy and complete the input-output table for the function $d = -12t$.

	t	d
6.	5	▪
7.	1	▪
8.	−12	▪
9.	−8	▪
10.	$\frac{1}{2}$	▪

11. **Mass** The function rule $M = 0.6t$ gives the total mass M in grams of a solid after h hours. What is the mass of the solid after 8 hr?

For Exercises 12–13, determine if the graph represents a function with a proportional relationship.

12.
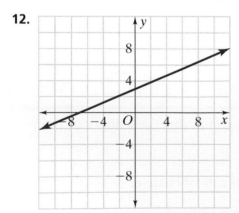

13.
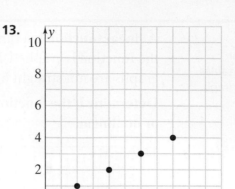

Find the slope of the line that passes through each pair of points.

14. $(5, 7)$ and $(-12, 4)$ 15. $(1, -1)$ and $(5, 6)$

For each function, find the slope and the y-intercept. Then graph the function.

16. $y = 5x - 3$ 17. $y = -\frac{3}{4}x + 10$

18. $y = x + 5$ 19. $y = \frac{2}{3}x$

20. A restaurant charges \$6.95 for a pizza, plus \$.50 for each topping. Write a function rule relating the cost of a pizza c to the number of toppings ordered t. What is the initial cost and the rate of change?

21. Which function has a greater rate of change?

x	1	3	4	7
y	4	10	13	22

$y = 2x + \frac{2}{3}$

22. Order functions E, F, G, and H from least to greatest rate of change.

E:
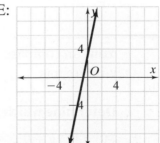

F: $y = \frac{3}{4}x - \frac{1}{2}$

G:

x	1	3	4	7
y	4	10	13	22

H: As x increases by 2 units, y increases by 3 units.

Reading Comprehension

Read each passage and answer the questions that follow.

Drive Sensibly Aggressive driving (speeding, rapid acceleration and braking) wastes gas. It can lower your gas mileage by 33 percent at highway speeds and by 5 percent around town. Sensible driving is also safer for you and others, so you may save more than gas money.

Observe the Speed Limit While each vehicle reaches its optimal fuel economy at a different speed (or range of speeds), gas mileage usually decreases rapidly at speeds above 50 mph. You can assume that each 5 mph you drive over 50 mph is like paying an additional $0.26 per gallon for gas. Observing the speed limit is also safer.

1. A driver is traveling 65 miles per hour on the highway. The function $c = 0.26\left(\dfrac{(s-50)}{5}\right)$ gives the additional charge per gallon where c is the amount in dollars and s is speed in miles per hour. What is the additional charge per gallon of gas when traveling at this speed?

   (A) $0.26
   (B) $0.52
   (C) $0.78
   (D) $3.90

2. Franklin is aggressively driving his car around town by rapidly braking and accelerating from a stop. His car gets 25 miles per gallon of gasoline. The function $m = 0.95g$, where m represents actual miles per gallon and g represents given miles per gallon, estimates the fuel economy of an aggressive driver. What is the most likely estimate of the miles per gallon for Franklin's car?

   (F) 5 mpg
   (G) 15.5 mpg
   (H) 16.75 mpg
   (J) 23.75 mpg

Fuel Economy According to the United States Department of Energy (DOE), hybrid vehicles can drive 40 to 70 miles on one gallon of gasoline, which helps drivers save money on fuel. Conventional cars usually get anywhere from 12 to 35 miles per gallon. While most hybrids cost significantly more upfront, savings at the fuel pump help offset the increased cost over the life of the car.

3. The function $c = 3.49\left(\dfrac{m}{g}\right)$ represents the cost c of fuel for an m mile trip in a car that gets g miles per gallon. Danielle's car gets 60 miles per gallon. How much would she pay for gas during a 480 mile trip?

   (A) $209.40
   (B) $27.92
   (C) $8.00
   (D) $0.44

4. Tori's hybrid car gets 50 miles per gallon of gasoline. Jacob's conventional car gets 20 miles per gallon. Tori and Jacob each take a 400 mile trip. Assuming that gas costs $3.49 per gallon, how much more does Jacob pay for gas than Tori?

   (F) $27.92
   (G) $41.88
   (H) $54.84
   (J) $69.80

What You've Learned

- In Chapter 3, you used inverse operations to solve one-step equations.
- In Chapter 5, you used cross products to solve proportions.
- In Chapter 6, you used equations and proportions to solve problems involving percents.

 Check Your Readiness

GO for Help

For Exercises	See Lesson
1–4	3-3
5–12	5-4
13–16	6-3

Solving One-Step Equations

(**Algebra**) Solve each equation.

1. $x + 13 = 28$

2. $n - 3.8 = 8.7$

3. $1.2c = 24$

4. $\frac{s}{4.5} = 10$

Solving Proportions

(**Algebra**) Solve each proportion.

5. $\frac{3}{4} = \frac{a}{24}$

6. $\frac{2}{b} = \frac{3}{21}$

7. $\frac{n}{52} = \frac{17}{13}$

8. $\frac{12}{5} = \frac{a}{45}$

9. $\frac{5}{12} = \frac{x}{84}$

10. $\frac{r}{16} = \frac{6}{24}$

11. $\frac{12}{m} = \frac{8}{10}$

12. $\frac{5}{7} = \frac{80}{t}$

Finding a Percent

Use an equation to find the percent.

13. What percent of 20 is 8?

14. 9 is what percent of 30?

15. What percent of 150 is 36?

16. 60 is what percent of 480?

What You'll Learn Next

- In this chapter, you will learn how to gather data about a population.

- You will use data from samples to make predictions and estimates about populations.

- You will also use data to compare two populations.

- Applying what you learn, you will solve problems involving data sets, such as estimating how many hours a typical police officer works each week based on a random sample of 30 police officers.

Key Vocabulary

- biased question (p. 317)
- box plot (p. 331)
- inference (p. 326)
- interquartile range (p. 331)
- mean absolute deviation (p. 332)
- population (p. 316)
- random sample (p. 316)
- sample (p. 316)
- variability (p. 331)

8-1 Random Samples and Surveys

Check Skills You'll Need

1. Vocabulary Review
A __?__ is a rate per 100.

Use a proportion to find the percent.

2. 4 is what percent of 5?

3. 10 is what percent of 40?

4. 14 is what percent of 200?

GO for Help
Lesson 6-2

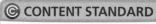

© **CONTENT STANDARD**
7.SP.1

What You'll Learn

To identify a random sample and to write a survey question

New Vocabulary population, sample, random sample, biased question

Why Learn This?

You can use a survey to gather information from a group of people. Pollsters use surveys to understand group preferences.

A **population** is a group of objects or people. You can gain information about a population by surveying a **sample**, or a part of the population.

In a **random sample**, each member of the population has the same chance of being selected. Random sampling tends to produce samples that are representative of the entire population. Generalizations based on representative samples are more likely to be correct.

EXAMPLE Identifying a Random Sample

1 You survey customers at a mall. You want to know which stores they shop at the most. Which sample is more likely to be random? Explain.

a. You survey shoppers in a computer store.

Customers that shop in a particular store may not represent all the shoppers in the entire mall. This sample is not random.

b. You walk around the mall and survey shoppers.

By walking around, you give everyone in the mall the same chance to be surveyed. This sample is more likely to be random.

✔ Quick Check

1. You survey a store's customers. You ask why they chose the store. Which sample is more likely to be random? Explain.
  a. You survey 20 people at the entrance from 5:00 P.M. to 8:00 P.M.
  b. You survey 20 people at the entrance throughout the day.

Bias means "slant."
A biased question slants
the answers in one
direction.

When you conduct a survey, ask questions that do not influence the answer. A **biased question** is a question that makes an unjustified assumption or makes some answers appear better than others.

EXAMPLE   Identifying Biased Questions

2 **Music** Is each question *biased* or *fair?* Explain.

a. "Do you think that soothing classical music is more pleasing than the loud, obnoxious pop music that teenagers listen to?"

This question is biased against pop music. It implies that all pop music is loud and that only teenagers listen to it. The adjectives "soothing" and "obnoxious" may also influence responses.

b. "Which do you think is the most common age group of people who like pop music?"

This question is fair. It does not assume that listeners of pop music fall into only one age group.

c. "Do you prefer classical music or pop music?"

This question is fair. It does not make any assumptions about classical music, pop music, or people.

✓ Quick Check

2. Is each question *biased* or *fair?* Explain.
   a. Do you prefer greasy meat or healthy vegetables on your pizza?
   b. Which pizza topping do you like best?

✓ Check Your Understanding

Vocabulary Match each description with the appropriate term.

1. a group of objects or people

2. makes some answers appear better

3. gives members of a group the same chance to be selected

A. biased question
B. random sample
C. population

You want to determine the favorite spectator sport of seventh-graders at your school. You ask the first 20 seventh-graders who arrive at a soccer game, "Is soccer your favorite sport to watch?"

4. What was the population of your survey? What was the sample?

5. The survey (was, was not) random.

6. You used a (biased, fair) question.

For more exercises, see Extra Skills and Word Problems.

GO for Help

For Exercises	See Example
7–10	1
11–15	2

Which sample is more likely to be random? Explain.

7. You want to survey teens about their snacking habits.
   a. You ask people at a party to name their favorite snack.
   b. You ask several teens entering a grocery store.

8. You want to know the most popular book among all the students at your school.
   a. You ask students from different grades at your school.
   b. You ask a group of your friends.

9. You want to know which baseball team is regarded as the best.
   a. You ask everyone seated in your section of the ballpark.
   b. You ask several visitors at a tourist attraction.

10. You want to survey seventh-grade students about computer use.
    a. You ask seventh-graders leaving the cafeteria after lunch.
    b. You ask seventh-graders entering a library on Friday night.

Is each question *biased* or *fair*? Explain.

11. Do you prefer to exercise or to watch television?

12. Do you prefer rock music or jazz?

13. Do you prefer harsh rock music or inspiring jazz?

14. Do you prefer unhealthy snacks or nutritious snacks?

15. What type of snack do you prefer?

16. **Guided Problem Solving** You are creating a survey to find out which weekend activity students prefer: shopping at the mall or watching a movie. Describe how you would find a random sample. Then write a question you could use for your survey.
    • What is the population you will need to survey?
    • Is your question fair or biased?

17. **Writing in Math** Which of the two surveys below would you use to determine attitudes about carnivals? Explain.

Survey	Question	Yes	No	Don't Know
A	Do you like going to noisy, overpriced carnivals?	53%	46%	1%
B	Do you like going to carnivals?	72%	27%	1%

GO Online
Homework Video Tutor
PearsonSuccessNet.com

18. Suppose you study the eating habits of college students. What question would you ask someone to determine whether he or she is a member of the population you want to study?

Careers A park ranger needs a college degree related to park management, natural history, forestry, or outdoor recreation.

19. Parks Suppose you are gathering information about visitors to Yosemite National Park. You survey every tenth person entering the park. Would you get a random sample of visitors? Explain.

Clothes A clothing company surveys women ages 18 to 35 to decide the price of a suit. Is each method a random sample? Explain.

20. Select names at random from a national telephone directory. Call these people and survey the person that answers.

21. Select names at random from a national telephone directory. Call these people and survey any woman 18 to 35 who answers.

22. Reasoning Jonas and Vanessa each survey a random sample of 25 students at their school. Jonas asks, "Should students at our school wear uniforms?" Vanessa asks, "Do you agree that wearing school uniforms is a good idea?" Which table likely shows Jonas's results, and which table likely shows Vanessa's results? Explain your reasoning.

Table A: School Uniforms

Response	Percent
In Favor	84%
Against	16%

Table B: School Uniforms

Response	Percent
In Favor	63%
Against	37%

23. Challenge A newspaper surveys 3 out of every 100 people of voting age in a community. The community has 38,592 people of voting age. How many people are surveyed?

Test Prep and Mixed Review   Practice

Multiple Choice

24. Alana wants to determine how many hours the players in a soccer league practice each week. Which sampling method is most likely to result in a sample that is representative of the population?
  Ⓐ Select a team at random, and survey each player on that team.
  Ⓑ Post a survey on a soccer website and ask visitors to fill it out.
  Ⓒ Survey every 5th player from an alphabetical list of the names of the players in the league.
  Ⓓ Choose the team with the most wins, and survey 5 randomly selected players from that team.

25. Emilio has a coupon for 20% off the price of any item. He wants to buy a beach towel priced at $24. Sales tax in his city is 8%. If Emilio uses his coupon, how much will he pay for the towel, including tax?
  Ⓕ $21.12   Ⓖ $20.74   Ⓗ $6.72   Ⓙ $5.18

GO for Help

For Exercises	See Lesson
26–28	3-2

Simplify each expression.

26. $4(x + 3) - 2x$ **27.** $8 + 6(2n - 4)$ **28.** $5t + 8 - 4t + 7$

8-2 Estimating Population Size

Check Skills You'll Need

1. **Vocabulary Review** A proportion is an equation stating that two __?__ are equal.

Solve each proportion.

2. $\frac{2}{3} = \frac{a}{15}$

3. $\frac{n}{36} = \frac{11}{9}$

4. $\frac{42}{63} = \frac{6}{k}$

for Help
Lesson 5-4

© CONTENT STANDARD
7.SP.2

For: Population Activity
Use: Interactive Textbook, 8-2

What You'll Learn

To estimate population size using proportions

Why Learn This?

Researchers use the *capture/recapture method* to estimate animal population size. They collect, mark, and release animals. Then they capture another group of animals. The number of marked animals in the second group indicates the population size.

The following proportion is used to estimate a deer population.

$$\frac{\text{number of marked deer counted}}{\text{total number of deer counted}} = \frac{\text{total number of marked deer}}{\text{estimate of deer population}}$$

EXAMPLE Using the Capture/Recapture Method

1 Gridded Response Researchers count 48 marked deer and a total of 638 deer on a flight over an area. They know there are 105 marked deer. Write a proportion to estimate the deer population in the area.

$$\frac{\text{number of marked deer counted}}{\text{total number of deer counted}} = \frac{\text{total number of marked deer}}{\text{estimate of deer population}}$$

$\frac{48}{638} = \frac{105}{x}$ ← **Write a proportion.**

$48x = 105 \cdot 638$ ← **Write the cross products.**

$48x = 66{,}990$ ← **Multiply.**

$\frac{48x}{48} = \frac{66{,}990}{48}$ ← **Divide each side by 48.**

$x \approx 1{,}396$ ← **Round to the nearest integer.**

There are about 1,396 deer.

Quick Check

1. Suppose the researchers in Example 1 count 638 deer, but only 35 marked deer. Estimate the total deer population in the area.

1. **Vocabulary** What is the capture/recapture method of estimating an animal population?

Use a proportion to estimate each animal population. Exercises 2 and 3 have been started for you.

2. total trout counted: 2,985
   tagged trout counted: 452
   total tagged trout: 1,956
   $$\frac{\text{tagged trout counted}}{\text{total trout counted}} = \frac{\text{total tagged trout}}{x}$$

3. total bass counted: 3,102
   tagged bass counted: 198
   total tagged bass: 872
   $$\frac{\text{tagged bass counted}}{\text{total bass counted}} = \frac{\text{total tagged bass}}{x}$$

4. total rabbits counted: 5,804
   marked rabbits counted: 3,214
   total marked rabbits: 5,398

5. total black bears counted: 218
   marked black bears counted: 25
   total marked black bears: 35

Homework Exercises

For more exercises, see Extra Skills and Word Problems.

GO for Help

For Exercises	See Example
6–14	1

Estimate the total deer population for each year in the table.

6. Year 1
7. Year 2
8. Year 3
9. Year 4
10. Year 5
11. Year 6
12. Year 7
13. Year 8
14. Year 9

Year	Total Deer Counted	Marked Deer Counted	Total Marked Deer
1	1,173	65	101
2	1,017	42	83
3	1,212	32	60
4	1,707	30	36
5	1,612	68	89
6	1,590	37	59
7	1,417	42	54
8	1,608	85	110
9	1,469	52	83

GPS 15. **Guided Problem Solving** In a study, a fish and game department worker catches, tags, and frees 124 catfish in a lake. A few weeks later, he catches and frees 140 catfish. Thirty-five have tags. Estimate the number of catfish in the lake.
   - number of marked catfish counted = ▇
   - total number of catfish counted = ▇
   - total number of marked catfish = ▇

16. **Data Analysis** Use your answers to Exercises 6–14 above. Describe how the deer population changed over time.

Use the report for Exercises 17 and 18.

17. A biologist spilled juice on the report. Find the number of alligators that were caught, tagged, and set free.

18. **Writing in Math** Explain how recapturing a higher percent of marked alligators affects the estimated total population.

Alligator Population	
Number caught, tagged, and set free	
Number recaptured	105
Number recaptured with tags	50
Estimated total population	132

19. **Sharks** A biologist is studying the shark population off the Florida coast. He captures, tags, and sets free 38 sharks. A week later, 8 out of 25 sharks captured have tags. He uses the proportion $\frac{25}{8} = \frac{38}{x}$ to estimate that the population is about 12.
   a. **Error Analysis** Find the error in the biologist's proportion.
   b. Estimate the shark population.

20. **Reasoning** A class helps determine the squirrel population in a park. Students capture, tag, and free squirrels. A few squirrels lose their tags. How will this affect the population estimate? Explain.

21. **Challenge** In a capture/recapture program, 30% of the animals recaptured have tags. Suppose 70 animals were originally captured, tagged, and released. Estimate the population.

Test Prep and Mixed Review — Practice

Gridded Response

22. The table at the right shows the results of a biologist who captures, tags, and sets free lake trout. What is the estimated trout population in the lake?

Trout Population	
Number Tagged	150
Number Recaptured	100
Number Recaptured with Tags	60

23. Alexandro needs 300 cubic inches of clay to make a sculpture. The clay comes in blocks that are 5 inches wide, 3 inches tall, and 4 inches deep. How many blocks does Alexandro need?

24. Partners A and B split their profits in a ratio of 2 : 3. If Partner A makes a profit of $2,700, how much profit, in dollars, does Partner B make?

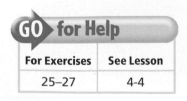
GO for Help

For Exercises	See Lesson
25–27	4-4

Solve each inequality. Graph the solution.

25. $-3x + 4 \geq 5$

26. $0.4n - 1 > 1.8$

27. $\frac{t}{4} - \frac{1}{2} < \frac{3}{4}$

1. Nichole wants to know whether students at her school support building a new gym. She surveyed a random sample of students on the school's basketball teams. The graph shows her results. Explain why the results of the survey may not be representative of the entire school.

Support for New Gym

No 14%

Yes 86%

Is each question *biased* or *fair*? Explain.

2. Should our city continue to waste money on expensive highway projects?

3. Do you support or oppose the new highway project?

4. **Open-Ended** Choose a survey topic and write a biased survey question and a fair survey question.

5. Which is the best way to survey a random sample of students from your school about their favorite radio station? Explain.
   - Ⓐ Survey 5 students in each first-period class.
   - Ⓑ Survey 12 students in the band.
   - Ⓒ Call 25 friends.
   - Ⓓ Survey each student in your math class.

Use a proportion to estimate each animal population.

6. total wild horses counted: 1,583
   marked wild horses counted: 496
   total marked wild horses: 1,213

7. total turtles counted: 51
   marked turtles counted: 32
   total marked turtles: 108

MATH AT WORK

Pollsters

Pollsters interview people to find out their opinions and their preferences about specific topics. They must understand the topic of interest well in order to ask the right questions. If pollsters ask poor-quality questions, they will not get accurate responses.

Pollsters use math to analyze the data they collect. They make predictions and estimates about the population that was surveyed. Their analysis gives us an overall view of the data. Pollsters often graph data to display their findings.

Go Online For more information about pollsters
PearsonSuccessNet.com

Describing Data

Poll A middle-school class was polled on whether the school should change its mascot. A 0 rating meant the student was strongly against the change. A 10 rating meant the student was strongly in favor of the change. The line plot below shows the data. Whitney computed the mean. Was the mean a good descriptor of how the students felt?

Mean: The sum of the data values divided by the number of data values
Median: The middle value, or the mean of the two middle values, when the data are arranged in numerical order
Mode: The value or values that occur with the greatest frequency

Mascot Survey Result

```
                    X
                    X
        X   X   X   X           X           X
  X     X   X   X   X           X           X
  X     X   X   X   X   X   X   X   X   X
  0   1   2   3   4   5   6   7   8   9   10
```

What You Might Think

What do I know? What do I want to find out?

What is the mean?

Does the mean represent the students' feelings?

What You Might Write

I know the students' ratings. I need to find the mean and decide whether the mean represents how the students felt.

total = (3 × 2) + (3 × 3) + (5 × 4) +
  (3 × 5) + 6 + 7 + (3 × 8) +
  9 + (4 × 10)
  = 136

mean = 136 ÷ 26, or about 5.2

I do not think so. Thirteen students were against the change. Ten students were for the change. The median of 4.5 or mode of 4 would better show how students felt.

Think It Through

1. **Reasoning** How did Whitney know to divide by 26 to find the mean? Explain.

2. Explain how to find the median of 4.5 and the mode of 4.

Exercises

Solve each problem. For Exercises 3 and 4, answer the questions first.

3. Jax has a weekly test in math. His scores on the last five tests were 78, 92, 86, 94, and 95. What score does he need on his next exam to have an average of 90?
   a. What do you know? What do you want to find out?
   b. How does a diagram like the one below help you understand what to do?

$600 \times 90\% = 540$					
78	92	86	94	95	■

4. Suppose a fox and a lizard compete in a 300-ft race. The fox runs at a rate of 30 ft/s. The lizard runs at a rate of 10 ft/s and starts 15 seconds before the fox. Who wins the race? Explain.
   a. What do you know? What do you want to find out?
   b. How does a table like the one below help you understand what to do?

Animal	Distance (ft)	Rate (ft/s)	Time (s)
Fox	300	30	■
Lizard	300	10	■

5. Annie has two part-time jobs during the summer. She earns $8.50 per hour working at a bakery and $7.50 per hour working at a grocery store. Last week, she worked a total of 40 hours. If 75% of her working hours were at the bakery, how much did Annie earn in all last week?

6. Parents were asked in a survey, "Should the school require uniforms?" A 0 rating meant the parent was strongly against uniforms. A 5 rating meant the parent was strongly for uniforms. The frequency table below shows the survey results. Which measure—the mean, the median, or the mode—would best describe the data? Explain.

   Parent Survey Results

Rating	0	1	2	3	4	5
Tally	〜〜〜 〜〜〜 ///	/	///	///	//	〜〜〜 //

8-3 Inferences

1. Vocabulary Review What are the *cross products* of a proportion?

Solve each proportion using cross products.

2. $\dfrac{x}{84} = \dfrac{25}{35}$

3. $\dfrac{18}{27} = \dfrac{n}{93}$

4. $\dfrac{7}{c} = \dfrac{8}{56}$

 **for Help**
Lesson 5-4

© **CONTENT STANDARD**
7.SP.2

What You'll Learn

To use data from random samples to draw inferences about populations

New Vocabulary inference

Why Learn This?

You can use data from a random sample of a population to draw inferences about the entire population. When you draw an **inference**, you make a prediction or conclusion based on data or reasoning.

EXAMPLE **Drawing Inferences about a Population**

1 **Multiple Choice** A restaurant manager selected a random sample of 20 customers and recorded the amount they spent on their meal. Based on the sample, which is the best estimate of the average, or mean, amount that customers spend on a meal at the restaurant?

Ⓐ $14   Ⓑ $16   Ⓒ $18   Ⓓ $20

Step 1 Find the average, or mean, of the sample data.

$$\text{mean} = \frac{\text{sum of the data values}}{\text{number of data values}}$$
$$= \frac{320}{20}$$
$$= 16$$

Random Sample of Amount Spent per Customer ($)				
21	9	23	12	15
16	10	17	17	15
14	16	13	17	17
14	25	14	23	12

Step 2 Use the average of the sample data to draw an inference.

The average amount spent by customers in the sample is $16, so the average amount spent by all customers is likely close to $16. The answer is B.

✓ Quick Check

1. Use the random sample from Example 1. Draw an inference about the percent of customers at the restaurant who spend more than $20. Support your answer.

Vocabulary Tip

The *mean* of a data set is the sum of the data values divided by the number of data values.

🖩 **Calculator Tip**

It can be helpful to use a calculator when finding the sum of a large number of values.

Different random samples from the same population may give different results. By comparing the samples, you can determine how much estimates or predictions made from the samples will vary.

EXAMPLE Comparing Random Samples

2 **Student Government** There are 360 students at a middle school. Sonya, Jane, and Danny each survey a random sample of 25 students about whom they plan to vote for in the election for student council president. Their results are shown in the table.

Votes for Student Council President

Candidate	Sonya's Sample	Jane's Sample	Danny's Sample
Emma	6	7	6
Ty	7	5	4
Carlos	12	13	15

a. For each sample, predict how many votes Carlos will get.

Use a proportion:

$$\frac{\text{votes for Carlos in sample}}{\text{students in sample}} = \frac{\text{predicted votes for Carlos}}{\text{students in school}}$$

Sonya's Sample:

$\frac{12}{25} = \frac{x}{360}$

$12 \cdot 360 = 25x$

$4{,}320 = 25x$

$173 \approx x$

about 173 votes

Jane's Sample:

$\frac{13}{25} = \frac{x}{360}$

$13 \cdot 360 = 25x$

$4{,}680 = 25x$

$187 \approx x$

about 187 votes

Danny's Sample:

$\frac{15}{25} = \frac{x}{360}$

$15 \cdot 360 = 25x$

$5{,}400 = 25x$

$216 = x$

about 216 votes

b. Describe the variation in the predictions.

The greatest prediction is 216 votes, and the least prediction is 173 votes. So the predictions vary by $216 - 173 = 43$ votes.

c. Draw an inference about the number of votes Carlos will get.

Carlos is likely to get about 187 votes, the median prediction.

GO for Help

For help with solving proportions, go to Lesson 5-4, Example 3.

Vocabulary Tip

The *median* of a data set is the middle value, or the mean of the two middle values, when the data are listed in numerical order.

Quick Check

2. The table shows the results of 3 random samples of 30 students each at a middle school with 420 students. The students were asked how many hours they spend online each week.

a. For each sample, predict how many students in the school spend at least 5 hours online per week.

Hours Spent Online Per Week

Time (h)	Sample 1	Sample 2	Sample 3
< 5	16	13	11
≥ 5	14	17	19

b. Describe the variation in the predictions.

c. Draw an inference about the number of students in the school who spend at least 5 hours online per week.

1. **Vocabulary** How is an inference different from a guess?

For each random sample of a fruit fly population, make a prediction about the number of flies in the population with white eyes.

2. population size: 275, sample: 5 out of 45 with white eyes

3. population size: 250, sample: 17 out of 40 with white eyes

4. population size: 443, sample: 10 out of 28 with white eyes

Homework Exercises

For more exercises, see Extra Skills and Word Problems.

GO for Help

For Exercises	See Example
5–8	1
9–11	2

Entertainment The table shows the ages of a random sample of 30 visitors at an amusement park. Use the sample to draw an inference about each measure. Support your answer.

Random Sample of Ages				
8	12	2	41	39
47	16	20	26	25
16	35	14	57	9
25	23	12	30	20
16	14	13	12	4
10	10	52	32	6

5. the mean age of visitors at the park

6. the percent of visitors under age 18

7. the percent of visitors age 35 and over

8. the median age of visitors at the park

The table shows the lengths of 3 random samples of 20 words each from a book.

Lengths of Words

Number of Letters	Sample 1	Sample 2	Sample 3
1	1	1	0
2	2	1	5
3	7	4	8
4	4	10	3
5	4	1	2
6	2	3	2

Test Prep Tip

When a test question asks you to draw an inference, be sure that you can use mathematics to support your answer.

9. For each sample, estimate the mean length of the words in the book to the nearest tenth.

10. Describe the variation in the estimates.

11. Draw an inference about the mean length of the words in the book.

12. Guided Problem Solving

A factory makes 60,000 MP3 players per day. On Friday, two inspectors test a random sample of MP3 players. Inspector 1 predicts that 480 MP3 players made on Friday are likely to be defective. Inspector 2 predicts that 180 MP3 players are likely to be defective. Whose prediction is likely to be more accurate? Justify your answer.

Test Results of MP3 Players		
Sample	Good	Defective
Inspector 1	496	4
Inspector 2	997	3

- What is the size of each sample?
- How is sample size likely to affect the accuracy of the predictions?

13. Reasoning A government inspector takes 5 random samples of the same size from a shipment of eggs. She determines the mean weight of a dozen eggs in each sample. What can the inspector conclude if the mean weights of the samples are very close to each other?

14. Writing in Math Explain why it is advantageous to draw inferences based on using multiple random samples from a population instead of using just one random sample.

15. Challenge A survey of a random sample of registered voters shows that 42% of males and 64% of females plan to vote to re-elect a senator. Predict the overall percent of the votes that the senator will get, assuming that the ratio of males to females who vote in the election is 3 to 2. Support your answer.

GO Online
Homework Video Tutor
PearsonSuccessNet.com

Test Prep and Mixed Review

Practice

Multiple Choice

16. Biologists selected a random sample of 20 wolf packs in a state and recorded the number of wolves in each pack. Based on the sample, which is the best estimate of the mean number of wolves per pack in the state?

Wolves Per Pack				
5	7	13	2	7
6	3	7	5	7
2	11	2	2	2
2	5	4	5	2

Ⓐ 2   Ⓑ 5   Ⓒ 7   Ⓓ 11

17. The depth of a lake at the beginning of summer is 62 feet. During the summer, the water level of the lake changes by $-5\frac{1}{2}$ feet. What is the depth of the lake at the end of the summer?

Ⓕ $56\frac{1}{2}$ ft   Ⓖ $57\frac{1}{2}$ ft   Ⓗ $66\frac{1}{2}$ ft   Ⓙ $67\frac{1}{2}$ ft

18. Which is the slope and y-intercept of the function $y = \frac{1}{3}x + 4$?

Ⓐ 4; 3   Ⓒ $\frac{1}{3}$; 4

Ⓑ 3; 4   Ⓓ 4; $\frac{1}{3}$

GO for Help

For Exercise	See Lesson
18	7-6

Vocabulary Builder

High-Use Academic Words

High-use academic words are words that you will see often in textbooks and on tests. These words are not math vocabulary terms, but knowing them will help you to succeed in mathematics.

Direction Words

Some words tell what to do in a problem. I need to understand what these words are asking so that I give the correct answer.

Word	Meaning
Represent	To replace with other words or symbols
Predict	To say in advance the outcomes or effects
Compare	To say how two things are similar or different

Exercises

1. Draw a picture to represent the weather outside today.

2. Predict the weather tomorrow.

3. Compare the weather today with the weather six months ago.

4. A rectangle has a width of 6 cm. Its length is x cm longer than its width. Which expression represents the area of the rectangle?

    Ⓐ $6x$ Ⓑ $6 + x$ Ⓒ $(6 + x)6$ Ⓓ $(6 + x) + 6$

5. Use the graph at the right. Predict the value of y when x is 10.

6. Ty lists the names of all his classmates, selects 5 names at random, and surveys those students. Jo surveys the 5 students who are on the swim team. Compare the two sampling methods.

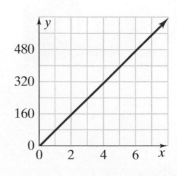

7. **Word Knowledge** Think about the word *conclude*.
    a. Choose the letter for how well you know the word.
       A. I know its meaning.
       B. I've seen it, but I don't know its meaning.
       C. I don't know it.
    b. **Research** Look up and write the definition of *conclude*.
    c. Use the word *conclude* in a sentence involving mathematics.

Data Variability

© **CONTENT STANDARDS**
7.SP.3, 7.SP.4

What You'll Learn

To compare data about two populations by using measures of center and measures of variability

New Vocabulary box plot, interquartile range (IQR), variability, mean absolute deviation (MAD)

Why Learn This?

You can use random samples to compare two populations.

A **box plot** uses 5 points on a number line to summarize a data set. The box shows the middle 50% of the data. With a box plot you can observe the visual overlap of two data sets.

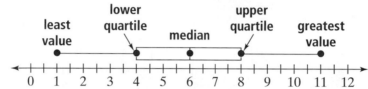

The **interquartile range** (IQR) of a data set is the difference between the upper and lower quartiles. The IQR is one measure of **variability**, which tells how much a data set is spread out.

EXAMPLE **Comparing Two Populations**

1. A veterinarian collects data about the weights of the dogs she treats. Compare the IQRs of the data sets to draw an inference about the dogs.

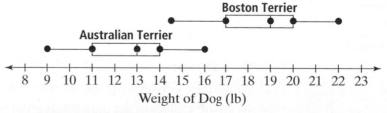

IQR for Australian terriers:	IQR for Boston terriers:
$14 - 11 = 3$	$20 - 17 = 3$

The IQRs of the data sets are the same. So, you can infer that the weights of Boston terriers vary about as much as the weights of Australian terriers.

✓ **Quick Check**

1. Compare the medians of the data sets in Example 1, and use the comparison to draw another inference about the dogs.

A second measure of variability is **mean absolute deviation** (MAD). The MAD of a data set is the average distance between the mean and each data value.

You can determine the amount of overlap of two data sets by expressing the difference between their centers as a multiple of the MAD or IQR. A multiple less than 1 indicates a large amount of overlap. A multiple greater than 1 indicates a small or no amount of overlap.

EXAMPLE Determining Overlap of Data Sets

② **Sports** The data table at the left shows the number of points scored by each player on two basketball teams during a game. Use measures of center and variability to express the amount of overlap between the data sets.

a. Calculate the mean of each data set.

Eagles: Mean $= \frac{56}{8} = 7$ **Vikings:** Mean $= \frac{16}{8} = 2$

b. Determine the MAD of each data set.

Eagles: Start by finding the MAD for points scored by the Eagles.

Points	4	6	6	7	7	8	9	9
Mean	7	7	7	7	7	7	7	7
Distance	3	1	1	0	0	1	2	2

$$\text{MAD} = \frac{\text{total of the distances}}{\text{number of data values}} = \frac{10}{8} = \frac{5}{4} = 1.25$$

Vikings: Follow the same steps. $\text{MAD} = \frac{10}{8} = \frac{5}{4} = 1.25$

The data sets have the same MAD, so their variability is similar.

c. What multiple n of the MAD equals the difference between the means?

$\text{MAD} \cdot n = \text{difference of means}$	← **Write an equation.**
$1.25n = 7 - 2$	← **Substitute.**
$1.25n = 5$	← **Simplify.**
$\dfrac{1.25n}{1.25} = \dfrac{5}{1.25}$	← **Divide each side by 1.25.**
$n = 4$	← **Simplify.**

d. What does this number tell you about the overlap of the data sets?

The difference between the means is 4 times the MAD. So, the distance between the centers of the data sets is greater than the variability of either data set. There is little overlap in the data sets, which the data table confirms.

✓ Quick Check

2. The data table at the left shows the number of commercials during a random sample of hour-long shows on two television stations.
   a. Calculate the mean of each data set.
   b. Determine the MAD for each data set.
   c. What multiple n of the MADs equals the difference between the means? What does this number tell you about the overlap?

Points Scored

Eagles		Vikings
	0	✗ ✗
	1	✗
	2	✗ ✗
	3	✗
✗	4	✗ ✗
	5	
✗ ✗	6	
✗ ✗	7	
✗	8	
✗ ✗	9	

Commercials During Hour-Long Shows

Station A		Station B
	32	✗
✗	33	
	34	✗ ✗ ✗
✗ ✗ ✗	35	✗ ✗
✗ ✗ ✗	36	✗ ✗
✗	37	✗ ✗
✗	38	
✗	39	

1. **Vocabulary** How does a measure of variability, such as the interquartile range, differ from a measure of center, such as the median?

2. **Sports** The box plot shows the heights in inches of the players on a women's college basketball team. What are the median and the IQR of the data?

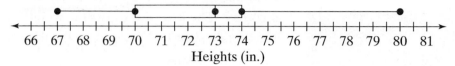

66 67 68 69 70 71 72 73 74 75 76 77 78 79 80 81
Heights (in.)

3. **Entertainment** The list below shows the lengths in minutes of a random sample of movies. Determine the mean and the MAD for the data.

$$90, 136, 109, 115, 106, 114, 105, 130, 110, 125$$

Homework Exercises

For more exercises, see Extra Skills and Word Problems.

GO for Help

For Exercises	See Example
4–6	1
7–9	2

Shopping The box-and-whisker plot shows the prices of shirts at store A and store B. Compare each pair of measures for the data sets in the box-and-whisker plot, and use each comparison to draw an inference.

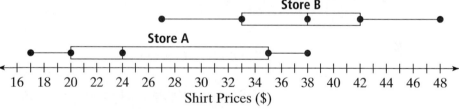

Store B

Store A

16 18 20 22 24 26 28 30 32 34 36 38 40 42 44 46 48
Shirt Prices ($)

Fish Lengths (in.)		
Bluegill		**Shoal bass**
✗ ✗	6	
✗ ✗	7	
✗ ✗ ✗	8	
	9	
✗ ✗ ✗	10	
	11	
	12	✗
	13	✗
	14	✗
	15	✗ ✗ ✗
	16	✗ ✗ ✗
	17	
	18	✗

4. the medians of the data sets

5. the IQRs of the data sets

6. the greatest price for store A and the median price for store B

Ecology The data table at the left shows the lengths of a random sample of two species of fish taken from a river. Use the data table for Exercises 7–9.

7. Calculate the mean of each data set.

8. Determine the MAD for each data set.

9. What number n multiplied by the MAD equals the difference between the means? What does this number tell you about the overlap of the data sets?

10. Guided Problem Solving The lists below show the daily high temperatures in °F in two cities over 10 days.

Chicago: 76, 79, 83, 66, 80, 78, 72, 75, 81, 80
Denver: 62, 63, 68, 61, 71, 69, 63, 68, 73, 72

Without making a data display, determine whether there is a large or small amount of overlap in the data sets. Support your answer.
- The mean of the Chicago temperatures is ■, and the mean of the Denver temperatures is ■.
- The MAD of each data set is ■.

Go Online
Homework Video Tutor
PearsonSuccessNet.com

Biology **The box plot shows the weights of a random sample of male and female spotted hyenas. Use the data for Exercises 11–13.**

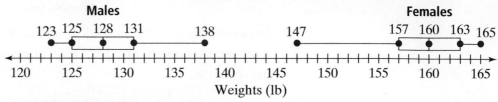

Weights (lb)

11. Determine the IQR of each data set.

12. Reasoning Biologists capture a spotted hyena that weighs 142 pounds. Can you tell from its weight whether it is male or female? Explain.

13. Writing in Math Two data sets have means that are very far apart, and the MADs of the data sets are very small. What can you conclude about the amount of overlap in the data sets? Explain.

14. Challenge The table below shows the lengths of a random sample of 50 words each from a magazine and a newspaper. Are the words in the newspaper generally longer than the words in the magazine? Explain.

Frequency

Letters per Word	1	2	3	4	5	6	7	8	9
Magazine	4	8	10	6	12	6	2	2	0
Newspaper	1	5	11	11	7	7	5	2	1

Test Prep and Mixed Review
Practice

Multiple Choice

15. The lists show the speeds in mi/h of a random sample of cars on a particular road at two different times of day. How much faster is the mean speed of the cars at 11:00 A.M. than at 8:00 A.M.?
8:00 A.M.: 36, 41, 35, 35, 30, 37, 39, 31, 43, 33
11:00 A.M.: 49, 40, 41, 47, 44, 48, 42, 46, 48, 45
(A) 9 mi/h   (B) 10 mi/h   (C) 12 mi/h   (D) 13 mi/h

Go for Help

For Exercises	See Lesson
16–19	1-4

Write each fraction as a decimal.

16. $\frac{7}{8}$ **17.** $\frac{1}{9}$ **18.** $\frac{4}{25}$ **19.** $\frac{5}{6}$

Interpreting Data

Before you answer a question that involves data, make sure you understand the information displayed in the graph. Then try to relate each of the answer choices to the data.

EXAMPLE

The line plot at the right shows the heights of a random sample of hardcover and paperback books at a bookstore. How much greater is the mean height of the hardcovers than the mean height of the paperbacks?

(A) 3.5 cm (B) 4.3 cm (C) 5 cm (D) 19.2 cm

The ✗'s on the left show the heights of the hardcovers, and the ✗'s on the right show the heights of the paperbacks. Choice A is the difference of the medians. Choice C is the difference of the greatest heights. Choice D is the mean of the paperback heights. The correct answer is B.

Book Heights (cm)		
Hardcovers		**Paperbacks**
	17	✗
	18	✗ ✗
	19	✗
	20	✗ ✗ ✗ ✗ ✗
	21	
✗	22	
✗ ✗ ✗ ✗	23	
✗ ✗ ✗ ✗	24	
✗	25	

Exercises

The box plot shows the finishing times in a 10-kilometer race for females 15–19 years old and 20–24 years old. Use the box plot to answer each question.

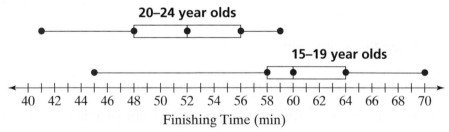

1. How much faster did the fastest 20–24 years old female finish the race than the fastest 15–19 years old female?
   (A) 4 minutes (B) 11 minutes (C) 18 minutes (D) 29 minutes

2. Which statement is NOT supported by the box plot?

   (F) Most 20–24 years old females beat the fastest 15–19 years old female.
   (G) All the 20–24 years old females finished the race in less than an hour.
   (H) At least half the 15–19 years old females did not beat any 20–24 years old females.
   (J) About half the 15–19 years old females took more than an hour to finish the race.

3. How much less is the median finishing time for 20–24 years old females than for 15–19 years old females?
   (A) 2 minutes (B) 6 minutes (C) 8 minutes (D) 10 minutes

Chapter 8 Review

Vocabulary Review

biased question (p. 317)
box plot (p. 331)
inference (p. 326)

interquartile range (p. 331)
mean absolute deviation (p. 332)
population (p. 316)

random sample (p. 316)
sample (p. 316)
variability (p. 331)

Choose the correct term to complete each sentence.

1. A (biased question, random sample) can influence the results of a survey.

2. A (box plot, sample) is used to gather data about part of a population.

3. The (population, variability) of a data set is a measure of how much the data are spread out.

Go Online

For vocabulary quiz
PearsonSuccessNet.com

4. The (interquartile range, mean absolute deviation) of a data set is a measure of the average distance from the mean to the data values.

5. A (population, random sample) is a whole group.

Skills and Concepts

Lesson 8-1
• To identify a random sample and to write a survey question

A **population** is a group of objects or people, and a **sample** is a part of a population. In a **random sample**, each member of the population has the same chance of being selected.

A **biased question** makes some answers appear better or worse than others.

Which sample is more likely to be random? Explain.

6. A clothing store manager wants to know the type of jeans customers most prefer.
   a. She asks every fifth customer entering the store one day.
   b. She asks all of the women trying on jeans in the store one day.

7. A team of biologists wants to know the heights of the trees in a forest.
   a. They measure the heights of 50 trees along a road in the forest.
   b. They divide the forest into equal squares and measure the heights of 2 trees in each square.

Is each question *biased* or *fair*? Explain.

8. What is your favorite activity after school?

9. Do you like the calm, soothing ocean?

Lesson 8-2

• To estimate population size using proportions

You can use the capture/recapture method to estimate population size. Use the following proportion to estimate an animal population.

$$\frac{\text{number of marked animals counted}}{\text{total number of animals counted}} = \frac{\text{total number of marked animals}}{\text{estimate of animal population}}$$

Use a proportion to estimate each animal population.

10. total eagles counted: 75
    tagged eagles counted: 10
    total tagged eagles: 60

11. total cheetahs counted: 21
    tagged cheetahs counted: 7
    total tagged cheetahs: 27

12. **Biology** Researchers know that there are 53 marked wolves in an area. On a flight over the area, they count 18 marked wolves and a total of 125 wolves. Estimate the total wolf population.

Lesson 8-3

• To use data from random samples to draw inferences about populations

Inferences are predictions or conclusions based on data or reasoning. You can use data from random samples of a population to draw inferences about the entire population.

Manufacturing A factory makes 10,000 cell phone batteries each day. On Monday, 3 inspectors test a random sample of 300 batteries each. The table shows the results.

13. For each sample, estimate how many batteries made at the factory on Monday are defective.

14. Describe the variation in the estimates.

15. Draw an inference about the number of defective batteries made at the factory on Monday.

Battery Test Results

Sample	Good	Defective
1	299	1
2	296	4
3	298	2

Lesson 8-4

• To compare data about two populations by using measures of center and measures of variability

A measure of **variability** indicates how much a data set is spread out. The **mean absolute deviation** (MAD) of a data set is the average distance between the mean and each data value.

Nutrition The line plot shows the number of raisins per package in random samples of two different brands of trail mix. Use the line plot for Exercises 16–18.

16. Calculate the mean of each data set.

17. Determine the MAD for each data set.

18. What multiple n of the MAD equals the difference between the means? What does this number tell you about the overlap of the data sets?

Raisins per Package

Brand A		Brand B
	33	X X X X
	34	X X X
X	35	X X
X X	36	X
X X X X	37	
X X	38	
X	39	

Chapter 8 Test

1. **Entertainment** Doyle wants to know which types of movies teenagers in his town like best. Which sample is more likely to be random? Explain.
   a. He surveys every fifth teenager leaving a showing of an action movie.
   b. He surveys every tenth teenager entering a grocery store.

Is each question *biased* or *fair*? Explain.

2. Do you prefer watching comedies or dramas?

3. Do you like watching violent sports or informative documentaries on TV?

4. **Writing in Math** Explain how you can get a random sample of the people who use a town library.

Use a proportion to estimate each population.

5. total counted: 102
   tagged counted: 38
   total tagged: 56

6. total counted: 958
   tagged counted: 210
   total tagged: 305

The table shows data for a random sample of 20 students at a middle school. Use the sample to draw an inference about each measure. Explain your reasoning.

Hours Slept per Night				
8	7.5	9	7	8
7.5	6	6.5	9.5	7.5
8	7.5	8	7	8
6.5	8	8.5	8.5	7.5

7. the median number of hours slept per night by students at the school

8. the percent of students at the school who sleep at least 8 hours per night

There are 482 students at a middle school. Gina, Brian, and Simon each survey a random sample of 25 students each about whether they plan to take a world languages class next year. Their results are shown in the table. Use the table for Exercises 9–12.

World Languages Class			
	Gina's Sample	Brian's Sample	Simon's Sample
Yes	11	13	10
No	14	12	15

9. For each sample, estimate how many students at the school plan to take a world languages class next year.

10. Describe the variation in the estimates.

11. Draw an inference about the number of students at the school who plan to take a world languages class next year.

12. **Reasoning** The school has 6 world languages classes that can fit 24 students each. Will all of the students who want to take a world languages class next year be able to take one? Support your answer.

The lists below show the heights in inches of a random sample of players in a basketball league and a soccer league. Use the data for Exercises 13–15.

Basketball players:
83, 75, 80, 75, 78, 79, 74, 73, 76, 77

Soccer players:
75, 73, 74, 69, 70, 76, 69, 74, 72, 68

13. Compare the means of the data sets, and use the comparison to draw an inference.

14. Determine the MAD for each data set.

15. What number n multiplied by the MAD equals the difference between the means? What does this number tell you about the overlap of the data sets?

Reading Comprehension

Read each passage and answer the questions that follow.

Bedroom Makeover Katy wants to remodel her bedroom. Her room is shaped like a rectangular prism with a length of 14 ft, a width of 10 ft, and a height of 8 ft. There are two doors in her room, each with a width of 30 in. and a height of 80 in. There is also a window with a width of 38 in. and a height of 48 in.

1. Katy wants to paint the 4 walls green. What is the area of the walls, not including the area of the doors and window?
   - Ⓐ 338 ft²
   - Ⓑ 384 ft²
   - Ⓒ 401 ft²
   - Ⓓ 513 ft²

2. Katy needs 2 gallons of paint for the walls. The paint costs $22.95 per gallon, and the sales tax rate is 8%. How much will Katy pay for the paint, including sales tax?
   - Ⓕ $42.23
   - Ⓖ $45.90
   - Ⓗ $47.74
   - Ⓙ $49.57

3. Katy wants to replace her old carpet. The store tells her to find the area of the floor and then increase that amount by 20% to determine how much carpet she will need to buy. The extra 20% is necessary because carpet is sold in standard lengths and must be cut to fit the floor. How much carpet will Katy need to buy?
   - Ⓐ 134 ft²
   - Ⓑ 160 ft²
   - Ⓒ 168 ft²
   - Ⓓ 224 ft²

4. Katy also wants to add a baseboard along the bottom of the walls where they meet the floor. How many feet of baseboard will Katy need if the baseboard does not extend across the doors?
   - Ⓕ 35 ft
   - Ⓖ 39 ft
   - Ⓗ 43 ft
   - Ⓙ 48 ft

Survey Says A recent survey of 2,254 randomly selected adults in the U.S. showed that 88% owned a cell phone. Of those who owned a cell phone, 55% used their phones to go online. In this survey, going online was defined as using the Internet or email.

5. The U.S. adult population at the time of the survey was approximately 239,000,000. Approximately how many adults owned a cell phone in the U.S.?
   - Ⓐ 272 million
   - Ⓑ 210 million
   - Ⓒ 131 million
   - Ⓓ 116 million

6. Approximately what percent of the U.S. adult population were cell phone owners who used their phones to go online?
   - Ⓕ 33%
   - Ⓖ 43%
   - Ⓗ 48%
   - Ⓙ 63%

7. Which of these survey questions would be least likely to give biased results?
   - Ⓐ If you have a cell phone, do you use it to check your email?
   - Ⓑ How much time do you waste surfing the Internet with your cell phone?
   - Ⓒ Don't you agree that owning a cell phone would make you more popular?
   - Ⓓ Why do you own a pricy cell phone even though a landline is so much cheaper?

What You've Learned

- In Chapter 5, you solved proportions.
- In Chapter 6, you converted between fractions, decimals, and percents.
- In Chapter 8, you analyzed data in tables, box-and-whisker plots, and stem-and-leaf plots.

 **Check Your Readiness**

GO for Help

For Exercises	See Lesson
1–6	5-1
7–12	5-4
13–22	6-1

Writing Ratios

Write each ratio in simplest form.

1. $\frac{9}{24}$ **2.** $\frac{20}{54}$ **3.** $\frac{15}{65}$

4. $\frac{16}{22}$ **5.** $\frac{21}{84}$ **6.** $\frac{18}{42}$

Using Proportional Reasoning

(Algebra) Solve each proportion.

7. $\frac{3}{10} = \frac{x}{30}$ **8.** $\frac{n}{14} = \frac{25}{8}$ **9.** $\frac{22}{c} = \frac{66}{15}$

10. $\frac{16}{35} = \frac{20}{y}$ **11.** $\frac{a}{24} = \frac{24}{9}$ **12.** $\frac{19}{38} = \frac{f}{21}$

Percents, Fractions, and Decimals

Write each decimal as a percent.

13. 0.46   **14.** 0.265   **15.** 0.07   **16.** 0.256   **17.** 0.82

Write each fraction as a percent. When necessary, round to the nearest tenth of a percent.

18. $\frac{4}{5}$ **19.** $\frac{5}{11}$ **20.** $\frac{8}{14}$ **21.** $\frac{12}{30}$ **22.** $\frac{15}{32}$

What You'll Learn Next

- In this chapter, you will use probability to express how likely an event is.

- You will make predictions based on probability.

- You will represent all possible outcomes of a probability experiment.

- Applying what you learn, you will solve problems involving probability, such as estimating how likely a basketball player is to make his or her next basket.

Key Vocabulary

- complement (p. 343)
- compound event (p. 360)
- counting principle (p. 354)
- dependent events (p. 361)
- event (p. 342)
- experimental probability (p. 347)
- independent events (p. 360)
- outcome (p. 342)
- sample space (p. 353)
- simulation (p. 369)
- theoretical probability (p. 342)
- trial (p. 369)

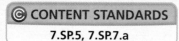

Check Skills You'll Need

1. **Vocabulary Review** In what three forms can you write a *rational number*?

Write each fraction as a decimal and as a percent.

2. $\frac{31}{50}$ 3. $\frac{19}{20}$

4. $\frac{11}{40}$ 5. $\frac{11}{10}$

 **for Help**
Lesson 6-1

CONTENT STANDARDS
7.SP.5, 7.SP.7.a

What You'll Learn

To find the probability and the complement of an event

New Vocabulary outcome, event, theoretical probability, complement

Why Learn This?

In sports, a coin toss often determines which team gets the ball first.

An **outcome** is the result of an action. For example, getting tails is a possible outcome of flipping a coin. An **event** is a collection of possible outcomes. If all the outcomes are equally likely, you can use a formula to find the theoretical probability.

KEY CONCEPTS **Theoretical Probability**

theoretical probability $= P(\text{event}) = \dfrac{\text{number of favorable outcomes}}{\text{total number of possible outcomes}}$

You can express probability as a fraction, a decimal, or a percent.

EXAMPLE **Finding Probability**

1. You select a letter at random from the letters shown. Find the probability of selecting a vowel. Express the probability as a fraction, a decimal, and a percent.

Each outcome is equally likely. The event *vowel* has 2 outcomes, A and E, out of 5 possible outcomes.

$P(\text{vowel}) = \dfrac{2}{5}$ ← **number of favorable outcomes**
← **total number of possible outcomes**

$= \dfrac{2}{5}, 0.4,$ or 40% ← **Write as a fraction, decimal, and percent.**

Vocabulary Tip

You read $P(\text{vowel})$ as "the probability of a vowel."

Quick Check

1. Find $P(\text{consonant})$ as a fraction for the letters in Example 1.

Video Tutor Help

PearsonSuccessNet.com

All probabilities range from 0 to 1. The probability of rolling a 7 on a number cube is 0, so that is an *impossible* event. The probability of rolling a positive integer less than 7 is 1, so that is a *certain* event.

← less likely   more likely →

0   0.5   1
Impossible   Certain
event   event

The **complement** of an event is the collection of outcomes not contained in the event. The sum of the probabilities of an event and its complement is 1. So $P(\text{event}) + P(\text{not event}) = 1$.

EXAMPLES **Finding Probabilities From 0 to 1**

2 **Clothes** The picture shows the jeans in Juanita's closet. She selects a pair of jeans with her eyes shut. Find $P(\text{dark color})$.

There are 8 possible outcomes. Since there are 3 black pairs and 2 blue pairs, the event *dark color* has 5 favorable outcomes.

$$P(\text{dark color}) = \frac{5}{8} \quad \begin{array}{l} \leftarrow \textbf{number of favorable outcomes} \\ \leftarrow \textbf{total number of possible outcomes} \end{array}$$

3 Refer to Juanita's closet. Find $P(\text{red})$.

The event *red* has no favorable outcome.

$$P(\text{red}) = \frac{0}{8}, \text{ or } 0 \quad \begin{array}{l} \leftarrow \textbf{number of favorable outcomes} \\ \leftarrow \textbf{total number of possible outcomes} \end{array}$$

4 Refer to Juanita's closet. Find $P(\text{not dark color})$.

$$P(\text{dark color}) + P(\text{not dark color}) = 1 \quad \leftarrow \begin{array}{l} \textbf{The sum of probabilities of an} \\ \textbf{event and its complement is 1.} \end{array}$$

$$\frac{5}{8} + P(\text{not dark color}) = 1 \quad \leftarrow \textbf{Substitute } \tfrac{5}{8} \textbf{ for } P(\text{dark color}).$$

$$\frac{5}{8} - \frac{5}{8} + P(\text{not dark color}) = 1 - \frac{5}{8} \quad \leftarrow \begin{array}{l} \textbf{Subtract } \tfrac{5}{8} \textbf{ from} \\ \textbf{each side.} \end{array}$$

$$P(\text{not dark color}) = \frac{3}{8} \quad \leftarrow \textbf{Simplify.}$$

GO for Help

For help with subtracting rational numbers go to Lesson 1-6, Example 2.

✓ Quick Check

You roll a number cube once. Find each probability.

2. $P(\text{multiple of } 3)$ **3.** $P(\text{not multiple of } 2)$ **4.** $P(9)$

1. **Vocabulary** Define *event* without using the word *outcome*.

2. $P(A) = \frac{1}{3}$. Write an expression for $P(\text{not A})$.

You select a marble from those shown. Match each event with its probability.

3. $P(\text{red})$ **A.** $\frac{5}{7}$

4. $P(\text{yellow})$ **B.** $\frac{2}{7}$

5. $P(\text{blue})$ **C.** 0

6. $P(\text{red or blue})$ **D.** 1

Homework Exercises

For more exercises, see Extra Skills and Word Problems.

GO for Help

For Exercises	See Examples
7–12	1
13–21	2

You mix the letters A, C, Q, U, A, I, N, T, A, N, C, and E thoroughly. Without looking, you select one letter. Find the probability of each event as a fraction, a decimal, and a percent.

7. $P(T)$ 8. $P(A)$ 9. $P(\text{vowel})$

10. $P(\text{consonant})$ 11. $P(N)$ 12. $P(Q \text{ or } C)$

You spin the spinner once. Find each probability.

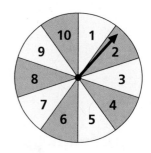

13. $P(12)$ 14. $P(2 \text{ or } 4)$

15. $P(\text{multiple of } 3)$ 16. $P(\text{even})$

17. $P(\text{not } 1)$ 18. $P(\text{not a factor of } 10)$

19. $P(\text{less than } 11)$ 20. $P(\text{not divisible by } 3)$

21. **Science** Six out of the 114 elements are noble gases. You write the names of all the elements on cards and select a card at random. What is the probability of *not* picking a noble gas?

22. **Guided Problem Solving** The table shows data about a group of people's hair colors. You select a person at random from the group. What is $P(\text{not black hair})$?
    - How many people are in the group?
    - How many people do *not* have black hair?

Hair Color	
Color	**Number**
Blond	58
Brown	64
Black	97

GO Online
Homework Video Tutor
PearsonSuccessNet.com

23. **Writing in Math** Describe a real-life situation where the probability of an event is 1. Then describe the complement of that situation.

You choose a card at random from a set of ten cards numbered 1 to 10. Classify each event as *unlikely*, *likely*, or *neither unlikely nor likely*.

24. Choosing a card numbered with a multiple of 2

25. Choosing a card numbered with a multiple of 4

Government The U.S. House of Representatives has 435 members. Each member's name is put into a hat and one name is chosen at random. Find each probability as a decimal to the nearest hundredth.

26. P(Florida)

27. P(Texas)

28. P(not Illinois)

29. P(Pennsylvania)

U.S. House of Representatives

State	Number	State	Number
Florida	27	Illinois	18
Pennsylvania	18	Texas	36

SOURCE: U.S. Census Bureau.

30. a. Suppose $P(E) = 0.3$. Find $P(\text{not } E)$.

   b. Suppose $P(\text{not } E) = 65\%$. Find $P(E)$.

31. Challenge A bag contains an unknown number of marbles. You know that $P(\text{red}) = \frac{1}{4}$ and $P(\text{green}) = \frac{1}{4}$. What can you conclude about how many marbles are in the bag?

Test Prep and Mixed Review   **Practice**

Multiple Choice

32. A weather forecast states that there is an 80% probability of rain tomorrow. Which term best describes the likelihood of rain tomorrow?
   - Ⓐ impossible
   - Ⓑ unlikely
   - Ⓒ likely
   - Ⓓ certain

33. The model represents the equation $3x + 5 = 14$. What is the value of x?
   - Ⓕ $x = \frac{11}{5}$
   - Ⓖ $x = 6$
   - Ⓗ $x = 3$
   - Ⓙ $x = \frac{19}{3}$

34. Karl buys a pair of jeans that regularly costs $38. They are on sale for 25% off. Karl also buys a shirt that costs $23. The sales tax is 4.5%. What other information is necessary to find Karl's correct change?
   - Ⓐ The sale price of the jeans
   - Ⓑ The total cost of the purchase
   - Ⓒ The amount he paid for the sales tax
   - Ⓓ The amount he gave the cashier

For Exercises	See Lesson
35–37	1-7

Find each product.

35. $1.2 \cdot (-3.4)$ **36.** $(-0.6) \cdot (-9.4)$ **37.** $-\frac{1}{3} \cdot \frac{3}{8}$

Exploring Probability

If you toss one coin 100 times, you might expect to get heads and tails about the same number of times. What happens when you toss *two* coins 100 times?

EXAMPLE

Toss two coins 10 times. Record the results. Use the results to determine which event is most likely: two heads (HH), two tails (TT), or one head and one tail (HT).

The table below shows one set of results.

Toss	1	2	3	4	5	6	7	8	9	10
Result	HH	HT	HT	TT	HH	HT	TT	HT	HH	HT

In all, there are three outcomes of HH, two outcomes of TT, and five outcomes of HT. One head and one tail is the most likely event.

Exercises

1. Conduct an experiment in which you use two coins, such as a penny and a nickel. Place them in a small paper cup. Cover the top, and shake the cup before each coin toss. Toss both coins 100 times. Make a table to record each result.

2. Are your results similar to other students' results? Explain.

3. **Reasoning** Are the three outcomes all equally likely? Or is one outcome more likely to occur than the others? Explain.

Three students play the game at the right.

4. Is a game with these rules fair? Explain why or why not.

5. **Open-Ended** How might you change the rules to make the game fair?

6. Conduct an experiment to test your new game. Do you still think your game is fair? Explain.

GAME RULES

1. Player A receives 1 point if two heads (HH) are tossed.

2. Player B receives 1 point if two tails (TT) are tossed.

3. Player C receives 1 point if one head and one tail (HT) are tossed.

Experimental Probability

Check Skills You'll Need

1. **Vocabulary Review** Explain the difference between an *event* and an *outcome*.

You roll a number cube once. Find each probability.

2. $P(4)$

3. $P(\text{multiple of } 2)$

4. $P(8)$

 **for Help**
Lesson 9-1

© **CONTENT STANDARDS**
7.SP.6, 7.SP.7, 7.SP.7.b

What You'll Learn

To find experimental probability and to use simulations

New Vocabulary experimental probability

Why Learn This?

Manufacturers collect data on the quality of their products. They use experimental probability to determine how many defective items they can expect to produce.

Probability based on experimental data or observations is called **experimental probability.**

KEY CONCEPTS **Experimental Probability**

$$P(\text{event}) = \frac{\text{number of times an event occurs}}{\text{total number of trials}}$$

EXAMPLE **Finding Experimental Probability**

Video Tutor Help
PearsonSuccessNet.com

1. You attempt 16 free throws in a basketball game. Your results are shown. What is the experimental probability of making a free throw?

Results of Free Throw Attempts

0 = miss			1 = make				
0	0	1	1	1	0	1	0
0	1	0	1	1	0	0	1

$P(\text{free throw}) = \dfrac{8}{16} \leftarrow$ **number of throws made**
$\phantom{P(\text{free throw}) = \dfrac{8}{16}} \leftarrow$ **total number of attempted free throws**

$\phantom{P(\text{free throw})} = \dfrac{1}{2} \quad \leftarrow$ **Simplify.**

The experimental probability of making a free throw is $\frac{1}{2}$.

Quick Check

1. In 60 coin tosses, 25 are tails. Find the experimental probability of getting tails.

2 **Multiple Choice** A bicycle company checks a random sample of bikes. The results are shown. If the trend continues, which is the best prediction of the number of defective bikes in a batch of 1,300?

Quality Control Results	
Defective Bikes	Bikes Checked
12	400

Ⓐ 430 bikes   Ⓑ 390 bikes   Ⓒ 43 bikes   Ⓓ 39 bikes

The experimental probability that a bike is defective is $\frac{12}{400}$, or $\frac{3}{100}$.

Let x represent the predicted number of defective bikes.

defective bikes → $\frac{3}{100} = \frac{x}{1,300}$ ← defective bikes
bikes checked →   ← bikes checked   ← **Write a proportion.**

$3(1,300) = 100x$ ← **Write the cross products.**

$3,900 = 100x$ ← **Simplify.**

$\frac{3,900}{100} = \frac{100x}{100}$ ← **Divide each side by 100.**

$39 = x$ ← **Simplify.**

You can predict that 39 bikes are defective. The correct answer is D.

✅ Quick Check

2. Predict the number of defective bikes in a batch of 3,500.

You can simulate, or model, events to find experimental probabilities.

EXAMPLE **Simulating an Event**

3 Find the experimental probability that 2 of 3 children in a family are girls. Assume that girls and boys are equally likely.

Simulate the problem by tossing three coins. Let "heads" represent a girl and "tails" represent a boy. A sample of 20 coin tosses is shown.

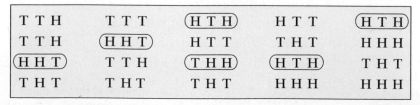

T T H	T T T	(H T H)	H T T	(H T H)
T T H	(H H T)	H T T	T H T	H H H
(H H T)	T T H	(T H H)	(H T H)	T H T
T H T	T H T	T H T	H H H	H H H

$P(\text{two girls}) = \frac{6}{20}$, or $\frac{3}{10}$ ← number of times *two heads* occur
← total number of tosses

The experimental probability that 2 of 3 children are girls is $\frac{3}{10}$.

✅ Quick Check

3. What is the experimental probability that 3 children are all boys?

1. **Vocabulary** What is the difference between theoretical probability and experimental probability? Explain.

You toss a coin 40 times and get 18 tails. Find each experimental probability.

2. $P(\text{heads}) = \frac{22}{\blacksquare}$

3. $P(\text{tails}) = \frac{\blacksquare}{40}$

4. **Mental Math** In a bird sanctuary, the experimental probability that any bird you see is a robin is about $\frac{1}{8}$. Suppose this trend continues. There are 48 birds. Predict the number of robins you see.

5. You want to find the probability that three out of five babies are boys. You decide to toss coins to simulate the problem. How many coins would you use? Explain.

Homework Exercises

For more exercises, see Extra Skills and Word Problems.

GO for Help

For Exercises	See Examples
6–8	1-2
9–12	3

Find each experimental probability.

6. tosses: 80; tails: 40; $P(\text{tails}) = \underline{\ ?\ }$

7. tosses: 250; heads: 180; $P(\text{heads}) = \underline{\ ?\ }$

8. **Manufacturing** The quality-control engineer of Top Notch Tool Company finds flaws in 8 of 60 wrenches examined. Predict the number of flawed wrenches in a batch of 2,400.

Baseball A baseball team averages one win to every one loss. Use a simulation to find each experimental probability for three games.

9. $P(\text{three wins})$

10. $P(\text{1 win and 2 losses})$

11. $P(\text{2 wins and 1 loss})$

12. $P(\text{three losses})$

13. **Guided Problem Solving** During hockey practice, Yuri blocked 19 out of 30 shots and Gene blocked 17 out of 24 shots. For the first game, the coach wants to choose the goalie with the greater probability of blocking a shot. Which player should he choose?
    - **Make a Plan** Find the experimental probability that each player will block the shot.

14. a. **Science** The probability that a male human is colorblind is 8%. Suppose you interview 1,000 males. About how many would you expect to be colorblind?
    b. **Reasoning** Will you always get the same number? Explain.

15. A company checks washers at four plants and records the number of defective washers. Find each experimental probability.

Plant	Number of Washers	Number Defective	P(Defective)
1	2,940	588	■
2	1,860	93	■
3	640	26	■
4	3,048	54	■

Data Analysis Use the data shown. Find each experimental probability.

16. P(Sunday) **17.** P(Monday)

18. P(Tuesday) **19.** P(Friday)

20. P(weekday) **21.** P(weekend)

Students' Birthdays

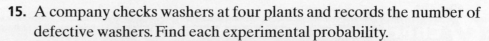

Su M Tu W Th F Sa

22. Writing in Math Describe a possible simulation to solve the following problem. You guess on six true-or-false questions. What is the probability that you guess exactly two answers correctly?

23. Challenge On any day, a company has x torn posters in stock. On Monday, the total number of posters is 252. Express P(torn) on Monday in terms of x. If $P(\text{torn}) = \frac{1}{42}$, what is x?

Test Prep and Mixed Review **Practice**

Multiple Choice

24. The picture shows the number of colored shirts sold this week at Joan's Clothing Shop. What is the experimental probability that the next shirt sold at the store will be blue?

10 Blue Shirts 3 Gray Shirts 5 Orange Shirts 8 Green Shirts

Ⓐ $\frac{1}{10}$ Ⓑ $\frac{1}{4}$ Ⓒ $\frac{5}{13}$ Ⓓ $\frac{5}{8}$

25. The scale on a map of Texas is 1 in. : 31 mi. Which distance on the map should represent the 420 mi from Amarillo to El Paso?

Ⓕ 1.25 in.   Ⓖ 13.5 in.   Ⓗ 135 in.   Ⓙ 13,824 in.

You spin the spinner once. Find each probability.

26. P(purple)   **27.** P(blue)

28. P(blue or yellow)   **29.** P(not yellow)

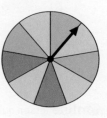

Random Numbers

You can use a random number table to simulate some problems. To generate a random number table in a spreadsheet, follow these steps.

Step 1 Highlight the group of cells to use for your table.

Step 2 Select the Format Cells menu.

Step 3 Choose the category Custom and enter 0000. Click OK.

Step 4 Use the formula RAND()*10,000. This will make a group of 4 digits in each cell of a spreadsheet. (*Note:* Each time you generate a random number table, you will get a different group of digits.)

	A	B	C	D
1	2260	1927	7807	0912
2	8879	6235	5897	8068
3	8121	4646	8368	1613
4	0821	8911	3022	0307
5	9393	5403	4930	4898

EXAMPLE

A rare lily bulb has a 50% chance of growing. You plant four bulbs. What is the experimental probability that all four will grow?

Use the random number table. Let even digits represent *grows*, and let odd digits represent *does not grow*. Then a 4-digit number of all even digits represents the event *all four grow*. Of 20 groups, 3 consist entirely of even digits. So the experimental probability of four bulbs growing is $\frac{3}{20}$, or 15%.

```
2260  1927  7807  0912
8879  6235  5897  8068
8121  4646  8368  1613
0821  8911  3022  0307
9393  5403  4930  4898
```

← Any group of 4 even digits represents *all four grow.*

Exercises

Use the random number table above or generate your own.

1. Suppose there is a 30% probability of being stopped by a red light at each of four stoplights. What is the experimental probability of being stopped by at least two red lights? Let 0, 1, and 2 represent red lights.

2. **Reasoning** Suppose there is a 60% chance of a red light at each stoplight. How many digits would you use to represent getting a red light? Explain.

3. **Writing in Math** Write a probability problem you can solve using a random number table. Solve your problem.

You spin the spinner at the right once. Write each probability as a fraction, a decimal, and a percent.

1. $P(2 \text{ or } 3)$ **2.** $P(\text{even})$ **3.** $P(\text{not } 4)$ **4.** $P(\text{not even})$

You roll a number cube. Classify each event as *unlikely, likely,* or *neither unlikely nor likely*.

5. Rolling a 3   **6.** Rolling a number less than 4

Forestry The table shows a sample of the number of spruce trees counted in a forest area. Use the table for Exercises 7 and 8.

7. Find the experimental probability of selecting a Serbian spruce.

8. The forest area includes approximately 68,000 spruce trees. To the nearest thousand, predict the number of Norway spruce trees in the forest area.

9. A true-or-false quiz has five questions. Use a simulation to find the probability of guessing at random and getting exactly three correct answers.

Spruce Trees

Tree Type	Number
Norway spruce	32
Serbian spruce	20
Colorado spruce	67

MATH AT WORK

Meteorologist

Meteorologists are scientists who study weather conditions. Some meteorologists work as weather reporters for television or radio stations. Others work for the National Weather Service or the Armed Forces.

One of the most important tools meteorologists use are computer models. These models take information about current weather conditions and use it to make predictions about future weather conditions.

For example, based on a computer model, a meteorologist might predict that there is a 60% probability of rain in your city tomorrow. This prediction indicates that rain is likely, so be sure to take an umbrella!

Go Online For information about meteorologists
PearsonSuccessNet.com

ⓒ **CONTENT STANDARDS**
7.SP.8, 7.SP.8.b

Test Prep Tip

When you construct a sample space for two events, pair each possible outcome for the first event with each possible outcome for the second event.

What You'll Learn

To make and use sample spaces and to use the counting principle

New Vocabulary sample space, counting principle

Why Learn This?

When you are at a salad bar, you can choose from different vegetables, fruits, and dressings. You may want to know all the possible combinations of ingredients you can use.

The collection of all possible outcomes in an experiment is the **sample space**. You can use the sample space to find the probability of an event.

EXAMPLE   Finding a Sample Space

1 **a.** Make a table to find the sample space for rolling two number cubes colored red and blue. Write the outcomes as ordered pairs.

	1	2	3	4	5	6
1	(1, 1)	(2, 1)	(3, 1)	(4, 1)	(5, 1)	(6, 1)
2	(1, 2)	(2, 2)	(3, 2)	(4, 2)	(5, 2)	(6, 2)
3	(1, 3)	(2, 3)	(3, 3)	(4, 3)	(5, 3)	(6, 3)
4	(1, 4)	(2, 4)	(3, 4)	(4, 4)	(5, 4)	(6, 4)
5	(1, 5)	(2, 5)	(3, 5)	(4, 5)	(5, 5)	(6, 5)
6	(1, 6)	(2, 6)	(3, 6)	(4, 6)	(5, 6)	(6, 6)

← There are 36 possible outcomes.

b. Find the probability of rolling at least one 3.

There are 11 outcomes with at least one 3. There are 36 possible outcomes. So the probability of rolling at least one 3 is $\frac{11}{36}$.

✓ Quick Check

1. Give the sample space for tossing two coins. Find the probability of getting two heads.

You can also show a sample space by using a tree diagram. Each branch of the tree represents one choice.

EXAMPLE Using a Tree Diagram

② **River Travel** Suppose you are going to travel on a river. You have two choices of boats—a kayak or a rowboat. You can go upstream on three smaller streams, to the north, northwest, and northeast.

a. What is the sample space for your journey?

Make a tree diagram for the possible outcomes.

Boat	Stream	Outcome
	North	Kayak, North
Kayak	Northwest	Kayak, Northwest
	Northeast	Kayak, Northeast
	North	Rowboat, North
Rowboat	Northwest	Rowboat, Northwest
	Northeast	Rowboat, Northeast

← There are six possible outcomes.

b. Suppose you select a trip at random. What is the probability of selecting a kayak and going directly north?

There is one favorable outcome (kayak, north) out of six possible outcomes. The probability is $\frac{1}{6}$.

✓ Quick Check

2. **a.** Suppose a canoe is added as another choice of boats in Example 2. Draw a tree diagram to show the sample space.
   b. Find the probability of selecting a canoe at random for the trip.

In Example 2 above, there are 2 choices of boats and 3 choices of direction. There are 2 × 3, or 6, total possible choices. This suggests a simple way to find the number of outcomes—using the **counting principle.**

KEY CONCEPTS The Counting Principle

Suppose there are *m* ways of making one choice and *n* ways of making a second choice. Then there are *m* × *n* ways to make the first choice followed by the second choice.

Example
If you can choose a shirt in 5 sizes and 7 colors, then you can choose among 5 × 7, or 35, shirts.

EXAMPLE **Using the Counting Principle**

3 **Gridded Response** How many different sandwiches can you order when you choose one bread and one meat from the menu?

Use the counting principle.

  Bread   **Meat**
number of choices × number of choices
      5   ×   6   =   30

There are 30 different sandwiches available.

THE DELI COUNTER
SANDWICHES

FRESH BREADS	DELI MEATS
Rye	Roast Beef
Wheat	Turkey
White	Ham
Pita	Pastrami
Wrap	Salami
	Liverwurst

✓ Quick Check

3. A manager at the Deli Counter decides to add chicken to the list of meat choices. How many different sandwiches are now available?

✓ Check Your Understanding

1. **Vocabulary** What is a sample space?

2. Complete the tree diagram for tossing a coin three times.

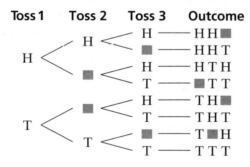

Toss 1   Toss 2   Toss 3   Outcome

H — HH■
H < ■ — HHT
H < H — HTH
    ■ < T — ■TT
    H — TH■
T < T — THT
T < ■ — T■H
    T — TTT

Use your completed diagram from Exercise 2 to find each probability.

3. $P(\text{HHH}) = \dfrac{■}{8}$ 4. $P(\text{TTT}) = \dfrac{1}{■}$

5. $P(\text{at least one H}) = \dfrac{■}{8}$ 6. $P(\text{exactly 2 T's}) = \dfrac{■}{8}$

7. If you toss 4 coins, how many possible outcomes are there?

8. Find the number of different couches that you can make using 16 different fabrics and 8 patterns.

9. **Multiple Choice** An architect has 3 different widths he can use for a rectangular building design. He also has 4 different lengths to use for the design. How many different designs are possible?
   Ⓐ 3   Ⓑ 4   Ⓒ 7   Ⓓ 12

For more exercises, see Extra Skills and Word Problems.

GO for Help

For Exercises	See Examples
10–12	1
13–14	2
15–16	3

Make a table to show the sample space for each situation and find the number of outcomes. Then find the probability.

10. You toss two coins. What is the probability of getting one tail and one head?

11. You roll a number cube once. What is the probability of rolling a number less than 4?

12. You toss a coin and spin a spinner. The spinner has four equal sections that are numbered from 1 to 4. Find the probability of getting tails and spinning a 4.

Make a tree diagram. Then find the probability of each event.

13. A spinner is half red and half blue. If you spin the spinner twice, what is the probability that you will get red both times?

14. You choose at random from the letters A, B, C, and D, and you roll a number cube once. What are the chances you get A and 5?

Use the counting principle.

15. **Cooking** You make a recipe with herbs and spices for a party. You have four herbs—basil, bay leaves, chives, and dill. You also have three spices—paprika, pepper, and garlic powder. How many different recipes with one herb and one spice can you make?

16. **Education** A school has four art teachers, three music teachers, and eight history teachers. In how many ways can a student be assigned an art teacher, a music teacher, and a history teacher?

GPS 17. **Guided Problem Solving** A traveler chooses one city tour at random from buses D, E, and F. He then chooses one harbor tour at random from boats 1, 2, and 3. What is the probability that he takes tours with bus D and boat 2?
- Draw a diagram of all the possible outcomes.
- How many outcomes include tours with bus D and boat 2?

A spinner has four equal sections numbered 1 through 4. You spin it twice. Use the sample space below to find each probability.

18. $P(1, 2)$

19. $P(1, \text{odd})$

20. $P(\text{even}, \text{odd})$

GO Online
Homework Video Tutor
PearsonSuccessNet.com

	Second Spin			
	1	**2**	**3**	**4**
First Spin 1	(1, 1)	(1, 2)	(1, 3)	(1, 4)
2	(2, 1)	(2, 2)	(2, 3)	(2, 4)
3	(3, 1)	(3, 2)	(3, 3)	(3, 4)
4	(4, 1)	(4, 2)	(4, 3)	(4, 4)

Find the number of outcomes for each situation.

21. Pick one of 7 boys and one of 12 girls.

22. Toss five coins once each.

23. a. Clothes Ardell has four suit jackets (white, blue, green, and tan) and four dress shirts in the same colors. How many different jacket-and-shirt outfits does Ardell have?

    b. Suppose he grabs a suit jacket and a dress shirt without looking. What is the probability that they will *not* be the same color?

24. <u>**Writing in Math**</u> Explain how to use the counting principle to find the number of outcomes in a sample space.

Careers Tailors fit designer clothes for important events.

Use the menu for Exercises 25–28.

25. List all the possible drink orders.

26. You order lemonade and popcorn. Draw a tree diagram to show the sample space.

27. Reasoning A manager uses the counting principle to find P(small popcorn, medium lemonade) $= \frac{1}{24}$. Do you agree? Explain.

28. Challenge Find the probability that you randomly select the same size popcorn and drink.

CITY CINEMA

POPCORN
small $3.00
medium . .$4.00
large $5.00

FRUIT PUNCH or LEMONADE
small $2.75
medium . .$3.00
large $3.25
jumbo . . . $3.75

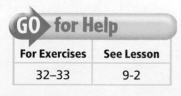

Test Prep and Mixed Review   **Practice**

Gridded Response

29. Trista has purple, yellow, and red wrapping paper. She can use blue or white ribbon. She has four shapes of gift tags. In how many different ways can she choose one wrapping paper, one ribbon, and one gift tag?

30. The 7th grade class had a vote for class president. There are 350 students in the 7th grade class, and 63% of the class voted for the winning candidate. About how many students voted for the winner?

31. Suppose $\frac{21}{25}$ of your classmates can attend your birthday party. What is this fraction expressed as a decimal?

Lee makes 3 goals out of 9 attempts in a hockey game. Use this information for Exercises 32 and 33.

32. What is the experimental probability that Lee does not make a goal?

33. Predict how many goals Lee will make out of 15 attempts.

For Exercises	See Lesson
32–33	9-2

Using Data to Predict

Katie and Tim play the following game to decide who should mow the lawn each week.

- Katie or Tim places three black marbles and three white marbles into a bag.
- Tim pulls out two marbles.
- If the marbles match, Katie mows the lawn. Otherwise, Tim mows the lawn.

The table below shows the results of the first 15 trials.

Marble Selection Results

Event	Number of Times
Marbles matched	6
No match	9

ACTIVITY

1. **Estimation** Use the data from the table above. Assume the data trend continues. For Katie and Tim, estimate the number of times that each one mows the lawn in 45 trials.

2. **Data Collection** Simulate the game with three red cubes and three yellow cubes. Put the cubes in a bag. Select two cubes at random. Record whether or not they match. Return the cubes to the bag, and repeat until you have recorded 45 trials.

3. **Reasoning** Describe how the results of your experiment compare to your predictions. Is the game fair? Explain.

4. Tim thinks the probability that the marbles match equals the probability that they do not match. Use diagrams and what you have learned to show why the probabilities are not equal. Find the probability that the two marbles match and the probability that they do not match.

5. Add a fourth cube of each color into the bag. Find the probability of selecting two cubes that match. Predict the number of matches in 49 trials.

6. **Data Analysis** Test your prediction. Record the results of 49 trials. Compare your results to your prediction. Is this game more fair or less fair than the original game? Explain.

Exploring Multiple Events

You want to make a necklace using two colors of beads. You decide which colors to use by selecting from the beads at the right. You select the first bead at random. You put the bead back and make another selection at random.

ACTIVITY

1. Copy and complete the table to show the sample space for the colors of the two beads. Use Y for yellow, G for green, R for red, and B for blue. Write the outcomes as ordered pairs.

First Bead

	Y	G	R	B
Y				
G				
R				
B				

Second Bead

2. What is the probability that you will select the yellow bead first?

3. If the first bead is yellow, what is the probability that you will select the blue bead second?

4. What is the probability that you will select the yellow bead first and the blue bead second? Explain how you know.

5. Suppose you now select a bead and do *not* replace it before selecting a second bead. How many beads are there to choose from when you select the second bead?

6. Make a tree diagram to show the sample space for selecting one bead and then selecting a second bead *without* replacing the first bead.

7. If the first bead is yellow, what is the probability that you will select the blue bead second if you do *not* replace the first bead?

8. What is the probability of selecting the yellow bead first and the blue bead second when the first bead is *not* replaced? Explain how you know.

9. **Reasoning** Does the probability of selecting the yellow bead first and the blue bead second depend on whether you replace the first bead? Explain.

Check Skills You'll Need

1. **Vocabulary Review** Use the terms *numerator* and *denominator* to describe how to multiply two rational numbers written as fractions.

Find each product.
2. $\frac{3}{4} \cdot \frac{3}{4}$ 3. $\frac{3}{5} \cdot \left(-\frac{2}{5}\right)$
4. $\frac{1}{5} \cdot \frac{1}{4}$ 5. $-\frac{3}{7} \cdot \left(-\frac{2}{7}\right)$

 **for Help**
Lesson 1-7

CONTENT STANDARDS
7.SP.8, 7.SP.8.a, 7.SP.8.b

What You'll Learn

To find the probability of independent and dependent events
New Vocabulary compound event, independent events, dependent events

Why Learn This?

You can find the probability of more than one event, such as winning a game twice.

A **compound event** consists of two or more events. Two events are **independent events** if the occurrence of one event does not affect the probability of the occurrence of the other.

KEY CONCEPTS **Probability of Independent Events**

If A and B are independent events, then $P(A, \text{then } B) = P(A) \times P(B)$.

EXAMPLE **Probability of Independent Events**

1 **Multiple Choice** You and a friend play a game twice. What is the probability that you win both games? Assume $P(\text{win})$ is $\frac{1}{2}$.

Ⓐ $\frac{1}{2}$ Ⓑ $\frac{4}{9}$ Ⓒ $\frac{1}{4}$ Ⓓ $\frac{1}{8}$

$P(\text{win, then win}) = P(\text{win}) \times P(\text{win})$ ← Winning is the first and second event.
$= \frac{1}{2} \times \frac{1}{2}$ ← Substitute $\frac{1}{2}$ for $P(\text{win})$.
$= \frac{1}{4}$ ← Multiply.

The probability of winning both games is $\frac{1}{4}$. The correct answer is C.

Quick Check

1. Find $P(\text{win, then lose})$.

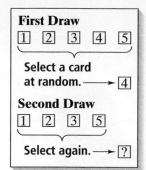

First Draw

| 1 | 2 | 3 | 4 | 5 |

Select a card
at random. ⟶ 4

Second Draw

| 1 | 2 | 3 | 5 |

Select again. ⟶ ?

Suppose you play a game with cards numbered 1–5. You draw two cards at random. You draw the first card and do not replace it. The probability in the second draw depends on the result of the first draw.

Two events are **dependent events** if the occurrence of one event affects the probability of the occurrence of the other event.

> **KEY CONCEPTS** **Probability of Dependent Events**
>
> If event B depends on event A, then
> $P(A, \text{ then } B) = P(A) \times P(B \text{ after } A)$.

EXAMPLES **Probability of Dependent Events**

2 You select a card at random from those below. The card has the letter M. Without replacing the M card, you select a second card. Find the probability that you select a card with the letter A after you select M.

| M | A | T | H | E | M | A | T | I | C | S |

There are 10 cards remaining after you select an M card.

$$P(A) = \frac{2}{10} \quad \leftarrow \text{ number of cards with the letter A} \atop \leftarrow \text{ number of cards remaining}$$

$$= \frac{1}{5} \quad \leftarrow \text{ Simplify.}$$

The probability of selecting an A for the second card is $\frac{1}{5}$.

**Online
active math**

For: Probability Activity
Use: Interactive
Textbook, 9-4

3 You select a card from a bucket that contains 26 cards lettered A–Z without looking. Without replacing the first card, you select a second one. Find the probability of choosing C and then M.

The events are dependent. After the first selection, 25 letters remain.

$$P(C, \text{ then } M) = P(C) \times P(M \text{ after } C) \quad \leftarrow \text{ Use the formula for} \atop \text{ dependent events.}$$

$$= \frac{1}{26} \times \frac{1}{25} \quad \leftarrow \text{ Substitute.}$$

$$= \frac{1}{650} \quad \leftarrow \text{ Multiply.}$$

The probability of choosing C and then M is $\frac{1}{650}$.

✓ Quick Check

2. Use the cards in Example 2. You select a T card at random. Without replacing the T card, you select a second card. Find $P(S)$.

3. Suppose another 26 cards lettered A–Z are put in the bucket in Example 3. Find $P(J, \text{ then } J)$.

More Than One Way

You toss a coin three times. What is the probability of getting three heads?

Brianna's Method

Each toss of a coin is an independent event. The probability of getting heads for one coin toss is $\frac{1}{2}$. I can multiply the probabilities of the three coin tosses.

$$P(\text{three heads}) = \frac{1}{2} \times \frac{1}{2} \times \frac{1}{2} = \frac{1}{8}$$

The probability of three heads is $\frac{1}{8}$.

Chris's Method

I can make a tree diagram for the coin tosses. A favorable outcome is one with 3 heads.

The tree diagram shows 1 favorable outcome out of 8 possible outcomes. The probability of three heads is $\frac{1}{8}$.

Toss 1	Toss 2	Toss 3	Outcome
		H	H H H
	H	T	H H T
H		H	H T H
	T	T	H T T
		H	T H H
	H	T	T H T
T		H	T T H
	T	T	T T T

Choose a Method

You toss a coin four times. What is the probability of getting tails all four times? Describe your method and explain why you chose it.

Check Your Understanding

1. **Vocabulary** How do independent and dependent events differ?

2. **Multiple Choice** Two independent events A and B both have a probability of $\frac{1}{3}$. Which expression represents $P(\text{A, then B})$?

   Ⓐ $\frac{1}{3} + \frac{1}{3}$ Ⓑ $\frac{1}{3} \times \frac{1}{3}$ Ⓒ $\frac{1}{3} + \frac{1}{2}$ Ⓓ $\frac{1}{3} \times \frac{1}{2}$

Are the two events *independent* or *dependent*?

3. You toss a nickel. Then you toss a dime.

4. You select a card. Then you select again without replacement.

GO for Help

For Exercises	See Examples
5–10	1
11–19	2
20–22	3

You roll a number cube twice. Find each probability.

5. $P(1, \text{then } 2)$

6. $P(3, \text{then even})$

7. $P(\text{less than } 4, \text{then } 1)$

8. $P(\text{odd, then even})$

9. $P(\text{divisible by } 2, \text{then } 5)$

10. $P(\text{greater than } 2, \text{then odd})$

An arrangement of 8 students is shown below. The numbers of all the students are in a basket. The teacher selects a number and replaces it. Then the teacher selects a second number. Find each probability.

11. $P(\text{student } 1, \text{then student } 8)$

12. $P(\text{student in row A, then student in row B})$

13. $P(\text{student in row A, then student } 6, 7, \text{or } 8)$

Row	Student			
A	1	2	3	4
B	5	6	7	8

You select the letter A from the group. Without replacing the A, you select a second letter. Find each probability.

14. $P(Z)$

15. $P(\text{vowel})$

16. $P(\text{red})$

17. $P(\text{blue})$

18. $P(\text{consonant})$

19. $P(\text{not K})$

A box contains 20 cards numbered 1–20. You select a card. Without replacing the first card, you select a second card. Find each probability.

20. $P(1, \text{then } 20)$

21. $P(3, \text{then even})$

22. $P(\text{even, then } 7)$

23. Guided Problem Solving Five girls and seven boys want to be the two broadcasters for a school show. To be fair, a teacher puts their names in a hat and selects two. Find $P(\text{girl, then boy})$.

- **Make a Plan** The selections of the two names are (dependent, independent) events. Find the probability of selecting a girl first. Then find the probability of selecting a boy after selecting a girl.
- **Carry Out the Plan** $P(\text{girl first}) = \frac{5}{\blacksquare}$; $P(\text{boy after girl}) = \frac{7}{\blacksquare}$

Two coins are dropped at random into the boxes in the diagram below.

24. What is the theoretical probability that both coins fall into a shaded box?

25. In 50 trials, both coins land in a shaded box twice. What is the experimental probability that both coins fall into a shaded box?

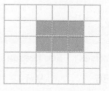

26. Events with no outcomes in common are called *disjoint events* or *mutually exclusive events*. To find the probability of mutually exclusive events, add the probabilities of the individual events. Suppose you select a number from 21 to 30 at random. What is the probability of selecting a number that is even or prime?

Choose a Method A bag contains 3 blue marbles, 4 red marbles, and 2 white marbles. Three times you draw a marble and return it. Find each probability.

27. P(red, then white, then blue)   28. P(all white)

29. **Reasoning** Events are complementary if they cover all possibilities with no overlap. Are the following sets of events *complementary, mutually exclusive,* or *neither?* Explain.
   a. A traffic light shows red, yellow, or green or is broken.
   b. A student receives an A, B, or C on a test.

30. <u>**Writing in Math**</u> When you select marbles without replacing them, are the events *independent* or *dependent?* Explain.

31. **Challenge** You have two spinners with colors on them. The probability of spinning green on both spinners is $\frac{5}{21}$. The probability of spinning green on the first one alone is $\frac{1}{3}$. What is the probability of spinning green on the second spinner alone?

Test Prep and Mixed Review   **Practice**

Multiple Choice

32. Dominica rolls a number cube once and spins the spinner shown at right once. What is the probability that she gets two odd numbers?

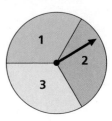

   Ⓐ $\frac{1}{18}$ Ⓑ $\frac{1}{6}$ Ⓒ $\frac{1}{4}$ Ⓓ $\frac{1}{3}$

33. Which number is NOT a perfect cube?
   Ⓕ 64   Ⓖ 125   Ⓗ 225   Ⓙ 343

34. William can spend no more than $15 at a carnival. The entrance fee to the carnival is $7, and rides cost $2 each. Which inequality best represents the number of rides r that William can afford?
   Ⓐ $r \le 4$ Ⓑ $r < 4$ Ⓒ $r \le 11$ Ⓓ $r < 11$

Make a table to show each sample space.

35. Spinning a spinner with equal sections numbered from 1 to 3 and tossing a coin

36. Guessing the answer to a true-false question and guessing the answer to a multiple-choice question with answer choices A, B, C, and D

GO for Help

For Exercises	See Lesson
35–36	9-3

Checkpoint Quiz 2

You spin the spinner twice.

1. Make a table to show the sample space.

2. Find P(green, then green).

3. Find P(purple, then blue).

4. In a board game, you randomly select one number card and one category card. The possible numbers are 1, 2, and 3. The possible categories are Science, History, Sports, Language, and Math. Assume that each outcome is equally likely. Make a tree diagram to show the sample space.

You select a letter at random from the group at the right. You replace the letter and make another selection. Find each probability.

5. P(vowel, then S)

6. P(vowel, then C)

7. P(C, then E)

8. P(T, then S)

9. P(U, then consonant)

You have 4 blue cards, 1 red card, and 3 green cards. You select a card at random, do not replace it, and select a second card. Find each probability.

10. P(green, then red)

11. P(blue, then green)

12. P(red, then blue)

MATH GAMES

Products of Winners

What You'll Need

- two number cubes

How To Play

- Take turns rolling two number cubes. Find the product of the two numbers. If the product is even, Player A scores a point. If the product is odd, Player B scores a point.
- After 15 rolls each, the player with more points wins. Who would you rather be, Player A or Player B?

Product Chart

	1	2	3	4	5	6
1	1	2	3	▪	▪	▪
2	2	4	▪	▪	▪	▪
3	▪	▪	▪	▪	▪	▪
4	▪	▪	▪	▪	▪	▪
5	▪	▪	▪	▪	▪	▪
6	▪	▪	▪	▪	▪	▪

High-Use Academic Words

High-use academic words are words that you will see often in textbooks and on tests. These words are not math vocabulary terms, but knowing them will help you succeed in mathematics.

Direction Words

Some words tell what to do in a problem. I need to understand what these words are asking so that I give the correct answer.

Word	Meaning
Analyze	To examine in detail to determine relationships
List	To present information in some order or to give examples
Persuade	To cause someone to do or believe something, especially by reasoning

Exercises

Match each situation with the correct word.

1. You do a survey in which you write the types of cereal people prefer and the number of times people choose each type of cereal.

2. You convince the manager of a diner to serve a certain type of cereal based on a survey.

3. You determine the cereal preferences of people based on a survey.

A. analyze
B. list
C. persuade

4. List all the possible outcomes of flipping a coin and rolling a number cube. Then find the probability that an outcome is heads and even.

5. Analyze the data at the right. How would you use the data to persuade a disc jockey to play hip-hop music? Explain.

6. **Word Knowledge** Think about the word *outcome*.
   a. Choose the letter for how well you know the word.
      A. I know its meaning.
      B. I've seen it, but I don't know its meaning.
      C. I don't know it.
   b. **Research** Look up and write the definition of *outcome*.
   c. Use the word in a sentence involving mathematics.

Music Preference Survey

Type of Music	Frequency
Hip-hop	𝖭𝖭𝖭 𝖭𝖭𝖭 𝖭𝖭𝖭
House	///
Country	////
Rock	𝖭𝖭𝖭 ////

Practice With Probability

Members of a math club have a drawing for three prizes based on the number of points members have earned.

Each student's name is put in a hat once for every point he or she earns. A name is drawn for first prize, then for second prize, then for third prize. A student can win only one prize. Based on the table below, what is the probability that Anna wins first prize, Cole wins second prize, and Dillon wins third prize?

Points Earned

Name	Frequency	Name	Frequency
Anna	𝟙𝟙𝟙 𝟙𝟙𝟙 𝟙𝟙𝟙 𝟙𝟙𝟙 𝟙𝟙𝟙 𝟙𝟙𝟙 𝟙𝟙𝟙 𝟙𝟙𝟙 𝟙𝟙𝟙 𝟙𝟙𝟙 𝟙𝟙𝟙 𝟙𝟙𝟙	Cole	𝟙𝟙𝟙 𝟙𝟙𝟙 𝟙𝟙𝟙 𝟙𝟙𝟙 𝟙𝟙𝟙 𝟙𝟙𝟙 𝟙𝟙𝟙 𝟙𝟙𝟙 𝟙𝟙𝟙 𝟙𝟙𝟙 𝟙
Dillon	𝟙𝟙𝟙 𝟙𝟙𝟙 𝟙𝟙𝟙 𝟙𝟙𝟙 𝟙𝟙𝟙 𝟙𝟙𝟙 𝟙𝟙𝟙 𝟙𝟙𝟙 𝟙𝟙𝟙 𝟙𝟙𝟙 𝟙𝟙𝟙 𝟙𝟙𝟙 ///	Raja	𝟙𝟙𝟙 𝟙𝟙𝟙 𝟙𝟙𝟙 𝟙𝟙𝟙 𝟙𝟙𝟙 𝟙𝟙𝟙 𝟙𝟙𝟙 𝟙𝟙𝟙 𝟙𝟙𝟙 //
Bailey	𝟙𝟙𝟙 𝟙𝟙𝟙 𝟙𝟙𝟙 𝟙𝟙𝟙 𝟙𝟙𝟙 𝟙𝟙𝟙 𝟙𝟙𝟙 /	Rosa	𝟙𝟙𝟙 𝟙𝟙𝟙 𝟙𝟙𝟙 𝟙𝟙𝟙 𝟙𝟙𝟙 𝟙𝟙𝟙 𝟙𝟙𝟙 𝟙𝟙𝟙 𝟙𝟙𝟙 ///

What You Might Think

What do I know? What do I want to find out?

How can I solve the problem?

What is the answer?

What You Might Write

I know each person's number of points. I want to know the probability that Anna wins first, Cole wins second, and Dillon wins third.

Anna's probability is $\frac{60}{300}$. After Anna wins first prize, she cannot win again. So Cole's probability of winning second is $\frac{51}{240}$. Then Dillon's probability of winning third is $\frac{53}{189}$.

The probability of the three winning in that order are $\frac{60}{300} \times \frac{51}{240} \times \frac{53}{189}$. This is about 0.01, or 1%.

Think It Through

1. Why is Anna's probability of winning first $\frac{60}{300}$? Why is Cole's probability of winning second $\frac{51}{240}$ if Anna wins first? Why is Dillon's probability of winning third $\frac{53}{189}$ if Cole wins second?

2. How can you use a calculator to verify $\frac{60}{300} \times \frac{51}{240} \times \frac{53}{189} \approx 0.01$?

Exercises

Solve each problem. For Exercise 3, answer parts (a) and (b) first.

3. Fran's probability of making a free throw in basketball is 80% based on her performance this season. If the trend continues, what is the probability she will make both of her next two free throws?
   a. What do you know? What do you want to find out?
   b. How can you solve the problem? Explain.

4. You play the card game In Between with the following rules.
   • Use 30 cards numbered 1–30.
   • You turn over two cards at random.
   • You win if the number on the next card turned over is between the numbers on the first two cards.

   For the cards displayed at the right, what is the probability you will win?

5. Janice agrees to work for her neighbor for a year. In return, her neighbor will pay her $480 and give her a car. Janice has to stop working after 9 months. Since she does not work the full year, she gets only $60 and the car. How much is the car worth?

6. George participates in a 3-mile charity walk. He averages 6 miles per hour for the first mile, 5 miles per hour for the next mile, and 4 miles per hour for the last mile. How long does it take him to walk the 3 miles?

7. Students study the advantages and disadvantages of year-round schools (YRS). They then express their opinions in a poll. A "0" means the student is strongly against YRS. A "10" means the student is strongly for YRS.

   YRS Survey Results

   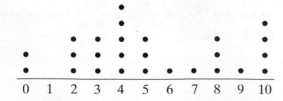

   The line plot shows the data collected. Find the mean, median, and mode of the data. Which measure best represents how the students feel about YRS? Explain.

Simulating Compound Events

What You'll Learn

To design and use simulations to estimate the probability of compound events

New Vocabulary simulation, trial

Why Learn This?

You can estimate the probability of compound events to help you determine how much you would need to spend to win a prize.

Recall that a **simulation** is a model used to estimate the probability of an event. Each **trial** of a simulation results in an outcome.

EXAMPLE   Designing a Simulation

1 A cereal company marks $\frac{1}{6}$ of its box lids with stars. If a customer gets a star, he or she wins a prize. Design a simulation for estimating the probability that a customer will need to buy at least 3 boxes to win a prize.

Step 1 Choose a simulation tool.

$\frac{1}{6}$ of the boxes are marked with stars, so use a tool that has 6 equally likely outcomes.

A number cube would be appropriate.

Step 2 Decide which outcomes are favorable.

$\frac{1}{6}$ of the outcomes should represent a box with a star.

Let rolling a 1 represent a box with a star. Let rolling any other number represent a box without a star.

Step 3 Describe a trial.

For each trial, roll the number cube until you get a 1. Keep track of the number of times you roll the cube. This number represents the number of boxes the customer must buy to win a prize.

✓ Quick Check

1. One-fourth of the deer in a population has a certain disease. Design a simulation for estimating the probability that a scientist will need to test no more than 3 deer before finding one with the disease.

Using a Simulation to Estimate Probability

2 Perform 20 trials of the simulation you designed in Example 1. Then estimate the probability that a customer will need to buy at least 3 cereal boxes to win a prize.

The table shows the results of 20 trials of the simulation. Of the 20 trials, 14 resulted in 3 or more boxes.

The probability that a customer will need to buy at least 3 boxes to win a prize is $\frac{14}{20}$, or $\frac{7}{10}$.

Boxes Needed to Win Prize	Frequency
1	IIII
2	II
3 or more	IIII IIII IIII

✓ Quick Check

2. Perform 20 trials of the simulation you designed in Quick Check 1. Then estimate the probability that a scientist will need to test no more than 3 deer before finding one that has the disease.

EXAMPLE

Using Random Digits as a Simulation Tool

3 **Journalism** In an election, 52% of voters chose Mayor Garner. Use random digits as a simulation tool to estimate the probability that a reporter will ask more than 2 voters before finding one who voted for Garner.

52% of voters, or $\frac{52}{100}$, chose Garner.

Use a simulation tool with 100 equally likely outcomes. You can use 2-digit random numbers from 00 to 99.

52 of the possible outcomes should represent voters for Garner. Use the numbers 00 to 51.

Each row of random numbers at the right represents one trial.

If either or both numbers are between 00 and 51, the reporter will need to ask 1 or 2 voters.

If neither number is between 00 and 51, the reporter will need to ask more than 2 voters.

Out of 10 trials, 3 resulted in more than 2 voters being asked.

So, the probability that a reporter will have to ask more than 2 voters before finding one who voted for Garner is approximately $\frac{3}{10}$.

Random Numbers	Outcome
06 82	← 1 voter
80 17	← 2 voters
87 65	← > 2 voters
96 96	← > 2 voters
60 68	← > 2 voters
47 39	← 1 voter
40 31	← 1 voter
66 17	← 2 voters
30 33	← 1 voter
20 68	← 1 voter

Medicine
91 04 81 49
72 45 45 96
54 93 14 81
70 28 66 00
67 37 29 45
33 77 57 22
58 84 14 80
49 45 20 59
78 05 88 88
21 83 16 98

✓ Quick Check

3. **Medicine** In the U.S., 42% of blood donors have type A blood. Use the random numbers at the left as a tool to estimate the probability that it will take at least 4 donors to find one with type A blood.

1. **Vocabulary** A particular simulation has 25 trials. What does this mean?

What is an appropriate simulation tool for each situation? Explain.

2. At birth, about $\frac{1}{2}$ of lion cubs are male. You want to estimate the probability that in a litter of 6 cubs, at least 3 are male.

3. In a certain city, 5% of the dogs are infected with heartworms. You want to estimate the probability that a vet will have to test at least 10 dogs from the city before finding one with heartworms.

Homework Exercises

For more exercises, see Extra Skills and Word Problems.

GO for Help

For Exercises	See Examples
4–5	1-2
6–7	3

4. **Music** The table shows the fraction of different song types on Jodie's MP3 player.
   a. Design a simulation that can be used to estimate the probability that Jodie will need to listen to more than 3 randomly played songs before hearing a jazz song.
   b. Perform 20 trials of the simulation. Then estimate the probability.

Jodie's Songs

Type	Fraction
Jazz	$\frac{1}{3}$
Pop	$\frac{1}{2}$
Rock	$\frac{1}{6}$

5. **Games** A board game includes a deck of cards. Unlike a standard deck of cards, $\frac{3}{4}$ of the cards in this deck are number cards.
   a. Design a simulation that can be used to estimate the probability that a player will need to draw no more than 2 randomly shuffled cards to get a number card.
   b. Perform 20 trials of the simulation. Then estimate the probability.

For Exercises 6 and 7, use the random digits in the boxes as a simulation tool. Each row represents one trial.

Sports
64 86
31 14
26 42
15 73
29 26
74 18
94 65
84 27
95 03
05 60

6. **Sports** A basketball player makes 37% of the 3-point baskets that he attempts. Estimate the probability that the player will have to attempt at least three 3-point baskets before making one.

7. **Travel** On average, 17% of an airline's flights are delayed. Estimate the probability that a passenger can take at least 5 of the airline's flights without any being delayed.

Travel
14 67 72 05 46
45 58 16 20 52
15 58 18 47 50
17 86 12 20 74
82 38 72 51 51
77 42 18 95 42
84 78 35 61 45
20 59 92 03 84
59 99 69 10 16
56 60 42 94 30

8. **Guided Problem Solving** A company puts 1 of 4 different baseball cards in each of its boxes of fruit snacks. There is an equal number of each card, and the cards are placed randomly. Design a simulation and perform 20 trials to estimate the probability that you will get all 4 different cards in the first 4 boxes you buy.
- How many equally likely outcomes does your simulation tool need?
- How will you perform one trial of your simulation?

9. **Consumer Math** A restaurant gives out a scratch-off ticket with each purchase of a $5 meal deal. Two thirds of the tickets are winners. Design a simulation and perform 20 trials to estimate the probability that a customer will need to spend at least $15 to get a winning ticket.

10. **Biology** The graph shows the frequency of gray and red screech owls in a particular forest. Design a simulation and perform 20 trials to estimate the probability that a biologist will need to tag at least 3 screech owls in this forest before tagging a red one.

Eastern Screech Owls

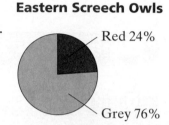

Red 24%

Grey 76%

Eastern screech owls:
Gray (left) and red (right)

11. **Error Analysis** A baseball player hits a home run on 3% of her times at bat. A coach wants to estimate the probability that the player will need to bat at least 10 times before hitting her next home run. He uses 2-digit random numbers between 00 and 99 as a simulation tool. He lets the numbers 00 to 03 represent a home run. Explain the coach's error.

12. **Challenge** You need a simulation tool for which 1 out of 9 equally likely outcomes is favorable. Describe how you could use one or more number cubes for this simulation.

Test Prep and Mixed Review   Practice

Multiple Choice

13. On average, $\frac{1}{4}$ of the customers a salesperson helps make a purchase. Which simulation tool could you use to estimate the probability that the salesperson must help at least 3 customers before making a sale?
- Ⓐ Roll a number cube; rolling a 4 represents a sale.
- Ⓑ Toss two coins; getting two heads represents a sale.
- Ⓒ Place 4 red marbles and 4 blue marbles in a bag; selecting a red marble represents a sale.
- Ⓓ Spin a spinner with 3 equal sections numbered from 1 to 3; spinning a 1 represents a sale.

Use a proportion to find the whole.

14. 168 is 84% of what number?   **15.** 15% of what number is 18?

16. 91 is 26% of what number?   **17.** 5% of what number is 9?

Eliminating Answers

Before you try to answer a multiple-choice question, you may be able to save time by eliminating some answer choices. Then you can choose your answer carefully from the remaining options.

EXAMPLE

A bag contains ten blue, six red, and four green pens. You select a pen at random. What is the probability of not choosing a green pen?

(A) $\frac{1}{5}$ (B) $\frac{4}{5}$ (C) $\frac{5}{6}$ (D) $\frac{9}{11}$

Look at the denominator of each choice. The number of possible outcomes is $10 + 6 + 4$, or 20. The denominator of the answer must be 20 or a factor of 20. Eliminate choices C and D because they have denominators of 6 and 11.

Estimate the magnitude of the answer. Since most of the pens are not green, the probability of *not* choosing a green pen is a fraction greater than $\frac{1}{2}$. Since choice A is less than $\frac{1}{2}$, you can eliminate choice A.

● The correct answer is choice B.

Exercises

1. A school has 1,060 students. The results of a survey are shown.

Students Surveyed	Students Who Produced Computer Art
40	24

   If the trend in the table continues, which is the best prediction of the total number of students who produced computer art?
   (A) 260 students   (C) 640 students
   (B) 480 students   (D) 790 students

2. A wheel is divided evenly into three sections labeled A, B, and C. You spin it twice. Which list shows all the possible outcomes?
   (F) (A, B), (B, A), (A, C), (C, A), (B, C), (C, B)
   (G) (A, A), (A, B), (B, A), (A, C), (C, A), (B, C), (C, C)
   (H) (A, A), (A, B), (B, A), (A, C), (C, A), (B, B), (B, C), (C, B), (C, C)
   (J) (A, B), (B, A), (A, C), (C, A), (B, C), (C, B), (A, A), (B, B)

Chapter 9 Review

Vocabulary Review

complement (p. 343)
compound event (p. 360)
counting principle (p. 354)
dependent events (p. 361)

event (p. 342)
experimental probability (p. 347)
independent events (p. 360)
outcome (p. 342)

sample space (p. 353)
simulation (p. 369)
theoretical probability (p. 342)
trial (p. 369)

Choose the correct term to complete each sentence.

1. The set of all possible outcomes of a probability experiment is the (compound event, sample space) of the experiment.

2. An outcome or a group of outcomes is called a(n) (event, simulation).

3. Two events are (dependent, independent) if the occurrence of one event does not affect the probability of the occurrence of the other.

4. You select a marble from a bag that contains 4 green marbles and 4 white marbles. Selecting a white marble is the (complement, trial) of selecting a green marble.

Go Online

For vocabulary quiz
PearsonSuccessNet.com

5. (Theoretical, Experimental) probability is based on observations.

Skills and Concepts

Lesson 9-1

• To find the probability and the complement of an event

You can find the **theoretical probability** of an event using this formula.

$$P(\text{event}) = \frac{\text{number of favorable outcomes}}{\text{total number of possible outcomes}}$$

You select a card at random from the cards shown at the right. Find each probability.

6. $P(\text{P})$ 7. $P(\text{vowel})$ 8. $P(\text{not P})$

Lesson 9-2

• To find experimental probability and to use simulations

You find the **experimental probability** of an event using this formula.

$$P(\text{event}) = \frac{\text{number of times an event occurs}}{\text{total number of trials}}$$

Games A computer game company makes random checks of its games. Of 200 games, 4 are found to be defective.

9. Find the experimental probability that a game is defective.

10. If the trend continues, predict the number of defective games in a batch of 1,600.

Lesson 9-3

- To make and use sample spaces and to use the counting principle

The collection of all possible outcomes in a probability experiment is called a **sample space.** You can use the **counting principle** to find the number of outcomes in a sample space.

Use the menu below for Exercises 11–13.

Appetizers	Soups
Egg Rolls	Won-ton
Fried Won-tons	Sizzling Rice

Main Dishes
Almond Chicken
Sweet & Sour Pork
Beef with Broccoli

11. At the China Panda, if you order the family dinner, you choose one appetizer, one soup, and one main dish from the menu. Draw a tree diagram to show the sample space.

12. You ask the restaurant to choose the meal for you at random. What is the probability of getting the egg rolls, won-ton soup, and almond chicken for your meal?

13. Use the counting principle to find the number of possible dinners.

Lesson 9-4

- To find the probability of independent and dependent events

A **compound event** consists of two or more events. Two events are **independent events** if the occurrence of one event does not affect the probabilty of the occurrence of the other. Two events are **dependent events** if the occurrence of one event affects the probability of the occurrence of the other.

A hat contains the names of eight girls and six boys. You select two names without replacing the first name. Find each probability.

14. $P(\text{boy, then boy})$ 15. $P(\text{girl, then boy})$ 16. $P(\text{girl, then girl})$

17. Two independent events A and B both have a probability of $\frac{1}{4}$. Find $P(A, \text{then } B)$.

Lesson 9-5

- To design and use simulations to estimate the probability of compound events

A **simulation** is a model used to estimate the probability of an event. Each **trial** of a simulation or probability experiment results in an outcome.

One third of the cards in a board game cause a player to lose points. Use this information for Exercises 18 and 19.

18. Design a simulation that can be used to estimate the probability that a player can draw at least 4 cards without losing any points.

19. Perform 20 trials of the simulation. Then estimate the probability.

Chapter 9 Test

Go Online For online chapter test PearsonSuccessNet.com

Use the data. Find the experimental probability of each event as a fraction, a decimal, and a percent.

Marker Color	Frequency
Purple	6
Green	2
White	3
Black	5

1. P(purple)

2. P(green)

3. P(orange)

4. **a. Quality Control** Factory workers test 80 batteries. Four batteries are defective. What is the experimental probability that a battery is defective?

   b. Assume this trend continues. Predict the number of defective batteries in a batch of 1,600.

There are six open containers arranged as shown. You toss a ball and it falls into one of the containers at random. Find each probability.

5. P(number greater than 4)

6. P(even number)

7. P(4)

8. P(7)

You have a bag that contains 6 blue, 2 green, 3 red, and 1 white marble. You select a marble at random. Find each probability.

9. P(blue)

10. P(white)

11. P(not green)

12. P(red)

13. P(green, then red when green is replaced)

14. P(red, then blue when red is not replaced)

15. Each of the letters D E T E R M I N E D is written on a card. You mix the cards thoroughly. What is the probability of selecting an E and then an M, if the first card is replaced before selecting the second card?

16. **Writing in Math** Suppose you toss a coin several times and record the results. Out of 20 trials, you get tails 9 times. What is the experimental probability of getting heads? Explain why this may differ from the theoretical probability.

A car comes in the colors and models listed in the table below. Assume there is the same chance of selecting any color or model.

Colors	Models
Silver	Hatchback
Gray	Coupe
Black	Sedan

17. Give the sample space.

18. Find the probability that a car selected at random is a silver hatchback.

19. Find the probability that a car selected at random is a yellow coupe.

20. Design a simulation that can be used to estimate the probability that a student will get at least 2 answers correct when guessing the answers to 3 true-false questions.

21. On average, 9% of the packages delivered by a shipping company are late. Use the random digits below as a simulation tool to estimate the probability that a customer can receive at least 4 packages without any being late. Each row represents one trial.

63	13	02	41
51	44	40	60
25	63	84	11
71	81	32	79
72	39	13	75
10	85	99	93
59	70	00	68
51	64	94	08
91	71	39	95
70	27	23	61

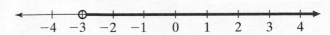

Multiple Choice

Read each question. Then write the letter of the correct answer on your paper.

1. A school has 424 students. In a random sample of 30 students, 4 would like to take a web design class. Which is the best prediction of the number of students at the school who would like to take a web design class?
   Ⓐ 10   Ⓑ 30   Ⓒ 60   Ⓓ 100

2. A deck has 12 cards numbered 1 to 12. Ashley needs a number greater than 9 to win a game. If she selects a card at random, what is the probability that she will win?
   Ⓕ $\frac{1}{4}$ Ⓖ $\frac{1}{3}$ Ⓗ $\frac{3}{4}$ Ⓙ $\frac{5}{6}$

3. What is the solution of $-15 = m - 9$?
   Ⓐ −24   Ⓑ −6   Ⓒ 6   Ⓓ 24

4. Which jar of peanut butter is the best buy?
   Ⓕ an 18-oz jar for $1.69
   Ⓖ a 30-oz jar for $2.59
   Ⓗ a 32-oz jar for $2.89
   Ⓙ a 24-oz jar for $2.09

5. The temperature at 6 P.M. is −4°C. By midnight, the temperature has decreased by 3°C. What is the temperature at midnight?
   Ⓐ −7°C   Ⓑ −1°C   Ⓒ 1°C   Ⓓ 7°C

6. Which choice does NOT equal the others?
   Ⓕ 4% of 3,000   Ⓗ 40% of 300
   Ⓖ 40% of 30   Ⓙ 30% of 400

7. Suppose you spin the spinners once. What is the probability that the sum of the numbers is 10?

   Ⓐ 0   Ⓑ $\frac{1}{4}$ Ⓒ $\frac{1}{2}$ Ⓓ $\frac{3}{4}$

8. Use the function rule $y = -2x - 3$. Which shows the outputs for $x = 3, x = 5, x = -2,$ and $x = -4$?
   Ⓕ −9, −13, 1, 5   Ⓗ 9, 13, −1, −5
   Ⓖ −9, −13, −1, −5   Ⓙ 9, 13, 1, 5

9. The graph below represents the solution set of which inequality?

   ```
   ◄──┼──⊕──┼──┼──┼──┼──┼──┼──►
     -4  -3  -2  -1   0   1   2   3   4
   ```
   Ⓐ $4x - 5 > 7$ Ⓒ $-x + 4 > 7$
   Ⓑ $3x + 4 > -5$ Ⓓ $-2x + 6 > 0$

10. If the area of a square is 81 square feet, which is the perimeter?
    Ⓕ 9 feet   Ⓗ 36 feet
    Ⓖ 9 square feet   Ⓙ 36 square feet

Gridded Response

11. Isabelle deposits $400 in an account that earns simple interest at an annual rate of 3%. If Isabelle makes no other deposits or withdrawals, how much money will be in the account at the end of 5 years?

Short Response

12. a. Write 0.9% as a decimal.
    b. Write 0.9% as a fraction.

13. A map with the scale 2 in. : 250 mi shows two ponds to be 4 in. apart. How many miles apart are the ponds? Show your work.

Extended Response

14. St. Francis, Torrey Pines, and Marina schools compete for the championship in field hockey.
    a. Make a table to find the sample space of possible outcomes of first, second, and third place.
    b. What is the probability of St. Francis winning with Marina in second place?
    c. What is the probability of Torrey Pines or Marina winning the championship?

What You've Learned

- In previous courses, you classified two-dimensional figures.
- You used a protractor to measure and draw angles.
- You used formulas to find the perimeter and area of rectangles.
- In Chapter 3, you evaluated expressions and solved one- and two-step equations.

Check Your Readiness

GO for Help

For Exercises	See Lesson
1–4	1-7
5–7	3-1
8–13	3-3
14–19	3-5

Multiplying Rational Numbers

Find each product.

1. $\frac{1}{2} \cdot 8$

2. $\frac{4}{5} \cdot 30$

3. $\frac{3}{4} \cdot 9$

4. $\frac{1}{3} \cdot 14$

Evaluating Expressions

(Algebra) **Evaluate each expression for** $x = \frac{1}{2}, y = 4,$ **and** $z = 6.$

5. xz

6. xyz

7. $x(y + z)$

Solving One-Step Equations

(Algebra) **Solve each equation.**

8. $19 = d + 17$

9. $m - 15 = 90$

10. $y + 86 = 180$

11. $28 = 2s$

12. $\frac{w}{4} = 56$

13. $3a = 180$

Solving Multi-Step Equations

(Algebra) **Solve each equation.**

14. $2(5 + c) = 30$

15. $\frac{1}{3}(z - 15) = 10$

16. $4(a - 6) = 40$

17. $60 = \frac{1}{2} \cdot 4 \cdot h$

18. $72 = 2(b + 12)$

19. $28 = \frac{2}{7}(d - 6)$

What You'll Learn Next

- In this chapter, you will classify angles and find unknown angle measures.

- You will draw geometric shapes and analyze the angles and sides of triangles.

- You will find the areas of parallelograms, triangles, trapezoids, and figures composed of these shapes.

- You will find the circumference and area of circles.

Key Vocabulary

- acute angle, angle (p. 381)
- adjacent angles (p. 381)
- base of a parallelogram (p. 389)
- base of a triangle (p. 394)
- bases of a trapezoid (p. 398)
- circumference (p. 404)
- complementary (p. 381)
- congruent angles (p. 382)
- diameter (p. 404)
- height of a parallelogram (p. 389)
- height of a trapezoid (p. 398)
- height of a triangle (p. 394)
- obtuse angle (p. 381)
- pi (p. 404)
- radius (p. 404)
- right angle, straight angle (p. 381)
- supplementary (p. 381)
- vertical angles (p. 382)

Drawing Geometric Figures

You can draw geometric figures freehand, by using tools such as a ruler and a protractor, and by using drawing software.

ACTIVITY

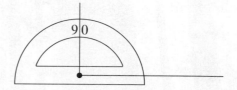

1. Using only a pencil, draw a rectangle 2 in. long and 4 in. wide. Remember, each angle of a rectangle measures 90°.

2. Check the accuracy of your freehand drawing. Use a ruler and protractor to draw the rectangle.
   a. Draw a 4-in. horizontal line segment.
   b. Draw a 90° angle at each end of the line segment.
   c. Draw the sides exactly 2 in. high.
   d. Draw a line segment that connects the tops of the sides.

3. **Technology** Draw the rectangle once more. This time use a software drawing program. Compare the computer-generated rectangle to the rectangles you created by hand.

4. Use freehand, tools, and software to draw each of these figures.
   a. a triangle with 3 side lengths of 5 cm and three 60° angles
   b. a rhombus with 4 side lengths of 3 cm, two 80° angles, and two 100° angles

5. 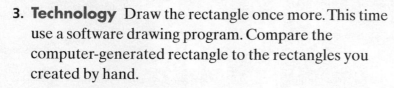 **Writing in Math** When is each of these methods most useful for drawing geometric figures: freehand, using tools, and using software?

✓ Check Skills You'll Need

1. Vocabulary Review
What do you call a mathematical sentence with an equal sign?

Solve each equation.

2. $3g - 14 = 13$

3. $24 + 6m = 72$

4. $24 = 12a - 24$

5. $8q - 9.1 = 38.9$

GO for Help
Lesson 3-5

© **CONTENT STANDARD**
7.G.5

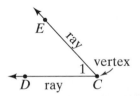

Vocabulary Tip

The ⌐ symbol indicates a right angle. Write "the measure of ∠C" as $m\angle C$.

What You'll Learn

To write and solve equations to find unknown angle measures

New Vocabulary angle, acute angle, right angle, obtuse angle , straight angle, complemetary, supplementary, adjacent angles, vertical angles, congruent angles

Why Learn This?

Architects think about angles in the structures they design. The design of a geodesic dome requires triangles. They make the dome stable.

An **angle** (∠) is a figure formed by two rays with a common endpoint. You can call the angle below left ∠DCE, ∠ECD, ∠C, or ∠1.

You can classify angles by their measures.

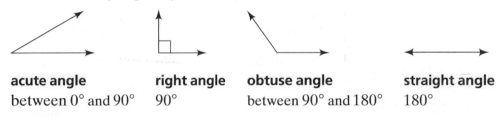

acute angle
between 0° and 90°

right angle
90°

obtuse angle
between 90° and 180°

straight angle
180°

If the sum of the measures of two angles is 90°, the angles are **complementary.** If the sum of the measures is 180°, the angles are **supplementary.**

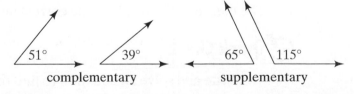

51° 39°
complementary

65° 115°
supplementary

Adjacent angles share a vertex and a side but have no interior points in common. Angles 1 and 2 are adjacent angles.

EXAMPLES **Finding Supplements and Complements**

1 **Algebra** Settling of the ground causes Italy's Leaning Tower of Pisa to tilt. The diagram on p. 382 describes the angles the tower makes with the ground. Find the measures of these angles.

Step 1 Write an equation.

The two angles are adjacent supplementary angles. You can write an equation by setting the sum of their degree measures equal to 180:

$$(3x - 35) + 2x = 180.$$

Step 2 Solve for x.

$$(3x - 35) + 2x = 180 \qquad \leftarrow \textbf{The angles are supplementary.}$$
$$2x + (3x - 35) = 180 \qquad \leftarrow \textbf{Use the Commutative Property.}$$
$$(2x + 3x) - 35 = 180 \qquad \leftarrow \textbf{Use the Associative Property.}$$
$$5x - 35 = 180 \qquad \leftarrow \textbf{Combine like terms.}$$
$$5x - 35 + 35 = 180 + 35 \qquad \leftarrow \textbf{Add 35 to each side.}$$
$$5x = 215 \qquad \leftarrow \textbf{Simplify.}$$
$$\frac{5x}{5} = \frac{215}{5} \qquad \leftarrow \textbf{Divide.}$$
$$x = 43 \qquad \leftarrow \textbf{Simplify.}$$

Step 3 Calculate the angle measures.

$$3(43) - 35 = 94 \quad \text{and} \quad 2(43) = 86$$

The angle measures are $94°$ and $86°$.

Multiple Choice If $\angle A$ and $\angle B$ are complementary, and $m\angle A$ is five times $m\angle B$, what is $m\angle B$?

(A) $15°$ (B) $18°$ (C) $30°$ (D) $36°$

Write and solve an equation. Let $x = m\angle B$ and $m\angle A = 5(m\angle B)$, or $5x$.

$$m\angle A + m\angle B = 90$$
$$5x + x = 90 \qquad \leftarrow \textbf{The angles are complementary.}$$
$$6x = 90 \qquad \leftarrow \textbf{Combine like terms.}$$
$$\frac{6x}{6} = \frac{90}{6} \qquad \leftarrow \textbf{Divide.}$$
$$x = 15 \qquad \leftarrow \textbf{Simplify.}$$

The measure of $\angle B$ is $15°$. The correct answer is choice A.

✓ Quick Check

1. Write and solve an equation to find the measures of the two angles described at the right.
2. $\angle A$ and $\angle B$ are complementary. $m\angle A = 2x + 30$ and $m\angle B = 4x$. What are the measures of $\angle A$ and $\angle B$?

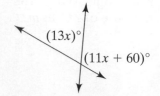

$(13x)°$

$(11x + 60)°$

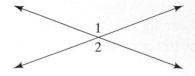

Angles 1 and 2 at the left are vertical angles. **Vertical angles** are formed by two intersecting lines and are opposite each other. Vertical angles have equal measures. Angles with equal measures are **congruent angles**.

$3x - 35°$ $\qquad$ $2x°$

GO **Online**

Video Tutor Help
PearsonSuccessNet.com

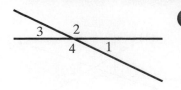

EXAMPLE Finding Angle Measures

3 Runway Design In the diagram of the runway layout for the Charles B. Wheeler Downtown Airport in Kansas City, Missouri, $m\angle 1 = 25.7°$. Find the measures of $\angle 2$, $\angle 3$, and $\angle 4$.

$m\angle 4 = 180° - 25.7°$ ← $\angle 1$ and $\angle 4$ are supplementary.

$\quad\quad = 154.3°$

$m\angle 3 = 25.7°$ ← $\angle 1$ and $\angle 3$ are vertical angles.

$m\angle 2 = 154.3°$ ← $\angle 2$ and $\angle 4$ are vertical angles.

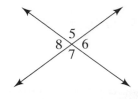

✓ Quick Check

3. In the diagram at the left, $m\angle 8 = 72°$. Find the measures of $\angle 5$, $\angle 6$, and $\angle 7$.

● More Than One Way

If $m\angle 1 = 140°$ and $m\angle 2 = 40°$, what is $m\angle 3$?

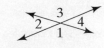

Carlos's Method

$\angle 3$ and $\angle 1$ are across from each other, so they are vertical angles. Since vertical angles have the same measure, $m\angle 3 = m\angle 1$.

So $m\angle 3 = 140°$.

Brianna's Method

$\angle 2$ and $\angle 3$ together form a straight angle, so their measures add up to $180°$. This means that they are supplementary angles.

$40° + m\angle 3 = 180°$

$40° - 40° + m\angle 3 = 180° - 40°$ ← Subtract 40° from each side.

$m\angle 3 = 140°$ ← Simplify.

So $m\angle 3$ is $140°$.

Choose a Method

In the figure at the right, $m\angle BEC = 25°$ and $m\angle CED = 155°$. Find $m\angle AEB$. Explain why you chose the method you used.

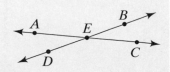

1. **Vocabulary** How are vertical angles and adjacent angles different?

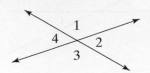

2. **Reasoning** What is the sum of the measures of the four angles formed by intersecting lines?

Classify each angle as *acute*, *right*, *obtuse*, or *straight*. Then find the measures of the complement and the supplement of each angle.

3. $m\angle A = 45°$ 4. $m\angle B = 105°$ 5. $m\angle C = 75°$

Homework Exercises

For more exercises, see Extra Skills and Word Problems.

Exercises	See Examples
6–10	1, 2
11–13	3

Write an equation relating the measures of the two angles and find the angle measures.

6.

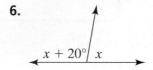

$x + 20°$ | x

7.

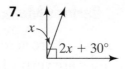

x
$2x + 30°$

8.

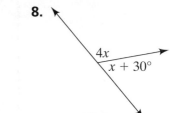

$4x$
$x + 30°$

9. If $\angle G$ and $\angle H$ are supplementary, and $m\angle G$ is 4 times $m\angle H$, what are the measures of $\angle G$ and $\angle H$?

10. $\angle J$ and $\angle K$ are complementary. $m\angle J = 3x + 10°$ and $m\angle K = 2x$. What are the measures of $\angle J$ and $\angle K$?

(**Algebra**) In the diagram at the right, $m\angle 2 = 123°$. Find the measure of each angle.

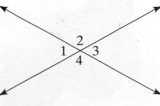

11. $m\angle 1$ 12. $m\angle 3$ 13. $m\angle 4$

14. **Guided Problem Solving** $\angle A$ and $\angle B$ are complementary. $m\angle A = 2x$ and $m\angle B = 4x + 30°$. What is the measure of the angle supplementary to $\angle A$?
   - What angle measure do you need to know to answer the question?
   - What equation describes the sum of the measures of $\angle A$ and $\angle B$?
   - How do you use the solution of the equation to find m$\angle A$?
   - How do you use $m\angle A$ to find the measure of the angle supplementary to it?

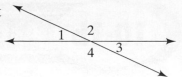

15. The measure of ∠1 in the diagram at the right is $2x - 25°$. The measure of ∠2 is $5x + 30°$. Find the measures of ∠3 and ∠4.

16. **Error Analysis** A student measured ∠XYZ and said that $m\angle XYZ = 120°$. Explain the student's error.

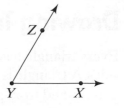

17. **Writing in Math** Can an angle ever have the same measure as its complement? Explain.

18. **Design** The diagram at the right describes the angles of a design outside Toronto's Royal Ontario Museum. What are the measures of ∠1, ∠2, ∠3, and ∠4?

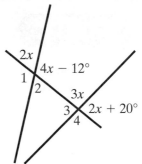

19. **Challenge** The measure of ∠1 in the design at the right is $2x - 5°$. The measure of ∠2 is $2x + 15°$. ∠4 and ∠8 are congruent. Find the measures of ∠9 and ∠10.

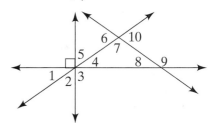

Test Prep and Mixed Review   **Practice**

Multiple Choice

20. Which equation describes a pair of complementary angles in the diagram?

    Ⓐ $m\angle 1 + m\angle 2 = 180°$
    Ⓑ $m\angle 2 + m\angle 4 = 180°$
    Ⓒ $m\angle 3 + m\angle 4 = 90°$
    Ⓓ $m\angle 4 + m\angle 1 = 90°$

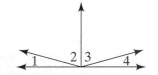

21. The five countries in northern Africa that border the Mediterranean Sea are shown in the table, along with the lowest elevation in each country. Which country contains the lowest point?

    Ⓕ Algeria   Ⓗ Egypt
    Ⓖ Morocco   Ⓙ Tunisia

Country	Elevation
Algeria	–40 m
Egypt	–133 m
Libya	–47 m
Morocco	–55 m
Tunisia	–17 m

GO for Help

For Exercise	See Lesson
22	5-6

22. For a scale of 1 cm : 12 km, find the actual length represented by the length 1.7 cm in a drawing.

Drawing Triangles

Every triangle has three measures of angles and three measures of sides. A triangle is unique if there is exactly one triangle that can be determined from given measures.

ACTIVITY

1. a. Use a ruler to draw a line segment. Measure and draw a 25° angle at one end of the line segment such as the one below.

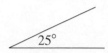
25°

Complete your triangle by drawing a line segment that intersects the other two line segments at 50° and 105°.

  b. Compare triangles with a classmate. Are your triangles the same?

  c. Do three angle measures determine a unique triangle? Explain.

2. a. Construct a triangle with angle measures of 30°, 40°, and 110° and a 2-inch side length. Describe the steps you followed.

  b. Compare your triangle with the triangle below. Are the triangles the same or different? Explain.

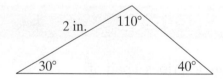
2 in.   110°
30°   40°

  c. Do three angle measures and a side measure determine a unique triangle? Explain.

3. a. One student started constructing a triangle, as shown below, with side lengths of 7.5 cm, 10 cm, and 12.5 cm. What information is not given? Why is this construction challenging?

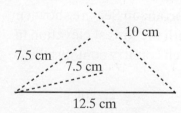
10 cm
7.5 cm
7.5 cm
12.5 cm

  b. Choose available tools and try to construct the triangle.

  c. Describe the strategy you used, explaining why you chose the tools that you did for the construction.

d. Can triangles with the same three side measures have different shapes? Explain your reasoning.

e. Is a triangle unique when only three side measures are given?

ACTIVITY

1. Cut straws to lengths of 2 cm, 3 cm, 4 cm, 5 cm, and 6 cm. For each combination of 3 straws, identify the type of a triangle you can make using three straws: unique, more than one, or none. Make a table to list the combinations.

Lengths	Type of Triangle
2 cm, 3 cm, and 4 cm	Unique
2 cm, 3 cm, and 5 cm	None

2. Is it possible to construct two different triangles using the same set of three straws? Explain.

3. What do you notice about the lengths of the straws when you cannot make a triangle?

Exercises

1. The table shows three measures for five triangles. Tell whether each determines a unique triangle, more than one triangle, or no triangle.

Triangle	Measure 1	Measure 2	Measure 3
A	75°	70°	35°
B	10 cm	6 cm	3 cm
C	7 cm	7 cm	9 cm
D	6 in.	5 in.	40°
E	36°	49°	4 in.

2. The triangle at the right has a 25-foot side and angle measures of 33° and 86°. How many different triangles also have a side measuring 25 feet and angle measures of 33° and 86°? Explain.

3. **Open Ended** List a set of measurements for each.
   a. three angle measures that cannot be used to construct a triangle
   b. three side lengths that cannot be used to construct a triangle

4. **Writing in Math** Write directions telling how to use a ruler and a protractor to construct a unique triangle that has a side measuring 4 centimeters connecting two angles with measures of 50° and 95°.

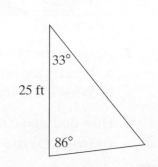

Generating Formulas for Area

You can generate the area of a figure by separating or combining the areas of two figures you know.

ACTIVITY

1. Using graph paper, draw a parallelogram like the one at the right. When you draw the perpendicular segment, what two polygons are formed?

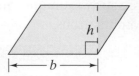

2. Cut out the parallelogram and then cut along the perpendicular segment.

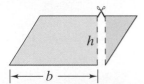

3. Rearrange the pieces to form a rectangle.
   a. What is the area of the rectangle?
   b. What was the area of the parallelogram?

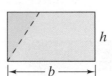

4. How do b and h relate to the length and width of the rectangle? Write a formula for the area of a parallelogram.

ACTIVITY

5. Fold a piece of graph paper in half. On one side, draw a right triangle like the one at the right.

6. Cut out the triangle, cutting through both layers of the folded paper. You now have two congruent triangles.

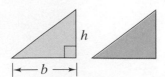

7. Arrange the pieces to form a rectangle.
   a. What is the area of the rectangle?
   b. What is the area of one triangle?

8. How do b and h relate to the length and width of the rectangle? Write a formula for the area of a triangle.

© **CONTENT STANDARD**
7.G.6

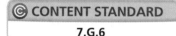
Vocabulary Tip

Perpendicular segments intersect to form right angles.

Video Tutor Help
PearsonSuccessNet.com

What You'll Learn

To find the area of a parallelogram and to relate perimeter and area
New Vocabulary height of a parallelogram, base of a parallelogram

Why Learn This?

The floor plan of the building at the right is in the shape of a parallelogram. You can calculate the area of the parallelogram to determine how much office space is available on a given floor of the building.

The **height of a parallelogram** is the length of a perpendicular segment connecting one **base of a parallelogram** to the other.

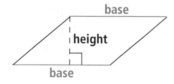

The diagram below relates the formula for the area of a rectangle to the formula for the area of a parallelogram.

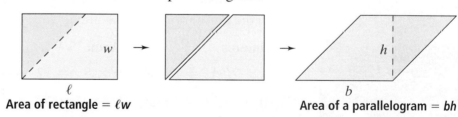

Area of rectangle = ℓw Area of a parallelogram = bh

KEY CONCEPTS **Area of a Parallelogram**

The area of a parallelogram is equal to the product of any base b and the corresponding height h.

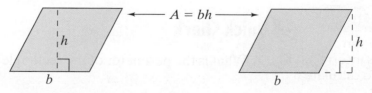

Finding the Area of a Parallelogram

1 Find the area of the parallelogram.

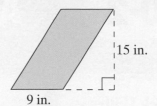

$A = bh$ ← **Use the area formula.**

$= (9)(15)$ ← **Substitute.**

$= 135$ ← **Simplify.**

The area is 135 in.^{2}.

✓ **Quick Check**

1. Find the area of the parallelogram.

10 cm

9 cm

You can also use lengths of the sides of a rectangle to find perimeter.

EXAMPLE **Relating Perimeter and Area**

The perimeter of a figure is the distance around the figure.

2 **Multiple Choice** Melinda wants to plant a rectangular garden and put a fence around it. She has 34 ft of fencing and she wants the area of her garden to be as big as possible. Which dimensions should she use?

Ⓐ Length of 9 ft and width of 8 ft

Ⓑ Length of 10 ft and width of 7 ft

Ⓒ Length of 12 ft and width of 6 ft

Ⓓ Length of 14 ft and width of 5 ft

Since all answer choices give the length ℓ and width w, you can calculate both the perimeter $2\ell + 2w$ and the area $\ell \times w$.

Perimeter   **Area**

$2(9) + 2(8) = 34$ ✔ $9 \times 8 = 72$ ← **Perimeter is correct; find the area.**

$2(10) + 2(7) = 34$ ✔ $10 \times 7 = 70$ ← **Perimeter is correct; the area in choice A is greater.**

$2(12) + 2(6) = 36$ ✘ ← **Perimeter is greater than 34 ft.**

$2(14) + 2(5) = 38$ ✘ ← **Perimeter is greater than 34 ft.**

The rectangle with a length of 9 ft and a width of 8 ft will have the correct perimeter and the greatest area. The answer is A.

Test Prep Tip

If the first part in an answer choice is incorrect, do not bother to calculate the second part.

✓ **Quick Check**

2. What is the perimeter of the rectangle?

5 cm

area = 30 cm^2

1. **Vocabulary** What kind of angle is formed by perpendicular lines?

Two parallelograms have a base and a height that are equal. Tell whether each statement is true or false. Explain your answer.

2. The two parallelograms must be congruent.

3. The areas of the two parallelograms are equal.

Use the parallelogram at the right. Fill in the blank.

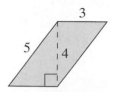

4. The area is $A = (3)(\blacksquare)$.

5. The perimeter is $P = 2(\blacksquare) + 2(5)$.

Homework Exercises

For more exercises, see Extra Skills and Word Problems.

GO for Help

For Exercises	See Examples
6–15	1
16	2

Find the area of each parallelogram.

6.
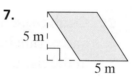

7.

8.

9.
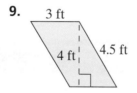

10.

11.

Find each area for base b and height h of a parallelogram.

12. $b = 14$ in.
$h = 6$ in.

13. $b = 25$ mi
$h = 25$ mi

14. $h = 40$ cm
$b = 0.5$ cm

15. $h = 1{,}000$ m
$b = 20$ m

16. A rectangular fish pond is 21 ft² in area. If the owner can surround the pond with a 20-foot fence, what are the dimensions of the pond?

17. **Guided Problem Solving** The diagram shows a park bounded by streets. The park is in the shape of a parallelogram. Each square is 10 yards on a side. What is the area of the park?
   - What are the base and the height of the parallelogram?
   - What formula should you use?

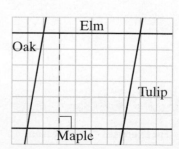

Find the unknown measures for each rectangle.

18. $\ell = 14$ in.
$w = \blacksquare$
$A = \blacksquare$
$P = 34$ in.

19. $\ell = \blacksquare$
$w = 4.2$ m
$A = 37.8$ m^2
$P = \blacksquare$

20. $\ell = 7$ ft
$w = \blacksquare$
$A = 18.2$ ft^2
$P = \blacksquare$

21. $\ell = \blacksquare$
$w = 2$ cm
$A = \blacksquare$
$P = 25$ cm

22. Geography The shape of the state of Tennessee is similar to a parallelogram. Estimate the area of Tennessee.

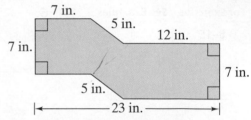

23. Reasoning The rectangle and the parallelogram at the left have the same perimeter. How do you know that the area of the rectangle is greater than the area of the parallelogram?

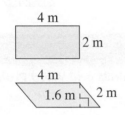

24. Writing in Math A rectangular lot is 70.2 m long and 59.8 m wide. Is 42,000 m^2 a reasonable estimate for the area of the lot? Explain.

25. Challenge Find the area and perimeter of the figure at the right.

Test Prep and Mixed Review   **Practice**

Multiple Choice

26. A playground has the shape of a parallelogram. If the base is 30 feet, and the corresponding height is 25 feet, what is its area?
Ⓐ 55 ft^2 Ⓑ 187.5 ft^2 Ⓒ 375 ft^2 Ⓓ 750 ft^2

27. An $11.76 fruit plate at a deli contains 6 oz each of watermelon and grapes and 4 oz each of cantaloupe, strawberries, and blackberries. What is the unit cost of the fruit plate?
Ⓕ $.49 per oz   Ⓗ $1.96 per oz
Ⓖ $1.18 per oz   Ⓙ $2.94 per oz

28. On a trip, your family wants to drive at least 150 miles in the next 3 hours. Which inequality represents the average speed s in miles per hour that your family needs to drive?
Ⓐ $s > 50$ Ⓑ $s \geq 50$ Ⓒ $s < 50$ Ⓓ $s \leq 50$

GO for Help

For Exercises	See Lesson
29–33	6-1

Write each percent as a decimal and as a fraction in simplest form.

29. 200%   **30.** 135%   **31.** 152%   **32.** 0.03%   **33.** 0.45%

Checkpoint Quiz 1

Find the measures of the complement and the supplement of each angle.

1. $m\angle T = 12°$ **2.** $m\angle R = 47°$ **3.** $m\angle U = 65°$

Write an equation relating the measures of the two angles and find the angle measures.

4.

x
$x - 40°$

5.

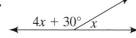

$4x + 30°$ x

In the diagram at the right, $m\angle 3 = 115°$. Find the measure of each angle.

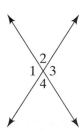

6. $m\angle 1$ **7.** $m\angle 2$ **8.** $m\angle 4$

Find the area of each parallelogram.

9.

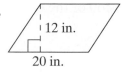

12 in.
20 in.

10.

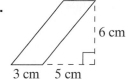

6 cm
3 cm   5 cm

MATH AT WORK

Architect

Do you have an eye for design? If so, then architecture could be a career for you. Architects use creativity, math, science, and art to plan buildings that are beautiful, functional, safe, and economical.

Architects use geometry to understand spatial relationships. They use ratios and percents to plan scale drawings and to build scale models, too.

Architects also must be able to manage projects, supervise people, and communicate complex ideas.

Go Online For information about architects
PearsonSuccessNet.com

What You'll Learn

To find the area of a triangle and to relate side lengths and area

New Vocabulary base of a triangle, height of a triangle

Why Learn This?

The wings of high-speed planes have a triangular shape, are usually thin, and are swept back to give the plane more lift. Engineers need to be able to calculate the area of the wings as they design such airplanes.

Any side of a triangle can be considered the **base of a triangle**. The **height of a triangle** is the length of the perpendicular segment from a vertex to the base opposite the vertex or to an extension of the base.

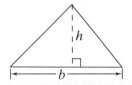 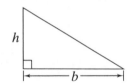 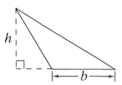

The formula for the area of a triangle follows from the formula for the area of a parallelogram.

The area of a parallelogram = *bh*.

Draw one diagonal.

Break the parallelogram into two triangles.

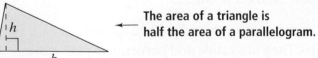

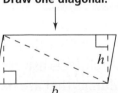

← **The area of a triangle is half the area of a parallelogram.**

KEY CONCEPTS **Area of a Triangle**

The area of a triangle is equal to half the product of any base *b* and the corresponding height *h*.

$$A = \frac{1}{2}bh$$

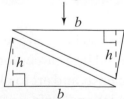

Finding the Area of a Triangle

1 Find the area of each triangle.

a.

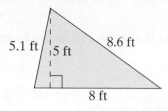

5.1 ft | 5 ft | 8.6 ft | 8 ft

b.

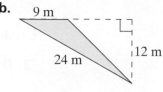

9 m | 24 m | 12 m

$$A = \frac{1}{2}bh \qquad \leftarrow \text{Use the area formula.} \rightarrow \qquad A = \frac{1}{2}bh$$

$$= \frac{1}{2}(8)(5) \qquad \leftarrow \text{Substitute.} \rightarrow \qquad = \frac{1}{2}(9)(12)$$

$$= 20 \qquad \leftarrow \text{Simplify.} \rightarrow \qquad = 54$$

The area is 20 ft². The area is 54 m².

Vocabulary Tip

Areas are always measured in *square units*.

✓ **Quick Check**

1. Find the area of each triangle.

a.

26.8 m | 12 m | 19 m | 36 m

b.

16 cm | 4 cm | 20.9 cm | 6 cm

EXAMPLE **Relating Side Lengths and Area**

2 **Crafts** A quilt has a design of small and large triangles. A small triangle is shown at the right. A large triangle has the same shape, but the sides are twice as long as the sides in a small triangle. How does the area of a large triangle compare to the area of a small triangle?

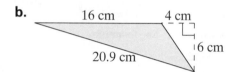

4.7 in. | 3.1 in. | 3.4 in.

Test Prep Tip

You can substitute 0.5 for $\frac{1}{2}$ in the formula for the area of a triangle if it makes the calculations easier.

Small triangle
$b = 3.4$ in., $h = 3.1$ in.
$$A = \frac{1}{2}(3.4)(3.1)$$
$$= 5.27$$

Large triangle
$b = 6.8$ in.; $h = 6.2$ in.
$$A = \frac{1}{2}(6.8)(6.2)$$
$$= 21.08$$

The area of a large triangle is 21.08 in.². The area of a triangle is 5.27 in.². So, the area of a large triangle is about 4 times as great as the area of a small triangle.

✓ **Quick Check**

2. What is the unknown side length of the triangle?

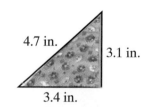

15 cm | area: 54 cm² | 12 cm

1. **Vocabulary** A triangle that has a 90° angle is a(n) ___?___ triangle.

Use the triangle at the right. Fill in the blank.

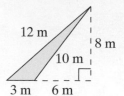

2. $b = $ ▇ m

3. $h = $ ▇ m

Find the area of each triangle.

4. $b = 4$ cm, $h = 5$ cm

5. $b = 2$ in., $h = 7$ in.

6. A carpenter has blueprints for a wooden, triangular patio. The base is 5 m and the height is 7 m. What is the area of the patio?

Homework Exercises

For more exercises, see **Extra Skills and Word Problems.**

Find the area of each triangle.

For Exercises	See Examples
7–12	1
13	2

GO for Help

7.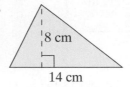

8.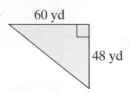

9.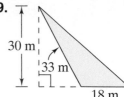

10.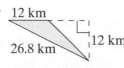

11.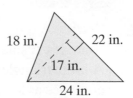

12.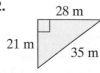

13. The perimeter of this triangle is 31.4 ft. What is its area?

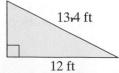

 14. **Guided Problem Solving** An equilateral triangle's perimeter is 27 ft. The height of the triangle is 7.8 ft. What is the triangle's area?
   - You can *Draw a Picture* to solve this problem. Sketch and label the triangle. Find the perimeter and then use the area formula.

15. A conservation group plans to buy a triangular plot of land. What is the area of the plot of land in the diagram?

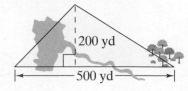

Find the area for base *b* and height *h* of each triangle.

16. $b = 4.2$ in. **17.** $b = 12$ m **18.** $h = 6.2$ ft **19.** $h = 100$ km
$h = 6.3$ in. $h = 17$ m $b = 2.5$ ft $b = 200$ km

20. **Writing in Math** The base of a triangle is doubled and the height remains the same. Explain how the area changes. Use examples.

21. A rescue helicopter receives a distress call from a ship at sea. The diagram at the right displays the search pattern the helicopter will use. Each pass from a central point forms an equilateral triangle. What is the area of one of the triangular regions?

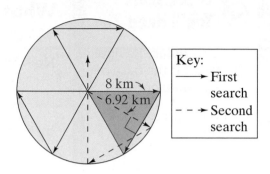

Key:
→ First search
- - → Second search

8 km
6.92 km

22. Two equilateral triangles with sides of length 6 inches are joined together to form a rhombus. What is the perimeter of the rhombus?

Careers Rescue swimmer is one of the jobs offered in the coast guard.

23. **Reasoning** One base of a triangle has a length of 6 ft and a corresponding height of 2 ft. This means that the area of the triangle is $\frac{1}{2}(6 \text{ ft} \cdot 2 \text{ ft}) = 6 \text{ ft}^2$. Another base of the same triangle has a length of 4 ft. What is its corresponding height? Explain.

24. **Challenge** The area of an isosceles right triangle is 121 ft^2. What is the approximate length of each of the two equal sides?

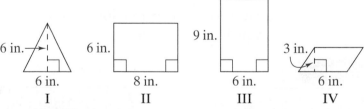

Test Prep and Mixed Review   **Practice**

Multiple Choice

25. Which two of the figures shown have the same area?

6 in. ⟋⟍
6 in.
I

6 in.
8 in.
II

9 in.
6 in.
III

3 in.
6 in.
IV

Ⓐ Figures I and II   Ⓒ Figures I and IV
Ⓑ Figures I and III   Ⓓ Figures II and IV

26. A square has a perimeter of *x* feet. What is its area in terms of *x*?

Ⓕ $\frac{x^2}{16}$ Ⓖ $4x^2$ Ⓗ $\frac{x^2}{4}$ Ⓙ $\frac{x}{16}$

GO for Help

For Exercises	See Lesson
27–29	5-4

Algebra Solve each proportion using mental math.

27. $\frac{m}{35} = \frac{4}{5}$ **28.** $\frac{55}{99} = \frac{5}{x}$ **29.** $\frac{9}{p} = \frac{180}{200}$

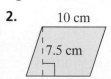

ⓒ **CONTENT STANDARD**

7.G.6

What You'll Learn

To find the area of a trapezoid and the areas of irregular figures

New Vocabulary bases of a trapezoid, height of a trapezoid

Why Learn This?

If you know how to find the area of simple figures, you can find the area of an irregular figure, such as the area of a backyard deck.

The formula for the area of a trapezoid follows from the formula for the area of a parallelogram.

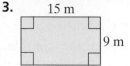

base

height

base

The two parallel sides of a trapezoid are the **bases of a trapezoid**, with lengths b_1 and b_2. The **height of a trapezoid** h is the length of a perpendicular segment connecting the bases.

If you put two identical trapezoids together, you get a parallelogram. The area of the parallelogram is $(b_1 + b_2)h$. The area of one trapezoid equals $\frac{1}{2}(b_1 + b_2)h$.

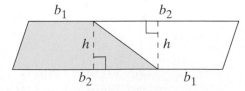

b_1 b_2

h h

b_2 b_1

Vocabulary Tip

A *trapezoid* is a quadrilateral that has exactly one pair of parallel sides. Read b_1 as "base 1" and b_2 as "base 2."

KEY CONCEPTS   Area of a Trapezoid

The area of a trapezoid is one half the product of the height and the sum of the lengths of the bases.

$$A = \frac{1}{2}h(b_1 + b_2)$$

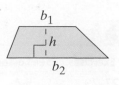

b_1

h

b_2

Finding the Area of a Trapezoid

1 Find the area of the trapezoid shown at the right.

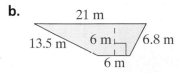

$A = \frac{1}{2}h(b_1 + b_2)$ ← **Use the area formula for a trapezoid.**

$= \frac{1}{2}(15)(8.5 + 13.5)$ ← **Substitute for h, b_1, and b_2.**

$= \frac{1}{2}(15)(22)$ ← **Add.**

$= 165$ ← **Multiply.**

The area of the trapezoid is 165 cm².

✓ Quick Check

1. Find the area of each trapezoid.

a.

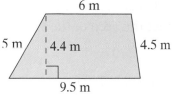

b.

You can estimate the area of states shaped like trapezoids.

EXAMPLE **Application: Geography**

2 Estimate the area of Arkansas by finding the area of the trapezoid shown.

$A = \frac{1}{2}h(b_1 + b_2)$ ← **Use the area formula for a trapezoid.**

$= \frac{1}{2}(242)(250 + 190)$ ← **Substitute for h, b_1, and b_2.**

$= \frac{1}{2}(242)(440)$ ← **Add.**

$= 53{,}240$ ← **Multiply.**

The area of Arkansas is about 53,240 mi².

At Crater of Diamonds State Park in Arkansas, visitors can search for and keep diamonds and other gems.

✓ Quick Check

2. Estimate the area of the figure at the right by finding the area of the trapezoid.

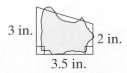

You can find the area of any figure by separating it into familiar figures.

● More Than One Way

Anna and Ryan are helping their friends build a large wooden deck. What is the area of the deck?

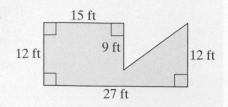

Anna's Method

I'll subtract the area of the triangle from the area of the rectangle.

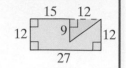

Area of the rectangle:

$A = bh$
$= (27)(12) = 324$

Area of the triangle:

$A = \frac{1}{2}bh$
$= \frac{1}{2}(12)(9) = 54$

Now I'll subtract the area of the triangle from the area of the rectangle.

$A = 324 - 54 = 270$

The area of the deck is 270 ft².

Ryan's Method

I'll add the areas of the rectangle and the trapezoid.

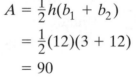

Area of the rectangle:

$A = bh$
$= (15)(12)$
$= 180$

Area of the trapezoid:

$A = \frac{1}{2}h(b_1 + b_2)$
$= \frac{1}{2}(12)(3 + 12)$
$= 90$

Now I'll add the two areas together.

$A = 180 + 90 = 270$

The area of the deck is 270 ft².

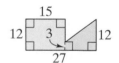

Choose a Method

Find the area of the figure.

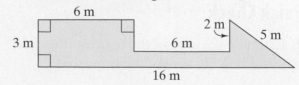

1. Vocabulary The perpendicular distance between the two parallel sides of a trapezoid is called the ___?___ of the trapezoid.

Identify the bases b_1 and b_2 and height h of each trapezoid below.

2.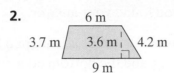

3.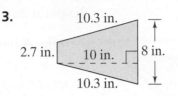

4.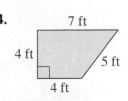

Homework Exercises

For more exercises, see **Extra Skills and Word Problems.**

GO for Help

For Exercises	See Examples
5–7	1-2

Find the area of each trapezoid.

5.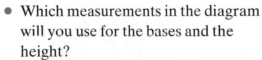

6.

7. Engineering When the Erie Canal opened in 1825, it was hailed as an engineering marvel. Find the area of the trapezoidal cross section of the Erie Canal at the right.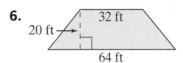

Not to scale

GPS

8. Guided Problem Solving Estimate the area of Nevada by finding the area of the trapezoid shown at the right.
- Which measurements in the diagram will you use for the bases and the height?
- How will you use the bases and height to calculate the area?

9. Choose a Method You plan to replace the carpeting in the room shown at the left. What is the area of the room?

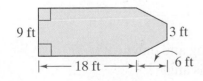

Use familiar figures to find the area of each irregular figure.

10.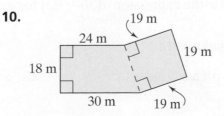

11.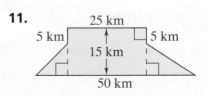

Find the area of each trapezoid, given the bases b_1 and b_2 and height h.

12. $b_1 = 3$ m
$b_2 = 7$ m
$h = 3$ m

13. $b_1 = 11$ in.
$b_2 = 16$ in.
$h = 9$ in.

14. $b_1 = 5.6$ cm
$b_2 = 8.5$ cm
$h = 6$ cm

15. $b_1 = 3\frac{1}{2}$ ft
$b_2 = 2\frac{1}{4}$ ft
$h = 2$ ft

16. **Writing in Math** Find the whole-number possibilities for the lengths of the bases of a trapezoid with a height of 1 m and an area of 3 m^2. Explain how you found your answer.

17. **Music** A hammered dulcimer is shaped like a trapezoid. The top edge is 17 in. long, and the bottom edge is 39 in. long. The distance from the top edge to the bottom edge is 16 in. What is the area of the dulcimer?

Use familiar figures to find the area and perimeter of each figure.

18.

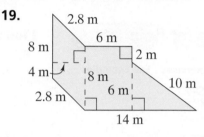

19.

20. **Challenge** A trapezoid has an area of 184 in.^{2}. The height is 8 in. and the length of one base is 16 in. Write and solve an equation to find the length of the other base.

Test Prep and Mixed Review
Practice

Gridded Response

21. The Hernandez family is purchasing tile for the kitchen shown in the diagram. If tile is not needed for the island area, how many square feet of tile will be needed?

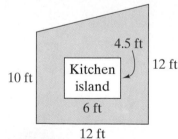

22. A carpenter finds that the measure of an angle formed between a vaulted ceiling and one wall is 67°. How many degrees is the supplement of this angle?

23. Evaluate the expression $a(3b - 2c)$ for $a = -2.75, b = -7,$ and $c = -3.5$.

GO for Help

For Exercises	See Lesson
24–25	6-4

Find each payment.

24. $453 with a 6% sales tax

25. $49.95 with a 5.5% sales tax

Checkpoint Quiz 2

Find the area of each figure. Where necessary, use familiar figures.

1.
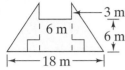
17.5 m 9 m
←12 m→

2.
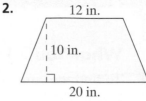
12 in.
10 in.
20 in.

3.
3 m
6 m
6 m
←— 18 m —→

4.
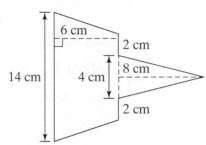
6 cm
2 cm
14 cm   4 cm   8 cm
2 cm

10-5a Activity Lab

Hands On

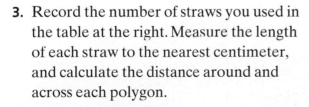

Modeling a Circle

When a regular polygon has many sides, it can be a model for a circle.

ACTIVITY

1. Form a chain of drinking straws by stapling them end to end.

2. Make a regular polygon using a chain of about 15 straws. Use another chain of straws to measure the widest distance across the polygon.

3. Record the number of straws you used in the table at the right. Measure the length of each straw to the nearest centimeter, and calculate the distance around and across each polygon.

Number of Straws		Distance (cm)		Around ÷ Across (cm)
Around	Across	Around	Across	
■	■	■	■	■
■	■	■	■	■

4. Repeat steps 2 and 3 using 20 straws and 30 straws.

5. Calculate and record the ratio of "distance around ÷ distance across" for each polygon. What pattern do you notice?

6. Suppose a regular polygon of 100 sides has a distance across of 100 cm. What is the distance around the polygon? Explain.

403

Circumference and Area of a Circle

© **CONTENT STANDARD**
7.G.4

What You'll Learn

To find the circumference and area of a circle

New Vocabulary circumference, diameter, radius, pi

Why Learn This?

If you know how to find the circumference of a circle, you can find how far you must travel to move all the way around the circle.

In the picture below, a Sacagawea dollar rolls along a surface. The distance the dollar rolls is the same as the distance around the edge of the dollar. This distance is the coin's circumference. **Circumference** is the distance around a circle.

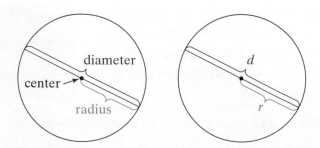

A **diameter** is a segment that passes through the center of a circle and has both endpoints on the circle. A **radius** is a segment that connects the center of a circle to the circle. For the same circle, the length of a radius, r, is half the length of a diameter, d.

Pi is the ratio of a circle's circumference C to its diameter d. Use the symbol π for this ratio. So, $\pi = \frac{C}{d}$. The formula for the circumference comes from this ratio.

> ### KEY CONCEPTS   Circumference of a Circle
>
> The circumference of a circle is π times the diameter d.
>
> $$C = \pi d \text{ or } C = 2\pi r$$

Pi is a nonterminating and nonrepeating decimal. Both $\frac{22}{7}$ and 3.14 are good approximations for π. Many calculators have a key for π and display it to nine decimal places. Your results will vary slightly, depending on which value for π you use.

EXAMPLE   Finding the Circumference of a Circle

1 **a.** Find the circumference of the circle using 3.14 for π.

13 m

b. Find the circumference of the circle using a calculator's π key.

5 ft

$C = \pi d$ ← Use the formula for a circumference. → $C = 2\pi r$

$= 3.14(13)$ ← Substitute. → $= 2\pi(5)$

$= 40.82$ Use a calculator. → ≈ 31.41592654

The circumference is about 40.8 m.

The circumference is about 31.4 ft.

✓ Quick Check

1. Find the circumference of the circle at the right. Round to the nearest tenth.

9 m

If you cut a circle into equal sectors and place them side by side, you make a shape that is close to a parallelogram.

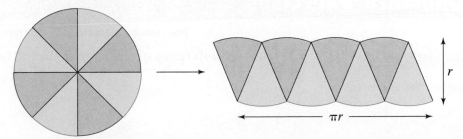

The length of the base of the "parallelogram" is half the circumference of the circle, $\frac{2\pi r}{2}$, or πr. The height of the "parallelogram" is r. So, the area of the "parallelogram" is $\pi r \cdot r$ or πr^2. The area of a circle is πr^2.

KEY CONCEPTS   Area of a Circle

The area of a circle is the product of π and the square of the radius r.

$$A = \pi r^2$$

EXAMPLE   Finding the Area of a Circle

2 A standard circus ring has a diameter of 13 m. What is the area of the ring? Round to the nearest tenth.

$r = \dfrac{13}{2} = 6.5$ ← **The radius is half of the diameter.**

$A = \pi r^2$ ← **Use the formula for the area of a circle.**

$= \pi(6.5)^2$ ← **Substitute 6.5 for the radius.**

$= 132.73328$ ← **Use a calculator.**

≈ 132.7 ← **Round to the nearest tenth.**

The area of a standard circus ring is about 132.7 m².

✓ Quick Check

2. Find the area of the circle. Round to the nearest square unit.

12 m

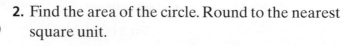
Check Your Understanding

1. **Number Sense** Is it possible to write out the exact value of pi as a decimal? Explain.

Identify the radius, the diameter, and the circumference.

2. 1, 2π, 2   **3.** 4π, 4, 2   **4.** 7, 3.5, 22   **5.** $\dfrac{2}{\pi}, \dfrac{1}{\pi}, 2$

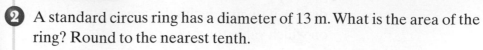
Homework Exercises

For more exercises, see Extra Skills and Word Problems.

GO for Help

For Exercises	See Examples
6–11	1
12–18	2

Find the circumference of each circle. Round to the nearest tenth.

6.
50 cm

7.
17 mm

8.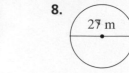
27 m

9.
40 in.

10.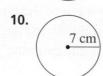
7 cm

11.
8 mi

Find the area of each circle. Round to the nearest square unit.

12.

6 in.

13.

10 m

14.

25 cm

15.

30 ft

16.

22 cm

17.

15 km

18. **Social Studies** The circular bases of the traditional tepees of the Sioux and Cheyenne tribes have a diameter of about 15 ft. What is the area of the base? Round to the nearest square unit.

19. **Guided Problem Solving** A Ferris wheel has a diameter of 135 m. How far does a rider travel in one full revolution of the wheel? Round to the nearest unit.
   • What is the diameter of the circle?
   • What is the formula for circumference, using diameter?

20. In a circle with radius 5 cm, how long can the longest chord be?

GO Online
Homework Video Tutor
PearsonSuccessNet.com

Use $\pi \approx \frac{22}{7}$ to estimate the circumference and area for each circle. Where necessary, round to the nearest tenth.

21. $r = 14$ m   22. $r = \frac{7}{10}$ cm   23. $d = 22$ in.   24. $d = 12$ ft

Use $\pi \approx \frac{22}{7}$ to estimate the unknown measures for each circle.

25. $C \approx 132$ in.
   $d \approx$ ▨
   $r \approx$ ▨
   $A \approx$ ▨

26. $C \approx$ ▨
   $d \approx$ ▨
   $r \approx$ ▨
   $A \approx 154$ m^2

27. $C \approx 220$ cm
   $d \approx$ ▨
   $r \approx$ ▨
   $A =$ ▨

28. $C \approx$ ▨
   $d \approx$ ▨
   $r \approx$ ▨
   $A \approx 616$ ft^2

29. **Bicycles** The front wheel of a high-wheel bicycle from the late 1800s was larger than the rear wheel to increase the bicycle's overall speed. The front wheel measured in height up to 60 in. Find the circumference and area of the front wheel of a high-wheel bicycle.

30. **Archaeology** The large stones of Stonehenge are arranged in a circle about 30 m in diameter. Find the area of the circle.

31. Sports The running track shown in the diagram has 2 straight sides. Both ends of the track are semi-circles, or half circles. What is the distance of one lap around the track?

100 m

30 m

32. Landscaping A circular garden with a radius of 4 ft is planted in the center of a 10-ft square. The part of the square that is NOT the garden is covered with small white rocks. What is the area of the region covered with white rocks?

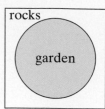
rocks
garden

33. Writing in Math Use the π key to calculate the area of the circle at the right to the nearest hundredth. Which is the better estimate, 98 m² or 99 m²? Explain.

5.6 m

34. Challenge The diagram shows a fountain at the center of a circular park. The radius of the circle is 30 ft. The circular region is divided into six equal parts. What is the length of the arc in the shaded region? Round to the nearest tenth.

Fountain
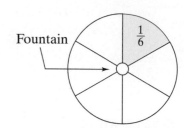
$\frac{1}{6}$

Ⓐ Ⓑ Ⓒ Ⓓ **Test Prep and Mixed Review**　　　**Practice**

Multiple Choice

35. Use a centimeter ruler to measure the radius of the button. What is the area of the button to the nearest square centimeter?

Ⓐ　3 cm²　　　　Ⓒ　7 cm²
Ⓑ　22 cm²　　　Ⓓ　89 cm²

36. A homebuilder wants to use the logo shown on a sign. Which of the following expressions can be used to find the area of the logo?

Ⓕ　$2x + 2y + \frac{1}{2}(4x)$

Ⓖ　$xy + \frac{1}{2}(2x)$

Ⓗ　$xy + \frac{1}{2}(2 \cdot 4)$

Ⓙ　$2x + 2y + \frac{1}{2}(2x)$

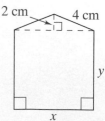
2 cm　　4 cm
y
x

GO for Help

For Exercises	See Lesson
37–39	6-1

Write each percent as a fraction in simplest form.

37. 65%　　　　**38.** 0.6%　　　　**39.** 37.5%

🌐nline lesson quiz, PearsonSuccessNet.com

Areas of Irregular Figures

You can find the area of an irregular-shaped figure by combining basic shapes such as rectangles or triangles, or removing them from an existing figure.

Mosaic Erin is creating a mosaic and needs to buy tiles for her artwork. She wants to buy 10% more than the area to be covered. How many square inches of tile does she need to purchase?

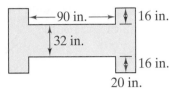

What You Might Think

> What do I know?
> What am I trying to find out?

> How do I solve the problem?

> What do I need to calculate?

> What is the answer?

What You Might Write

I know the dimensions of the artwork. I need to find the area, plus 10%.

I'll subtract the area of the two smaller rectangles from the area of the whole rectangle. Then I'll add 10%.

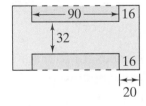

The area of each smaller rectangle is 90 in. × 16 in., or 1,440 in.^{2} The area of the larger rectangle is 130 in. × 64 in., or 8,320 in.^{2}

The area of the artwork is 8,320 in.^{2} − 2(1,440 in.^{2}), or 5,440 in.^{2}
Then I need to add 10%.
5,440 in.^{2} × 1.10 = 5,984 in.^{2}

Erin needs to buy 5,984 in.^{2} of tile.

Think It Through

1. Why does multiplying by 1.1 add 10% to the area?

2. Is there a way to find the total area by adding instead of subtracting? Explain.

Exercises

Solve the problems. For Exercises 3 and 4, answer the questions first.

3. You plan to replace the carpeting in the room shown below. What is the area of the room?

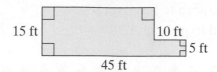

15 ft   10 ft

5 ft

45 ft

   a. What do you know? What do you need to find out?

   b. Can you find the answer in two different ways? Explain.

4. Sam wants to paint the wall below. What is the area of the wall to the nearest tenth?

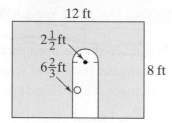

12 ft

$2\frac{1}{2}$ ft

$6\frac{2}{3}$ ft

8 ft

   a. What shapes make up the door?

5. Data from the 2010 U.S. Census for four states are in the table below. Order the states from smallest population per square mile, to greatest. Explain what this means.

State	Population	Area (mi^2)
Alaska	710,231	663,267
Florida	18,801,310	65,755
New Jersey	8,791,894	8,721
Texas	25,145,561	268,581

6. Wilma agreed to cut the grass on the infield of the school track for $0.35 /yd^2 on her riding lawnmower. How much would she make each time she cut the grass?

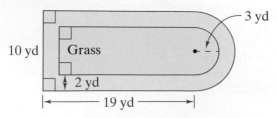

3 yd

10 yd   Grass

2 yd

19 yd

Measuring to Solve

Some test questions ask you to measure with a centimeter ruler before solving a problem.

EXAMPLE

The bottom of a bottle is circular, as shown at the right. Measure the radius of the bottle in centimeters.

Which of the following is closest to the circumference of the bottom of the bottle?

- (A) 6 cm
- (B) 9 cm
- (C) 15 cm
- (D) 19 cm

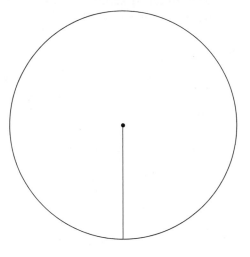

Use a centimeter ruler to measure the radius of the bottle. Label the radius. To find the circumference of the bottle, use the formula for the circumference of a circle.

$C = 2\pi r$, or πd
$C = 2\pi r = 2 \times \pi \times 3 \approx 18.84955\ldots$

The circumference of the bottle is about 19 cm. The answer is D.

Exercises

1. A vase has a circular base, as shown at the right. Measure the radius of the base in centimeters. Which of the following is the closest to the area of the circular base?

   - (A) 2 cm^2
   - (B) 6 cm^2
   - (C) 12 cm^2
   - (D) 24 cm^2

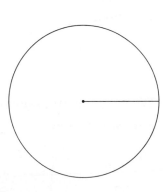

2. Celine is making a frame for a mirror. She bought tiles in the shape of trapezoids, like the one at the right, to glue onto the frame. Measure the bases and the height in centimeters. Which best represents the area of one tile?

   - (F) 5 cm^2
   - (G) 8 cm^2
   - (H) 15 cm^2
   - (J) 16 cm^2

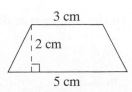

Chapter 10 Review

Vocabulary Review

acute angle (p. 381)
adjacent angles (p. 381)
angle (p. 381)
base of a parallelogram (p. 389)
base of a triangle (p. 394)
bases of a trapezoid (p. 398)
circumference (p. 404)

complementary (p. 381)
congruent angles (p. 382)
diameter (p. 404)
height of a parallelogram
  (p. 389)
height of a trapezoid (p. 398)
height of a triangle (p. 394)

obtuse angle (p. 381)
pi (p. 404)
radius (p. 404)
right angle (p. 381)
straight angle (p. 381)
supplementary (p. 381)
vertical angles (p. 382)

1. Two angles whose measures have a sum of 180° are (complementary, supplementary).

2. A perpendicular segment connecting one base of a parallelogram to another is the (height, radius) of the parallelogram.

3. The (base, height) of a triangle is always one side of the triangle.

Go Online

For vocabulary quiz
PearsonSuccessNet.com

4. An (acute, obtuse) angle measures less than 90°.

5. The distance around a circle is the (diameter, circumference) of the circle.

Skills and Concepts

Lesson 10-1

• To write and solve equations to find unknown angle measures

An **angle** is formed by two rays with a common endpoint. The sum of two **complementary** angles is 90°. The sum of two **supplementary** angles is 180°.

Two intersecting lines form four angles. The angles that are opposite each other are **vertical angles.** They have equal measures, so they are **congruent angles.** The angles next to each other are **adjacent angles.** They are supplementary.

Write an equation relating the measures of the two angles and find the angle measures.

6.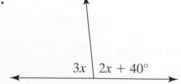
   $3x$ | $2x + 40°$

7. $3x - 10°$
   $2x$

In the diagram at the right, $m\angle 1 = 143.7°$. Find the measure of each angle.

8. $\angle 2$

9. $\angle 3$

10. $\angle 4$

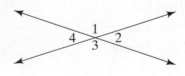

Lesson 10-2

- To find the area of a parallelogram and to relate perimeter and area

The **height of a parallelogram** is the length of a perpendicular segment connecting one **base of a parallelogram** to the other. To find the area of a parallelogram, use the formula $A = bh$.

Find the area of each parallelogram.

11.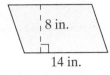
8 in.
14 in.

12.
2.4 m
6 m

13.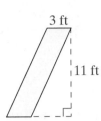
3 ft
11 ft

Lesson 10-3

- To find the area of a triangle and to relate side lengths and area

The **height of a triangle** is the length of the perpendicular segment from a vertex of the triangle to the **base** opposite the vertex or to an extension of the base. To find the area of a triangle, use the formula $A = \frac{1}{2} bh$.

Find the area of each triangle.

14.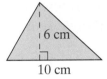
6 cm
10 cm

15.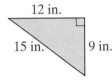
12 in.
15 in.
9 in.

16.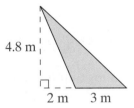
4.8 m
2 m   3 m

Lesson 10-4

- To find the area of a trapezoid and the areas of irregular figures

parallelogram
$A = bh$

triangle
$A = \frac{1}{2}bh$

trapezoid
$A = \frac{1}{2}h(b_1 + b_2)$

To find the area of an irregular figure, first separate it into familiar figures and find the area of each piece. Then add the areas.

Use familiar figures to find the area of each figure.

17.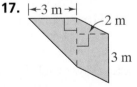
|←3 m→|
2 m
3 m

18.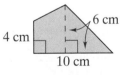
4 cm
6 cm
10 cm

19.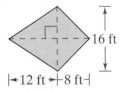
16 ft
|←12 ft→|←8 ft→|

Lesson 10-5

- To find the circumference and area of a circle

To find the **circumference** of a circle, use the formula $C = \pi d = 2\pi r$. To find the area of a circle, use the formula $A = \pi r^2$.

Find the circumference and area of each circle.

20.
8 in.

21.
14 mi

22.
7 km

Go Online For online chapter test
PearsonSuccessNet.com

Find the measures of both angles in each diagram.

1.
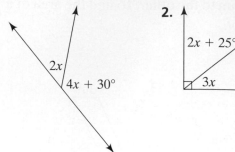

2.
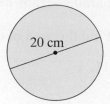

Name each of the following for the diagram below.

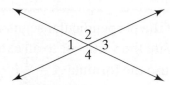

3. an angle congruent to $\angle 2$

4. two pairs of congruent angles

5. two pairs of vertical angles

6. two angles that are supplementary to $\angle 3$

If $m\angle 4 = 130.2°$ in the diagram above, find each measure.

7. $m\angle 1$

8. $m\angle 2$

Find the area of each figure.

9.
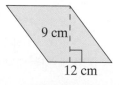

10.
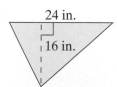

11.
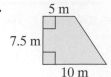

12.
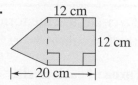

Find the circumference and area of each circle. Round to the nearest tenth.

13.
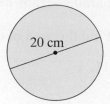

14.
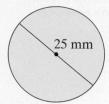

15. **Construction** The area of a window is 18 ft^2. The length of the window is two times the width of the window. What are the dimensions of the window?

16. Draw a triangle with a 5-cm side that connects angles of 60° and 50°.

Tell whether each set of measures for a triangle determines a unique triangle, more than one triangle, or no triangle.

17. 5 cm, 10 cm, 2 cm

18. 60°, 60°, 60°

19. 7 ft, 7 ft, 30°

You are planning a circular garden with a diameter of 16 ft. Use this information to answer questions 22 and 23.

20. How much ground area will you need for the garden?

21. How much fencing do you need to completely surround the garden?

22. **Algebra** A trapezoid with an area of 48 m^2 has a height of 6 m. One of its bases is 12 m. Write and solve an equation to find the length of its other base.

23. **Writing in Math** One of the four angles formed when two lines intersect measures 95°. Explain how to find the measures of the other three angles without using a protractor.

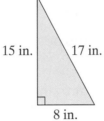
Multiple Choice

Read each question. Then write the letter of the correct answer on your paper.

1. Which number has the greatest value?

   (A) -1.3 (B) 9 (C) 1 (D) -12

2. What are the area and perimeter of the triangle?

   (F) $A = 60$ in.^{2}, $P = 23$ in.

   (G) $A = 60$ in.^{2}, $P = 40$ in.

   (H) $A = 68$ in.^{2}, $P = 40$ in.

   (J) $A = 60$ in.^{2}, $P = 46$ in.

   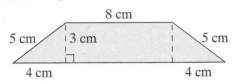

   15 in. 17 in.

   8 in.

3. Which of the following could NOT be the lengths of the sides of a triangle?

   (F) 5 m, 6 m, 8 m (H) 4 m, 7 m, 11 m

   (G) 10 m, 10 m, 15 m (J) 3 m, 3 m, 3 m

4. Which expression could you use to find the area of the trapezoid?

   8 cm

   5 cm 3 cm 5 cm

   4 cm 4 cm

   (A) $3 \cdot 8 \div 2$

   (B) $\frac{1}{2} \cdot 3 \cdot (8 + 16)$

   (C) $\frac{1}{2} \cdot 5 \cdot (8 + 16)$

   (D) $3 \cdot (8 + 8) \div 2$

5. Which figure has the greatest area?

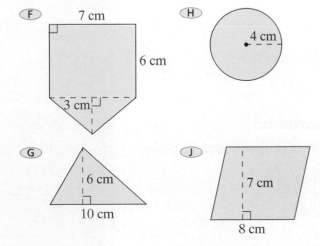

6. Which equation can you use to represent the following? Five more than half of the people (p) on the bus are students (s).

   (A) $\frac{p}{2} + 5 = s$ (C) $\frac{p}{2} - 5 = s$

   (B) $(p - 5) \div 2 = s$ (D) $(p + 5) \div 2 = s$

7. Which number is NOT equivalent to $\frac{6}{8}$?

   (F) 0.75 (H) 0.75%

   (G) $\frac{9}{12}$ (J) $\frac{3}{4}$

8. What is the measure of an angle that is supplementary to a $23°$ angle?

   (A) $23°$ (C) $157°$

   (B) $67°$ (D) $203°$

Gridded Response

Record your answer in a grid.

9. A triangle has a height of 8 ft and a base of 15 ft. Find the triangle's area in square feet.

10. **Sewing** You sew 34 squares for a quilt. This is 5% of the squares used in the quilt. How many squares are there to sew in all?

Short Response

11. Define a variable and write an inequality to model "To qualify for the long-jump finals, I need to jump at least 14 ft."

12. The area of a circular rug is 113.04 ft^2. What is the diameter of the rug? Use $\pi = 3.14$. Show your work.

Extended Response

13. The ratio of the corresponding sides of two similar triangles is $3 : 5$. The sides of the smaller triangle are 9 m, 12 m, and 18 m. Find the perimeter of the larger triangle. Show your work.

Geometry Continued

What You've Learned

- In Chapter 3, you wrote and solved algebraic equations.
- In Chapter 5, you determined whether the relationship between two variables is proportional.
- In Chapter 10, you explored some of the properties of triangles.

 Check Your Readiness

GO for Help

For Exercises	See Lessons
1–4	10-1
5–10	3-5
11–12	7-3

Classifying and Measuring Angles

Measure each angle. Classify it as *acute*, *right*, *obtuse*, or *straight*.

1.

2.

3.

4.

Solving Two-Step Equations

Solve each equation. Check the solution.

5. $3x + 5 = 14$

6. $5b - 80 = 10$

7. $-4n + 6 = -2$

8. $24 = 18 + 2c$

9. $\dfrac{p}{4} + 3 = 6$

10. $\dfrac{s}{6} - 1 = 9$

Determining Whether Relationships Are Proportional

Determine whether the relationship shown in each table is proportional. Explain.

11.

x	2	4	6	8
y	8	16	24	32

12.

x	3	6	9	12
y	9	15	21	27

What You'll Learn Next

- In this chapter, you will use the properties of pairs of angles and parallel lines to find angle measures.

- You will explore properties of figures that have the same shape but may or may not have the same size.

- You will investigate relationships among the angle measures of triangles.

- Applying what you learn, you will solve problems involving side lengths and angle measures of geometric figures, such as those found in bridges, buildings, observatories, and other objects.

Key Vocabulary

- alternate interior angles (p. 418)
- congruent polygons (p. 422)
- corresponding angles (p. 418)
- exterior angle (p. 441)
- interior angle (p. 440)
- similar figures (p. 428)
- similar polygons (p. 428)
- transversal (p. 418)

What You'll Learn

To identify parallel lines and the angles formed by parallel lines and transversals

Why Learn This?

Carpenters must know about angles and parallel lines in order to make correct measurements and cuts.

A line that intersects two other lines at different points is a **transversal**. In the diagrams below, line *t* is a transversal. Some pairs of angles formed by two lines and a transversal have special names.

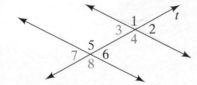

Corresponding angles lie on the same side of the transversal and in corresponding positions.

∠1 and ∠5   ∠2 and ∠6

∠3 and ∠7   ∠4 and ∠8

Alternate interior angles lie within a pair of lines and on opposite sides of the transversal.

∠1 and ∠4   ∠2 and ∠3

EXAMPLE   **Identifying Angles**

1 Identify a pair of corresponding angles and a pair of alternate interior angles.

   ∠1 and ∠3 are corresponding angles.

   ∠2 and ∠7 are alternate interior angles.

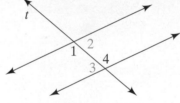

✔ Quick Check

1. Use the diagram in Example 1. Identify each pair of angles as *corresponding, alternate interior,* or *neither.*

   a. ∠3, ∠6   **b.** ∠5, ∠7   **c.** ∠1, ∠8

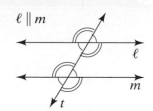

Vocabulary Tip

Recall that parallel lines lie in the same plane and do not intersect.

KEY CONCEPTS **Transversals and Parallel Lines**

When a transversal intersects two parallel lines,
- corresponding angles are congruent, and
- alternate interior angles are congruent.

$\ell \parallel m$

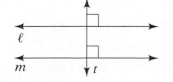

EXAMPLE **Finding Angle Measures**

2 **Gridded Response** A carpenter wants to make the hat rack at the left and needs to find all the angle measurements. He knows that line r is parallel to line s, and $m\angle 4 = 63°$. What is $m\angle 5$ measured in degrees?

$m\angle 5 = m\angle 4 = 63°$ ← Alternate interior angles are congruent.

The correct answer is 63 degrees.

✓ Quick Check

● **2.** In Example 2, $m\angle 3 = 117°$. Find $m\angle 6$ and $m\angle 7$.

When a transversal intersects two parallel lines, some pairs of angles are congruent. The reverse is also true. If the corresponding angles or the alternate interior angles are congruent, the lines are parallel.

To show that $\overleftrightarrow{AB}$ is parallel to $\overleftrightarrow{CD}$, you write $\overleftrightarrow{AB} \parallel \overleftrightarrow{CD}$.

EXAMPLE **Identifying Parallel Lines**

3 In the diagram at the right, $m\angle 1 = 60°$, $m\angle 2 = 60°$, and $m\angle 3 = 60°$. Explain how you know $\overleftrightarrow{LP} \parallel \overleftrightarrow{MN}$ and $\overleftrightarrow{LM} \parallel \overleftrightarrow{PN}$.

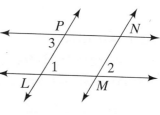

$\overleftrightarrow{LP} \parallel \overleftrightarrow{MN}$ because $\angle 1$ and $\angle 2$ are congruent corresponding angles. $\overleftrightarrow{LM} \parallel \overleftrightarrow{PN}$ because $\angle 1$ and $\angle 3$ are congruent alternate interior angles.

✓ Quick Check

3. Transversal t at the left is perpendicular to lines ℓ and m. Explain how you know $\ell \parallel m$.

The reasoning used in Example 3 is called *deductive reasoning*. Deductive reasoning is the logical process of drawing conclusions from given facts.

In the diagram at the right, $\overleftrightarrow{PQ} \parallel \overleftrightarrow{ST}$.

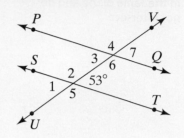

1. Name a pair of corresponding angles.

2. Name a pair of alternate interior angles.

3. Which line is the transversal?

4. What other angles have measures of 53°?

5. **Reasoning** Is the following statement *true* or *false*? Corresponding angles can also be alternate interior angles. Explain.

Homework Exercises

For more exercises, see Extra Skills and Word Problems.

Identify the angles as *corresponding*, *alternate interior*, or *neither*.

For Exercises	See Examples
6–13	1
14–19	2
20–22	3

6. ∠6, ∠3   7. ∠8, ∠4

8. ∠2, ∠1   9. ∠2, ∠4

10. ∠1, ∠5   11. ∠2, ∠7

12. ∠3, ∠5   13. ∠4, ∠3

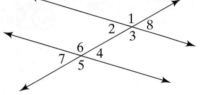

In the diagram, $\ell \parallel m$. If $m\angle 3 = 122°$, find the measure of each angle.

14. ∠4   15. ∠2   16. ∠6

17. ∠7   18. ∠8   19. ∠5

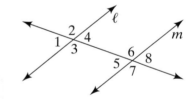

For each diagram, explain how you know $a \parallel b$.

GO Online
Homework Video Tutor
PearsonSuccessNet.com

20.   21.   22.

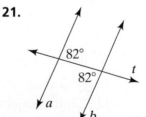
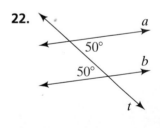

GPS 23. **Guided Problem Solving** Two lines are cut by a transversal. The corresponding angles are not congruent. Are the two lines parallel?
- **Understand the Problem** If a transversal cuts two parallel lines, corresponding angles are congruent. The question is, are two lines parallel if corresponding angles are not congruent?
- **Make a Plan** Draw pictures of corresponding angles that are not congruent. Conclude whether or not the two lines are parallel.

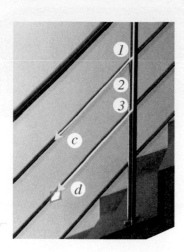

24. **Architecture** The railings in the photo at the left are parallel. If $m\angle 1 = 138°$, find $m\angle 2$ and $m\angle 3$.

Which pairs of lines, if any, are parallel? Explain.

25.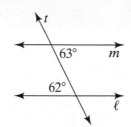

26.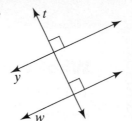

27.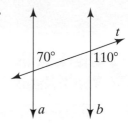

28. **Writing in Math** A transversal t cuts parallel lines m and n. If t is perpendicular to m, what is the relationship between t and n?

Use the diagram at the right for Exercises 29–30.

29. Find the measure of each numbered angle.

30. *Alternate exterior angles* lie outside a pair of lines and on opposite sides of a transversal. What do you notice about the measures of alternate exterior angles of parallel lines?

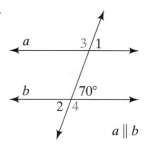

31. **a.** In the diagram at the left, $\overleftrightarrow{PQ} \parallel \overleftrightarrow{ST}$. Find the measure of each numbered angle.
    b. What is the sum of the angle measures of the triangle?

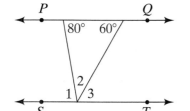

32. **Challenge** Which pair of angles is always congruent?
    Ⓐ alternate interior angles   Ⓒ corresponding angles
    Ⓑ vertical angles   Ⓓ alternate exterior angles

Test Prep and Mixed Review   **Practice**

Gridded Response

33. In the diagram at the right, line ℓ is parallel to line m. What is the measure, in degrees, of $\angle 1$?

34. What is the slope of the line that passes through the points $(0, 1)$ and $(2, 9)$?

35. Amy sells wooden coasters online. The function $t = 5c + 4$ represents the total cost t, in dollars, of a customer's order when he or she buys c coasters. One of Amy's customers buys 6 coasters. What is the total cost, in dollars, of the order?

Find each cube root.

36. $\sqrt[3]{27}$ 37. $\sqrt[3]{1,000}$ 38. $\sqrt[3]{216}$

For Exercise	See Lesson
36–38	1-10

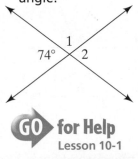
© CONTENT STANDARD
8.G.2

What You'll Learn

To identify congruent figures and use them to solve problems

New Vocabulary congruent polygons

Why Learn This?

Land surveyors measure angles and distances on land. To do so, they may use congruent polygons.

Congruent polygons are polygons that have the same size and shape. The symbol ≅ means "is congruent to." When two polygons are congruent, you can slide, flip, or turn one so that it fits exactly on top of the other one.

Corresponding angles and corresponding sides of congruent polygons are congruent. The two polygons below are congruent.

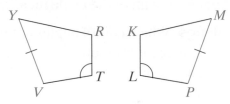

∠T corresponds to ∠L.

$\overline{YV}$ corresponds to $\overline{MP}$.

R corresponds to K.

You can write VTRY ≅ PLKM.

The tick marks in the diagram tell you which sides are congruent. The arcs tell you which angles are congruent. When you name congruent polygons, you must list the corresponding vertices in the same order.

EXAMPLE Writing Congruence Statements

1 Write a congruence statement for the congruent figures at the right.

∠R ≅ ∠L, ∠S ≅ ∠K, ∠T ≅ ∠J, and ∠W ≅ ∠N. So RSTW ≅ LKJN.

✓ Quick Check

1. Write a congruence statement for the congruent figures at the right.

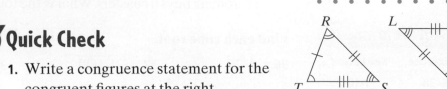

You can use corresponding parts of triangles to show that two triangles are congruent. You do not need to know that *all* the corresponding parts are congruent to show the triangles are congruent. You can show congruence in several ways.

KEY CONCEPTS **Showing Triangles Are Congruent**

To demonstrate that two triangles are congruent, show that the following parts of one triangle are congruent to the corresponding parts of the other triangle.

| Side-Side-Side (SSS) | Side-Angle-Side (SAS) | Angle-Side-Angle (ASA) |

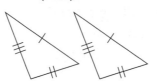 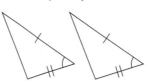 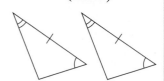

Vocabulary Tip

The abbreviations SSS, SAS, and ASA are easy ways to remember how to show triangles are congruent.

The order of the angles and sides is important in deciding whether two triangles are congruent.

EXAMPLE **Congruent Triangles**

2 Show that each pair of triangles is congruent.

a.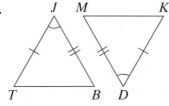

$\overline{TJ} \cong \overline{KD}$	**S**ide
$\angle J \cong \angle D$	**A**ngle
$\overline{BJ} \cong \overline{MD}$	**S**ide

$\triangle TJB \cong \triangle KDM$ by SAS.

b.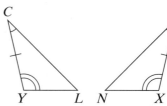

$\angle C \cong \angle D$	**A**ngle
$\overline{CY} \cong \overline{DX}$	**S**ide
$\angle Y \cong \angle X$	**A**ngle

$\triangle CYL \cong \triangle DXN$ by ASA.

✓ Quick Check

2. Show that each pair of triangles is congruent.

a.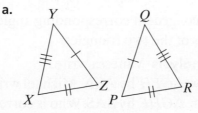

b.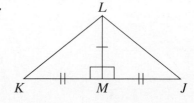

You can use corresponding parts of congruent figures to find distances.

EXAMPLE **Application: Surveying**

3 A surveyor drew the picture below. A bridge will be built across the river from point *A* to point *B*. Show that the two triangles are congruent. Then find *AB*.

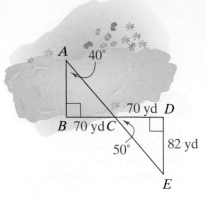

$\angle B \cong \angle D$ ← **Both are right angles.**

$BC = DC$ ← **Both measure 70 yd.**

$\angle ACB \cong \angle ECD$ ← **They are vertical angles.**

So $\triangle ABC \cong \triangle EDC$ by ASA.

Corresponding parts of congruent triangles are congruent. $\overline{AB}$ corresponds to $\overline{ED}$, so *AB* is 82 yd.

✓ Quick Check

3. Use the diagram in Example 3 to find each measure.

 a. $m\angle E$ **b.** $m\angle ACB$

✓ Check Your Understanding

1. **Vocabulary** What two characteristics do congruent polygons have in common?

2. Is the following statement *true* or *false*? When two polygons are congruent, you can slide, flip, or turn one so that it fits on top of the other one.

State whether each pair of triangles is congruent by SSS, SAS, or ASA.

3.

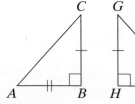

4.

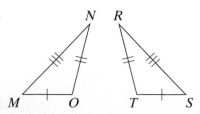

Use the two congruent triangles below for Exercises 5 and 6.

5. List the congruent corresponding angles and sides of the two triangles.

6. **Error Analysis** Vanessa writes $\triangle EFH \cong \triangle GFH$ by ASA. Michael writes $\triangle EFH \cong \triangle GHF$ by SAS. Who is correct?

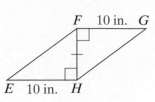

For more exercises, see Extra Skills and Word Problems.

GO for Help

For Exercises	See Examples
7–8	1
9–10	2
11–18	3

Write a congruence statement for each pair of congruent figures.

7.

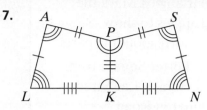

8.

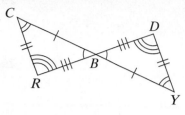

Show that each pair of triangles is congruent.

9.

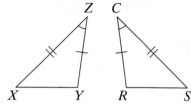

10.

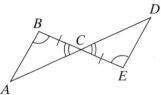

In the diagram below, *LMRC* ≅ *TXND*. **Find each measure.**

11. *m∠N*　　**12.** *m∠T*

13. *RM*　　**14.** *ND*

15. *m∠C*　　**16.** *m∠M*

17. *XT*　　**18.** *CL*

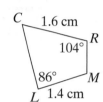
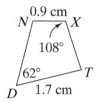

GPS

19. Guided Problem Solving A truss is a support structure made up of triangular units. Trusses are commonly used to strengthen roofs and bridges.

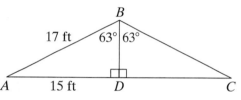

The diagram at the right shows a truss for a roof. What is the length of $\overline{AC}$?

- You know that △*ABD* ≅ △*CBD* by ■.
- Because congruent parts of congruent triangles are congruent, the length of $\overline{DC}$ is ■, which means that the length of $\overline{AC}$ is ■.

Is each pair of triangles congruent? Explain.

20.

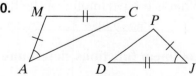

21.

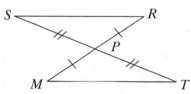

22. Writing in Math Are all squares congruent to each other? Explain. Use the terms *corresponding sides* and *corresponding angles* in your explanation.

23. Reasoning Can you show that two triangles are congruent by Angle-Angle-Angle? Draw figures to support your answer.

Maps Use the map at the right for Exercises 24–27.

24. Show that the triangles in the map are congruent.

25. Copy the triangles. Mark the sides and angles to show congruent corresponding parts.

26. How far is Porter Square from the intersection of Lee Street and Washington Road?

27. Find the distance along the road from Porter Square to Green Street.

28. **Challenge** Show that the two triangles at the right are congruent. Then find the missing measures.

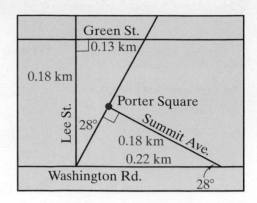

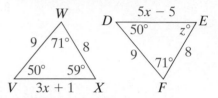

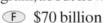

Test Prep and Mixed Review   **Practice**

Multiple Choice

29. Based on the figure at the right, which statement about *JK* is correct?
    Ⓐ $JK = JN$ Ⓒ $JK = LM$
    Ⓑ $JK > JN$ Ⓓ $JK < LM$

30. The volume of Earth's oceans is approximately 1.335×10^9 cubic kilometers, and each cubic kilometer of ocean water holds about 1.3×10^4 grams of dissolved gold. If the price of gold is $50.60 per gram, about how much is the dissolved gold in the oceans worth?
    Ⓕ $70 billion   Ⓗ $20 trillion
    Ⓖ $300 billion   Ⓙ $900 trillion

31. A flower bed is shaped like a right triangle with legs that measure 8 ft and 8 ft. What is the perimeter of the flower bed to the nearest foot?
    Ⓐ 11 ft   Ⓑ 24 ft   Ⓒ 27 ft   Ⓓ 32 ft

For each pair of linear functions, determine which has the greater rate of change.

32. $2y - 3x = 8$;

x	2	4	6	8
y	7	11	15	19

33. $y = 4 + x$;

x	3	6	9	12
y	1	2	3	4

34. $y = 5x + 3$;

x	−4	−2	0	2
y	−30	−18	−6	6

35. $2y = x - 3$;

x	0	8	16	24
y	3	5	7	9

GO for Help

For Exercises	See Lesson
32–35	7-7

Identify each pair of angles as *corresponding*, *alternate interior*, or *vertical*.

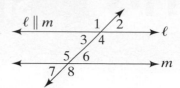

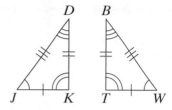

$\ell \parallel m$

1. ∠6, ∠7

2. ∠4, ∠5

3. ∠2, ∠6

In the diagram, $m\angle 1 = 135°$. Find the measure of each angle.

4. ∠5

5. ∠6

6. ∠8

7. Show that the pair of triangles at the right is congruent.

8. Let $m\angle C = 67°$. Find the measures of the complement and the supplement.

In the diagram below, $APKS \cong OFND$. Find each measure.

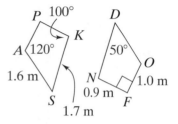

9. $m\angle N$

10. $m\angle P$

11. $m\angle O$

12. PK

13. DO

14. DN

Dancers

Modern dance allows for freedom of movement and self-expression. Other types of dance include folk, classical ballet, ethnic, tap, and jazz.

You might wonder how math applies to dance. Dancers often perform as a group. The choreography, or arranged movements of the dance, often consists of repeated steps. Knowledge of patterns helps dancers memorize the steps and synchronize themselves with the other dancers.

Go Online For information on dancers
PearsonSuccessNet.com

11-3 Similar Figures

What You'll Learn

To identify similar figures and to use proportions to find missing measurements in similar figures

New Vocabulary similar figures, similar polygons

Why Learn This?

Sometimes you want an image to be larger or smaller than the original.

Similar figures have the same shape but not necessarily the same size. The ratios of the lengths of corresponding sides in similar figures are proportional.

The symbol ~ means "is similar to."

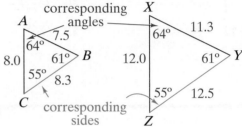

If two polygons are **similar polygons,** then corresponding angles are congruent and the lengths of corresponding sides are in proportion. Recall that in a proportion, the *cross products* are equal. In the diagram above, $\triangle ABC \sim \triangle XYZ$.

EXAMPLE Identifying Similar Polygons

1 Is rectangle *LMNO* similar to rectangle *HIJK*? Explain.

$$\angle L \cong \angle H \quad \angle M \cong \angle I \quad \angle N \cong \angle J \quad \angle O \cong \angle K$$

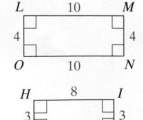

$$\frac{MN}{IJ} \overset{?}{=} \frac{LM}{HI} \quad \leftarrow \text{Write a proportion.}$$

$$\frac{4}{3} \overset{?}{=} \frac{10}{8} \quad \leftarrow \text{Substitute.}$$

$$4 \cdot 8 \overset{?}{=} 3 \cdot 10 \quad \leftarrow \text{Write the cross products.}$$

$$32 \neq 30 \quad \leftarrow \text{Simplify.}$$

The corresponding angles are congruent, but the corresponding sides are not in proportion. So the rectangles are *not* similar.

✓ Quick Check

1. Rectangle *EFGH* has side lengths of 18 and 27. Rectangle *LMNO* has side lengths of 36 and 54. Are the rectangles similar? Explain.

You can use proportions to find unknown lengths in similar figures.

EXAMPLE **Application: Design**

2️⃣ You are designing a poster. A sketch for the letter H is shown. The letter will be 9 in. tall on the poster. If the two letters are similar, what is the width on the poster?

$$\frac{5 \text{ in.}}{9 \text{ in.}} = \frac{4 \text{ in.}}{w} \quad \leftarrow \textbf{Write a proportion.}$$

$$5 \cdot w = 9 \cdot 4 \quad \leftarrow \textbf{Write the cross products.}$$

$$5w = 36 \quad \leftarrow \textbf{Simplify.}$$

$$\frac{5w}{5} = \frac{36}{5} \quad \leftarrow \textbf{Divide each side by 5.}$$

$$x = 7.2 \quad \leftarrow \textbf{Simplify.}$$

5 in. |← 4 in. →|

The width of the letter is 7.2 inches.

✓ Quick Check

🔴 **2.** If the letter H on the poster has a height of 14 in., what is its width?

When similar figures overlap, you can separate them.

EXAMPLE **Overlapping Similar Triangles**

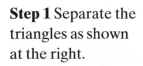

3️⃣ **Multiple Choice** In the figure at the left, $\triangle ABC \sim \triangle DEC$. Find the value of x.

   Ⓐ 8 ft   Ⓑ 9 ft   Ⓒ 12 ft   Ⓓ 18 ft

Step 1 Separate the triangles as shown at the right.

Step 2 Write a proportion using corresponding sides of the triangles.

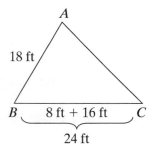

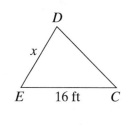

$$\frac{18}{x} = \frac{24}{16} \quad \leftarrow \textbf{Write a proportion.}$$

$$18 \cdot 16 = 24 \cdot x \quad \leftarrow \textbf{Write the cross products.}$$

$$288 = 24x \quad \leftarrow \textbf{Simplify.}$$

$$\frac{288}{24} = \frac{24x}{24} \quad \leftarrow \textbf{Divide each side by 24.}$$

$$12 = x \quad \leftarrow \textbf{Simplify.}$$

The value of x is 12 ft. The correct answer is choice C.

✓ Quick Check

🔴 **3.** If DC is 14 ft, what is the length of $\overline{AC}$?

Test Prep Tip ✏️

You can reduce $\frac{24}{16}$ in the first step. This uses more steps but makes calculations easier.

1. **Vocabulary** Can a triangle and square be similar figures? Explain.

Complete each statement for the similar figures at the right.

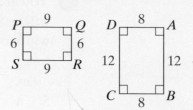

2. $\angle P \cong \angle A$, $\angle R \cong \angle$ ■

3. $\angle Q \cong \angle B$, $\angle S \cong \angle$ ■

4. $\dfrac{PQ}{AB} = \dfrac{■}{BC}$

Homework Exercises

For more exercises, see Extra Skills and Word Problems.

GO for Help

For Exercises	See Examples
5–6	1
7–9	2
10–11	3

Are the figures in each pair similar? Explain.

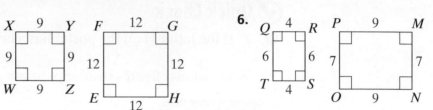

Exercises 7–8 show pairs of similar figures. Find the unknown lengths.

7.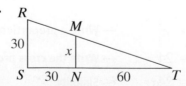

8.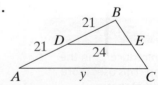

9. **Movies** A frame of movie film is 35 mm wide and 26.25 mm high. The film projects an image 8 m wide. How high is the image?

Exercises 10–11 show similar figures. Find the unknown lengths.

10.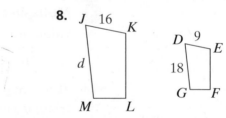

11.

12. **Guided Problem Solving** You have a class photo that is 10 in. long and 8 in. wide. If you want to enlarge your photo to be 15 in. long, how wide will the photo be?
   • **Understand the Problem** You know the dimensions of the original photo and the length of the enlarged photo. Find the width of the enlarged photo.
   • **Make a Plan** Draw the figures and label their sides.

Exercises 13–14 show pairs of similar figures. Find the unknown lengths.

13.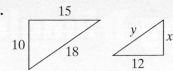

14.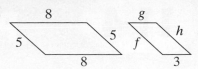

15. **Clothing** A T-shirt comes in different sizes. A large T-shirt is 21.5 in. wide and 26.5 in. long. If a small youth T-shirt is 15.5 in. wide, what is its length to the nearest inch?

16. **Writing in Math** Are squares always similar? Explain.

17. **Multiple Choice** Which statement is *true*?
    - (A) Corresponding sides of similar polygons are equal.
    - (B) Not all circles are similar.
    - (C) Corresponding sides of similar polygons are congruent.
    - (D) Not all rectangles are similar.

For Exercises 18–19 use the similar triangles shown below.

18. Find the length of side c.

19. **Challenge** Find the ratio of corresponding sides and the ratio of the perimeters. What do you notice?

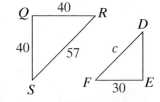

Test Prep and Mixed Review   **Practice**

Multiple Choice

20. The figures shown at the right are similar. What is the value of w?

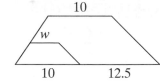

    - (A) 4.0
    - (B) 4.4
    - (C) 6.3
    - (D) 8.0

21. Each day, the International Space Station orbits the Earth about 15.6 times and travels about 6.62×10^5 kilometers. Approximately how many kilometers does the International Space Station travel in 1 orbit around the Earth?
    - (F) 4.24×10^4 km
    - (G) 1.03×10^5 km
    - (H) 4.24×10^5 km
    - (J) 1.03×10^7 km

22. Judy spends 3 more than twice as many hours studying for history as she does for math. She studies 4 hours for history. Which equation can be used to find x, the number of hours she studies for math?
    - (A) $3x + 3 = 4$
    - (B) $3x + 2 = 4$
    - (C) $2x + 2 = 4$
    - (D) $2x + 3 = 4$

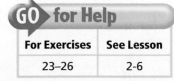
GO for Help

For Exercises	See Lesson
23–26	2-6

Algebra Solve each equation. Check the solution.

23. $-3(n + 5) = 27$

24. $0.9(s - 4) = 3.6$

25. $-16 = -8(g + 4)$

26. $3 = \frac{1}{2}(12 + t)$

Proving Triangles Similar

© **CONTENT STANDARD**
8.G.5

What You'll Learn

To determine measures of the angles of triangles and use them to help prove that triangles are similar

Why Learn This?

Architects and engineers often make use of triangles when designing buildings and other structures.

Three copies of the same triangle have been arranged as shown. Lines ℓ and m are parallel because their alternate interior angles are congruent.

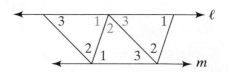

The angles labeled in blue show that ∠1, ∠2, and ∠3 form a straight angle along line ℓ, which means that the sum of their measures is 180°. Therefore, the sum of the measures of the angles of each of the triangles is 180°.

KEY CONCEPTS   Angle Sum of a Triangle

The sum of the measures of the angles of any triangle is 180°.

EXAMPLE   Finding an Angle Measure

1 Multiple Choice △RST forms part of the front of a cabin as shown at the left. What is the measure of ∠S?

Ⓐ 55°   Ⓑ 70°   Ⓒ 125°   Ⓓ 110°

$$m\angle R + m\angle S + m\angle T = 180°$$ ← **Angle sum of a triangle**

$$55° + m\angle S + 55° = 180°$$ ← **Substitute.**

$$m\angle S + 110° = 180°$$ ← **Simplify.**

$$m\angle S + 110° - 110° = 180° - 110°$$ ← **Subtract 110° from each side.**

$$m\angle S = 70°$$ ← **Simplify.**

∠S measures 70°. The correct answer is choice B.

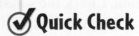

✓ Quick Check

1. What is the measure of ∠E in △DEF?

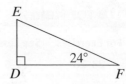

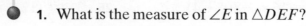

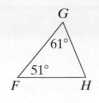

G

61°

51°

F   H

If all pairs of corresponding angles of two triangles are congruent, then the triangles have the same shape and the triangles are similar. In the diagram at the left, $\angle F \cong \angle X$ and $\angle G \cong \angle Y$.

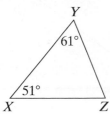

Y

61°

51°

X   Z

What about the third pair of corresponding angles? By using the angle sum of a triangle, you can determine that $m\angle H = 68°$ and $m\angle Z = 68°$. Because all three pairs of corresponding angles are congruent, $\triangle FGH \sim \triangle XYZ$.

This example shows that if two pairs of corresponding angles of two triangles are congruent, then the third pair of corresponding angles must also be congruent and the triangles are similar.

KEY CONCEPTS   **Angle-Angle (AA) Similarity**

If two angles of one triangle are congruent to the corresponding angles of another triangle, then the triangles are similar.

EXAMPLE   **Similar Triangles**

2 Show that the pair of triangles is similar.

Step 1 Use the angle sum of a triangle to find $m\angle R$.

$$91° + 37° + m\angle R = 180°$$
$$128° + m\angle R = 180°$$
$$128° - 128° + m\angle R = 180° - 128°$$
$$m\angle R = 52°$$

Q

37°

P 91°

R

Step 2 Use AA similarity.

$\angle P \cong \angle L$ ← **Each measures 91°.**

$\angle R \cong \angle K$ ← **Each measures 52°.**

$\triangle PQR \sim \triangle LMK$ by AA similarity.

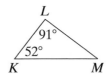

L

91°

52°

K   M

GO for Help

For help solving equations, go to Lesson 3-3.

Test Prep Tip

There is often more than one way to show that two triangles are similar. For example, you could have started by finding $m\angle M$ instead of $m\angle R$.

✓ Quick Check

2. Show that each pair of triangles is similar.

a.

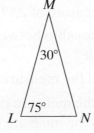

M

30°

75°

L   N

T   U
75°   75°

S

b.

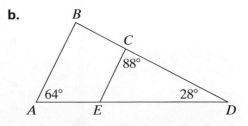

B

C
88°

64°   28°
A   E   D

For each triangle, find $m\angle 1$.

1.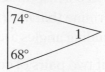

2.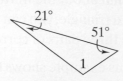

3.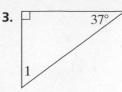

Use the triangles below for Exercises 4 and 5.

4. List the congruent corresponding angles of the two triangles.

5. **Error Analysis** Daisy writes $\triangle DEF \sim \triangle TRS$ by AA similarity. Erika writes $\triangle DEF \sim \triangle RST$ by AA similarity. Who is incorrect? Explain.

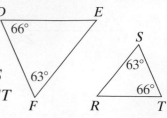

Homework Exercises

For more exercises, see Extra Skills and Word Problems.

Determine the unknown angle measure in each triangle.

GO for Help

For Exercises	See Examples
6–9	1
10–11	2

6.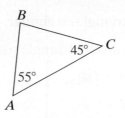

7.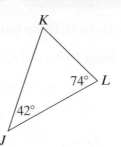

8.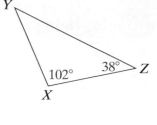

9. A triangular flag has two angles that each measure 74°. What is the measure of the third angle of the flag?

Show that each pair of triangles is similar.

10.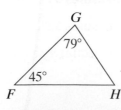

11.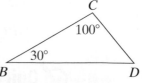

GPS 12. **Guided Problem Solving** The diagram shows a cross-section of a portion of a dam. What is the measure of $\angle 1$?

- What is the relationship between $\angle 2$ and the 135° angle?

- How can you find the measure of $\angle 2$?

- Once you know the measure of $\angle 2$, how can you find the measure of $\angle 1$?

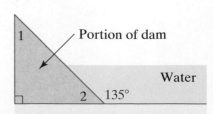

13. City workers are laying out the paths in a new park, as shown in the diagram. Do the workers have enough information to determine $m\angle Q$? If so, explain how to find its measure. If not, explain why not.

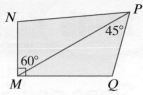

14. Engineering The diagram shows a portion of a bridge support. If the support was built correctly, $\triangle FGH$ should be similar to $\triangle FHK$. Given that $\overline{GJ} \parallel \overline{FK}$, was the support built correctly? Justify your answer.

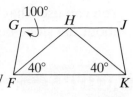

(**Algebra**) **For each triangle, determine the value of x.**

15.

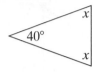

16.

17.

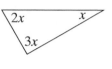

18. <u>**Writing in Math**</u> Is the following statement *true* or *false*? A triangle can have two angles that measure $100°$. Explain.

19. Challenge Another way to show that two triangles are similar is to show that one pair of corresponding angles is congruent and that the corresponding sides that make up those angles are in proportion. This method is called *side-angle-side (SAS) similarity*. Use this method to show that the triangles at the left are similar.

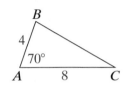

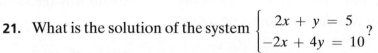
Test Prep and Mixed Review   **Practice**

Multiple Choice

20. What is the measure of $\angle F$ in the triangle shown at the right?

  Ⓐ $33°$ Ⓒ $57°$

  Ⓑ $45°$ Ⓓ $135°$

21. What is the solution of the system $\begin{cases} 2x + y = 5 \\ -2x + 4y = 10 \end{cases}$?

  Ⓕ $(-5, 0)$ Ⓖ $(1, 3)$ Ⓗ $(2, 1)$ Ⓙ $(4, -3)$

22. What is the function rule for the linear function shown in the table?

  Ⓐ $y = -2x - 3$ Ⓒ $y = 2x + 1$

  Ⓑ $y = x - 1$ Ⓓ $y = 3x + 3$

x	-2	-1	0	1
y	-3	-1	1	3

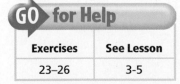
GO for Help

Exercises	See Lesson
23–26	3-5

(**Algebra**) **Solve each equation.**

23. $-2x + 6 = 28$ **24.** $1.4n - 0.3 = 8.1$

25. $\dfrac{t}{8} - 7 = 3$ **26.** $\dfrac{c}{4} + 8 = 20$

Slope and Similar Triangles

You can use what you know about similar triangles to learn more about the slope between different points on a line.

ACTIVITY

Use the diagram below to explore slope and similar triangles.

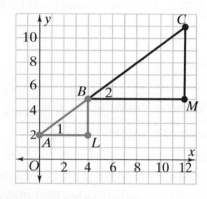

1. $\overline{BL}$ and $\overline{CM}$ are both vertical. Are they parallel?
2. The line containing points A, B, and C is a transversal that intersects $\overline{BL}$ and $\overline{CM}$. Why is $\angle 1$ congruent to $\angle 2$?
3. Is $\triangle ABL$ similar to $\triangle BCM$? Justify your answer.
4. Write a ratio in the form $\dfrac{\text{vertical side length}}{\text{horizontal side length}}$ for each triangle. How do the two ratios compare?
5. How does the ratio of the vertical and horizontal side lengths of $\triangle ABL$ compare to the slope of its hypotenuse?
6. Is the slope of $\overline{AB}$ the same as the slope of $\overline{BC}$? Justify your answer.
7. Use the diagram below and similar triangles to explain why the slope m is the same between any two distinct points on a line.

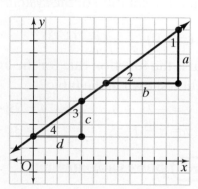

You can use slope and similar triangles to derive formulas for lines in the coordinate plane.

The graph shows points *E*, *F*, and *H* that lie on a line that passes through the origin. $\triangle FMH$ was formed by drawing a vertical segment from point *H* and a horizontal segment from point *F*. The same method was used to form $\triangle FNE$.

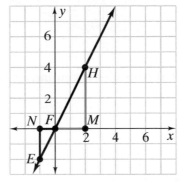

1. Are $\triangle FMH$ and $\triangle FNE$ similar figures? Explain.

2. Write a ratio for each triangle in the form $\dfrac{\text{vertical side length}}{\text{horizontal side length}}$.

3. How do the ratios of the vertical and horizontal side lengths relate to the slope *m* of $\overline{EH}$?

4. Use the slope to write the equation of $\overline{EH}$: $y = \blacksquare\,x$.

5. Write a general equation for a line with slope *m* passing through the origin. Explain your reasoning.

6. How does the position of $\triangle FNE$ in the graph below compare to the position of $\triangle FNE$ in the original graph above?

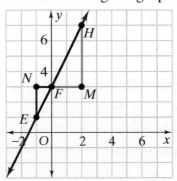

7. Did the ratios of the vertical and horizontal side lengths for the two triangles change?

8. Each point in the second graph is shifted up. Complete the equation that relates *y* to *x* for $\overline{EH}$ in the second graph: $y = \blacksquare\,x + \blacksquare$.

9. Write a general equation for a line with slope *m* that intercepts the vertical axis at $(0, b)$. Explain how you found your answer.

1. Are the figures at the right similar? Explain.

2. A rectangular photograph has a length of 6 in. and a width of 4 in. A similar photograph has a length of 9 in. What is the width of the similar photograph?

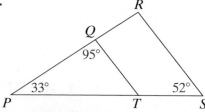

Determine the unknown angle measure in each triangle.

3.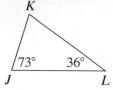

4.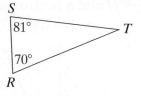

5.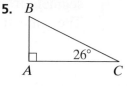

6.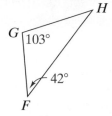

Show that each pair of triangles is similar.

7.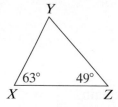

8.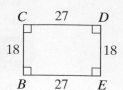

MATH GAMES

Triangle Triples

What You'll Need

- 25 index cards labeled from 20° to 140° in increments of 5°

How To Play

- Shuffle the index cards. Deal the same number to each player.

- If a player has a group of three cards labeled with angle measures that could form a triangle, the three cards form a Triangle Triple. Players should remove any Triangle Triples from their hand and place those cards to one side.

- Choose a player to go first. That player draws a card from another player's hand and tries to use the card to form a Triangle Triple.

- Players should take turns drawing cards from each other. The first player to get three Triangle Triples is the winner.

Angle Sums

An *interior angle* of a polygon is an angle inside the polygon formed by two adjacent sides. An *exterior angle* is an angle outside the polygon formed by a side and an extension of an adjacent side.

In the figure at right, ∠1, ∠2, and ∠3 are interior angles, and ∠4, ∠5, and ∠6 are exterior angles.

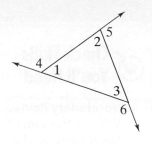

ACTIVITY

You can develop formulas for finding the sum of the angle measures of a polygon.

1. Draw polygons with 4, 5, 6, and 7 sides. Draw all the diagonals from one vertex of each figure. Count the number of triangles formed.

2. Copy and complete the table below.

Number of Sides	Number of Triangles Formed	Sum of Interior Angle Measures
3	1	180°
■	■	■
■	■	■
■	■	■
■	■	■
8	6	6 · 180° = 1,080°

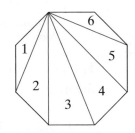

3. **a. Patterns** Describe how the sum of the interior angle measures changes as the number of sides of a polygon increases by 1.

   b. Reasoning What relationship do you notice between the number of sides of a polygon and the number of triangles formed? Explain.

4. **a.** Draw polygons with 3, 4, 5, and 6 sides. Draw and measure the exterior angles of each polygon.

   b. Find the sum of the measures of the exterior angles of each polygon. Record your information in a table.

   c. Make a conjecture about the sum of the exterior angles of a polygon.

✓ Check Skills You'll Need

1. **Vocabulary Review** What is the sum of the measures of a pair of *supplementary angles*?

Find the measure of the supplement of each angle.
2. 54° 3. 90°
4. 108° 5. 18°
6. 76° 7. 150°

GO for Help
Lesson 11-2

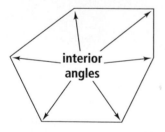

interior angles

What You'll Learn

To find the angle measures of a polygon

New Vocabulary interior angle, exterior angle

Why Learn This?

Polygons often appear in art and architecture. In designing tile patterns, it helps to know about the angles of polygons.
Here is a list of common polygons.

Polygon Name	Number of Sides
Triangle	3
Quadrilateral	4
Pentagon	5
Hexagon	6
Heptagon	7

Polygon Name	Number of Sides
Octagon	8
Nonagon	9
Decagon	10
Dodecagon	12

Two consecutive sides of a polygon form one **interior angle.** The sum of the measures of the interior angles depends on the number of sides.

KEY CONCEPTS   Polygon Angle Sum

For a polygon with n sides, the sum of the measures of the interior angles is $(n - 2)180°$.

EXAMPLE   Sum of the Interior Angle Measures

1 What is the sum of the measures of the interior angles of a nonagon?

$$(n - 2)180° = (9 - 2)180°$$ ← A nonagon has nine sides. Substitute 9 for n.

$$= 1{,}260°$$ ← Simplify.

The sum of the interior angle measures of a nonagon is 1,260°.

✓ Quick Check

1. What is the sum of the measures of the interior angles of a heptagon?

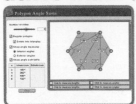

You can use the same formula to find angle measures in a polygon.

EXAMPLE **Angle Measures of a Polygon**

2 (**Algebra**) Find the unknown angle measure in the
pentagon at the right.

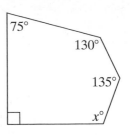

Step 1 Find the sum of the angle measures.

$$(n - 2)180° = (5 - 2)180° \quad \leftarrow \text{Substitute 5 for } n.$$
$$= 540° \quad \leftarrow \text{Simplify.}$$

Step 2 Write an equation. Let x = the unknown angle measure.

$$540° = 90° + 75° + 130° + 135° + x° \quad \leftarrow \text{Write an equation.}$$
$$540° = 430° + x° \quad \leftarrow \text{Simplify.}$$
$$110° = x° \quad \leftarrow \text{Subtract 430° from each side.}$$

The unknown angle measure is 110°.

✓ Quick Check

2. A hexagon has five angles with measures of 142°, 84°, 123°, 130°, and
90°. What is the measure of the sixth angle?

An **exterior angle** of a polygon is an angle formed
by a side and an extension of an adjacent side.

The measure of an exterior angle of a triangle is
equal to the sum of the measures of the interior
angles at the other two vertices.

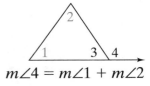

$$m\angle 4 = m\angle 1 + m\angle 2$$

EXAMPLE **Finding the Measure of an Exterior Angle**

3 **Art** The diagram shows a portion of the design of a mosaic. $\angle 2$ is an
exterior angle of $\triangle ABC$. What is $m\angle 2$?

$$m\angle 2 = m\angle A + m\angle B \quad \leftarrow \text{Exterior angle of triangle}$$
$$= 45° + 90° \quad \leftarrow \text{Substitute.}$$
$$= 135° \quad \leftarrow \text{Simplify.}$$

$\angle 2$ measures 135°.

An ancient Roman
mosaic made of tiles

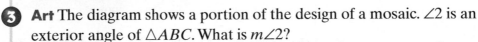

Check By the angle sum of a triangle, $m\angle 1 = 180° - 45° - 90° = 45°$.

$\angle 1$ and $\angle 2$ are supplementary, so $m\angle 2 = 180° - 45° = 135°$. ✔

✓ Quick Check

3. In $\triangle RST$, $m\angle R = 63°$ and $m\angle S = 84°$. What is the measure of the
exterior angle at vertex T?

1. **Vocabulary** How does an interior angle of a polygon differ from an exterior angle?

Classify each polygon by the number of its sides.

2. 　　3. 　　4. 　　5.

6. **Error Analysis** Jason knows the sum of the angle measures of a hexagon is 720°. To find the sum of the angle measures of a dodecagon, he multiplies 720° by 2 since 12 = 6 · 2. Miranda multiplies 180° by 10. Who is correct? Explain.

Homework Exercises

For more exercises, see Extra Skills and Word Problems.

Find the sum of the measures of the interior angles of each polygon.

GO for Help

For Exercises	See Examples
7–12	1
13–15	2
16–19	3

7. pentagon　　8. octagon　　9. hexagon

10. decagon　　11. triangle　　12. dodecagon

Algebra Find the missing angle measure in each figure.

13. 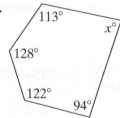　　14. 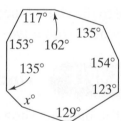　　15.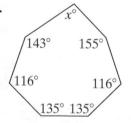

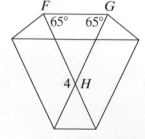

Find the measure of each exterior angle of the triangle below.

16. ∠1　　17. ∠2　　18. ∠3

19. The diagram at the left shows the plans for a kite. ∠4 is an exterior angle of △FGH. What is $m\angle 4$?

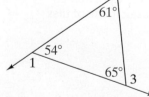

20. **Guided Problem Solving** The measure of each interior angle of a polygon is 157.5°. How many sides n does the polygon have?
   - What two expressions can you write for the sum of the measures of the interior angles of the polygon?
   - What is the solution for n when you set the two expressions equal to each other?

Algebra Find the missing angle measures in each figure.

21.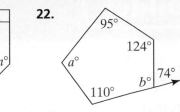

22.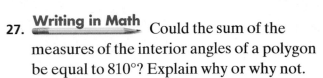

23.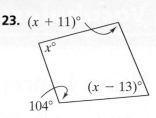

In the diagram, line *m* intersects line *n*. Find the measure of each angle, and justify your answers.

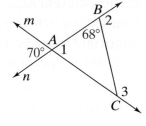

24. ∠1   25. ∠2   26. ∠3

27. <u>**Writing in Math**</u> Could the sum of the measures of the interior angles of a polygon be equal to 810°? Explain why or why not.

28. The measures of six angles of a heptagon are 145°, 115°, 152°, 87°, 90°, and 150°. Find the measure of the seventh angle.

29. **Baseball** In the home plate at the left, ∠1 ≅ ∠2. Find *m*∠1.

30. **Challenge** Use the triangle at the right and what you have learned about the exterior angles of triangles to show that the sum of the measures of the exterior angles of a triangle is 360°.

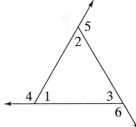

Test Prep and Mixed Review   **Practice**

Multiple Choice

31. The following statements are true about △*ABC*.
    • *m*∠*A* is less than *m*∠*B*.
    • *m*∠*B* is less than *m*∠*C*.
    • An exterior angle at vertex *C* measures 100°.

    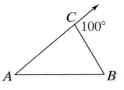

    Which are possible measures of ∠*A* and ∠*B*?
    Ⓐ *m*∠*A* = 10°, *m*∠*B* = 90°   Ⓒ *m*∠*A* = 40°, *m*∠*B* = 60°
    Ⓑ *m*∠*A* = 20°, *m*∠*B* = 80°   Ⓓ *m*∠*A* = 50°, *m*∠*B* = 50°

32. The area of a square is 275 square feet. Which is closest to the side length of the square?
    Ⓕ 15.8 ft   Ⓖ 16.1 ft   Ⓗ 16.4 ft   Ⓙ 16.6 ft

GO **for Help**

For Exercises	See Lesson
33–38	11-1

In the diagram, line ℓ ∥ *m*, and *m*∠5 = 63°. Find the measure of each angle.

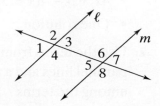

33. ∠1   34. ∠2   35. ∠3
36. ∠4   37. ∠6   38. ∠7

Vocabulary Builder

Using Concept Maps

Concept maps are visual tools that show how you can relate different ideas and terms you have used. Connecting new knowledge to existing knowledge is important in understanding mathematics.

To build a concept map, follow these steps:

- Place each concept or term inside a geometrical shape.
- Draw lines connecting the concepts or terms that are related.

EXAMPLE

In this chapter, you learned about the angles formed by two intersecting lines. You can show the relationships among the angles with the concept map below.

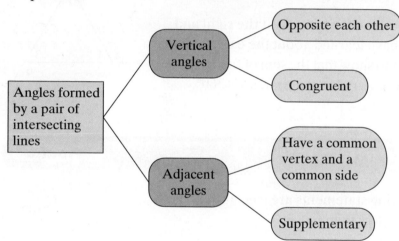

Exercises

1. Make a concept map for "Types of Solutions of Linear Equations" using the following types of solutions and examples from Chapter 3.

   - No solutions
   - $4x + 5 = 4(x - 3)$
   - One solution

   - $3x + 4 = 2x - 5$
   - Infinitely many solutions
   - $5x + 6 = 3(x + 2) + 2x$

2. Use the terms from Lesson 11-1 that are related to the angles formed by a pair of parallel lines and a transversal. Make a concept map showing the relationships among the terms.

Finding Angle Measures

Today, the Great Pyramid at Giza in Egypt is shorter than it was when it was originally built. One of the exterior angles at the base of the pyramid measures 128.5°. If the base angles of the pyramid are congruent, what was the measure of the angle at the top of the pyramid when it was originally built?

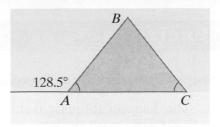

What You Might Think

> What do I know? What do I want to find out?

> How can I find $m\angle BAC$?

> How can I find $m\angle C$?

> How can I find $m\angle B$?

> What is the answer?

What You Might Write

I know the measure of the exterior angle at vertex A. I also know that $\angle C \cong \angle BAC$. I need to find $m\angle B$.

The angle that measures 128.5° and $\angle BAC$ are supplementary.

$$128.5° + m\angle BAC = 180°$$
$$m\angle BAC = 51.5°$$

$\angle C \cong \angle BAC$, so $\angle C$ also measures 51.5°.

The sum of the measures of the interior angles of a triangle is 180°.

$$m\angle BAC + m\angle C + m\angle B = 180°$$
$$51.5° + 51.5° + m\angle B = 180°$$
$$103° + m\angle B = 180°$$
$$m\angle B = 77°$$

When the pyramid was originally built, the angle at the top measured 77°.

Think It Through

1. How do you know that the angle that measures 128.5° and $\angle BAC$ are supplementary?

2. **Reasoning** What is one way that you could check the answer to this problem?

Exercises

Solve each problem. For Exercises 3 and 4, answer parts (a) and (b) first.

3. The diagram at the right shows the plans for a triangular swimming pool. $\overline{HK}$ marks the boundary between the shallow end and the deep end of the pool. Given that $\overline{HK} \parallel \overline{GL}$, what is the measure of $\angle G$?

   a. What do you know and what do you want to find out?

   b. What is the relationship between $\angle JHK$ and $\angle G$?

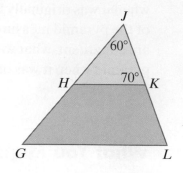

4. The polygon below represents one face of a barn. Given that the left half of the polygon is congruent to the right half of the polygon, what is the measure of $\angle U$?

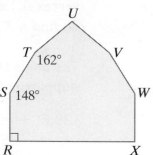

   a. What do you know and what do you want to find out?

   b. What type of polygon is the face of the barn? What is the sum of the measures of the interior angles of this type of polygon?

5. A graphic artist made the logo shown at the right for a company. Given that $\triangle LMP \cong \triangle NMP$, what is the measure of $\angle LMN$?

6. The diagram below shows the design for a rectangular metal gate. What is the measure of $\angle CED$?

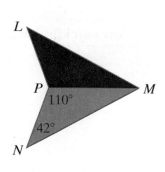

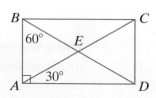

Drawing a Picture

The problem-solving strategy *Draw a Picture* may help you answer test questions using given information.

EXAMPLE

Blanca has a rectangular exercise pen for her rabbits that has a length of 6 ft and a width of 3 ft. She plans to build a similar pen with a length of 9 ft. What will be the perimeter of the new pen?

  Ⓐ 13.5 ft   Ⓑ 22 ft   Ⓒ 27 ft   Ⓓ 54 ft

You can draw a picture to model the situation. Let w = the width of the new pen.

Original Pen

3 ft

6 ft

$$\frac{3}{w} = \frac{6}{9} \qquad \leftarrow \text{Use the picture to write a proportion.}$$
$$3 \cdot 9 = 6 \cdot w \qquad \leftarrow \text{Write the cross products.}$$
$$27 = 6w \qquad \leftarrow \text{Simplify.}$$
$$\frac{27}{6} = \frac{6w}{6} \qquad \leftarrow \text{Divide each side by 6.}$$
$$4.5 = w \qquad \leftarrow \text{Simplify.}$$

New Pen

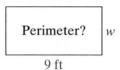

Perimeter? w

9 ft

The width of the new pen is 4.5 ft, so the perimeter of the new pen is $2(9) + 2(4.5) = 27$ ft. The answer is C.

Exercises

1. A window has the shape of a triangle with one obtuse angle and two acute angles. The obtuse angle measures 95°, and the two acute angles are congruent. What is the measure of each of the acute angles?

  Ⓐ 27.5°   Ⓑ 42.5°   Ⓒ 55°   Ⓓ 85°

2. Pine Ln., Main St., and Central Ave. intersect at the same point. Main St. and Central Ave. are perpendicular. The acute angle between Pine Ln. and Main St. measures 40°. What is the measure of the acute angle between Pine Ln. and Central Ave.?

  Ⓕ 40°   Ⓖ 50°   Ⓗ 60°   Ⓙ 140°

3. A pentagon has two right angles. The remaining three angles of the pentagon are congruent. What is the measure of each of the three remaining angles?

  Ⓐ 60°   Ⓑ 72°   Ⓒ 120°   Ⓓ 150°

Vocabulary Review

alternate interior angles (p. 418)   exterior angle (p. 441)   similar polygons (p. 428)
congruent polygons (p. 422)   interior angle (p. 440)   transversal (p. 418)
corresponding angles (p. 418)   similar figures (p. 428)

Choose the correct vocabulary term to complete each sentence.

1. A (transversal, perpendicular line) intersects two lines at different points.

2. (Exterior, interior) angles are found outside the parallel lines cut by a transversal.

3. (Alternate interior angles, Corresponding angles) are on the same side of a transversal.

4. A pair of (adjacent exterior angles, corresponding angles) share both a common vertex and a common side.

5. If two polygons have the same shape but different sizes, then they are (congruent polygons, similar polygons).

Go Online

For vocabulary quiz
PearsonSuccessNet.com

Skills and Concepts

Lesson 11-1

- To identify types of angles and to find angle measures using the relationship between angles

- To identify parallel lines and the angles formed by parallel lines and transversals

Vertical angles have the same measure, so they are congruent angles. The sum of the measures of a pair of supplementary angles is $180°$. The sum of the measures of a pair of complementary angles is $90°$.

If two parallel lines are cut by a **transversal,** the **corresponding angles** are congruent, and the **alternate interior angles** are congruent.

Find the measures of $\angle 1$ and $\angle 2$ in each diagram.

6.

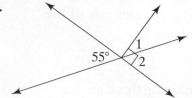

7.

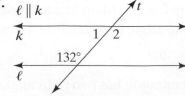

Lesson 11-2

• To identify congruent figures and use them to solve problems

Congruent polygons have exactly the same size and shape. You can use SAS, ASA, or SSS to decide whether two triangles are congruent.

Write a congruence statement and show that the triangles are congruent.

8.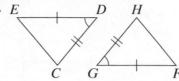

9.

Lesson 11-3

• To identify similar figures and to use proportions to find missing measurements in similar figures

Figures that have the same shape but not necessarily the same size are **similar figures. Similar polygons** have corresponding angles that are congruent and corresponding sides that are in proportion.

In the figure, $\triangle ACE \sim \triangle BCD$. Find each unknown length.

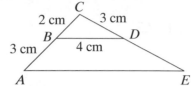

10. *AE*　　　**11.** *CE*　　　**12.** *DE*

Lesson 11-4

• To determine measures of the angles of triangles and use them to help prove that triangles are similar.

The sum of the measures of the angles of any triangle is 180°.

You can show that two triangles are similar by using AA similarity. In other words, if two angles of one triangle are congruent to the corresponding angles of another triangle, then the triangles are similar.

Show that each pair of triangles is similar.

13.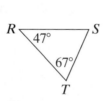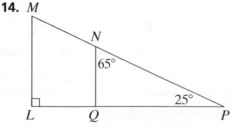

14.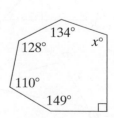

Lesson 11-5

• To find the angle measures of a polygon

For a polygon with *n* sides, the sum of the measures of the **interior angles** is $(n - 2)180°$.

The measure of an **exterior angle** of a triangle is equal to the sum of the measures of the interior angles at the other two vertices.

15. Find the unknown angle measure in the figure at the right.

16. In $\triangle JKL$, $m\angle J = 42°$ and $m\angle K = 63°$. What is the measure of an exterior angle at vertex *L*?

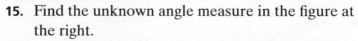
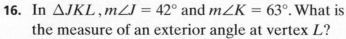

Chapter 11 Test

Go Online For online chapter test
PearsonSuccessNet.com

Identify each pair of angles in the diagram below as *corresponding*, *alternate interior*, *vertical*, or *none of these*.

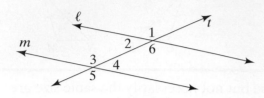

1. ∠2, ∠4
2. ∠1, ∠5
3. ∠1, ∠3
4. ∠3, ∠4
5. ∠4, ∠6
6. ∠3, ∠5

7. Find the measures of the numbered angles in the diagram below.

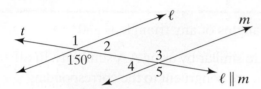
ℓ ∥ m

The measure of ∠D is 68°.

8. Find the measure of its supplement.

9. Find the measure of its complement.

Determine whether each pair of triangles is congruent. If so, write a congruence statement and explain how you know the triangles are congruent.

10.

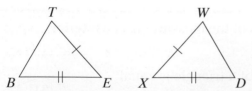

11.

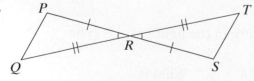

12. **Writing in Math** Explain why the order in which you list the vertices of two polygons in a congruence statement is important.

△ABC ~ △EDC. **Find each unknown length.**

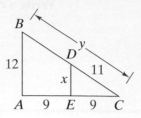

13. x
14. y

15. **Art** A rectangular painting in a museum has a length of 36 in. and a width of 30 in. The museum plans to sell a similar poster at its gift store. If the length of the poster will be 24 in., what will be the width of the poster?

Determine the unknown angle measure in each triangle.

16.

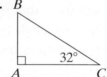

17.

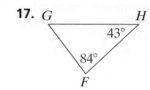

18. Show that the pair of triangles is similar.

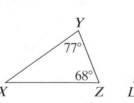

Find the sum of the measures of the interior angles of a polygon with the given number of sides.

19. 4 sides
20. 7 sides
21. 15 sides

Find the measure of each exterior angle of the triangle.

22. ∠1
23. ∠2
24. ∠3

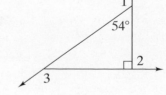

Multiple Choice

For Exercises 1–9, choose the correct letter.

1. Which square root lies between the whole numbers 11 and 12?

   Ⓐ $\sqrt{101}$ Ⓑ $\sqrt{120}$ Ⓒ $\sqrt{135}$ Ⓓ $\sqrt{144}$

2. How many solutions does the equation $4x + 6 = 2(x + 1) + 2x$ have?

   Ⓕ none   Ⓗ exactly two
   Ⓖ exactly one   Ⓙ infinitely many

3. $\triangle ABC \sim \triangle DEC.$ Which proportion can be used to find the length of $\overline{DE}$?

   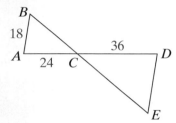

   Ⓐ $\dfrac{18}{24} = \dfrac{36}{DE}$ Ⓒ $\dfrac{24}{DE} = \dfrac{36}{18}$

   Ⓑ $\dfrac{DE}{18} = \dfrac{36}{24}$ Ⓓ $\dfrac{24}{36} = \dfrac{DE}{18}$

4. Which of the following functions is a linear function?

   Ⓕ $y = 3^x$ Ⓗ $y = 8/x$
   Ⓖ $y = \frac{1}{3}x$ Ⓙ $y = x^2 - 4$

5. Which power is equivalent to $5^3 \cdot 5^3$?

   Ⓐ 5^5 Ⓒ 25^5
   Ⓑ 5^6 Ⓓ 25^6

6. Which is a pair of corresponding angles?

   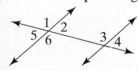

   Ⓕ $\angle 1$ and $\angle 6$ Ⓗ $\angle 3$ and $\angle 6$
   Ⓖ $\angle 1$ and $\angle 4$ Ⓙ $\angle 2$ and $\angle 4$

7. Joni is cutting out a triangular piece of fabric to use in a quilt. The first angle of the triangle measures 60°. What could be the measures of the other two angles?

   Ⓐ 45° and 45°   Ⓒ 30° and 90°
   Ⓑ 40° and 100°   Ⓓ 10° and 20°

8. What is the solution of $\begin{cases} y = 2x + 3 \\ y = 3x - 8 \end{cases}$?

   Ⓕ $(-11, -19)$ Ⓗ $(1, 5)$
   Ⓖ $(-1, 1)$ Ⓙ $(11, 25)$

9. $\angle 1$ and $\angle 2$ are exterior angles of $\triangle RST$. If $m\angle 1 = 102°$, what is $m\angle 2$?

   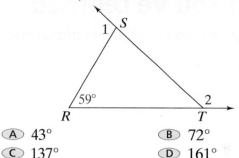

   Ⓐ 43°   Ⓑ 72°
   Ⓒ 137°   Ⓓ 161°

Gridded Response

10. The Berry family bought 2 adult tickets and 3 child tickets to a play for $48. The Martinez family bought 2 adult tickets and 1 child ticket to the play for $32. What is the cost, in dollars, of 1 adult ticket to the play?

Short Response

11. Write 9.972 as a mixed number in simplest form.

Extended Response

12. A system of two linear equations can have no solution, one solution, or infinitely many solutions. Write a short paragraph explaining how a graph of two equations would appear for each of these possibilities.

13. On the first day of gym class, students do 6 push-ups. The number of push-ups the students do will increase by 2 each time they come to class.
   a. Write a function rule to show the number of push-ups p the class does after c classes.
   b. How many push-ups will the class do on the ninth day of class? Justify your answer.

CHAPTER 12 · Surface Area and Volume

What You've Learned

- In Chapter 1, you multiplied rational numbers.
- In Chapter 10, you found the areas of parallelograms, triangles, and other figures.
- You found the circumference and area of a circle.

✔ Check Your Readiness

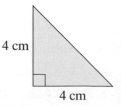

GO for Help

For Exercises	See Lesson
1–4	1-7
5	10-4
6	10-2
7	10-3
8–10	10-5

Multiplying Rational Numbers

Find each product.

1. $0.25 \cdot 3.14 \cdot 4$ **2.** $2 \cdot 20.5 \cdot 2$

3. $\frac{1}{2} \cdot 5 \cdot 8$ **4.** $2.8 \cdot (-4.3)$

Areas of Parallelograms, Triangles, Circles, and Other Figures

Find the area of each figure. Round to the nearest tenth.

5.

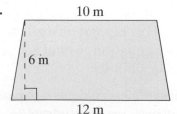

10 m
6 m
12 m

6.

5 yd
3 yd

7.

4 cm
4 cm

Circumference of a Circle

Find the circumference of each circle. Round to the nearest tenth.

8.

7 m

9.

12 cm

10.

2.5 mi

What You'll Learn Next

- In this chapter, you will identify three-dimensional solids, such as prisms, cylinders, and pyramids.

- You will find the surface area and volume of prisms, cylinders, cones, and pyramids.

- Applying what you learn, you will identify cross sections of real-world three-dimensional solids.

Key Vocabulary

- bases (p. 454)
- center of a sphere (p. 455)
- cone (p. 455)
- cross section (p. 473)
- cube (p. 454)
- cubic unit (p. 465)
- cylinder (p. 454)
- edge (p. 454)
- face (p. 454)
- height (p. 454)
- net (p. 458)
- prism (p. 454)
- pyramid (p. 454)
- sphere (p. 455)
- surface area (p. 459)
- three-dimensional figure (p. 454)
- vertex (p. 454)
- volume (p. 465)

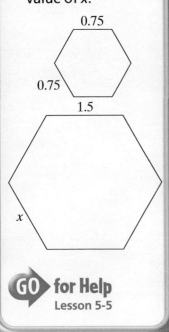

What You'll Learn

To classify and draw three-dimensional figures

New Vocabulary three-dimensional figure, face, edge, bases, prism, height, cube, cylinder, pyramid, vertex, cone, sphere, center

Why Learn This?

You already know about some three-dimensional figures. You see them in many ordinary objects around you. If you know how to classify three-dimensional figures, you can describe the shapes of the objects you see.

A **three-dimensional figure,** or solid, is a figure that does not lie in a plane. A flat surface of a solid shape like a polygon is called a **face.** Each segment formed by the intersection of two faces is an **edge.**

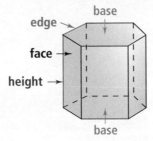

A **prism** is a three-dimensional figure with two parallel and congruent polygonal faces, called **bases.** The other faces are rectangles. The **height** of a prism is the length of a perpendicular segment that joins the bases. A prism is named for the shape of its bases.

A **cube** is a rectangular prism with faces that are all squares.

A **cylinder** has two congruent parallel bases that are circles. The height of a cylinder is the length of a perpendicular segment that joins the bases.

A **pyramid** has triangular faces that meet at one point, a **vertex,** and a base that is a polygon. A pyramid is named for the shape of its base.

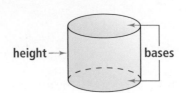

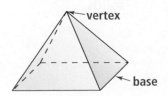

A **cone** has one circular base and one vertex.

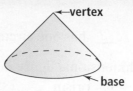

A **sphere** is the set of all points in space that are the same distance from a **center** point.

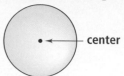

EXAMPLE **Naming Figures**

1 **Architecture** Look at the architectural blocks. Name Figure 3.

Figure 3 has two parallel, congruent bases that are circles.

Figure 3 is a cylinder.

✓ Quick Check

● **1.** Name Figures 1 and 2.

You can use graph paper to draw three-dimensional figures.

EXAMPLE **Drawing Three-Dimensional Figures**

Vocabulary Tip

Notice the word hexagon inside *hexagonal*. A hexagon has six sides, so a *hexagonal* prism is a prism with a six-sided base.

2 Draw a hexagonal prism.

Step 1 Draw a hexagon.

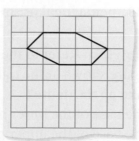

Step 2 Draw a second hexagon congruent to the first.

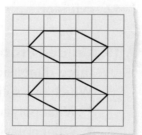

Step 3 Connect the vertices. Use dashed lines for hidden edges.

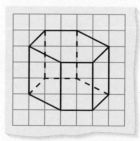

✓ Quick Check

● **2.** Use graph paper to draw a triangular prism.

1. **Vocabulary** A __?__ has one circular base and one vertex.

2. Which three-dimensional figure does NOT have a base?
   Ⓐ cone   Ⓑ prism   Ⓒ pyramid   Ⓓ sphere

Describe each base and name each prism.

3.    4. 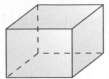   5.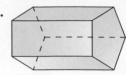

Homework Exercises

For more exercises, see Extra Skills and Word Problems.

GO for Help

For Exercises	See Example
6–11	1
12–14	2

Name each figure.

6. 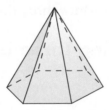   7.    8.

9.    10. 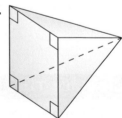   11.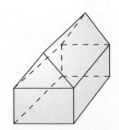

Use graph paper to draw each figure.

12. cylinder   13. pentagonal prism   14. square pyramid

GPS 15. **Guided Problem Solving** Refer to the three-dimensional figure shown at the right. Which two solids make up the figure?
   • What polygon is the base of the lower portion?
   • What polygon is the base of the upper portion?

16. A solid has a rectangle for its base and four faces that are triangles. What is the solid?

Name the three-dimensional figure that each object resembles.

17.

18.

19.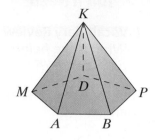

Use the pentagonal pyramid at the right.

20. Name four edges that intersect $\overline{AB}$.

21. Name any edges that are parallel to $\overline{AB}$.

22. Name the five edges that are *not* parallel to $\overline{AB}$ and do *not* intersect $\overline{AB}$.

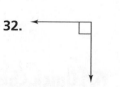

23. What is the total area of the two bases of the figure at the left?

24. **Writing in Math** Are the edges of a cube congruent? Explain.

25. **Challenge** Identify the number of faces, edges, and vertices a hexagonal pyramid has.

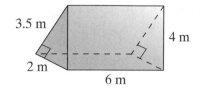

Test Prep and Mixed Review   **Practice**

Multiple Choice

26. Which of the following has two bases that are congruent polygons?
- Ⓐ Pyramid
- Ⓑ Cylinder
- Ⓒ Cone
- Ⓓ Prism

27. The circular base of a soup can has a diameter of 3 in. What is the area of the base of the can? Round to the nearest square unit.
- Ⓕ 5 in.^{2}
- Ⓖ 7 in.^{2}
- Ⓗ 9 in.^{2}
- Ⓙ 28 in.^{2}

28. The perimeter of an equilateral triangle is 45 ft. The height of the triangle is 13 ft. What is the triangle's area?
- Ⓐ 7.5 ft^2
- Ⓑ 15 ft^2
- Ⓒ 97.5 ft^2
- Ⓓ 195 ft^2

Classify each angle as *acute, right, obtuse,* or *straight*.

29.

30.

31.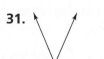

32.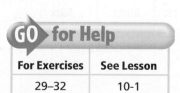

Surface Areas of Prisms and Cylinders

Check Skills You'll Need

1. **Vocabulary Review** What is the *height of a triangle*?

Find the area of each triangle.

2.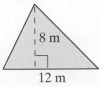
8 m
12 m

3.
3 ft   6.7 ft
3.6 ft
2 ft   4 ft

GO for Help
Lesson 10-3

© CONTENT STANDARD
7.G.6

What You'll Learn

To find the surface areas of prisms and cylinders using nets

New Vocabulary net, surface area

Why Learn This?

When you wrap a birthday gift or cover a textbook, you are working with surface area. Surface area tells you how much material you need to cover something. You can use a net to solve surface area problems.

A **net** is a two-dimensional pattern that you can fold to form a three-dimensional figure. You can use nets to design boxes.

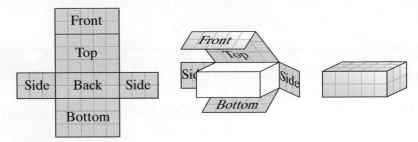

You can draw many different nets for a three-dimensional figure.

EXAMPLE   Drawing a Net

1 Draw a net for the triangular prism at the right.

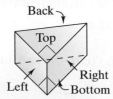
Back
Top
Left   Right
Bottom

← Begin by labeling the bases and faces.

First draw one base. Then draw one face that connects both bases. Next, draw the other base. Draw the remaining faces. →

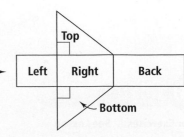
Top
Left   Right   Back
Bottom

Quick Check

1. Draw a different net for the right triangular prism in Example 1.

The **surface area** of a prism is the sum of the areas of its faces. You measure surface area of a prism in square units. You can find the surface area by finding the area of its net.

For help with finding the area of a triangle, go to Lesson 10-3, Example 2.

EXAMPLE   Finding the Surface Area of a Prism

2 Find the surface area of the triangular prism.

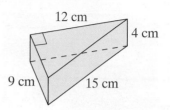

First draw a net for the prism.

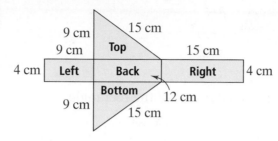

Then find the total area of the five faces.

left side	back	right side	top	bottom

$$4(9) \ + \ 4(12) \ + \ 4(15) \ + \ \tfrac{1}{2}(12)(9) \ + \ \tfrac{1}{2}(12)(9) = 252$$

The surface area of the triangular prism is 252 cm².

✓ Quick Check

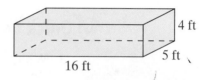

2. Find the surface area of the rectangular prism.

If you cut a label from a can, you will see that the label is a rectangle. The height of the rectangle is about the height of the can. The base length of the rectangle is the circumference of the can.

Similarly, if you cut up a cylinder, you get a rectangle and two circles.

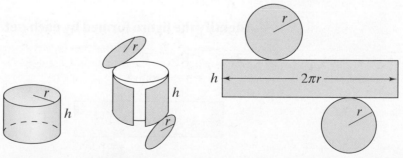

You can use a net of a cylinder to find its surface area.

EXAMPLE   **Finding the Surface Area of a Cylinder**

③ Crafts You plan to make a birthday present for your friend. The first step is to cover a coffee can with construction paper. How much construction paper do you need?

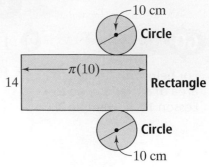

Step 1 Draw a net.

Step 2 Find the area of one circle.

$$A = \pi r^2$$
$$= \pi(5)^2$$
$$= \pi(25)$$
$$\approx 78.54$$

Step 3 Find the area of the rectangle.

$$(\pi d)h = \pi(10)(14)$$
$$= 140\pi$$
$$\approx 439.82$$

Step 4 Add the areas of the two circles and the rectangle.

Surface area = 78.54 + 78.54 + 439.82 = 596.9

The amount of construction paper needed is about 597 cm².

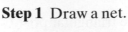

✓ Quick Check

3. What is the surface area of the cylinder at the right? Round to the nearest tenth.

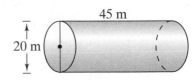

✓ Check Your Understanding

1. **Vocabulary** The __?__ of a prism is the sum of the areas of its faces.

2. **Reasoning** What kind of polygon is included in both a net of a triangular prism and a net of a rectangular prism?

Identify the figure formed by each net. Then find its surface area.

3.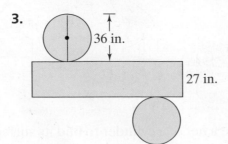

4.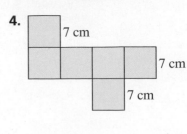

For more exercises, see Extra Skills and Word Problems.

GO for Help

For Exercises	See Example
5–8	1
9–11	2
12–14	3

Draw a net for each three-dimensional figure.

5.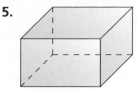

6.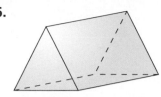

7.

8.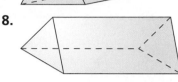

Find the surface area of each prism.

9.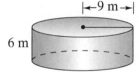
9 m, 6 m, 10 m, 8 m

10.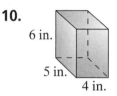
6 in., 5 in., 4 in.

11.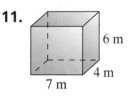
6 m, 4 m, 7 m

Find the surface area of each cylinder. Round to the nearest tenth.

Vocabulary Tip

Cylindrical means "in the shape of a cylinder."

12.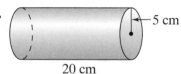
|←9 m→| 6 m

13.
5 cm, 20 cm

14. The diameter of the base of a cylindrical can is 4 in. The height of the can is 6.5 in. Find the can's surface area to the nearest tenth.

GPS

15. Guided Problem Solving The tent at the right is similar to a triangular prism. Calculate the surface area of the tent to find the amount of fabric needed to make the tent.

- A triangular prism has ▧ faces.
- Find and add the areas of the faces: surface area = ▧ + ▧ + ▧ + ▧ . . .

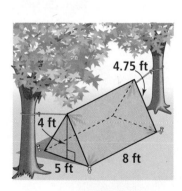
4.75 ft, 4 ft, 8 ft, 5 ft

16. Some cans are cut from a large sheet of metal. Find the amount of metal needed to make a can similar to the one at the right. Round to the nearest tenth.

17. Calculate the surface area of a rectangular prism with a height of 4 in., a width of 16 in., and a length of 10 in.

6 cm, 12 cm

Find the surface area of each cylinder given the base radius and height of the cylinder. Round to the nearest square unit.

18. $r = 3$ cm
$h = 10$ cm

19. $r = 7$ ft
$h = 25$ ft

20. $r = 12$ m
$h = 16$ m

21. $r = 10$ in.
$h = 3$ ft

22. A cosmetics company that makes small cylindrical bars of soap wraps the bars in plastic prior to shipping. Find the surface area of a bar of soap if the diameter is 5 cm and the height is 2 cm. Round to the nearest tenth.

14 in.
24 in.

23. Suppose you wish to make a cylindrical case that will exactly fit the bass drum at the left. What is the surface area of the case to the nearest tenth?

24. Error Analysis A student says the two cylinders at the right have the same surface area. Explain the student's error.

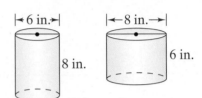

25. Writing in Math Which has a greater effect on the surface area of a cylinder—doubling the radius or doubling the height? Explain.

26. Open-Ended Draw a net for a prism that has a surface area of 72 cm².

27. Challenge Find the surface area of the figure at the right. Round to the nearest square unit.

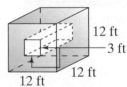
12 ft
3 ft
12 ft
12 ft

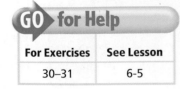
Test Prep and Mixed Review   **Practice**

Multiple Choice

28. Which solid can be formed from the net shown at the right?
Ⓐ Triangular prism
Ⓑ Rectangular prism
Ⓒ Triangular pyramid
Ⓓ Rectangular pyramid

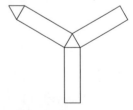

29. Chip grows $\frac{3}{4}$ inch in January, $\frac{5}{8}$ inch in February, and $\frac{1}{2}$ inch in March. Altogether, how much does Chip grow in January, February, and March?

Ⓕ $\frac{15}{24}$ in.   Ⓖ $\frac{9}{14}$ in.   Ⓗ $\frac{7}{8}$ in.   Ⓙ $1\frac{7}{8}$ in.

Find the simple interest on a $360 loan at each rate.

30. 5% annual interest, 5 years

31. 3.2% annual interest, 2 years

GO for Help

For Exercises	See Lesson
30–31	6-5

Patterns in 3-Dimensional Figures

You can explore number patterns using unit cubes.

Suppose you use unit cubes to make a larger cube with two unit cubes on an edge. You paint the outside of the larger cube. You need eight unit cubes to form the larger cube. Each cube has three sides painted.

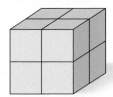

ACTIVITY

Number of Unit Cubes on an Edge	Total Number of Unit Cubes	Total Number Expressed as a Power	Number of Unit Cubes With Given Number of Sides Painted			
			0	1	2	3
2	8	2^3	0	0	0	8
3	▪	▪	▪	▪	▪	▪
4	▪	▪	▪	▪	▪	▪
5	▪	▪	▪	▪	▪	▪
6	▪	▪	▪	▪	▪	▪
7	▪	▪	▪	▪	▪	▪

1. Copy and complete the table above. Use the figure at the right to help you fill in the row for 3 unit cubes on an edge.

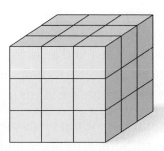

2. a. **Patterns** Describe the number pattern you see in each of the last four columns of your table.
   b. Use the number patterns and extend the table for 8 number cubes on an edge.

3. a. **Number Sense** What is the total number of unit cubes in a cube with 10 unit cubes on an edge?
   b. If there are 15 unit cubes on an edge, how many unit cubes will have no side painted? One side painted? Two sides painted?
   c. **Reasoning** If 144 unit cubes have two sides painted, how many unit cubes are on one edge of the cube?

Name each figure.

1.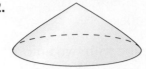

2.

3.

4. A solid is the set of all points in space that are the same distance from a center point. What is the solid?

Draw each figure.

5. cone

6. hexagonal pyramid

7. pentagonal prism

Find the surface area of each figure. Round to the nearest tenth.

8.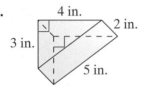
4 in.
2 in.
3 in.
5 in.

9.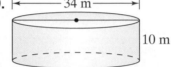
|← 34 m →|
10 m

10. Malik made a wooden jewelry box with a height of 6 in., a width of 12 in., and a length of 10 in. He plans on staining the outside of the box with a walnut finish. What is the surface area of the jewelry box that will be stained?

MATH AT WORK

Songwriter

Songwriters need to know what types of music are "in" to compose a song that will sell. Then a songwriter must find an artist to record the song. Producers and record companies decide whether they will promote a song as a potential hit.

Many hip-hop or rap beats use rhythms that follow a pattern. Songwriters use musical notes that have fractional names to create the pattern. Common musical notes are half notes and quarter notes.

Go Online For information about songwriters
PearsonSuccessNet.com

Volumes of Prisms and Cylinders

12-3

✓ Check Skills You'll Need

1. **Vocabulary Review**
   How is π related to the circumference and the diameter of a circle?

Find the area of each circle. Round to the nearest square unit.

2.

12 m

3.

15 in.

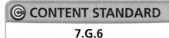
for Help
Lesson 10-5

© **CONTENT STANDARD**
7.G.6

 **nline**

Video Tutor Help
PearsonSuccessNet.com

What You'll Learn

To find the volumes of prisms and cylinders

New Vocabulary volume, cubic unit

Why Learn This?

Many storage silos are shaped like cylinders. You can use volume formulas to find the amount of storage space inside a figure like a silo.

The **volume** of a three-dimensional figure is the number of cubic units needed to fill the space inside the figure.

A **cubic unit** is a cube with edges one unit long. A cubic centimeter is a cube with edges one centimeter long.

1 cm
1 cm
1 cm

Consider filling the rectangular prism below with cubic centimeters.

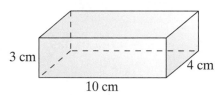
3 cm
4 cm
10 cm

The bottom layer of the prism contains 10 · 4, or 40, cubes.

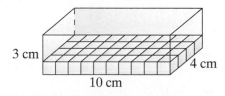
3 cm
4 cm
10 cm

Three layers of 40 cubes fit in the prism. 3 · 40 = 120

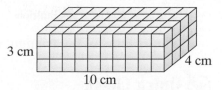
3 cm
4 cm
10 cm

The volume of the prism is 120 cm³.

The previous calculation of volume suggests the following formula.

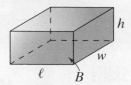

KEY CONCEPTS **Volume of a Rectangular Prism**

V = area of base · height
  = Bh
  = ℓwh

EXAMPLE **Finding the Volume of a Rectangular Prism**

1 **Gridded Response** Mr. Cho is building a craft box like the one shown at the right. What is the volume of the craft box in cubic inches?

$V = \ell wh$ ← Use the formula.

= $(3)(4)(5)$ ← Substitute.

= 60 ← Multiply.

The volume of the craft box is 60 cubic inches.

✓ Quick Check

1. If the height of the prism above is doubled, what is the volume?

The volume formulas for rectangular and triangular prisms are similar.

Test Prep Tip 🖉

When finding volume, remember to calculate the area of the base first.

KEY CONCEPTS **Volume of a Triangular Prism**

V = area of base · height
  = Bh

EXAMPLE **Finding the Volume of a Triangular Prism**

2 Find the volume of the triangular prism.

$V = Bh$ ← Use the formula.

= $(6)(6)$ ← Substitute: $B = \frac{1}{2} \times 3 \times 4 = 6.$

= 36 ← Multiply.

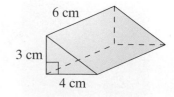

The volume of the triangular prism is 36 cm^3.

✓ Quick Check

2. If the height of the prism above is doubled, what is the volume?

The volume formula for a cylinder is also similar to the volume formula for a prism.

> **KEY CONCEPTS** | **Volume of a Cylinder**
>
> $V = $ area of base $\cdot$ height
> $\quad = Bh$
> $\quad = \pi r^2 h$
>
>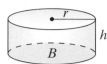

EXAMPLE | **Finding the Volume of a Cylinder**

3 **Painting** Estimate the volume of the cylindrical paint can. Then find the volume to the nearest cubic unit.

Estimate

$$V = \pi r^2 h \qquad \leftarrow \text{Use the formula.}$$
$$\approx (3)(4)^2(9) \quad \leftarrow \text{Use 3 to estimate } \pi.$$
$$\approx (50)(9) \qquad \leftarrow \text{Use 50 to estimate 48 (3 } \cdot \text{ 16).}$$
$$\approx 450$$

The estimated volume is 450 in.³

Calculate

$$V = \pi r^2 h \qquad \leftarrow \text{Use the formula.}$$
$$\approx (\pi)(4)^2(9) \quad \leftarrow \text{Substitute.}$$
$$\approx 452.38934 \quad \leftarrow \text{Use a calculator.}$$
$$\approx 452 \qquad\quad \leftarrow \text{Round to the nearest whole number.}$$

The calculated volume is about 452 in.³

Check for Reasonableness The calculated volume is close to the estimated volume, so the answer is reasonable.

✓ Quick Check

3. a. Estimate the volume of the cylinder. Then find the volume to the nearest cubic centimeter.
  b. Reasoning Suppose you estimate using 20 for 4^2 instead of 16 in Example 3. Will your estimate be reasonable?

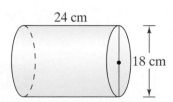

1. **Vocabulary** The number of cubic units needed to fill the space inside a three-dimensional figure is called the __?__ .

2. How does the volume of a cylinder change if the height is doubled?

   Ⓐ It does not change.   Ⓒ It quadruples.
   Ⓑ It doubles.   Ⓓ It halves.

Find the volume of each figure, given the following dimensions.

3. triangular prism
   $B = 20$ in.^{2}; $h = 3$ in

4. cylinder
   $r = 5$ cm; $h = 7$ cm

For more exercises, see Extra Skills and Word Problems.

Find the volume of each rectangular prism.

For Exercises	See Example
5–7	1
8–10	2
11–13	3

GO for Help

5.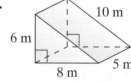
5.5 in.
5.5 in.
5.5 in.

6.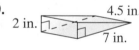
2 cm
2 cm
6 cm

7.
7.5 ft
7.5 ft
7.5 ft

Find the volume of each triangular prism.

8.
10 m
6 m
8 m
5 m

9.
2 in.
4.5 in.
7 in.

10.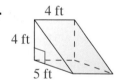
4 ft
4 ft
5 ft

Packaging Estimate the volume of each cylinder. Then find the volume to the nearest cubic unit.

11.
2 in.
7 in.

12.
13 cm
33 cm

13.
7 in.
6.5 in.

GPS 14. **Guided Problem Solving** What is the volume of the object shown at the right?
   • Identify the two familiar solids that make up the object. What are they?
   • What is the volume of each familiar solid?

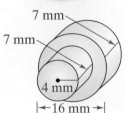
7 mm
7 mm
4 mm
16 mm

Find the height of each rectangular prism.

15. $V = 455$ cm^3
$\ell = 10$ cm
$w = 7$ cm

16. $V = 525$ m^3
$\ell = 7.5$ m
$w = 3.5$ m

17. $V = 5{,}832$ in.^{3}
$\ell = 18$ in.
$w = 18$ in.

18. Reasoning Compare the volumes of the figures. Why are their volumes different?

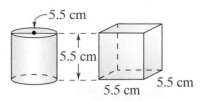

19. <u>Writing in Math</u> Explain how you can find the radius of a cylinder with a height of 10 in. and a volume of 385 in.^{3}. (Use $\pi = 3.14$.)

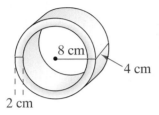

20. Find the volume of the figure at the left to the nearest cubic centimeter.

21. Aquariums A large aquarium is built in the shape of a cylinder. The diameter is 203 ft and the height is 25 ft. About how many million gallons of water does this tank hold? (1 gal $\approx$ 231 in.^{3})

22. A rectangular prism has a length of 3.1 m, a width of 2.2 m, and a height of 5.6 m. Find the volume to the nearest cubic meter.

23. Challenge A soft-drink can has a height of about 4.8 in. and a diameter of about 2.5 in. Suppose you need to put 12 cans in a rectangular case about 5 in. tall, 11 in. long, and 7.6 in. wide. Will the cans fit in the case? Explain.

Test Prep and Mixed Review

Practice

Gridded Response

24. Mrs. Panosian has a can of concentrated orange juice like the one at the right. What is the volume of the can in cubic centimeters?

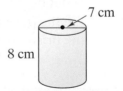

25. Nina created a project on water conservation. She found that you use 1.6 gallons of water each time you flush a toilet. At this rate, how many gallons of water would you use flushing 7 times?

26. Ethan collected five rocks with a total mass of 43.4 kg. Two of the rocks were identical, and each had a mass of 13.3 kg. If two of the other rocks had masses of 4.7 kg and 5.3 kg, what was the mass of the fifth rock in kilograms?

GO for Help

For Exercises	See Lesson
27–30	10-1

Find the measures of the complement and supplement of each angle.

27. $m\angle A = 40°$ **28.** $m\angle B = 65°$ **29.** $m\angle C = 37°$ **30.** $m\angle D = 5°$

Generating Formulas for Volume

In this activity, you will relate the volume of a pyramid to the volume of a prism.

ACTIVITY

Step 1 Using poster board, draw and cut out four congruent isosceles triangles like the one below.

5 cm

├── 6 cm ──┤

Step 2 Tape the edges of the four triangles to form a pyramid without a base. What is the area of the missing base?

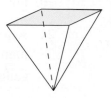

Step 3 Using poster board, draw and cut out four congruent rectangles and one square like the one below.

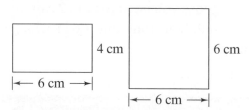

4 cm   6 cm

├── 6 cm ──┤   ├── 6 cm ──┤

Step 4 Tape the edges of the polygons to form a prism without a base. Compare the areas of the missing base of the prism and the missing base of the pyramid.

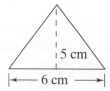

Step 5 Place the pyramid and the prism side by side. What do you notice about their heights?

Step 6 Fill the pyramid with rice. Pour the rice from the pyramid into the prism. Repeat until the prism is full.

Exercises

1. **a.** How many pyramids full of rice did you need to fill the prism?
   b. How does the volume of the pyramid compare to the volume of the prism?
   c. Make a conjecture about the formula for volume of a pyramid.

2. **Reasoning** To fill a cylinder with base area B and height h, you need 3 cones as shown at the right. Make a conjecture about the formula for volume of a cone.

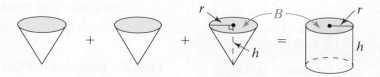

Practice Solving Problems

Painting A painter uses a roller in the shape of a cylinder to paint a wall. The length of the roller is 9 in. The diameter of the roller is 2 in. What is the area covered by one full turn of the roller?

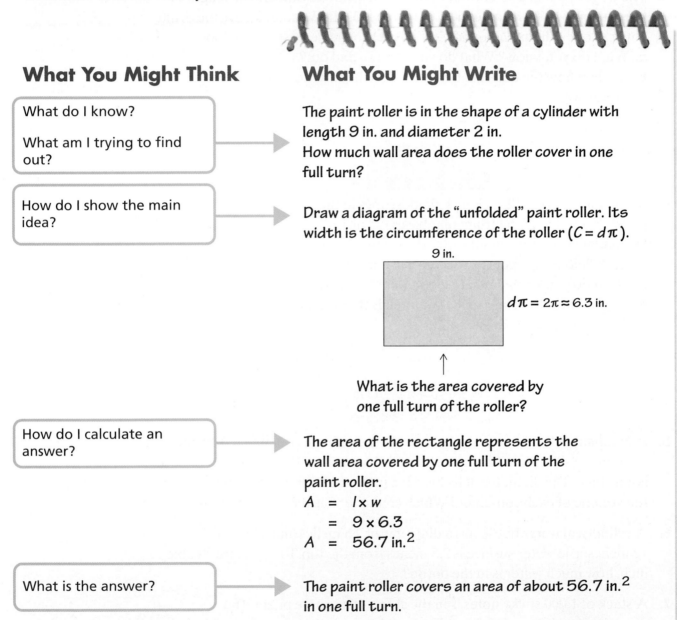

What You Might Think	**What You Might Write**
What do I know? What am I trying to find out?	The paint roller is in the shape of a cylinder with length 9 in. and diameter 2 in. How much wall area does the roller cover in one full turn?
How do I show the main idea?	Draw a diagram of the "unfolded" paint roller. Its width is the circumference of the roller ($C = d\pi$).

9 in.

$d\pi = 2\pi \approx 6.3$ in.

↑
What is the area covered by one full turn of the roller?

How do I calculate an answer?	The area of the rectangle represents the wall area covered by one full turn of the paint roller. $A = l \times w$ $= 9 \times 6.3$ $A = 56.7$ in.^{2}
What is the answer?	The paint roller covers an area of about 56.7 in.^{2} in one full turn.

Think It Through

1. The paint roller is in the shape of a cylinder. Why does the diagram not include the two circular bases of the cylinder?

2. In the diagram, why is the width of the rectangle 6.3 in.?

Exercises

Solve each problem. For Exercises 3 and 4, answer parts (a) and (b) first.

3. The large drum of a steamroller is in the shape of a cylinder. The length of the drum is 6 ft. The diameter of the drum is 3.5 ft. What area does the drum cover in one full turn? Round your answer to the nearest square foot.
   a. What do you know? What do you want to find out?
   b. Explain how the diagram below models the situation. Then calculate the answer.

   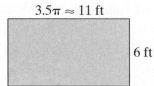

   $3.5\pi \approx 11$ ft

   6 ft

4. A company makes 12-in. long kaleidoscopes in the shape of a triangular prism. Each side of the triangular bases is 2 in. long. All surfaces except the triangular bases are coated with a decorative finish. How much surface area of the kaleidoscope gets the decorative finish?
   a. What do you know? What do you want to find out?
   b. Explain how the diagram below models the situation. Then calculate the answer.

   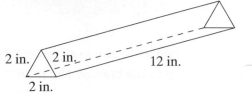

   2 in.　2 in.　12 in.
   2 in.

5. A company sells oatmeal and cornmeal in cylindrical containers. The oatmeal container is 6 in. high. The diameter of its base is 4 in. The cornmeal container is 4 in. high. The diameter of its base is 6 in. To the nearest cubic inch, what is the volume of each container? Which container has the greater volume?

6. A cylindrical water bottle has a diameter of 2.5 inches and a height of 12 inches. The water surface is 2.5 inches from the top. To the nearest cubic inch, how much water is in the bottle?

7. A stack of 1,000 sticky notes is in the shape of a square prism. The prism has a volume of 13.5 in.^{3}. Each sticky note measures 3 in. by 3 in.
   a. What is the height of the stack of sticky notes?
   b. What is the thickness of one sticky note?

8. You have two gift boxes, both in the shape of a rectangular prism. The area of the base of box B is twice the area of the base of box A. The height of box B is half the height of box A. Compare the volumes of the two gift boxes.

12-4 Cross Sections

 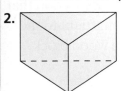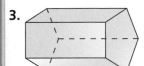
What You'll Learn

To describe cross sections that result from slicing three-dimensional figures

New Vocabulary cross section

Why Learn This?

You can see cross sections when you slice through an apple or cut through a tree trunk.

A **cross section** is the two-dimensional shape that you see after slicing through a three-dimensional object.

cross section of an apple

cross section of a tree trunk

© CONTENT STANDARD
7.G.3

EXAMPLE Identifying a Cross Section

1 John made a clay model of a square pyramid. He shows the cross section of the pyramid by slicing the pyramid with a string. What is the shape of each cross section?

a.    This slice makes a triangle.

Vertical Slice

b.   This slice makes a square.

Horizontal Slice

Quick Check

1. Jorge and Patti are eating sushi rolls shaped like cylinders. Jorge cut his sushi roll vertically. Patti cut her sushi roll horizontally. What is the shape of each cross section?

a. Jorge
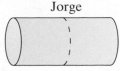

b. Patti
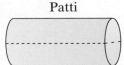

You are using reasoning when you describe the cross section formed by the intersection of a solid and a plane. You can also sketch a picture.

EXAMPLE **Describing a Cross Section**

② **Wood Working** Ripping means cutting wood in the same direction as the grain of the wood. Crosscutting means cutting wood across the grain of the wood. Describe the cross section formed by the cuts below.

a.

Ripping the rectangular prism makes a cross section that is a rectangle congruent to the side face of the wood block.

b.

Crosscutting the rectangular prism makes a cross section that is a rectangle congruent to the front face of the wood block.

✓ Quick Check

2. Describe the cross section formed by the slices through the hexagonal pyramid.

a.

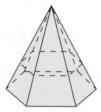

b.

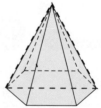

✓ Check Your Understanding

1. **Vocabulary** A ____?____ is the two-dimensional shape that you see after slicing through a three-dimensional object.

Describe each cross section.

2.

3.

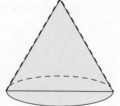

4.

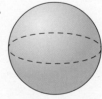

For more exercises, see Extra Skills and Word Problems.

GO for Help

For Exercises	See Examples
5–11	1-2

Describe each cross section.

5.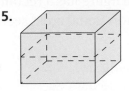

6.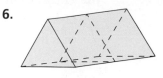

7.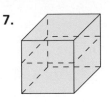

8.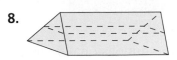

9.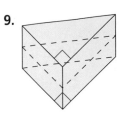

10.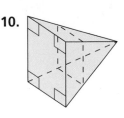

11. Sasha cut an orange shaped like a sphere through the center. Describe the cross section that Sasha sees.

12. **Guided Problem Solving** Parallel vertical slices are made through a rectangular pyramid as shown below.

   • What are the shapes of the cross sections?
   • Describe how the cross sections will change as additional cuts are made.

13. You have a block of cheese in the shape shown at the right.
   a. What shape will the slice of cheese be if the cheese is sliced horizontally?
   b. What shape will the slice of cheese be if the cheese is sliced vertically?
   c. Does it matter where the cuts are made? Explain your reasoning.

14. A barn silo has the shape of the figure shown at the right.
   a. If it is sliced in half with a vertical cut, what geometric shapes make up the cross section?
   b. Discuss how the two-dimensional shapes that make up the cross section relate to the three-dimensional shapes that make up the silo.

15. Writing in Math What three-dimensional figure can have a cross section in the same shape as the triangle shown at the right? Explain your reasoning.

16. A three-dimensional figure has a rectangular vertical cross section and a horizontal cross section in the shape of a hexagon.

vertical
cross section

horizontal
cross section

What is the three-dimensional figure?

17. Challenge A cross section of a rectangular prism is a rectangle with sides measuring 5 cm and 7 cm. Can the exact dimensions of the prism be determined? Explain your reasoning.

Test Prep and Mixed Review

Practice

Multiple Choice

18. A plane parallel to the base of the cone intersects a cross-section through the cone. What best describes the shape of the cross section?

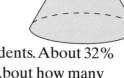

  Ⓐ circle   Ⓒ triangle

  Ⓑ rectangle   Ⓓ square

19. Stewart Middle School has 243 seventh-grade students. About 32% of them attended the high school football game. About how many seventh-grade students attended the football game?

  Ⓕ Fewer than 75   Ⓗ Between 85 and 100

  Ⓖ Between 75 and 85   Ⓙ More than 100

20. A standard basketball rim has a circumference of about 56.6 inches. Which expression can be used to find the diameter of the rim?

  Ⓐ $\dfrac{56.6}{2\pi}$ Ⓒ $\dfrac{56.6}{\pi}$

  Ⓑ $56.6 \times \pi$ Ⓓ $56.6 \times 2\pi$

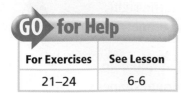

For Exercises	See Lesson
21–24	6-6

Find each percent of increase or decrease. Round to the nearest tenth.

21. 20 to 50   **22.** 32 to 8   **23.** 99 to 55   **24.** 75 to 110

Finding Volume Using Models

ACTIVITY

Draw and cut out the nets shown below. Fold them to make a cube, a square pyramid, a cylinder, and a cone. Each model will have one open base.

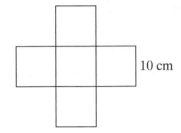

10 cm

1. For each model, what shape is the base? What is the height?

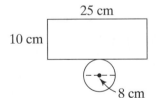

2. Fill the pyramid with sand. Then pour the sand from the pyramid into the cube. How many pyramids full of sand does the cube hold?

3. What fractional part of the volume of the cube is the volume of the pyramid?

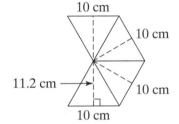

4. Fill the cone with sand. Then pour the sand from the cone into the cylinder. How many cones full of sand does the cylinder hold?

5. What fractional part of the volume of the cylinder is the volume of the cone?

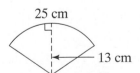

6. Make a conjecture about the formulas for the volume of a pyramid and the volume of a cone.

12-5 Volumes of Pyramids and Cones

✓ Check Skills You'll Need

1. **Vocabulary Review** How are the shapes of *pyramids* and *cones* different?

2. What shape is the base of each of the figures below?

a.

b.

GO for Help
Lesson 12-1

What You'll Learn

To find the volumes of pyramids and cones

Why Learn This?

You consider volume when you fill an ice cream cone or use a funnel.

The contents you need to fill a prism with base area B will fill exactly three pyramids with the same base area and height as the prism.

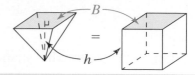

KEY CONCEPTS Volume of a Pyramid

The volume V of a pyramid is one third the product of the base area B and the height h.

$V = \frac{1}{3}Bh$

© **CONTENT STANDARD**
8.G.9

EXAMPLE Finding Volume of a Square Pyramid

① Find the volume of the pyramid below to the nearest cubic centimeter.

Step 1 Find the area of the base.

$B = s^2$ ← **area of a square**

$= 10^2$ ← **Substitute.**

$= 100$ ← **Simplify.**

Step 2 Find the pyramid's height.

$h^2 + 5^2 = 13^2$ ← **Pythagorean Theorem**

$h = 12$ ← **Simplify.**

Step 3 Find the volume.

$V = \left(\frac{1}{3}\right)Bh$ ← **volume of a pyramid**

$= \left(\frac{1}{3}\right)(100)12$ ← **Substitute.**

$= 400$ ← **Multiply.**

The volume of the pyramid is 400 cm³.

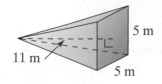

✓ Quick Check

1. Find the volume of the pyramid at the left to the nearest cubic meter.

The contents of three cones fill a cylinder with the same dimensions.

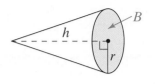

> ### KEY CONCEPTS   Volume of a Cone
>
> The volume V of a cone is one third the product of base area B and height h.
>
> $$V = \frac{1}{3}Bh$$

You can use the formula to find the volume or missing dimensions.

EXAMPLES   Using the Volume Formula

2 Find the volume of the cone at the left to the nearest cubic meter.

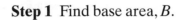

Step 1 Find base area, B.

$B = \pi r^2$ ← area of a circle

$\quad = \pi(4^2)$ ← Substitute.

$\quad = 16\pi$ ← Simplify.

Step 2 Find the volume.

$V = \frac{1}{3}Bh$ ← volume of a cone

$\quad = \frac{1}{3}(16\pi)10$ ← Substitute 16π for B and 18 for h.

$\quad \approx 168$ ← Simplify.

The volume of the cone is about 168 m^3.

3 Food An ice cream shop owner designs a new ice cream cone. He wants the volume to be about 240 cm³. The cone is 14 cm tall. What is its radius?

$240 = \frac{1}{3}(\pi r^2)(14)$ ← Substitute 240 for V, πr² for B, and 14 for h in the formula for the volume of a cone.

$240 = \frac{14\pi}{3}r^2$ ← Simplify.

$\frac{3}{14\pi} \cdot 240 = \frac{3}{14\pi} \cdot \frac{14\pi}{3}r^2$ ← Multiply each side by the reciprocal of $\frac{14\pi}{3}$.

$\frac{3(240)}{14\pi} = r^2$ ← Simplify.

$\sqrt{\frac{3(240)}{14\pi}} = \sqrt{r^2}$ ← Find the positive square root of each side.

$4.046013188 \approx r$ ← Use a calculator.

The radius of the cone is about 4 cm.

GO ⬤**nline**

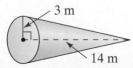

Video Tutor Help
PearsonSuccessNet.com

✓ Quick Check

2. Find the volume of the cone at the right. Round to the nearest cubic meter.

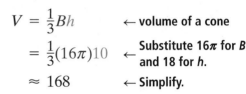

3. Find the radius of a cone with a volume of 360 cm³ and a height of 9 cm.

1. **Mental Math** A square pyramid has a base area of 9 m². Its height is 5 m. The volume of the pyramid is (15 m³, 45 m³).

Match each pyramid or cone with the equation you can use to find the area of its base.

2.
5 cm
4 cm
4 cm

3.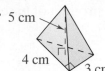
5 cm
4 cm
3 cm

4.
3 cm
4 cm

A. $B = \pi(4^2)$ **B.** $B = \frac{1}{2}(4)(3)$ **C.** $B = 4^2$

Homework Exercises

For more exercises, see Extra Skills and Word Problems.

GO for Help

For Exercises	See Examples
5–7	1
8–10	2
11	3

Find the volume of each pyramid to the nearest whole cubic unit.

5.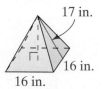
17 in.
16 in.
16 in.

6.
6 cm
6 cm
8 cm

7.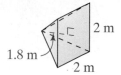
2 m
1.8 m
2 m

Find the volume of each cone to the nearest whole cubic unit.

8.
30 cm
12 cm

9.
3 ft
4 ft

10.
5 m
15 m

11. A party hat has the shape of a cone. The volume of the hat is about 419 cm³. If the hat has a height of 16 cm, what is its radius?

12. **Guided Problem Solving** The funnel shown at the right can hold 500 cm³ of fluid. Its height (without the stem) is 12 cm. Find the diameter of the cone part of the funnel.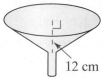
12 cm

- **Estimation** You can use the strategy *Systematic Guess and Check* to estimate the radius. Select radius values for the formula $V = \frac{1}{3}\pi r^2 h$ until you calculate a volume of about 500 cm³. Then estimate the diameter.
- Use the formula for the volume of a cone to solve the problem. Use your estimation to check that your answer is reasonable.

Find the volume of the following solids to the nearest whole cubic unit.

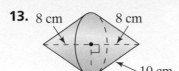

13. 8 cm · 8 cm · 10 cm

14. 2.5 m · 3 m · 1 m · 2.5 m

15. Reasoning Does the volume of a cone stay the same if you add 1 unit to the radius and subtract 1 unit from the height? Explain.

16. A glassblower decides to make an hourglass that will hold about 47 in.³ in each cone. If the radius of each cone is 3 in., what is the height of each cone h?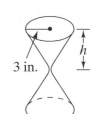

17. (**Algebra**) The volume of a square pyramid is 15 ft³. Its base area is 27 ft². What is its height?

18. Error Analysis Lian says that if you double the dimensions of a square pyramid, you double its volume. What is her error?

19. Writing in Math Explain how you might use the area formulas for rectangles, triangles, and circles to help you remember volume formulas for pyramids, cones, prisms, and cylinders.

20. Challenge Find the volume of a cone with a slant height of 7.5 in. and a lateral area of about 106 in.²

Test Prep and Mixed Review   **Practice**

Multiple Choice

21. Which is closest to the volume of the pyramid at the right? (9.7 m, 11 m, 11 m)

Ⓐ 323 m³   Ⓒ 88 m³
Ⓑ 121 m³   Ⓓ 16 m³

22. Casey works 3 days each week. She worked 24 hours this week. This is 12 hours less than twice the number of hours she worked last week. Which equation can you use to find the number of hours Casey worked last week?

Ⓕ $n = \dfrac{24+12}{2}$ Ⓗ $n = \dfrac{24-12}{2}$

Ⓖ $n = 2(24) - 12$ Ⓙ $n = 2(24) + 12$

23. The microwaves used in a microwave oven have a wavelength of about 1.2×10^{-1} m. A meter is about 3.9×10^{1} in. What is this wavelength in inches?

Ⓐ 0.47 in.   Ⓒ 4.7×10^{-2} in.
Ⓑ 4.7 in.   Ⓓ 4.7×10^{2} in.

GO for Help

For Exercise	See Lesson
23	2-4

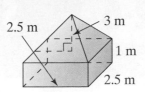
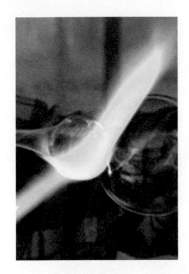

Check Skills You'll Need

1. **Vocabulary Review** What does a number's *exponent* show?

Simplify each expression.

2. 3^4

3. 6^2

4. $7(8)^3$

5. 2.1^2

GO for Help
Skills Handbook
p. 601

© **CONTENT STANDARD**
8.G.9

What You'll Learn

To find the surface area and volume of a sphere

Why Learn This?

Many objects have the shape of a sphere, including toys. To make these objects, it is helpful to know about the surface area and volume of spheres.

A sphere is the set of all points in space that are the same distance from a center point.

KEY CONCEPTS **Surface Area of a Sphere**

The surface area of a sphere is four times the product of π and the square of the radius r.

$$\text{S.A.} = 4\pi r^2$$

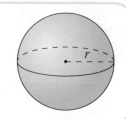

EXAMPLE **Finding the Surface Area of a Sphere**

1 Find the surface area of the sphere at the right to the nearest square centimeter.

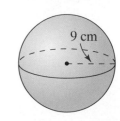

9 cm

$$
\begin{aligned}
\text{S.A.} &= 4\pi r^2 &&\leftarrow \text{surface area of a sphere} \\
&= 4\pi(9^2) &&\leftarrow \text{Substitute.} \\
&= 324\pi &&\leftarrow \text{Simplify.} \\
&\approx 1017.87602 &&\leftarrow \text{Use a calculator.}
\end{aligned}
$$

The surface area of the sphere is about 1,018 cm^2.

Test Prep Tip

Simplify the product of whole numbers before you multiply by the decimal values.

✓ Quick Check

1. A sphere has a radius of 7 ft. Find its surface area to the nearest square foot.

Consider a sphere with radius *r* inside a cylinder with radius *r* and height 2*r*. You know how to find the volume of the cylinder.

$$V = Bh \qquad \leftarrow \text{volume of a cylinder}$$
$$= (\pi r^2)(2r) \quad \leftarrow \text{Substitute } \pi r^2 \text{ for } B \text{ and } 2r \text{ for } h.$$
$$= 2\pi r^3 \qquad \leftarrow \text{Simplify.}$$

The volume of the sphere is two thirds of the volume of the cylinder.

KEY CONCEPTS | **Volume of a Sphere**

The volume of a sphere is four thirds of the product of π and the radius *r* cubed.

$$V = \frac{4}{3}\pi r^3$$

EXAMPLE | **Finding the Volume of a Sphere**

② Gridded Response The diameter of a sphere in a water fountain is 4 ft. What is the volume of the sphere to the nearest cubic foot?

Estimate Use 3 for π. The radius of the sphere is 2 ft. The volume of the sphere is about $\frac{4}{3}(3)(2)^3 = 32$ ft³.

$$V = \frac{4}{3}\pi r^3 \qquad \leftarrow \text{volume of a sphere}$$

$$= \frac{4}{3}\pi(2^3) \qquad \leftarrow \text{Substitute 2 for } r.$$

$$= \frac{32}{3}\pi \qquad \leftarrow \text{Simplify.}$$

$$\approx 33.51032164 \quad \leftarrow \text{Use a calculator.}$$

The volume of the sphere is about 34 ft³.

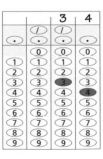

Check for Reasonableness The answer 34 ft³ is close to the estimate of 32 ft³. The answer is reasonable.

✓ Quick Check

2. **Globes** A globe in a brass stand has a diameter of 40 in. What is the volume of the globe to the nearest cubic inch?

Vocabulary Match each solid's definition with the correct term.

1. exactly one circular base and one vertex

2. two bases that are parallel, congruent circles

3. set of all points in space that are the same distance from a center point

A. cylinder
B. sphere
C. cone

Use the sphere at the right for Exercises 4–6.

4. Which is the correct expression for the surface area of the sphere: $\frac{4}{3}(3.14)(1)^3$ or $4(3.14)(1)^2$?

5. What is the surface area of the sphere?

6. What is the volume of the sphere?

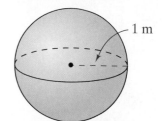
1 m

Homework Exercises

For more exercises, see Extra Skills and Word Problems.

GO for Help

For Exercises	See Examples
7–12	1 and 2
13	2

Find each sphere's surface area and volume to the nearest whole number.

7.
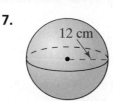
12 cm

8.
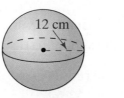
10 in.

9.
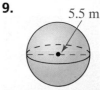
5.5 m

10.

8 yd

11.

11 ft

12.

6.4 mm

13. **Mental Math** A model of the moon has a radius of about 3 cm. Find the volume of the model to the nearest cubic centimeter.

GPS 14. **Guided Problem Solving** Water covers approximately 70% of Earth's surface. The diameter of Earth is about 13,000 km. Find the approximate area of Earth that is covered by water.
 • What is the formula for the surface area of a sphere?
 • What is the surface area of Earth?
 • What is 70% of Earth's surface area?

GO Online
Homework Video Tutor
PearsonSuccessNet.com

15. **Baseball** Balls used in major league baseball have diameters that range from 2.86 in. to 2.94 in. What is the difference in surface area between the largest and the smallest baseball?

16. The circumference of a glass terrarium in the shape of a sphere is about 12.5 in. What is the surface area of the terrarium to the nearest square inch?

17. Error Analysis Your classmate found the volume of a sphere with a radius of 5 ft to be 500π ft³. What error did your classmate make?

Gemstones **A jeweler sells spherical gemstones for pendants. Find the surface area and volume of each gemstone to the nearest whole number.**

18. jasper: $r = 3$ cm

19. rose quartz: $d = 40$ mm

20. topaz: $d = 4$ mm

21. pearl: $r = 0.6$ cm

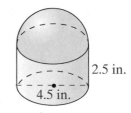

22. Tennis Tennis balls have a diameter of 2.5 in. A can holds three balls and has the shape of a cylinder.
   a. Find the total volume of the balls to the nearest whole cubic unit.
   b. Find the volume of the can to the nearest whole cubic unit. Assume the balls touch the can on the sides, top, and bottom.

23. Find the surface area and volume of the figure at the right. Round to the nearest whole number.

24. Writing in Math Suppose you know the surface area of a sphere. Explain how you would find the volume of the sphere.

25. Challenge The volume of Mars is about 1.642×10^{11} km³. What is the radius of Mars to the nearest kilometer?

Gridded Response

26. A bowling ball is required to have a radius of no more than 4.3 inches and a weight of no more than 16 pounds. To the nearest cubic inch, what is the volume of a ball with radius 4.3 inches?

27. A cylinder has a height of 19 ft. and a diameter of 10 ft. What is the volume of the cylinder to the nearest cubic foot?

28. There are a total of 1,127 students enrolled in three grades at Washington Junior High School. There are 427 students in the seventh grade and 397 students in the eighth grade. How many students are in sixth grade?

Find the volume of each figure to the nearest cubic unit.

GO for Help

For Exercises	See Lesson
29–31	12–5

29.

4 in.
3 in.
3.5 in.

30.
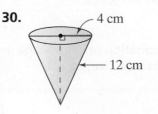
4 cm
12 cm

31.
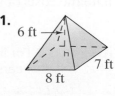
6 ft
7 ft
8 ft

Find the volume of each figure to the nearest whole number.

1.
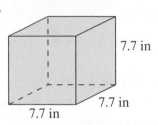
13 cm   17 cm   21 cm   21 cm

2.
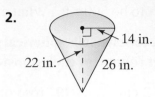
14 in.   22 in.   26 in.

3.
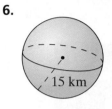
3 cm   3 cm   7 cm

4.
7.7 in   7.7 in   7.7 in

5.
4 cm   9 cm

6.
15 km

7. Find the surface area of a sphere with a radius of 5 in. Round to the nearest whole number.

8. Mike cut a plum shaped like a sphere through the center, and drew a view of the cross section. Draw a picture of the the cross section Mike drew.

MATH AT WORK

Landscape Architect

Landscape architects are involved in planning and designing residential areas, parks, shopping centers, golf courses, and college campuses. Landscape architects make detailed plans that include the location of buildings, roads, and walkways, and the arrangement of shrubs, trees, and flowers. A knowledge of geometry helps them prepare sketches and models of proposed sites. They also use their mathematical skills to estimate the costs of their projects.

Go Online For information on lansdscape architects
PearsonSuccessNet.com

Drawing a Picture

Sometimes a picture is not supplied with a problem. Then you can draw a picture to help you solve the problem. Make sure your picture is large enough to allow you to label all the parts.

EXAMPLE

A farmer has bales of hay in the shape of a cylinder. The radius of the base of each bale is 2 ft, and the height of each bale is 5 ft. The farmer wraps each bale in plastic for storage. How much plastic does she need to wrap one hay bale? Round to the nearest whole number.

Step 1 Draw and label a net for a cylinder. Label the radius of its bases 2 feet. Label the height of the cylinder 5 feet. The length of the rectangle is the circumference of the base ($C = 2\pi r$). So, label the length of the rectangle $2\pi^2$, or 12.57 ft.

Step 2 Find the area of one circle.

$$A = \pi r^2$$
$$= \pi(2)^2$$
$$= \pi(4)$$
$$\approx 12.57$$

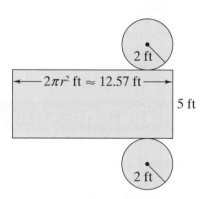

Step 3 Find the area of the rectangle.

$$(2\pi r)h = 2\pi(2)(5)$$
$$= 20\pi$$
$$\approx 62.83$$

Step 4 Add the areas of the two circles and the rectangle.

$$\text{S.A.} = 12.57 + 12.57 + 62.83 = 87.97$$

The surface area of the hay bale is 87.97 ft². So the farmer needs about 88 ft² of plastic.

Exercises

Draw a picture to solve each problem. If necessary, round to the nearest hundredth.

1. A gift box is in the shape of a square prism. The base of the box has sides that are 5 cm long. The height of the box is 8 cm. You plan to wrap the gift box with wrapping paper. How much wrapping paper do you need?

2. A wading pool is in the shape of a cylinder. The diameter of the pool is 2 m and its height is 0.5 m. You plan to fill the pool with water. How much water will the pool hold?

Vocabulary Review

bases (p. 454)
center of a sphere (p. 455)
cone (p. 455)
cross section (p. 473)
cube (p. 454)
cubic unit (p. 465)

cylinder (p. 454)
edge (p. 454)
face (p. 454)
height (p. 454)
net (p. 458)
prism (p. 454)

pyramid (p. 454)
sphere (p. 455)
surface area (p. 459)
three-dimensional
    figure (p. 454)
vertex (p. 454)
volume (p. 465)

Choose the correct term to complete each sentence.

1. Each segment formed by the intersection of two faces of a solid is a(n) (base, edge).

2. A rectangular prism with faces that are all squares is a (cube, sphere).

3. A (prism, pyramid) has two parallel and congruent bases.

4. A two-dimensional shape that you see after slicing through a solid is called a (cross section, face).

Go **Online**

For vocabulary quiz
PearsonSuccessNet.com

5. A three-dimensional figure that has one circular base and one vertex is a (cone, cylinder).

Skills and Concepts

Lesson 12-1

• To classify and draw three-dimensional figures

Some **three-dimensional figures** have only flat surfaces. **Prisms** and **pyramids** are named for the shape of their bases. **Cones** and pyramids have one **vertex.**

Name each figure.

6.

7.

8.

9.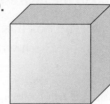

10.

11.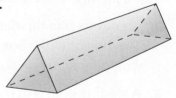

Lessons 12-2, 12-3

- To find the surface areas of prisms and cylinders using nets
- To find the volumes of prisms and cylinders

To find the **surface area** of a prism or cylinder, draw a **net** and find the area of the net.

To find the **volume** of a prism, use the formula $V = Bh$. To find the volume of a cylinder, use the formula $V = \pi r^2 h$.

Find the surface area for each figure. Round to the nearest hundredth.

12.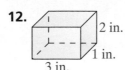
2 in.
1 in.
3 in.

13.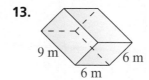
9 m 6 m
6 m

14.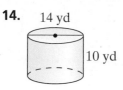
14 yd
10 yd

Find the volume for each figure. Round to the nearest hundredth.

15.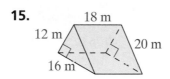
18 m
12 m
20 m
16 m

16.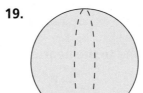
9 m
4 m

17.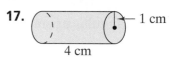
1 cm
4 cm

Lesson 12-4

- To describe cross sections that result from slicing three-dimensional figures

A **cross section** is the two-dimensional shape that you see after slicing through a three-dimensional object.

Describe each cross section.

18.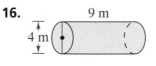

19.

20.

Lessons 12-5, 12-6

- To find the volumes of pyramids and cones
- To find the surface area and volume of a sphere

For a pyramid and a cone, the volume is one third the product of the area of the base B and the height h of the solid. Volume formula for pyramids and cones, $V = \frac{1}{3}Bh$.

A **sphere** is the set of all points in space that are the same distance from a center point. The formula for the surface area of a sphere is S.A. $= 4\pi r^2$. The formula for volume is $V = \frac{4}{3}\pi r^3$.

Find the volume of each to the nearest whole number. Find the surface area of the spheres to the nearest whole number.

21.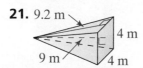
9.2 m
4 m
9 m 4 m

22.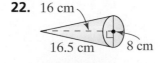
16 cm
16.5 cm 8 cm

23.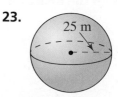
25 m

24.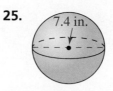
6 cm

25.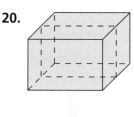
7.4 in.

Chapter 12 Test

Name each solid and describe its base(s).

1.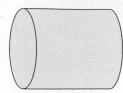

2.

Draw each figure.

3. triangular prism

4. rectangular pyramid

Draw a net of each solid.

5.

6.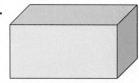

Find the surface area of each solid to the nearest square unit.

7.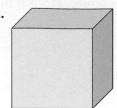
12 m   16 m   4 m   20 m

8. 28 in.   30 in.

9.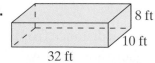
8 ft   10 ft   32 ft

10.
7 m   5 m   8 m

Find the volume of each solid. When using π, round to the nearest cubic unit.

11.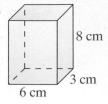
8 cm   3 cm   6 cm

12.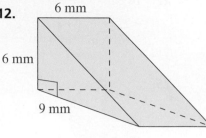
6 mm   6 mm   9 mm

13.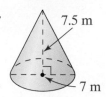
|← 6 m →| 4 m

14.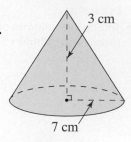
3 cm   7 cm

15.
1 ft   0.75 ft   0.9 ft

16.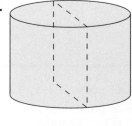
7.5 m   7 m

17. 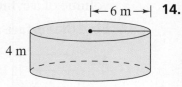 **Writing in Math** A fountain in the shape of a cylinder sits in the center of a park. The height of the fountain is 3 ft. Its volume is 235.6 ft³. Explain how you would find the radius of the fountain.

Describe each cross section.

18.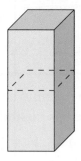

19.

Find the surface area and volume of each sphere. When using π, round to the nearest cubic unit.

20.
7 m

21.
24 mm

Multiple Choice

Read each question. Then write the letter of the correct answer on your paper.

1. Which number has the greatest value?

    (A) 8   (B) −5   (C) −10   (D) 0

2. Rectangle *ABCD* has dimensions 3 in. × 4 in. What are the area and perimeter of *ABCD*?

    (F) $A = 12$ in.^{2}, $P = 12$ in.

    (G) $A = 12$ in.^{2}, $P = 14$ in.

    (H) $A = 6$ in.^{2}, $P = 12$ in.

    (J) $A = 12$ in.^{2}, $P = 7$ in.

3. The rectangles are similar. Which proportion could NOT be used to find the value of *x*?

    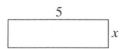

    (A) $\dfrac{7}{5} = \dfrac{2}{x}$

    (C) $\dfrac{x}{5} = \dfrac{2}{7}$

    (B) $\dfrac{x}{2} = \dfrac{7}{5}$

    (D) $\dfrac{2}{7} = \dfrac{x}{5}$

4. Jeremy wants to fence part of his backyard for his dog. He has 44 ft of fencing and wants the fenced-in area to be as big as possible. Which dimensions should he use?

    (F) Length of 14 ft and width of 8 ft

    (G) Length of 12 ft and width of 10 ft

    (H) Length of 11 ft and width of 11 ft

    (J) Length of 10 ft and width of 13 ft

5. Which expression could you use to find the area of the cylinder's base?

    (A) $2 \cdot \pi \cdot 5$

    (B) $\pi \cdot 2.5 \cdot 2.5$

    (C) $\pi \cdot 5 \cdot 5$

    (D) $2 \cdot \pi \cdot 2.5 \cdot 6$

    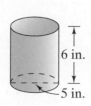

6. Which figure has the greatest volume?

    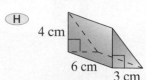

    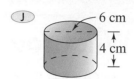

7. If $\angle C$ and $\angle D$ are complementary and the measure of $\angle C$ is 47°, what is the measure of $\angle D$?

    (A) 43°   (B) 53°   (C) 133°   (D) 143°

Gridded Response

Record your answer in a grid.

8. Jay has 180 baseball cards. The cards make up 75% of Jay's sports card collection. How many sports cards does Jay have in all?

Short Response

9. Define a variable and write an inequality to model "Kate rides her bike at least 12 miles each day."

10. The volume of a cylindrical can of tomato juice is 100.48 in.^{3} The diameter of the can is 4 in. What is the height of the can? Use $\pi = 3.14$. Show your work.

Extended Response

11. The ratio of the corresponding sides of two similar right triangles is 3 : 5. The sides of the smaller right triangle are 9 m, 12 m, and 15 m. Find the area of the larger right triangle. Show your work.

What You've Learned

- In Chapter 5, you identified similar figures and used proportions to find missing measurements in similar figures.
- In Chapter 7, you graphed points in the coordinate plane.
- In Chapter 11, you determined whether two figures were congruent and wrote congruence statements.

Check Your Readiness

GO for Help

For Exercises	See Lesson
1–4	7-6
5–6	11-2
7	11-3
8	11-4

The Coordinate Plane

Graph each point on the same coordinate plane.

1. $A(3, -4)$

2. $B(-5, 6)$

3. $C(0, 5)$

4. $D(-2, -3)$

Congruent Figures

Write a congruence statement for each pair of congruent figures.

5.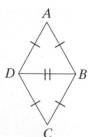

6.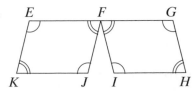

Similar Figures

Are the figures in each pair similar? Explain.

7.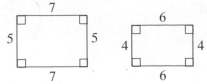

8.

What You'll Learn Next

- In this chapter, you will graph translations, reflections, and rotations.

- You will graph dilations and determine the scale factor of a dilation.

- You will identify sequences of transformations that produce congruent figures and those that produce similar figures.

- Applying what you learn, you will determine whether everyday figures, such as flowers, have rotational symmetry.

Key Vocabulary

- angle of rotation (p. 505)
- center of rotation (p. 505)
- dilation (p. 517)
- enlargement (p. 518)
- image (p. 494)
- line of reflection (p. 499)
- line of symmetry (p. 500)
- reduction (p. 518)
- reflection (p. 499)
- reflectional symmetry (p. 500)
- rotation (p. 505)
- rotational symmetry (p. 505)
- scale factor (p. 517)
- transformation (p. 494)
- translation (p. 494)

Translations

Check Skills You'll Need

1. Vocabulary Review
In what *quadrant* is $(-3, 5)$ located?

Name the coordinates of each point.

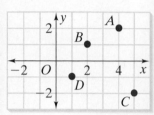

2. *A*   **3.** *B*

4. *C*   **5.** *D*

 **for Help**
Lesson 7-6

© **CONTENT STANDARDS**
8.G.1, 8.G.1.a, 8.G.1.b,
8.G.1.c, 8.G.3

Vocabulary Tip

Each corner of a triangle is a *vertex*. The plural of vertex is *vertices*.

What You'll Learn

To graph and describe translations in the coordinate plane

New Vocabulary transformation, translation, image

Why Learn This?

Translations are used in games and in the arts. You can use translations to plan a winning chess strategy or choreograph a figure-skating routine.

A **transformation** is a change in the position, shape, or size of a figure. A **translation** is a transformation that moves each point of a figure the same distance and in the same direction.

The figure you get after a transformation is an **image** of the original figure. To identify the image of point A, use prime notation (A'). You read A' as "A prime."

EXAMPLE Graphing a Translation

1 **Multiple Choice** If $\triangle PQR$ below is translated 6 units to the right and 3 units down, what are the coordinates of point P'?

Ⓐ $P'(-1, -2)$ Ⓑ $P'(-2, 1)$ Ⓒ $P'(-2, -1)$ Ⓓ $P'(1, -2)$

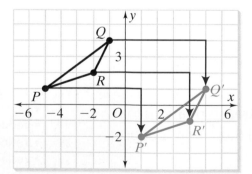

Slide each vertex right 6 units and down 3 units. Label and connect the images of the vertices.

The answer is D.

✓ Quick Check

1. $\triangle JKL$ has vertices $J(0, 2)$, $K(3, 4)$, and $L(5, 1)$. Translate $\triangle JKL$ 4 units to the left and 5 units up. What are the coordinates of J'?

Notice in Example 1 that $\triangle P'Q'R'$ is congruent to $\triangle PQR$. A translation of a figure preserves the side lengths and angle measures of the figure. You can use arrow notation to describe the translation. The translation of each point is shown below.

$$P(-5, 1) \rightarrow P'(1, -2) \quad \leftarrow \text{Read } P \rightarrow P' \text{ as "point } P \text{ goes to point } P \text{ prime."}$$
$$Q(-1, 4) \rightarrow Q'(5, 1)$$
$$R(-2, 2) \rightarrow R'(4, -1)$$

The arrow notation for the translation of the triangle is $\triangle PQR \rightarrow \triangle P'Q'R'$.

You can use arrow notation to write a general rule that describes a translation. For Example 1, $(x, y) \rightarrow (x + 6, y - 3)$ shows an ordered pair (x, y) and describes a translation to the right 6 units and down 3 units.

EXAMPLE **Describing a Translation**

2 Write a rule to describe the translation of the black triangle to the blue triangle.

Each point has moved 4 units to the right and 2 units down. So the translation adds 4 to the x-coordinate and subtracts 2 from the y-coordinate.

The rule is $(x, y) \rightarrow (x + 4, y - 2)$.

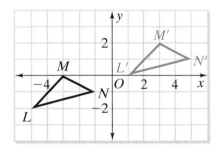

Test Prep Tip

Draw arrows from each original point to its image to help you see the translation.

Quick Check

2. Write a rule that describes the translation shown on the graph at the right.

Check Your Understanding

1. **Vocabulary** A (transformation, image) is a change in the position, shape, or size of a figure.

2. **Sports** The graph at the left shows an ice skater moving across the ice. How far and in what direction does the skater move?

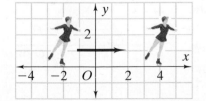

Graph each point and its image after the given translation.

3. $T(1, 3)$, left 2 units

4. $V(-4, 4)$, down 6 units

5. $S(4, 0)$, right 1 unit, down 3 units

6. $X(0, -2)$, right 7 units

For more exercises, see Extra Skills and Word Problems.

GO for Help

For Exercises	See Examples
7–10	1
11–14	2

Copy each figure. Then graph the image after the given translation.

7. up 2 units

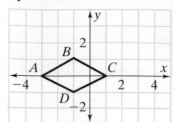

8. left 3 units, down 4 units

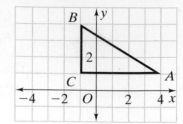

9. right 4 units, up 3 units

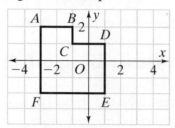

10. left 2 units, up 1 unit

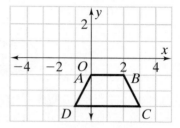

Write a rule that describes the translation shown on each graph.

11.

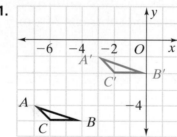

12.

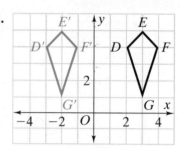

13.

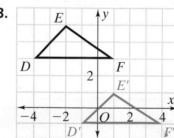

14.

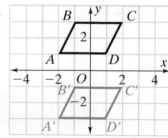

15. Guided Problem Solving Suppose the figure at the right is translated 6 units to the right and 5 units down. Without graphing, what are the coordinates of the image points?
- What are the coordinates of the vertices?
- To translate to the right, do you add to or subtract from the *x*-coordinate?
- To translate down, do you add to or subtract from the *y*-coordinate?

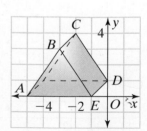

Match each rule with the correct translation.

16. $(x, y) \rightarrow (x - 6, y + 2)$ **A.** $P(4, -1) \rightarrow P'(3, -6)$

17. $(x, y) \rightarrow (x + 3, y)$ **B.** $Q(3, 0) \rightarrow Q'(-3, 2)$

18. $(x, y) \rightarrow (x - 1, y - 5)$ **C.** $R(-2, 4) \rightarrow R'(1, 4)$

19. Use graph paper to complete parts (a)–(e).
   a. Draw a rectangle with vertices $A(1, 6), B(4, 6), C(4, 2),$ and $D(1, 2)$.
   b. What are the lengths of the sides of rectangle $ABCD$? What are the angle measures?
   c. Perform any translation of rectangle $ABCD$. Use arrow notation to describe your translation.
   d. How do the lengths of the sides of rectangle $A'B'C'D'$ compare with the lengths of the sides of rectangle $ABCD$? How do the angle measures compare?
   e. Do you think that your answer to part (d) is true for any translation of a figure? Explain your reasoning.

20. Games The chessboard at the left shows four possible moves for the white knight. Write a rule to describe each move as a translation, using the knight's original position as the origin.

21. Writing in Math Suppose you translate a point to the left 1 unit and up 3 units. Describe what you would do to the coordinates of the original point to find the coordinates of the image.

22. Challenge Graph the equation $y = \frac{1}{2}x$. Translate the line up 3 units. Describe the image.

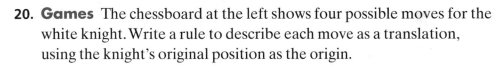
Test Prep and Mixed Review   **Practice**

Multiple Choice

23. Point $A(2, 3)$ is translated 2 units to the right and 4 units down. What are the coordinates of point A'?
   Ⓐ $(0, 0)$ Ⓑ $(0, -1)$ Ⓒ $(4, 0)$ Ⓓ $(4, -1)$

24. Which is the slope and y-intercept of a line that passes through $(3, 6)$ and $(0, 8)$?
   Ⓕ $-\frac{2}{3}; 8$ Ⓗ $\frac{2}{3}; -6$

   Ⓖ $-\frac{3}{2}; 8$ Ⓙ $\frac{3}{2}; -8$

Graph each linear equation.

25. $y = \frac{1}{3}x$ **26.** $y = -5x + 2$

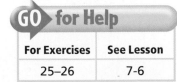
GO for Help

For Exercises	See Lesson
25–26	7-6

Exploring Reflections

A reflection reflects, or flips, a figure over a line. You can use tracing paper, a ruler, and a protractor to explore reflections.

ACTIVITY

Step 1 Fold a piece of tracing paper in half. Unfold the paper. Label the halves I and II. Draw $\triangle DEF$ on half I.

Step 2 Refold the paper. Trace the triangle on the back of half II.

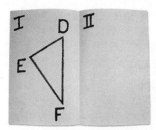 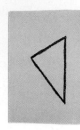

Step 3 Unfold the paper and trace the second triangle onto the front of half II. Label the vertices of the last triangle D', E', and F' to correspond to the vertices of $\triangle DEF$.

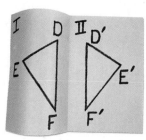

Exercises

1. Compare the lengths of $\overline{DE}$ and $\overline{D'E'}$. Do the same for the other corresponding side lengths. What appears to be true?

2. Compare the measures of $\angle D$ and $\angle D'$. Do the same for the other corresponding angle measures. What appears to be true?

3. Compare the distances of D and D' from the fold. Do the same for the other corresponding vertices. What appears to be true?

4. Use your ruler to connect vertices D and D'. This segment intersects the fold to form four angles. Measure one of the angles. Do the same for the other angles formed by the fold and the segments connecting the corresponding vertices. What appears to be true?

What You'll Learn

To graph reflections in the coordinate plane and to identify lines of symmetry

New Vocabulary reflection, line of reflection, reflectional symmetry, line of symmetry

Why Learn This?

Reflections appear everywhere in the world around us. You can see reflections in a mirror or a pool of water, or in shapes in art and nature.

A **reflection** is a transformation that flips a figure over a line. This line is the **line of reflection**. Like translations, reflections change the position of a figure but not its size or shape.

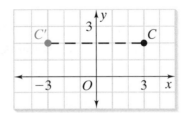

In the diagram at the left, C and C' are the same distance from the line of reflection. The segment connecting C and C' is perpendicular to the line of reflection, the y-axis.

EXAMPLE Graphing Reflections of a Point

1   Graph the point $A(3, 2)$. Then graph its image after it is reflected over the x-axis. Name the coordinates of A'.

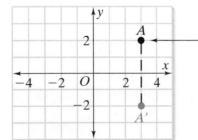

Since A is 2 units *above* the x-axis, A' is 2 units *below* the x-axis.

The coordinates of A' are $(3, -2)$.

✓ Quick Check

1. Graph the point $D(-2, 1)$. Then graph its image after it is reflected over the y-axis. Name the coordinates of D'.

When you reflect a figure over a line, the image is congruent to the original figure.

EXAMPLE Graphing Reflections of a Shape

② Graph △*BCD* and its image after it is reflected over the line through (1, 3) and (1, 0). Name the coordinates of the vertices of △*B′C′D′*.

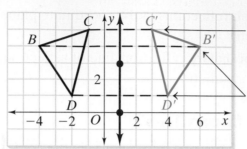

Since *C* is 2 units to the left of the red line, *C′* is 2 units to the right of the line.

Reflect the other vertices. Draw △*B′C′D′*.

The coordinates of the vertices are *B′*(6, 4), *C′*(3, 5), and *D′*(4, 1).

✓ Quick Check

2. △*EFG* has vertices *E*(4, 3), *F*(3, 1), and *G*(1, 2). Graph △*EFG* and its image after it is reflected over the *x*-axis. Name the coordinates of the vertices of △*E′F′G′*.

If a figure can be reflected over a line so that the reflected image matches the original figure, then the figure has **reflectional symmetry.** The line that divides the figure into mirror images is called a **line of symmetry.**

Many shapes in nature have reflectional symmetry. In the leaf at the left, the black line approximates a line of symmetry.

EXAMPLE Identifying Lines of Symmetry

③ Draw the lines of symmetry for the snowflake below.

There are six ways to fold the figure so both halves match. The figure has six lines of symmetry.

✓ Quick Check

3. Copy the flag at the right. Draw the lines of symmetry.

1. **Vocabulary** Line *a* divides a figure into two halves. How can you tell whether *a* is a line of symmetry?

Use the graph at the right. Match each point with its image after a reflection over the given axis.

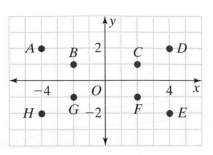

2. *A*, *y*-axis

3. *B*, *x*-axis

4. *H*, *y*-axis

5. *F*, *y*-axis

6. *E*, *x*-axis

7. *C*, *x*-axis

For more exercises, see Extra Skills and Word Problems.

GO for Help

For Exercises	See Examples
8–13	1
14–16	2
17–19	3

Graph the given point and its image after each reflection over the given axis. Name the coordinates of the reflected point.

8. $H(-3, 2)$, *x*-axis

9. $G(2, 4)$, *y*-axis

10. $B(-3, -4)$, *y*-axis

11. $D(0, -2)$, *x*-axis

12. $C(4, -3)$, *x*-axis

13. $M(5, 0)$, *y*-axis

$\triangle MPS$ **has vertices** $M(4, 5)$, $P(1, 2)$, **and** $S(5, 1)$. **Graph** $\triangle MPS$ **and its image after a reflection over each line. Name the new coordinates.**

14. *x*-axis

15. *y*-axis

16. line through $(1, -2)$ and $(4, -2)$

Copy each figure that has reflectional symmetry. Draw the lines of symmetry. Write *no reflectional symmetry* where applicable.

17.

18.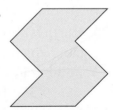

19.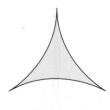

GPS 20. **Guided Problem Solving** Does the flag at the right have reflectional symmetry? If so, state how many lines of symmetry it has.

• **Understand the Problem** Find whether you can fold the figure so both halves match.

• **Make a Plan** Copy the figure and try folding it in different ways.

21. The word **COB** has reflectional symmetry. Which capital letters in the alphabet have reflectional symmetry?

22. **a.** Graph the image of $\triangle JKL$ after it is reflected over the red line. Name the coordinates of $\triangle J'K'L'$. What do you notice about the y-coordinates?

   b. Translate $\triangle J'K'L'$ to the left 3 units. Name the coordinates of $\triangle J''K''L''$.

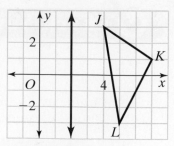

Figure $EFGH$ has vertices $E(2,5)$, $F(4,5)$, $G(6,1)$, and $H(3,1)$. Graph figure $EFGH$ and its image after a reflection over each line. Name the coordinates of the vertices of the reflected figure.

23. y-axis   24. x-axis   25. line through $(0,2)$ and $(-3,2)$

26. **Art** The figure at the right is folded along a red line of symmetry. Copy the figure and sketch the unfolded figure.

27. **Writing in Math** How many lines of symmetry does a circle have? Explain your answer.

28. **Challenge** When connected in order, the points $(-3, -3)$, $(-4, -1)$, $(-1, 2)$, $(2, 5)$, and $(4, 4)$ form half of a figure. The line of symmetry of the complete figure is $y = x$. Draw the complete figure.

Test Prep and Mixed Review

Practice

Multiple Choice

29. If $\triangle ABC$ is reflected over the x-axis, what are the coordinates of C'?

   (A) $(2, -4)$ (C) $(-2, 4)$
   (B) $(4, -2)$ (D) $(-4, 2)$

30. Earth is about 93,000,000 miles from the sun. Which expression represents this number in scientific notation?

   (F) 9.3×10^{-7} (H) 9.3×10^6
   (G) 9.3×10^{-6} (J) 9.3×10^7

31. Which list shows the numbers in order from least to greatest?

   (A) $\sqrt{5}$, 2.4, $\frac{7}{3}$, $\sqrt{2}$ (C) $\sqrt{5}$, $\frac{7}{3}$, 2.4, $\sqrt{2}$
   (B) $\sqrt{2}$, $\sqrt{5}$, $\frac{7}{3}$, 2.4 (D) $\sqrt{2}$, 2.4, $\sqrt{5}$, $\frac{7}{3}$

GO for Help

For Exercises	See Lesson
32–34	5-4

Solve each proportion.

32. $\dfrac{3}{5} = \dfrac{6}{x}$ 33. $\dfrac{4}{6} = \dfrac{x}{75}$ 34. $\dfrac{9}{12} = \dfrac{150}{x}$

Graph each point and its image after the given translation. Name the coordinates of the translated point.

1. $M(2,5)$, left 5 units

2. $N(-4,7)$, down 8 units

3. $P(-1,-3)$, right 2 units, up 3 units

4. Copy $\triangle JKL$ at the right. Graph the image after a translation to the left 3 units and up 4 units. What are the coordinates of J', K', and L'?

5. Write a rule to describe the translation in Exercise 4.

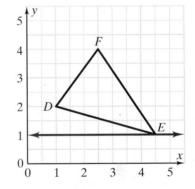

Graph the given point and its image after a reflection over each line. Name the coordinates of the reflected point.

6. $Q(3,4)$, x-axis

7. $R(2,-5)$, y-axis

8. $S(0,9)$, line through $(0,0)$ and $(5,5)$

9. Copy $\triangle DEF$ at the right. Graph the image after a reflection over the red line. What are the coordinates of D', E', and F'?

10. Which of the following letters have lines of symmetry: A, C, G, J? Draw the lines of symmetry.

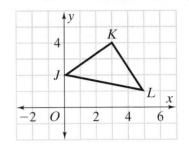

MATH AT WORK

Video Game Programmers

Video game programmers write the code that drives the actions in video games.

Video game programmers need a strong background in mathematics and computer programming. They use logic to design their programs. Then they use algebra to write the detailed instructions that the computer understands. The result is a game that is fun to play.

 **Go Online** For information on video game programmers
PearsonSuccessNet.com

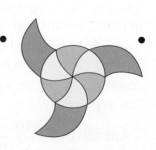

Exploring Rotations

ACTIVITY

Begin with a square piece of paper that has 4-inch sides.

Step 1 Place the piece of paper over the figure below. Trace everything in black: the center point, the kite, and the vertices of $\triangle ABC$.

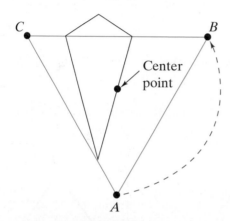

Step 2 Place the point of your pencil on the center point. Rotate the paper until vertex A overlaps vertex B. Trace the kite in its new location.

Step 3 Repeat Step 2, but this time, rotate the paper until vertex A overlaps vertex C.

Exercises

1. How does the image of the kite after a rotation compare with the original kite? Explain your reasoning.

2. The *angle of rotation* is the number of degrees a figure rotates. What is the angle of rotation of the kite in Step 2?

3. Make a new design using a square rather than $\triangle ABC$. What angle do you rotate the figure for each vertex of the square?

The diagram at the right was made by rotating and copying a figure.

4. Make a sketch of the original figure.

5. **Reasoning** Consider the steps in the activity above. How do you transform the figure so that the image is congruent to the original figure?

What You'll Learn

To graph rotations and to identify rotational symmetry

New Vocabulary rotation, center of rotation, angle of rotation, rotational symmetry

Why Learn This?

When you learn to recognize rotational symmetry, you can see it in everything from art and nature to architecture and science.

A **rotation** is a transformation that turns a figure about a fixed point called the **center of rotation.** A figure has **rotational symmetry** if it can be rotated 180° or less and exactly matches its original figure.

When you rotate a figure about a point, the image is congruent to the original figure. A rotation changes only the position of a figure. The **angle of rotation** is the number of degrees the figure rotates. A complete rotation is 360°.

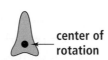 center of rotation 90° 180° 270° 360°

EXAMPLE Rotational Symmetry

1. **Nature** Find the angle of rotation of the figure.

The image matches the original after $\frac{1}{5}$ of a complete rotation.

$$\frac{1}{5} \cdot 360° = 72°$$

The angle of rotation is 72°.

✓ Quick Check

1. If the figure at the right has rotational symmetry, find the angle of rotation. If it does not, write *no rotational symmetry.*

You can use the coordinate plane to graph rotations. In this book, all rotations are counterclockwise.

EXAMPLE **Graphing Rotations**

2 Graph △ABC and its image after a rotation of 90° about the origin. Name the coordinates of the vertices of △A′B′C′.

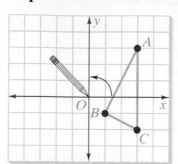

Step 1 Draw and trace.

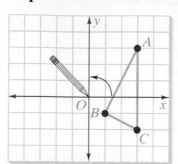

- Draw △ABC on a piece of graph paper. Place a piece of tracing paper over your graph.
- Trace the vertices of the triangle, the x-axis, and the y-axis, as shown in blue.
- Place your pencil at the origin to rotate the paper.

Step 2 Rotate and mark each vertex of the image.

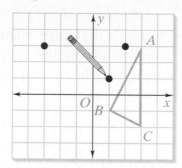

- Rotate the tracing paper 90° counterclockwise. The axes should line up.
- Mark the position of each vertex of the image by pressing your pencil through the paper.

Step 3 Draw the image.

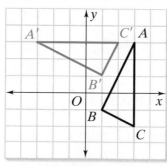

- Remove the tracing paper.
- Draw △A′B′C′.
- Label the vertices to complete the image.

The coordinates of the vertices of △A′B′C′ are A′(−3, 3), B′(1, 1), and C′(2, 3).

✓ Quick Check

2. Graph △ABD and its image after a rotation of the given number of degrees about the origin. Name the coordinates of the vertices of the image.
   a. 180°   **b.** 270°

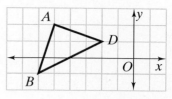

1. **Vocabulary** A figure has rotational symmetry if it can be rotated ■ degrees or less and exactly match its original figure.

Graph each point. Then rotate it the given number of degrees about the origin. Give the coordinates of the image.

2. $L(3, 3)$, 90°
3. $M(-4, -2)$, 270°
4. $N(3, -5)$, 180°

Homework Exercises

For more exercises, see Extra Skills and Word Problems.

GO **for Help**

For Exercises	See Examples
5–7	1
8–10	2

Determine whether each figure has rotational symmetry. If it does, find the angle of rotation. Write *no rotational symmetry* if applicable.

5.

6.

7.

Copy △PQR. Draw the image of △PQR after a rotation of the given number of degrees about the origin. Give the coordinates of the vertices of the image.

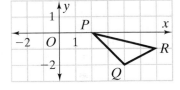

8. 90°
9. 180°
10. 270°

 11. **Guided Problem Solving** Figure B is an image formed by rotating Figure A. Give the angle of rotation for Figure B.
   • Draw Figure A on graph paper. Be sure to graph the center of the figure on the origin.
   • Trace Figure A onto tracing paper and rotate counterclockwise.

Figure A

Figure B

12. Graph △JKL with vertices $J(1, -3)$, $K(6, -2)$, and $L(6, -4)$. Graph the three images formed by rotating the triangle 90°, 180°, and 270° about the origin. Give the coordinates of the vertices of each image.

13. **Error Analysis** A square has rotational symmetry because it can be rotated 180° so that its image matches the original. Your friend says the angle of rotation is 180° ÷ 4 = 45°. What is wrong with this statement?

GO **Online**
Homework Video Tutor
PearsonSuccessNet.com

Draw the image of the figure at the right after the following rotations.

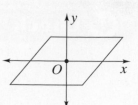

14. 90°   **15.** 180°   **16.** 270°

17. 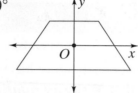 Explain how the design in the tie at the left can be made by using rotations and translations.

Copy each figure. Then draw the image of the figure after the given rotation about the origin.

18. 180°

19. 270°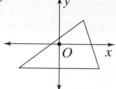

20. Challenge Graph $\triangle PQR$ with vertices $P(3, 2)$, $Q(1, 0)$, and $R(3, -2)$. Draw the triangle after it is reflected across the y-axis. How can you get the same image using a rotation? Explain.

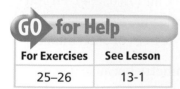
Test Prep and Mixed Review   Practice

Gridded Response

21. How many degrees is the least angle of rotation of the snowflake?

22. A bee keeper wants to know the measure of each angle in a honeycomb. The honeycomb is made up of a grid of regular hexagons. What is the measure of each angle, in degrees?

23. The distance between the sun and Mars is about 2.28×10^{11} meters. Light travels about 3.0×10^8 meters per second. Using the formula time $= \dfrac{\text{distance}}{\text{speed}}$, about how many minutes does it take sunlight to reach Mars?

24. What is the slope of the line that passes through the points $(3, 2)$ and $(2, -5)$?

GO for Help

For Exercises	See Lesson
25–26	13-1

For $M(0, -3)$, give the coordinates of its image after each translation.

25. right 2 units and down 1 unit   **26.** left 3 units and up 3 units

Transformations and Congruence

✓ Check Skills You'll Need

1. Vocabulary Review
The __?__ is the number of degrees a figure rotates about a fixed point.

Give the coordinates of the image of each point after being rotated the given number of degrees about the origin.

2. *A* (2, 1), 90°

3. *B* (0, 3), 180°

4. *C* (−1, 4), 270°

 **for Help**
Lesson 13-3

What You'll Learn

To describe a sequence of transformations that maps one figure onto another; to determine whether two figures are congruent by using a sequence of transformations

Why Learn This?

When you walk in the sand, you leave a trail of footprints that are congruent to each other. You can use transformations to map one footprint onto another.

If two figures are congruent, then a transformation, or a sequence of transformations, will map one figure onto the other.

EXAMPLE **Recognizing a Series of Transformations**

1 The three trapezoids are congruent. Describe the sequence of transformations that maps *WXYZ* onto *W″X″Y″Z″*.

A reflection over the *y*-axis maps *WXYZ* onto *W′X′Y′Z′*.

A translation 7 units down maps *W′X′Y′Z′* onto *W″X″Y″Z″*.

So, a reflection over the *y*-axis, followed by a translation 7 units down, maps *WXYZ* onto *W″X″Y″Z″*.

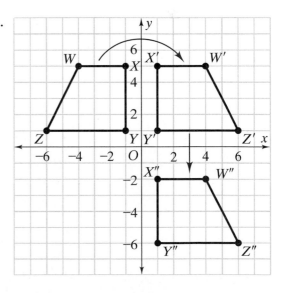

✓ Quick Check

1. Describe the sequence of transformations that maps *W″X″Y″Z″* onto *WXYZ*.

If you can use a sequence of transformations to map one figure onto another, then the two figures are congruent.

EXAMPLE Using Transformations to Determine Congruence

Vocabulary Tip

Two figures have the same *orientation* if you can use a translation, a rotation, or a combination of the two to map one figure onto the other.

2 Determine whether the two triangles in the diagram are congruent. If they are, write a congruence statement. If they are not congruent, explain why.

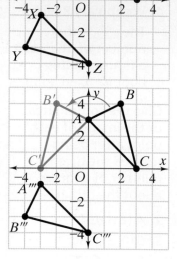

$\triangle ABC$ and $\triangle XYZ$ have opposite orientations and are on opposite sides of the y-axis, so start by reflecting $\triangle ABC$ over the y-axis to get $\triangle A'B'C'$.

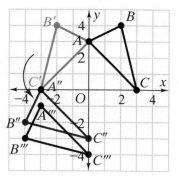

Since $\triangle A'B'C'$ and $\triangle XYZ$ are in different positions, rotate $\triangle A'B'C'$ 90° about the origin to get $\triangle A''B''C''$.

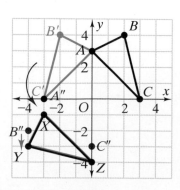

Each vertex of $\triangle XYZ$ is 1 unit down from the corresponding vertex of $\triangle A''B''C''$. So translating $\triangle A''B''C''$ 1 unit down will map it onto $\triangle XYZ$.

A reflection over the y-axis, followed by a rotation of 90° about the origin, followed by a translation 1 unit down maps $\triangle ABC$ onto $\triangle XYZ$. So, $\triangle ABC \cong \triangle XYZ$.

✓ Quick Check

2. Determine whether △ *EFG* is congruent to △ *MNP*. If the triangles are congruent, tell what sequence of transformations will map △ *EFG* onto △*MNP*. Then write a congruence statement. If they are not congruent, explain why.

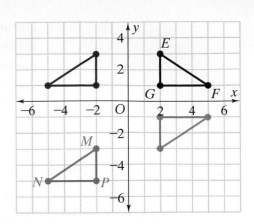

✓ Check Your Understanding

1. Reasoning What three transformations can you use to prove that two figures are congruent? Explain your reasoning.

Use the graph at the right. Match each point with its image after the given sequence of transformations.

2. *A*, reflection over *y*-axis, 90° rotation about origin, translation 3 units down

3. *B*, reflection over *x*-axis, 180° rotation about origin, translation 2 units down

4. *C*, reflection over *y*-axis, 270° rotation about origin, translation 3 units right

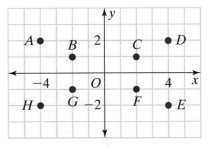

Homework Exercises

For more exercises, see Extra Skills and Word Problems.

The three figures in each diagram are congruent. Describe the sequence of transformations that maps the original figure onto the final image.

GO for Help

Exercise	See Examples
5–6	1
7–8	2

5.

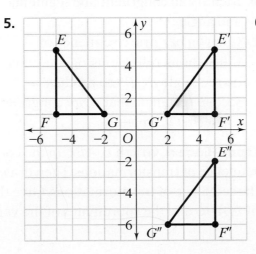

6.

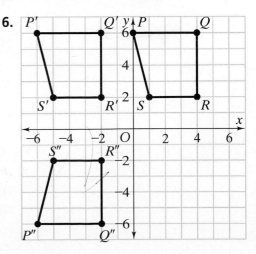

13-4 Transformations and Congruence **511**

Determine whether the black figure is congruent to the green figure. If the figures are congruent, tell what sequence of transformations will map the black figure onto the green figure. Then write a congruence statement. If they are not congruent, explain why.

7.

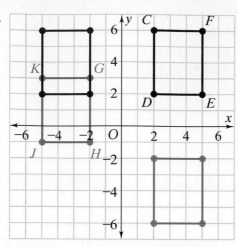

8.

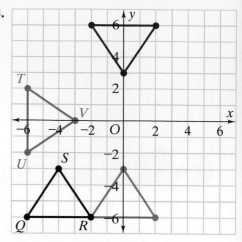

GPS **9. Guided Problem Solving** Draw $\triangle EFG$ with vertices at $E(-2, 3)$, $F(0, 4)$, and $G(0, 0)$ and $\triangle JKL$ with vertices at $J(3, -2)$, $K(4, -4)$, and $L(0, -4)$.

Describe two sequences of transformations that you can use to map $\triangle EFG$ onto $\triangle JKL$.

• To map $\triangle EFG$ onto $\triangle JKL$, should you start by translating, reflecting, or rotating $\triangle EFG$?
• What transformation should you perform second?
• Does the order in which you perform the sequence of transformations matter?

10. Rectangle $PQRS$ is transformed to rectangle $P'Q'R'S'$ as shown on the graph.

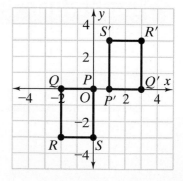

a. Describe a sequence of transformations to map rectangle $PQRS$ to rectangle $P'Q'R'S'$.
b. Identify all congruent line segments and angles.
c. Can you perform a sequence of translations, reflections, or rotations on rectangle $PQRS$ to produce a second rectangle that is *not* congruent to the first? Explain.

11. Open-Ended Graph $\triangle ABC$ in the coordinate plane. Describe a sequence of transformations. Then draw the image of $\triangle ABC$ after the sequence of transformations. Give the coordinates of the vertices of $\triangle ABC$ and the coordinates of the vertices of its image.

12. **Geometry** A *glide reflection* is a transformation that is made up of a translation and a reflection across a line that is parallel to the direction of the translation.
    a. Graph $\triangle DEF$ with vertices $D(1, -1), E(7, -3)$, and $F(2, -7)$.
    b. Graph the image of $\triangle DEF$ under a glide reflection where the translation is $(x, y) \rightarrow (x, y + 8)$ and the reflection line is the y-axis. Give the coordinates of the vertices of the image.
    c. Are the two figures congruent? Explain your reasoning.

13. **Writing in Math** Suppose you reflect a point over the y-axis and then translate its image 5 units down. Describe what you would do to the coordinates of the original point to find the coordinates of the final image.

14. **Challenge** Graph $\triangle MNP$ with vertices $M(-2, 2), N(-4, 2)$, and $P(-4, 5)$. Reflect $\triangle MNP$ across the y-axis. Then reflect its image across the x-axis. How can you get the same final image using a single rotation? Explain.

Test Prep and Mixed Review
Practice

Multiple Choice

15. What is the image of $T(1, 3)$ after a reflection over the y-axis, followed by a rotation of $180°$ about the origin, followed by a translation 4 units left?

   Ⓐ $T'''(-5, 3)$ Ⓑ $T'''(-3, -3)$ Ⓒ $T'''(3, 3)$ Ⓓ $T'''(5, -3)$

16. The graph of $y = \frac{1}{2}x + 1$ is shown on the coordinate grid at the right. Which table of ordered pairs contains only points on this line?

Ⓕ

x	y
−4	1
2	2
3	2.5

Ⓖ

x	y
−2	0
1	1.5
4	3

Ⓗ

x	y
0	−2
1	0
2	2

Ⓙ

x	y
−3	−1.5
0	2
5	3.5

17. Audrey bought a box of cereal and some bananas for $4.69. If the cereal cost $3.99 and the bananas were on sale for $0.28 per pound, how many pounds of bananas did Audrey buy?

   Ⓐ 0.42 lb   Ⓑ 2.2 lb   Ⓒ 2.5 lb   Ⓓ 4.2 lb

GO for Help

Exercise	See Lesson
18–20	3-5

Solve each equation.

18. $2b + 6 = 20$ 19. $3k - 2 = 24$ 20. $-5n + 4 = 29$

Vocabulary Builder

High-Use Academic Words

High-use academic words are words that you will see often in textbooks and on tests. These words are not math vocabulary terms, but knowing them will help you to succeed in mathematics.

Direction Words

Some words tell what to do in a problem. I need to understand what these words are asking so that I give the correct answer.

Word	Meaning
Sketch	To draw something without using a scale
Compare	To say how two things are similar or different
Show	To explain or prove using logic or examples

Exercises

1. The figure at the right is folded along a red line of symmetry. Copy the figure and sketch the unfolded figure.

2. Compare what you are doing now with what you were doing 3 hours ago.

3. Show that, in the same calendar year, there are always at least 90 days between Memorial Day and Labor Day.

Use the graph at the right for Exercises 4–6.

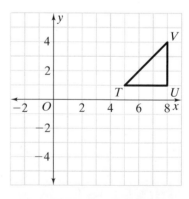

4. Copy the figure at the right. Sketch the image of $\triangle TUV$ after a reflection over the x-axis.

5. Compare the image of $\triangle TUV$ after a translation 6 units left and the image of $\triangle TUV$ after a translation 6 units down.

6. Show that the image of $\triangle TUV$ after a rotation of $180°$ about the origin is in Quadrant III.

7. **Word Knowledge** Think about the word *verify*.
   a. Choose the letter for how well you know the word.
      A. I know its meaning.
      B. I've seen it, but I don't know its meaning.
      C. I don't know it.
   b. **Research** Look up and write the definition of *verify*.
   c. Use the word in a sentence involving mathematics.

Copy △*TUV*. Draw the image of △*TUV* after a rotation of the given number of degrees about the origin. Give the coordinates of the vertices of the image.

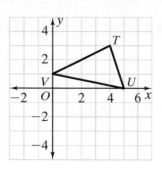

1. 90°

2. 180°

3. 270°

Determine whether the two figures in each diagram are congruent by performing the given sequence of transformations. If they are congruent, write a congruence statement. If they are not congruent, explain why.

4. Rotate *JKLM* 90° about the origin. Translate *J′K′L′M′* 6 units right.

5. Reflect △*UVW* over the *y*-axis. Rotate △*U′V′W′* 180° about the origin.

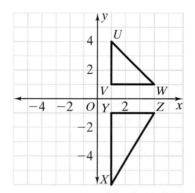

MATH AT WORK

Graphic Designer

Graphic designers are artists who produce images, typography, or motion graphics, either by hand or with computer software. Many graphic designers work for design services, publishers, advertisers, or in public relations.

The ability to transform an image is a skill that graphic designers sometimes use when creating a logo, or a visual symbol for a company. The designer will start with a basic image and then use translations, reflections, rotations, or any combination of the three transformations, to generate the logo. Using transformations helps ensure that a logo is both visually appealing and memorable to the general public.

Exploring Dilations

A dilation is a transformation that enlarges or reduces a figure. You can use graph paper, a ruler, and a protractor to explore dilations.

ACTIVITY

1. Graph points $A(4,2)$, $B(8,2)$, $C(4,5)$, and $O(0,0)$ on graph paper. Draw $\triangle ABC$.

2. Use a different color to draw rays $\overrightarrow{OA}$, $\overrightarrow{OB}$, and $\overrightarrow{OC}$.

3. Use a ruler to locate A' on $\overrightarrow{OA}$ so that $\overline{OA} = \overline{AA'}$, as shown.

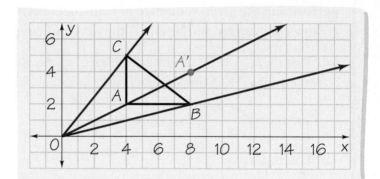

4. Use the same method to locate points B' and C'. Then draw $\triangle A'B'C'$.

5. Compare the lengths of $\overline{AB}$ and $\overline{A'B'}$. Do the same for the other corresponding side lengths. What appears to be true?

6. Compare the measures of $\angle A$ and $\angle A'$. Do the same for the other corresponding angle measures. What appears to be true?

7. Compare the distances of A and A' from the origin. What appears to be true?

8. What appears to be true about $\triangle ABC$ and $\triangle A'B'C'$? Explain.

9. Suppose you locate A' on $\overrightarrow{OA}$ so that $\overline{OA'} = \overline{A'A}$, B' on $\overrightarrow{OB}$ so that $\overline{OB'} = \overline{B'B}$, and C' on $\overrightarrow{OC}$ so that $\overline{OC'} = \overline{C'C}$. What do you think would be true about $\triangle ABC$ and $\triangle A'B'C'$? Explain your reasoning.

© CONTENT STANDARDS
8.G.3, 8.G.4

Vocabulary Tip

You can think of the *scale factor* of a dilation as a multiplier.

What You'll Learn

To graph dilations and to determine the scale factor of a dilation

New Vocabulary dilation, scale factor, enlargement, reduction

Why Learn This?

Photos can be enlarged or reduced using scale factors.

A **dilation** is a transformation in which a figure and its image are similar. The ratio of a length in the image to the corresponding length in the original figure is the **scale factor**.

EXAMPLE Finding a Dilation

1 Find the image of $\triangle ABC$ after a dilation with center A and a scale factor of $\frac{1}{2}$.

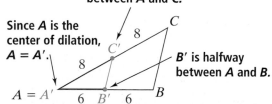

C' is halfway between **A** and **C.**

Since **A** is the center of dilation, **A = A'.**

B' is halfway between **A** and **B.**

$\triangle A'B'C'$ is the image of $\triangle ABC$ after a dilation with a scale factor of $\frac{1}{2}$. $\triangle ABC \sim \triangle A'B'C'$.

✓ Quick Check

1. Find the image of $\triangle DEF$ with vertices $D(-2, 2), E(1, -1),$ and $F(-2, -1)$ after a dilation with center D and scale factor 2.

You can use the coordinate plane to graph dilations. In this book, all dilations are centered at $(0, 0)$. To find the image of a figure in the coordinate plane after a dilation, you multiply the *x*- and *y*-coordinates of its vertices by the scale factor.

For: Similar Figures
Activity
Use: Interactive
Textbook, 13-5

EXAMPLE Graphing Dilation Images

2 Find the coordinates of the vertices of the image of quadrilateral *KLMN* after a dilation with scale factor of $\frac{3}{2}$. Then graph the image.

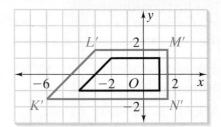

Step 1 Multiply the coordinates of each vertex by $\frac{3}{2}$.

$K(-4, -1) \rightarrow K'\left(-6, -\frac{3}{2}\right)$

$L(-2, 1) \rightarrow L'\left(-3, \frac{3}{2}\right)$

$M(1, 1) \rightarrow M'\left(\frac{3}{2}, \frac{3}{2}\right)$

$N(1, -1) \rightarrow N'\left(\frac{3}{2}, -\frac{3}{2}\right)$

Step 2 Graph the vertices of the image. Draw $K'L'M'N'$.

✓ Quick Check

2. *ABCD* has vertices $A(0,0), B(0,3), C(3,3),$ and $D(3,0)$. Find the coordinates of the vertices of the image of *ABCD* after a dilation with a scale factor of $\frac{4}{3}$. Then graph the image.

A dilation with a scale factor greater than 1 is called an **enlargement**. The image is bigger than the original. A dilation with a scale factor less than 1 is called a **reduction**. The image is smaller than the original.

EXAMPLE Application: City Planning

3 *TRSV* shows the outline of a park. A city planner dilates the figure to show the area of the park that can be used for concerts. What is the scale factor of the dilation?

The image is smaller than the original figure, so the dilation is a reduction. The scale factor must be less than 1.

$$\begin{array}{l} \text{image} \rightarrow \\ \text{original} \rightarrow \end{array} \quad \frac{T'R'}{TR} = \frac{2}{8} = \frac{1}{4}$$

The correct answer is choice B.

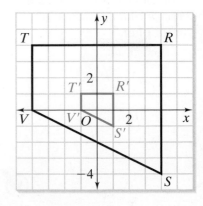

✓ Quick Check

3. The blue figure at the left shows the outline of a yard. The black figure is a doghouse. The blue figure is a dilation image of the black figure. Find the scale factor. Is the dilation an enlargement or a reduction?

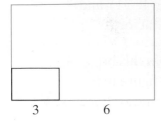

3   6

1. **Vocabulary** A rectangle is dilated with a scale factor of 0.6. Is the image a reduction or an enlargement? Explain.

The blue figure is a dilation image of the red figure.

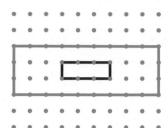

2. Is the blue figure an enlargement or a reduction of the red figure?

3. What is the scale factor?

Homework Exercises

For more exercises, see **Extra Skills and Word Problems**.

GO for Help

For Exercises	See Examples
4–5	1
6–7	2
8–10	3

Copy △ABC. Find the image of △ABC after a dilation with the given center and scale factor.

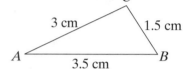

4. center C, scale factor $\frac{1}{2}$

5. center B, scale factor 2

Find the coordinates of the vertices of the image of ABCD after a dilation with the given scale factor. Graph the image.

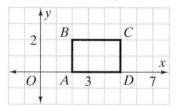

6. scale factor 2

7. scale factor $\frac{1}{2}$

The blue figure is a dilation image of the original figure. Find the scale factor. Classify each dilation as an *enlargement* or a *reduction*.

8.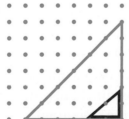

9.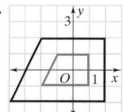

10.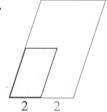

11. **Guided Problem Solving** You are reducing a digital photo that is 2 in. high and 3 in. wide. If the reduced photo is $1\frac{1}{4}$ in. high, what is its width? Write your answer as a mixed number in simplest form.

   • **Understand the Problem** You know the height and width of the original photo and the height of the reduced photo. You want to find the width of the reduced photo.
   • **Make a Plan** Draw and label the original photo and the reduced photo. Label the missing width *w*.

Graph quadrilateral EFGH with the given vertices. Find the coordinates of the vertices of its image after a dilation with the given scale factor. Graph the image.

12. $E(-2, -1)$, $F(2, 0)$, $G(2, 2)$, $H(-1, 2)$; scale factor of 2

13. $E(-3, 0)$, $F(1, -4)$, $G(5, 0)$, $H(1, 4)$; scale factor of $\frac{1}{2}$

14. Computers A window on a computer screen is $1\frac{1}{2}$ in. high and 2 in. wide. After you click the "size reduction" button, the window is reduced to $1\frac{1}{8}$ in. high and $1\frac{1}{2}$ in. wide. What is the scale factor?

15. $\triangle A'B'C'$ is the image of $\triangle ABC$ after a dilation. $AB = 7$ cm, $AC = 10$ cm, $A'B' = 28$ cm, and $B'C' = 24$ cm. What is the ratio of the perimeter of $\triangle ABC$ to the perimeter of $\triangle A'B'C'$?

16. Writing in Math Explain how to dilate a figure in the coordinate plane.

17. Challenge $\triangle ABC$ has three angles that measure 60° each and three sides that measure 60 cm each. With what scale factor should you dilate $\triangle ABC$ so that its image $\triangle A'B'C'$ has sides that measure 21 cm each?

Test Prep and Mixed Review

Practice

Multiple Choice

18. The blue figure is a dilation image of the black figure. What is the scale factor?

(A) $\frac{1}{4}$ (B) $\frac{1}{2}$ (C) 2   (D) 4

19. The number of people a restaurant can hold is proportional to the area of its floor space. One restaurant has a length of 45 feet, a width of 40 feet, and a ceiling height of 25 feet. It can hold 115 people. Which piece of information do you NOT need in order to find the amount of space needed for 200 people?

(F) The length of the restaurant
(G) The number of people the restaurant can hold
(H) The ceiling height of the restaurant
(J) The width of the restaurant

20. Cory is putting strips of tape along the diagonals of windows to prepare for a storm. Each window is 54 inches high and 40 inches wide. Which estimate is closest to the total length of the strips of tape Cory needs to cover 12 windows?

(A) 11 ft   (B) 67 ft   (C) 134 ft   (D) 185 ft

GO for Help

For Exercises	See Lesson
21–23	1-2

Find each sum or difference.

21. $29 - 37$

22. $139 + -98$

23. $97 - 148$

Geometry Software and Dilations

You can use the dilation command in geometry software to dilate a figure. The software will ask you to specify a center of dilation and a scale factor.

ACTIVITY

Graph $\triangle ABC$ with vertices $A(0,0), B(5,4)$, and $C(6,1)$. Find the image of $\triangle ABC$ after a dilation with center $(0,0)$ and a scale factor of 2. Then find the coordinates of the vertices of the image of $\triangle ABC$.

Step 1 Plot points A, B, and C. Construct the triangle.

Step 2 Use the dilation command. Enter $(0,0)$ for the center and 2 for the scale factor.

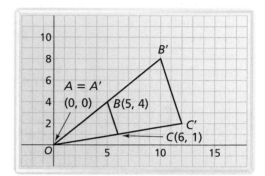

The coordinates of the vertices of $\triangle A'B'C'$ are $A'(0,0)$, $B'(10,8)$, and $C'(12,2)$.

Exercises

Use $\triangle ABC$ above for Exercise 1.

1. Find the image of $\triangle ABC$ after a dilation with center $(0,0)$ and a scale factor of 2.5.

2. Find the coordinates of the vertices of the image of $\triangle ABC$ that you drew in Exercise 1.

3. Graph rectangle $HIJK$ with vertices $H(1,2), I(1,7), J(14,7)$, and $K(14,2)$. Label the vertices.

4. Find the image of rectangle $HIJK$ after a dilation with center $(0,0)$ and a scale factor of 0.5. Label the image $LMNO$.

5. Use the Measure menu to find the perimeters of rectangle $HIJK$ and rectangle $LMNO$. Write a ratio comparing the perimeter of $LMNO$ to the perimeter of $HIJK$. What appears to be true?

6. Use the Measure menu to find the areas of $HIJK$ and $LMNO$. Write a ratio comparing the area of $LMNO$ to the area of $HIJK$. What appears to be true?

Transformations and Similarity

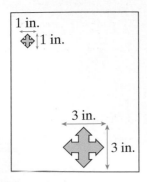
✓ Check Skills You'll Need

1. **Vocabulary Review** If two polygons are __?__, then the corresponding angles are congruent and the lengths of the corresponding sides are proportional.

2. In the figure below, △VWX ~ △YZX. Find the value of p.

X

6 ft

Y   Z
   p
2 ft

V   8 ft   W

GO for Help
Lesson 11-3

© CONTENT STANDARD
8.G.4

What You'll Learn

To describe a sequence of transformations that maps one figure onto a figure that is similar; to determine whether two figures are similar by using a sequence of transformations

Why Learn This?

Smartphones and tablets have a "zoom" feature that makes a figure larger or smaller. A "swipe" feature lets you slide the figure around on the screen. When you use these two features together, the final figure is similar to the original figure.

If two figures are similar, but not congruent, then a dilation, or a dilation and a sequence of transformations, will map one figure onto the other.

EXAMPLE **Determining Similarity using Transformations**

① You use the zoom and swipe features on your smartphone to enlarge and then move an image of a bee on the screen. Describe the sequence of transformations that maps the original image of the bee onto an image that is similar.

Original Image   Zoomed-In Image   Final Image

A dilation with a scale factor of 3.5 maps the original image of the bee onto the first zoomed-in image. A translation to the left maps the zoomed-in image onto the final image similar to the original image.

✓ Quick Check

1. Using a computer, a graphic designer moves a company logo from the top left of a page to the bottom center of the page and then enlarges the logo, as shown at the left. Describe the sequence of transformations that maps the original logo onto the final logo.

More Than One Way

Determine whether $\triangle ABC$ is similar to $\triangle ZYX$. Explain your reasoning.

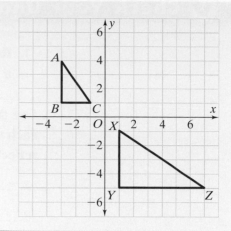

GO for Help

For help rotating a figure about the origin, go to Lesson 13-3, Example 2.

Tina's Method

I can use a sequence of transformations to prove that $\triangle ABC$ is similar to $\triangle ZYX$.

Rotate $\triangle ABC$ $90°$ about the origin to get $\triangle A'B'C'$.

Reflect $\triangle A'B'C'$ over the y-axis to get $\triangle A''B''C''$.

Dilate $\triangle A''B''C''$ by the scale factor 2 with center C'' to get $\triangle ZYX$.

I can map $\triangle ABC$ onto $\triangle ZYX$ using transformations with a dilation, so the triangles are similar.

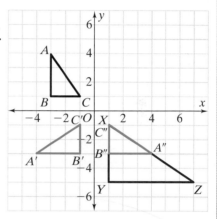

Roberto's Method

I can use the SAS Similarity Theorem to prove that the two triangles are similar.

$\angle B \cong \angle Y$ because they are right angles.

$\dfrac{AB}{BC} = \dfrac{3}{2}$ and $\dfrac{ZY}{YX} = \dfrac{6}{4} = \dfrac{3}{2}$.

So, $\triangle ABC$ is similar to $\triangle ZYX$ by the SAS Similarity Theorem.

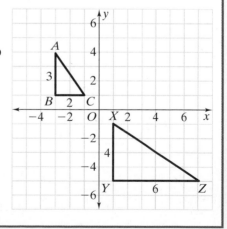

Choose a Method

Quadrilateral $QRST$ has vertices $Q(1,1)$, $R(3,1)$, $S(4,3)$, and $T(2,3)$. Quadrilateral $JKLM$ has vertices $J(-2,2)$, $K(-6,2)$, $L(-8,6)$, and $M(-4,6)$. Determine whether Quadrilateral $QRST$ is similar to Quadrilateral $JKLM$. Explain your reasoning.

1. **Reasoning** What type of transformation can change the size of a figure? Explain your reasoning.

Use the graph at the right. Identify each mapping as a translation, reflection, rotation, or dilation.

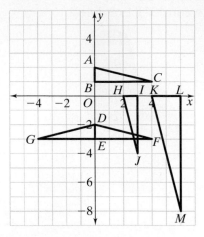

2. $\triangle ABC \rightarrow \triangle DEF$

3. $\triangle DEF \rightarrow \triangle DEG$

4. $\triangle DEG \rightarrow \triangle HIJ$

5. $\triangle HIJ \rightarrow \triangle KLM$

6. What sequence of transformations maps $\triangle ABC$ onto $\triangle KLM$?

Homework Exercises

For more exercises, see Extra Skills and Word Problems.

GO for Help

Exercise	See Examples
6–8	1
9–10	More Than One Way

7. You use a word-processing program to create invitations for a party. You decrease the font size from 32 to 16 points. Then you move the words from the left side to the center of the invitation. Describe the sequence of transformations that maps the original words onto their final size and placement.

The two figures in each diagram are similar. Describe the sequence of two transformations that maps the original figure onto the final image.

8.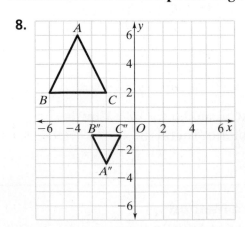

9.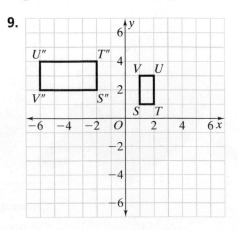

Determine whether the two figures are similar. If they are similar, describe a sequence of transformations that can be used to map one figure onto the other figure. If they are not similar, explain why.

10. Quadrilateral $ABCD$ with vertices $A(-1,1), B(-4,1), C(-4,3),$ and $D(-2,3);$ quadrilateral $JKLM$ with vertices $J(6,1), K(0,1), L(0,5),$ and $M(4,5)$

11. $\triangle DEF$ with vertices $D(0,0), E(-3,0),$ and $F(-3,6); \triangle PQR$ with vertices $P(0,0), Q(0,2),$ and $R(4,2)$

GPS 12. **Guided Problem Solving** Point $P''(-12,-9)$ is the image of point P after the following sequence of transformations: a reflection over the x-axis, followed by a dilation with a scale factor of 3 centered at $(0,0)$. What are the coordinates of point P?
- What do you need to do in order to find the coordinates of P'?
- What are the coordinates of P'?
- How does knowing the coordinates of P' help you find the coordinates of P?

13. A translation 6 units down followed by a dilation with scale factor $\frac{1}{2}$ maps $\triangle ABC$ onto $\triangle A''B''C''$. If $\overline{AB} = 8$ units, what is the length of $\overline{A''B''}$?

14. **Open Ended** Copy $\triangle ABC$.
    a. Describe a sequence of two different transformations in which the final image is *congruent* to $\triangle ABC$.
    b. Describe a sequence of two different transformations in which the final image is *similar*, but not congruent, to $\triangle ABC$.
    c. How are the sequences of transformations you described in parts (a) and (b) different?

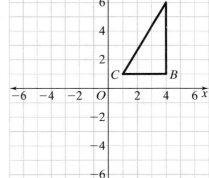

15. **Writing in Math** Does a 90° rotation about $(0,0)$, followed by a dilation with scale factor 2 centered at $(0,0)$ produce the same final image as a dilation with scale factor 2 centered at $(0,0)$ followed by a 90° rotation about $(0,0)$? Explain.

16. **Challenge** Is a dilation with a scale factor of 2, followed by a dilation with a scale factor of 3, the same as a single dilation with a scale factor of 5? Explain your reasoning.

Multiple Choice

17. Quadrilateral $ABCD$ is similar to quadrilateral $WXYZ$. $ABCD$ has vertices $A(2, 1)$, $B(6, 1)$, $C(6, 4)$, and $D(2, 4)$. $WXYZ$ has vertices $W(4, 2)$, $X(12, 2)$, $Y(12, 8)$, and $Z(4, 8)$. What is the scale factor of the dilation that maps $ABCD$ onto $WXYZ$?

   Ⓐ $\frac{1}{2}$

   Ⓑ $\frac{1}{4}$

   Ⓒ 2

   Ⓓ 4

18. The three parallelograms are congruent. Describe the sequence of transformations that maps $LMNP$ onto $L''M''N''P''$.

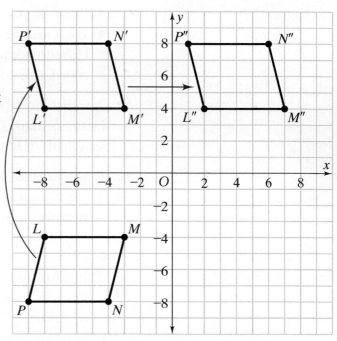

19. For every 3 runs that Margo's team scored during a softball game, Addison's team scored 4 runs. What additional information is needed to find the number of runs Margo's team scored?

   Ⓕ Addison's team's score

   Ⓖ The score after the first inning.

   Ⓗ The number of players on Margo's team

   Ⓙ The number of players on both teams

GO for Help

Exercise	See Lesson
20–24	11-1

Find the measure of the complement and supplement of each angle.

20. 37°   **21.** 74°   **22.** 83.2°   **23.** 47.1°   **24.** 5.8°

Transformations

Tourism Luz is visiting Salt Lake City. From her hotel near Pioneer Park, she walks 4 blocks north and 2 blocks east to the Utah Museum of Contemporary Art. Then she walks 5 blocks south and 3 blocks east to the Leonardo Museum. How many blocks is she from her hotel?

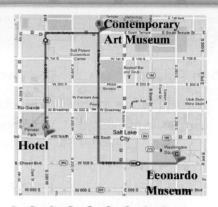

What You Might Think

(What do I know?)

(What am I trying to find out?)

(How do I show the main idea?)

(How do I calculate an answer?)

(What is the answer?)

What You Might Write

From her hotel, Luz walks 4 blocks north and 2 blocks east. Then she walks 5 blocks south and 3 blocks east.

How far is Luz from her hotel?

Draw and label a diagram of Luz's route. Use (0, 0) to represent Luz's hotel.

$(x, y) \rightarrow (x + 2, y + 4)$ represents a walk of 4 blocks north and 2 blocks east.

$(x, y) \rightarrow (x + 3, y - 5)$ represents a walk of 5 blocks south and 3 blocks east.

Luz's current position is the combination of the two translations.

$(0, 0)$ translates to $(0 + 2, 0 + 4)$, or $(2, 4)$. Then, $(2, 4)$ translates to $(2 + 3, 4 - 5)$, or $(5, -1)$.

Luz is 5 blocks east and 1 block south of her hotel.

Think It Through

1. **Error Analysis** Your friend says that the rule $(x, y) \rightarrow (x + 4, y + 2)$ represents a walk of 4 blocks north and 2 blocks east. Explain why your friend is incorrect.

2. Write a rule to represent Luz's current position relative to her hotel.

Exercises

Solve each problem. For Exercises 3 and 4, answers parts (a) and (b) first.

3. Tripp rides his bicycle 6 blocks south and 10 blocks west of a pizza shop to deliver a pizza. Then he rides 2 blocks north and 4 blocks east to make a second delivery. How many blocks is he now from the pizza shop?
   a. What do you know? What do you want to find out?
   b. Explain how the diagram below models the situation. Then calculate the answer.

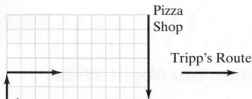

Pizza Shop

Tripp's Route

4. Elison uses a sequence of transformations to model a trail of her footprints in the snow. The quadrilateral with vertices $A(1,1)$, $B(1,2)$, $C(4,2)$, and $D(5,1)$ represents her first left footprint in the trail. A reflection over the x-axis, followed by a translation 5 units right, maps her first left footprint onto her first right footprint. What are the coordinates of the vertices of her first right footprint?
   a. What do you know? What do you want to find out?
   b. Explain how the diagram below models the situation. Then calculate the answer.

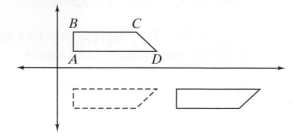

5. a. The word KICKBOX has a horizontal line of symmetry. Find two other words with a horizontal line of symmetry.
   b. The word TOMATO, when stacked vertically and upright, has a vertical line of symmetry. Find two other words that, when stacked vertically and upright, have a vertical line of symmetry.

   T
   O
   M
   A
   T
   O

6. Find a single transformation that has the same effect as the sequence of transformations.
   a. $(x,y) \rightarrow (x+3, y+5)$, followed by $(x,y) \rightarrow (x-4, y-3)$
   b. a rotation 90° about the origin, followed by another rotation 90° about the origin
   c. a dilation centered at $(0,0)$ with scale factor 4, followed by a dilation centered at $(0,0)$ with scale factor $\frac{1}{2}$

Answering the Question Asked

When answering a question, be sure to answer the question that is asked. Read the question carefully and identify the information you need to find. Eliminate answer choices that are not related to the question that is asked.

EXAMPLE

Quadrilateral *MATH* has vertices $M(1,1), A(3,1), T(2,3)$, and $H(1,3)$. What are the coordinates of the image of *T* after a reflection over the *x*-axis, followed by a translation 4 units left?

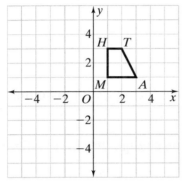

(A) $(-6,3)$ (B) $(6,-3)$ (C) $(2,-3)$ (D) $(-2,-3)$

Choice A gives the coordinates of the image of *T* after a reflection over the *y*-axis, followed by a translation 4 units left. Choice B gives the coordinates of the image of *T* after a reflection over the *x*-axis, followed by a translation 4 units right. Choice C gives the coordinates of the image of *T* after only a reflection over the *x*-axis. The correct answer is D.

Exercises

1. △*FUN* has vertices $F(-1,1), U(-2,4)$, and $N(-5,2)$. What are the coordinates of the image of *F* after a translation 5 units down, followed by a reflection over the *y*-axis?

    (A) $(-1,-4)$
    (B) $(-1,4)$
    (C) $(1,-4)$
    (D) $(1,1)$

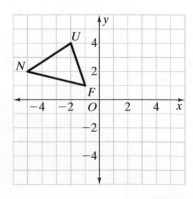

Vocabulary Review

angle of rotation (p. 505)
center of rotation (p. 505)
dilation (p. 517)
enlargement (p. 518)
image (p. 494)

line of reflection (p. 499)
line of symmetry (p. 500)
reduction (p. 518)
reflection (p. 499)
reflectional symmetry (p. 500)

rotation (p. 505)
rotational symmetry (p. 505)
scale factor (p. 517)
transformation (p. 494)
translation (p. 494)

Choose the correct vocabulary term(s) above to complete each sentence.

1. A(n) __?__ is a dilation with a scale factor less than one.

2. Three types of transformations that change the position of a figure are __?__, __?__, and __?__.

3. If a figure has a(n) __?__ of 180° or less for which its image matches the original figure, then the figure has __?__.

4. If a figure has a(n) __?__ that divides the figure into two mirror images, then the figure has __?__.

Go Online

For vocabulary quiz
PearsonSuccessNet.com

5. A __?__ is a transformation that can change the size of a figure.

Skills and Concepts

Lessons 13-1, 13-2, 13-3

- To graph and describe translations in the coordinate plane
- To graph reflections in the coordinate plane and to identify lines of symmetry
- To graph rotations and to identify rotational symmetry

A **transformation** is a change in the position, shape, or size of a figure. The figure you get after a transformation is called the **image.** You can transform figures in a plane by a **translation,** a **reflection,** or a **rotation.**

Copy △ABC for Exercises 6–8. Graph the image of △ABC after each transformation.

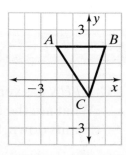

6. translation 2 units left and 1 unit up

7. translation 1 unit right and 3 units down

8. reflection over the x-axis

9. reflection over the y-axis

10. rotation of 90° about the origin

11. rotation of 180° about the origin

Lesson 13-4

- To describe a sequence of transformations that maps one figure onto another
- To determine whether two figures are congruent by using a sequence of transformations

If two figures are congruent, then a transformation, or a sequence of transformations, will map one figure onto the other. If you can use a sequence of transformations to map one figure onto another, then the two figures are congruent.

The three figures in each diagram are congruent. Describe the sequence of transformations that maps the original figure onto the final image.

12.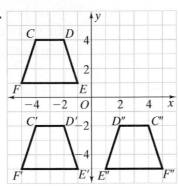

13.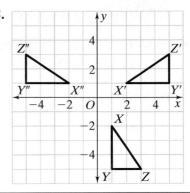

Lesson 13-5

- To graph dilations and to determine the scale factor of a dilation

A **dilation** is a transformation in which a figure and its image are similar. Every dilation has a center and a scale factor. The **scale factor** describes the change in size from the original figure to the image.

A dilation is an **enlargement** if the scale factor is greater than 1.
A dilation is a **reduction** if the scale factor is less than 1.

14. The blue figure is a dilation of the original figure. Find the scale factor and classify the dilation as an *enlargement* or a *reduction*.

Lesson 13-6

- To describe a sequence of transformations that maps one figure onto a figure that is similar
- To determine whether two figures are similar by using a sequence of transformations

If two figures are similar, but not congruent, then a dilation, or a dilation and a sequence of transformations, will map one figure onto the other. If you can use a sequence of transformations and a dilation to map one figure onto another, then the two figures are similar.

The three figures in each diagram are similar. Describe the sequence of transformations that maps the original figure onto the final image.

15.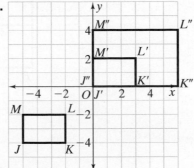

16.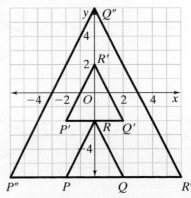

Go Online For online chapter test
PearsonSuccessNet.com

△*JKL* has vertices *J*(4, 5), *K*(6, 2), and *L*(3, 2).
Graph △*JKL* and its image after each
transformation.

1. translation 6 units left

2. translation 3 units left and 3 units down

3. reflection over the *y*-axis

4. reflection over the line through
   (1, −2) and (1, 2)

5. rotation of 90° about the origin

6. rotation of 180° about the origin

7. Write a rule to
   describe the
   translation at
   the right.

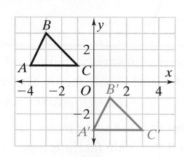

8. **Open-Ended** Draw and describe a figure that
   has exactly three lines of symmetry.

9. After a certain reflection, the image of
   P(3, −1) is *P*′(−1, −1). What are the
   coordinates of the image of *Q*(−2, 4) after the
   same reflection?

10. The three figures in the diagram are
    congruent. Describe the sequence of
    transformations that maps the original figure
    onto the final image.

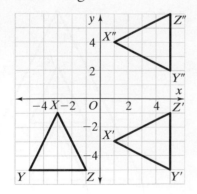

11. △*ABC* has vertices *A*(1, 2), *B*(4, 3) and
    C(−2, 5). Find the coordinates of the image
    of △*ABC* after a dilation with a scale
    factor of 3.

12. **Writing in Math** Suppose you know the
    coordinates of the vertices of a triangle.
    Explain how you would find the coordinates
    of the vertices of its image after a dilation with
    a scale factor of *r*.

13. Copy △*ABC* below. Draw the image of
    △*ABC* after a dilation with a scale factor of 2.

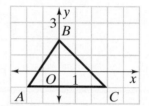

14. In the figure below, △*XBY* is the image of
    △*ABC* after a dilation. What is the
    scale factor?

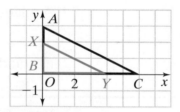

15. The three figures in the diagram are similar.
    Describe the sequence of transformations that
    maps the original figure onto the final image.

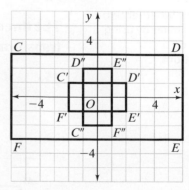

Multiple Choice

Read each question. Then write the letter of the correct answer on your paper.

1. In the diagram at the right, which two angles are adjacent angles?

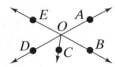

   (A) $\angle EOD, \angle DOC$ (C) $\angle AOE, \angle BOC$

   (B) $\angle BOC, \angle BOD$ (D) $\angle AOB, \angle EOD$

2. A circle has circumference 56.52 ft. What is its area? Use 3.14 for π.

   (F) 28.26 ft^2 (H) 254.34 ft^2

   (G) 56.52 ft^2 (J) 1,017.36 ft^2

3. What is the solution of the inequality $-4p < 36$?

   (A) $p > 9$ (C) $p > -9$

   (B) $p < -9$ (D) $p < 9$

4. What percent of the letters of the alphabet are the vowels a, e, i, o, and u?

   (F) about 15%   (H) about 30%

   (G) about 19%   (J) about 33%

5. What is the order of the numbers from least to greatest? $\frac{1}{8}, -0.18, 0.2, -\frac{2}{13}$

   (A) $-\frac{2}{13}, -0.18, \frac{1}{8}, 0.2$

   (B) $-0.18, -\frac{2}{13}, 0.2, \frac{1}{8}$

   (C) $-0.18, -\frac{2}{13}, \frac{1}{8}, 0.2$

   (D) $-\frac{2}{13}, 0.2, \frac{1}{8}, -0.18$

6. What is the solution of $\frac{x}{6} = \frac{20}{32}$?

   (F) 3   (G) 3.75   (H) 4.8   (J) 5

7. Which equation has the solution $x = 4$?

   (A) $x + 3 = -7$ (C) $x - 8 = 12$

   (B) $5 + x = 9$ (D) $1 + x = 3$

8. Shauna slices a cone vertically through both its vertex and a diameter of its base. What shape is the cross section?

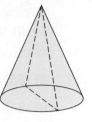

   (F) a triangle   (H) a circle

   (G) a rectangle   (J) a half circle

9. Rectangle $ABCD$ and rectangle $AXYZ$ are similar. How long is $\overline{XY}$?

   (A) 2.5 cm   (C) 1.6 cm

   (B) 2 cm   (D) 1.5 cm

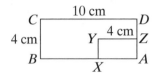

10. At the beginning of June, the level of water in a lake compared to normal is $-2\frac{1}{2}$ feet. During June the water level decreases by $3\frac{1}{4}$ feet. What is the water level of the lake compared to normal at the end of June?

   (F) $-\frac{3}{4}$ feet   (H) $-5\frac{1}{4}$ feet

   (G) $-1\frac{1}{4}$ feet   (J) $-5\frac{3}{4}$ feet

11. A diver's elevation is decreasing at a rate of 30 feet per minute. If the diver starts at sea level, what will her elevation be after 2.5 minutes?

   (A) -75 feet   (C) 12 feet

   (B) -12 feet   (D) 75 feet

12. Which expression is equal to 54?

   (F) $-3 \times 3 \times 6$ (H) $-3 \times 3 \times (-6)$

   (G) $3 \times 3 \times (-6)$ (J) $-3 \times (-3) \times (-6)$

13. The monthly bill for Ramon's cell phone increased by 8%. The new monthly bill is $59.40. What was the monthly bill before the price increase?

Ⓐ $51.00 Ⓒ $58.32

Ⓑ $55.00 Ⓓ $64.15

14. A contractor has built 8 new homes in the past 6 months. If her rate of building remains the same, which equation can be used to find n, the number of homes she will build in a 3-year period?

Ⓕ $\frac{8}{6} = \frac{36}{n}$ Ⓗ $\frac{6}{8} = \frac{n}{36}$

Ⓖ $\frac{8}{6} = \frac{n}{36}$ Ⓙ $\frac{8}{36} = \frac{n}{6}$

15. Which statement is true?

Ⓐ $1 < \sqrt{3} < 2$

Ⓑ $2 < \sqrt{3} < 3$

Ⓒ $3 < \sqrt{3} < 4$

Ⓓ $4 < \sqrt{3} < 5$

16. Which is closest to the volume of the cylinder?

Ⓕ 301.6 m^3

Ⓖ 251.3 m^3

Ⓗ 100.5 m^3

Ⓙ 75.4 m^3

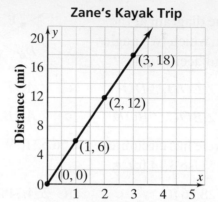

2 m

6 m

17. A cone is 5 inches wide and 6 inches tall. Which is closest to the surface area of the cone?

Ⓐ 201.1 in.^2 Ⓒ 70.7 in.^2

Ⓑ 157.1 in.^2 Ⓓ 39.3 in.^2

18. Point $T(2, 3)$ is rotated 90° about the origin. What are the coordinates of T'?

Ⓕ $(-3, 2)$ Ⓗ $(2, -3)$

Ⓖ $(-2, -3)$ Ⓙ $(3, -2)$

19. Which object is not an example of a prism?

Ⓐ a shoe box Ⓒ a domino

Ⓑ a file cabinet Ⓓ a soup can

Gridded Response

Use the graph below for Exercises 20 and 21. Zane is paddling a kayak down a river. The graph shows how far he travels over time.

Zane's Kayak Trip

20. What is the constant of proportionality of the relationship shown in the graph?

21. If Zane continues at the same speed, how many miles will he have traveled in 4 hours?

22. A farmer's field is shaped like a parallelogram. The base of the field is 4 times the height. What is the area of the field in square kilometers? Round to the nearest hundredth.

1.03 km

23. Sonya takes beads at random from a large bag of beads and threads them on a bracelet. Of the first 40 beads, 12 are red, 16 are white, and 12 are blue. What is the experimental probability, expressed as a decimal, that the next bead Sonya picks will be red?

24. What is $\frac{9}{20}$ written as a decimal?

25. What is the solution of the equation $x^3 = 216$?

26. How many dollars can you save on your grocery bill if you have 4 coupons, each for $1 off, and 2 coupons, each for $2 off?

27. The temperature outside is $-3°F$ and rising 3.4 degrees every hour. After 4 hours, what will be the temperature to the nearest tenth of a degree?

Short Response

28. Cards A through G are in a hat. You select a card at random. You select a second card without replacement. Find the probability that both cards are vowels. Show your work.

29. It costs $14 per hour to rent a paint sprayer plus a $40 delivery fee. Mr. Bolton rents a paint sprayer for 6 hours. He is charged $138. Was Mr. Bolton charged the correct amount? Support your answer by writing and solving an equation.

30. Fatima wants to know how long the volunteers at an animal shelter have been working there. She plans to sample 30 of the shelter's 140 volunteers. Describe a way that Fatima could choose her sample so that it is likely to be representative of the population.

31. Solve $x - 6 \geq -8$. Then graph the solution set.

32. Write 3 different expressions that are equivalent to $2(x + 8) + 5x - 10$.

33. Solve the equation $-3(n + 6) = 18$. Show your work, and justify each step.

34. Which has a greater volume: a cone with radius 2 cm and height 6 cm, or a cone with height 2 cm and radius 6 cm? Explain.

35. The graph shows the relationship between the number of miles driven x and the number of gallons y of gasoline left in the car's tank. Explain what the slope and y-intercept represent in this situation.

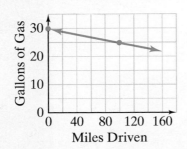

Extended Response

36. The box plots show the number of points scored per game by two college football teams in the 2011−2012 season.

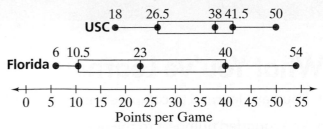

a. Determine the medians of the data sets.
b. Compare the medians and draw an inference about the teams.
c. Determine the IQRs of the data sets.
d. Compare the IQRs, and use the comparison to draw an inference about the teams.

37. a. Draw a net of the cylinder shown.

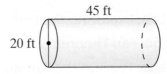

b. Find the surface area of the cylinder to the nearest tenth. Show your work.

38. You treat a friend to dinner. The cost of the food items from the menu totals $20.46. The sales tax on the food is 5%. You give a tip of 25% (before tax) for excellent service.
a. How much is the sales tax?
b. How much is the tip?
c. What is the total cost of the dinner?

39. Fifty students were surveyed about their favorite type of music.

   4 boys and 10 girls chose "Pop" music.

   10 boys and 9 girls chose "Country" music.

   5 boys and 2 girls chose "Rap" music.

   5 boys and 5 girls chose "Classical" music.

Is there evidence that Pop music is more popular with girls than Country music is? Use a two-way table. Show your work.

APPENDIX A
The Pythagorean Theorem

What You've Learned

- You have learned to compare and order positive rational numbers.
- You rounded numbers to the nearest integer, to the nearest tenth, and to the nearest hundredth.
- You divided decimals by whole numbers.
- You have found square roots of perfect squares, and you have solved equations involving square roots.

List of Lessons

Key Vocabulary

- Converse of the Pythagorean Theorem (p. 548)
- coordinate plane (p. 552)
- hypotenuse (p. 538)
- legs (p. 538)
- ordered pair (p. 552)
- origin (p. 552)
- Pythagorean Theorem (p. 538)
- quadrants (p. 552)
- Triangle Inequality Theorem (p. 547)
- x-axis (p. 552)
- x-coordinate (p. 552)
- y-axis (p. 552)
- y-coordinate (p. 552)

Exploring the Pythagorean Theorem

ACTIVITY

Step 1 Use centimeter grid paper to draw a right triangle. The right angle should be included between sides that are 3 cm and 4 cm long.

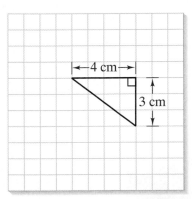

Step 2 Draw a 3-by-3 square along the side that is 3 cm long. Label the square A. Draw a 4-by-4 square along the side that is 4 cm long. Label the square B.

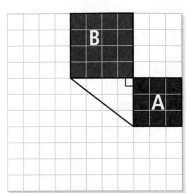

Step 3 Cut out another piece of grid paper to make a square on the side opposite the right angle. Label the square C.

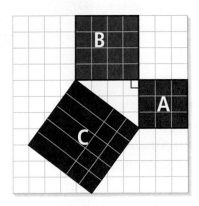

Exercises

1. a. Repeat the activity for the triangles shown in the table. Copy and complete the table.

b. Patterns What is the relationship between the areas of the two smaller squares (A and B) and the area of the largest square (C)?

2. (**Algebra**) Use variables to write an equation that relates the side lengths of a right triangle.

Sides of Triangle	Area of Square A	Area of Square B	Area of Square C
3, 4, 5	9	16	25
5, 12, ■	■	■	■
6, 8, ■	■	■	■
9, 12, ■	■	■	■

Check Skills You'll Need

1. **Vocabulary Review** What is the *square root* of a number?

Estimate the value of each expression to the nearest integer.

2. $\sqrt{60}$ 3. $\sqrt{111}$

4. $\sqrt{80}$ 5. $\sqrt{22}$

GO for Help
Lesson 1-9

What You'll Learn

To use the Pythagorean Theorem to find the length of the hypotenuse of a right triangle

New Vocabulary legs, hypotenuse, Pythagorean Theorem

Why Learn This?

The Pythagorean Theorem describes the special relationship among the sides of a right triangle. You can use the theorem to find the side lengths of right triangles in structures such as bridges.

In a right triangle, the two shortest sides are **legs.** The longest side, which is opposite the right angle, is the **hypotenuse.** The **Pythagorean Theorem** is an equation that shows the relationship between the legs and the hypotenuse.

KEY CONCEPTS **The Pythagorean Theorem**

In any right triangle, the sum of the squares of the lengths of the legs is equal to the square of the length of the hypotenuse.

$$a^2 + b^2 = c^2$$

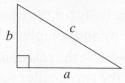

You can use the Pythagorean Theorem to find the length of the hypotenuse of a right triangle if you know the lengths of the two legs.

EXAMPLES **Finding the Hypotenuse**

① Find the length of the hypotenuse of the triangle.

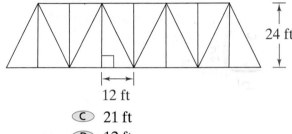

$a^2 + b^2 = c^2$ ← **Use the Pythagorean Theorem.**

$5^2 + 12^2 = c^2$ ← **Substitute 5 for *a* and 12 for *b*.**

$25 + 144 = c^2$ ← **Simplify.**

$169 = c^2$ ← **Add.**

$\sqrt{169} = \sqrt{c^2}$ ← **Find the positive square root of each side.**

$13 = c$ ← **Simplify.**

The length of the hypotenuse is 13 cm.

② **Multiple Choice** An architect drew the sketch of a bridge shown below. The bridge has 12-ft-long horizontal members and 24-ft-long vertical members. What is the length in feet of each diagonal member? Round to the nearest foot.

24 ft

12 ft

Ⓐ 720 ft   Ⓒ 21 ft

Ⓑ 27 ft   Ⓓ 12 ft

Each diagonal member is the hypotenuse of a right triangle.

$a^2 + b^2 = c^2$ ← **Use the Pythagorean Theorem.**

$12^2 + 24^2 = c^2$ ← **Substitute 12 for *a* and 24 for *b*.**

$144 + 576 = c^2$ ← **Simplify.**

$720 = c^2$ ← **Add.**

$\sqrt{720} = \sqrt{c^2}$ ← **Find the positive square root of each side.**

$\sqrt{}$ 720 $\boxed{=}$ 26.83281573 ← **Use a calculator.**

$27 \approx c$ ← **Simplify.**

The length of each diagonal member is about 27 ft. The answer is B.

Test Prep Tip
Draw and label a picture of a right triangle like the one below to match the problem situation.

24 ft | ?

12 ft

✓ Quick Check

1. Find the length of the hypotenuse of a right triangle with legs of 12 cm and 16 cm.

2. A bridge has 22-ft horizontal members and 25-ft vertical members. Find the length of each diagonal member to the nearest foot.

1. **Vocabulary** The side lengths of a right triangle are 5, 12, and 13. How do you know that the length of the hypotenuse is 13? Explain.

2. Fill in the blanks for each step to find the missing hypotenuse length of the triangle below.

   a. $12^2 + \blacksquare^2 = c^2$

   b. $\blacksquare + 256 = c^2$

   c. $\blacksquare = c^2$

   d. $\blacksquare = c$

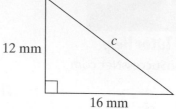

Homework Exercises

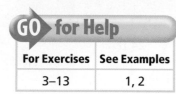

For Exercises	See Examples
3–13	1, 2

Find the length of the hypotenuse of each triangle. For Exercises 7–12, *a* and *b* represent the lengths of the two legs. If necessary, round to the nearest tenth.

3.
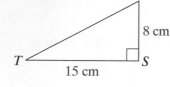

4.

5.
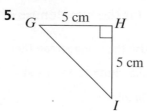

6.
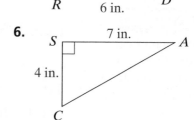

7. $a = 3, b = 4$

8. $a = 9, b = 12$

9. $a = 7, b = 24$

10. $a = 6, b = 5$

11. $a = 11, b = 14$

12. $a = 18, b = 22$

13. **Ramps** A ramp is 1 ft high. The base of the ramp extends 14 ft along the side of a building. How long is the sloped part of the ramp to the nearest hundredth of a foot?

14. **Guided Problem Solving** Find the perimeter of a right triangle with legs of 6 cm and 8 cm.
   - **Make a Plan** First use the Pythagorean Theorem to find the length of the hypotenuse. Then find the perimeter of the triangle.
   - **Carry Out the Plan** The hypotenuse is ▓ cm long. The perimeter of the triangle is ▓ cm.

15. **Television** A television is measured by the diagonal dimension of its screen. For example, a 24-in. television has a diagonal measure of 24 in.
   a. A television screen is 16 in. high and 22 in. wide. What is its diagonal dimension to the nearest integer?
   b. Find the dimensions of a television screen with the same diagonal measure as the one in part (a), but with a different height and width.

The legs of a right triangle are equal. Given the length of the legs, find the length of the hypotenuse. Round to the nearest tenth.

16. 5 cm   17. 2 cm   18. 10 in.   19. 12 m

20. Two hikers start a trip from a camp walking 1.5 km due east. They turn due north and walk 1.7 km to a waterfall. To the nearest tenth of a kilometer, how far is the waterfall from the camp?

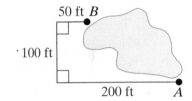

21. **Writing in Math** Explain how you would find the distance AB across the lake at the right. Then find AB to the nearest foot.

22. **Reasoning** If $\sqrt{w}$ is an integer, how many values of w are between 20 and 120?

23. (**Algebra**) Is $m = 3$ a solution to $m^2 + (m + 1)^2 = (m + 2)^2$?

24. **Challenge** The sum of the squares of the lengths of all three sides of a right triangle is 200. What is the length of the hypotenuse?

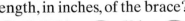
Test Prep and Mixed Review   **Practice**

Multiple Choice

25. A carpenter is attaching a brace to the back of the frame shown at the right. What is the length, in inches, of the brace?
   Ⓐ 2,500 in. Ⓑ 50 in. Ⓒ 26.5 in. Ⓓ 10 in.

30 in.   Brace   40 in.

26. Nicole makes 15 free throws. She attempts a total of 24 free throws. What decimal represents the portion of free throws that Nicole does NOT make?
   Ⓕ 0.375 Ⓖ $0.\overline{375}$ Ⓗ 0.625 Ⓙ $0.\overline{625}$

27. A cube-shaped packing box has a side length of 7 inches. What is the volume of the packing box?
   Ⓐ 14 cubic inches   Ⓒ 49 cubic inches
   Ⓑ 21 cubic inches   Ⓓ 343 cubic inches

GO for Help

For Exercises	See Lesson
28–31	1-10

Solve each equation by finding the value of x.

28. $x^3 = 729$ 29. $x^3 = -512$ 30. $x^3 = \dfrac{1}{1,000}$ 31. $x^3 = \dfrac{343}{512}$

Proving the Pythagorean Theorem

A proof is a series of logical steps that leads from given information to the statement that is being proven. You can write a proof of the Pythagorean Theorem.

ACTIVITY

1. Write an algebraic expression for the area of the large red square.

2. Trace and cut out the pieces of the large red square. Rearrange the pieces to cover exactly the green and blue square. How do the areas compare?

3. What is the side length of the green square? The blue square?

4. Write an algebraic expression for the area of the figure composed of the green and blue squares.

5. Write an equation relating the area of the blue figure to the area of the large red square. What do you notice about the equation?

6. Summarize your findings. How does this relate to the Pythagorean Theorem?

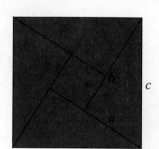

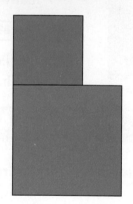

Exercise

1. The two squares below represent another proof of the Pythagorean Theorem. Explain the proof.

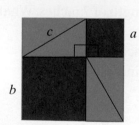 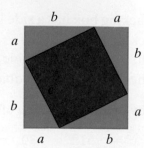

Check Skills You'll Need

1. **Vocabulary Review**
State the
*Pythagorean
Theorem.*

Find the length of the hypotenuse given the lengths of the two legs, *a* and *b*. Round to the nearest tenth.

2. $a = 3, b = 4$

3. $a = 7, b = 5$

 **for Help**

Lesson A-1

What You'll Learn

To use the Pythagorean Theorem to find missing measurements of triangles

Why Learn This?

You can use the Pythagorean Theorem to find distances without measuring, including distances in space.

When you know the length of one leg and the hypotenuse of a right triangle, you can use the Pythagorean Theorem to find the length of the other leg.

EXAMPLE   Finding a Leg of a Right Triangle

1   Find the missing leg length of the triangle below.

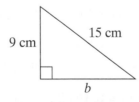

9 cm   15 cm

b

$a^2 + b^2 = c^2$ ← Use the Pythagorean Theorem.

$9^2 + b^2 = 15^2$ ← Substitute 9 for *a* and 15 for *c*.

$81 + b^2 = 225$ ← Simplify.

$b^2 = 144$ ← Subtract 81 from each side.

$\sqrt{b^2} = \sqrt{144}$ ← Find the positive square root of each side.

$b = 12$ ← Simplify.

The length of the other leg is 12 cm.

✓ Quick Check

1. The hypotenuse of a right triangle is 20.2 ft long. One leg is 12.6 ft long. Find the length of the other leg to the nearest tenth.

You can substitute the known leg length for either a or b in the Pythagorean Theorem.

EXAMPLE **Application: Satellites**

2 Multiple Choice Satellites that relay television signals to Earth cruise at a distance of about 22,200 miles above Earth's surface. The radius of Earth is about 4,000 miles. Find the distance a from the satellite to point T in the diagram below. Round to the nearest hundred miles.

  Ⓐ 670,440 mi
  Ⓑ 26,000 mi
  Ⓒ 25,900 mi
  Ⓓ 22,500 mi

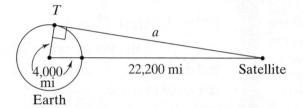

The diagram above shows a right triangle with a hypotenuse of 22,200 miles + 4,000 miles, or 26,200 miles. The length of the known leg is 4,000 miles. The variable a represents the length of the other leg.

$$a^2 + b^2 = c^2$$ ← Use the Pythagorean Theorem.
$$a^2 + 4{,}000^2 = 26{,}200^2$$ ← Substitute 4,000 for b and 26,200 for c.
$$a^2 + 16{,}000{,}000 = 686{,}440{,}000$$ ← Find $4{,}000^2$ and $26{,}200^2$.
$$a^2 = 670{,}440{,}000$$ ← Subtract 16,000,000 from each side.
$$\sqrt{a^2} = \sqrt{670{,}440{,}000}$$ ← Find the positive square root of each side.

$\sqrt{}$ 670,440,000 $\boxed{=}$ *25892.85616* ← Use a calculator.
$$a \approx 25{,}900$$ ← Round to the nearest hundred.

The distance from the satellite to the horizon is about 25,900 mi. The answer is C.

✔ Quick Check

2. **Construction** The bottom of an 18-ft ladder is 5 ft from the side of a house. Find the distance from the top of the ladder to the ground. Round to the nearest tenth of a foot.

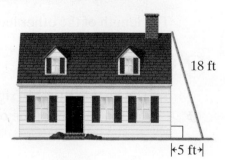

18 ft

⊢5 ft⊣

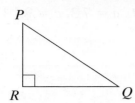

1. **Vocabulary** Name the two legs and the hypotenuse of the triangle at the left.

2. Fill in the blanks for each step to find the missing leg length of the triangle below.

   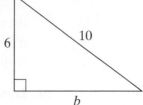

   a. $6^2 + b^2 = \blacksquare^2$

   b. $\blacksquare + b^2 = 100$

   c. $b^2 = \blacksquare$

   d. $b = \blacksquare$

Homework Exercises

GO for Help

For Exercises	See Examples
3–13	1, 2

Find the missing leg length. For Exercises 7–12, a and b represent leg lengths and c represents the length of the hypotenuse. If necessary, round to the nearest tenth.

3.

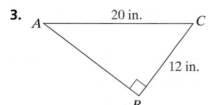

4.

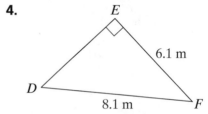

5.

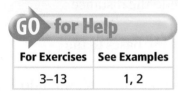

6.

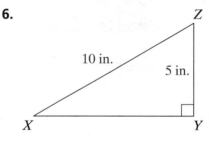

7. $a = 5, c = 12$ 8. $a = 7, c = 25$ 9. $b = 10.5, c = 20.1$

10. $a = 3.4, c = 6.7$ 11. $b = 8.3, c = 16.9$ 12. $b = 11, c = 15$

13. A 10-ft-long slide is attached to a deck that is 5 ft high. Find the distance from the bottom of the deck to the bottom of the slide to the nearest tenth.

14. **Guided Problem Solving** A computer screen has a diagonal length of 17 in. and a height of 9 in. To the nearest tenth of an inch, what is the area of the screen?
    • To the nearest tenth, what is the width of the computer screen?
    • What is the formula for the area of a rectangle?

Use the formula $A = \frac{1}{2}bh$ to find the area of a right triangle with a leg of length a and hypotenuse of length c.

15. $a = 4$, $c = 5$ **16.** $a = 8.6$, $c = 10$ **17.** $a = 7.3$, $c = 9.1$

18. Diving A diver swims 20 m under water to the anchor of a buoy that is 10 m below the surface of the water. On the surface, how far is the buoy located from the place where the diver started? Round to the nearest meter.

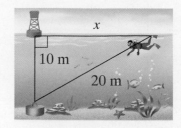

19. Error Analysis One leg of a right triangle is 3 cm and the hypotenuse is 4 cm. A student evaluates $\sqrt{3^2 + 4^2}$ to find the length of the other leg. What error did the student make?

20. The distance from home plate to second base is about 127.3 ft.

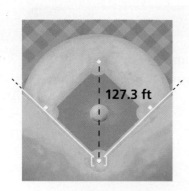

127.3 ft

a. **Writing in Math** Explain how you would find the distance between the bases.

b. **Estimation** Estimate the distance between the bases to the nearest foot.

c. When you hit a home run, you run around all the bases. How far do you run?

21. Challenge The sides of a right triangle are labelled a, b, and c. Can $a + b = c$? Explain.

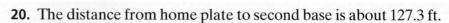
Test Prep and Mixed Review   **Practice**

Multiple Choice   **22.** The top of a badminton net is 5 feet high. Ropes connect the top of each pole to stakes in the ground. The ropes are 8.5 feet long. Which is closest to the distance from a stake to the base of a pole?

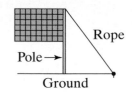
Rope
Pole →
Ground

     Ⓐ 4 ft   Ⓑ 7 ft   Ⓒ 9 ft   Ⓓ 15 ft

23. Which integer is closest to $\sqrt{10}$?

     Ⓕ 2   Ⓖ 3   Ⓗ 4   Ⓙ 5

24. A park has a walking path shaped like a right triangle. Its legs are 50 yards and 120 yards long. What is the total length of the path, in yards?

     Ⓐ 130 yd   Ⓑ 255 yd   Ⓒ 300 yd   Ⓓ 340 yd

GO **for Help**

For Exercises	See Lesson
25–28	1-9

Compare. Use $<$, $>$, or $=$.

25. $\sqrt{24}$ ▧ 5.1   **26.** 6.9 ▧ $\sqrt{37}$ **27.** $\sqrt{56}$ ▧ 8   **28.** 12.1 ▧ $\sqrt{120}$

Converse of the Pythagorean Theorem

Check Skills You'll Need

1. **Vocabulary Review**
   In a right triangle, the length of a __?__ cannot be longer than the length of the __?__.

Find the missing leg length *b* given one leg length *a* and the length of the hypotenuse *c*. Round to the nearest tenth.

2. $a = 6, c = 10$
3. $a = 9, c = 15$

for Help
Lesson A-2

What You'll Learn

To solve problems using the Triangle Inequality Theorem and the Converse of the Pythagorean Theorem

New Vocabulary Triangle Inequality Theorem, Converse of the Pythagorean Theorem

Why Learn This?

You can use the Converse of the Pythagorean Theorem to determine if a triangle is a right triangle.

Notice that the segments on the left below do *not* form a triangle. The segments on the right below do form a triangle. The lengths of three segments must be related in a special way in order to form a triangle.

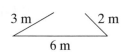
3 m   2 m
6 m

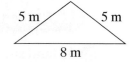
5 m   5 m
8 m

KEY CONCEPTS   **Triangle Inequality Theorem**

The sum of the lengths of any two sides of a triangle is greater than the length of the third side.

EXAMPLE   **Using the Triangle Inequality Theorem**

1 Is it possible to construct a triangle with the given side lengths? Explain.
   a. 6 cm, 5 cm, 4 cm

$4 + 5 > 6$ ✔
$5 + 6 > 4$ ✔
$4 + 6 > 5$ ✔

Yes. The sum of any two lengths is greater than the third length.

   b. 7 mi, 15 mi, 6 mi

$6 + 15 > 7$ ✔
$15 + 7 > 6$ ✔
$7 + 6 > 15$ ✗

No. The sum of 7 and 6 is *not* greater than 15.

Quick Check

1. Is it possible to construct a triangle with the given side lengths? Explain.
   a. 6 mi, 10 mi, 20 mi   **b.** 1.5 m, 2.5 m, 3.5 m

If the equation $a^2 + b^2 = c^2$ is true for the lengths of the sides of a triangle, then the triangle is a right triangle. This method is called the **Converse of the Pythagorean Theorem**. You can use the Converse of the Pythagorean Theorem to determine if a triangle is a right triangle.

EXAMPLE Identifying a Right Triangle

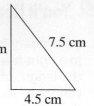

2 Determine whether the triangle is a right triangle. Explain.

$$a^2 + b^2 \stackrel{?}{=} c^2$$ **Use the Pythagorean Theorem.**

$$6^2 + 4.5^2 \stackrel{?}{=} 7.5^2$$ **Substitute 6 for a, 4.5 for b, and 7.5 for c.**

$$36 + 20.25 \stackrel{?}{=} 56.25$$ **Simplify. Use a calculator.**

$$56.25 = 56.25$$

7.5 cm

6 cm

4.5 cm

Vocabulary Tip

When using the Converse of the Pythagorean Theorem, substitute the greatest side length for c.

The equation is true, so the triangle is a right triangle.

✓ Quick Check

2. Determine whether the given lengths can be side lengths of a right triangle. Explain.
   a. 10 in., 24 in., 26 in.   b. 8 cm, 9 cm, 12 cm

EXAMPLE Application: Surveying

3 A land surveyor determines that a triangular plot of land has boundary lines that are 400 yd, 600 yd, and 720 yd in length. The 400-yd boundary line runs east-west. Determine whether either of the other two boundary lines runs north-south.

If either of the other two boundary lines runs north-south, then the boundary lines must form a right triangle. So use the Converse of the Pythagorean Theorem.

$$a^2 + b^2 \stackrel{?}{=} c^2$$ **Use the Pythagorean Theorem.**

$$400^2 + 600^2 \stackrel{?}{=} 720^2$$ **Substitute 400 for a, 600 for b, and 720 for c.**

$$160{,}000 + 360{,}000 \stackrel{?}{=} 518{,}400$$ **Simplify.**

$$520{,}000 \neq 518{,}400$$

The equation is not true, so the boundary lines do not form a right triangle. Neither of the other two boundary lines runs north-south.

✓ Quick Check

3. A triangular field has boundary lines that are 40 yd, 75 yd, and 85 yd long. Determine whether the boundary lines form a right triangle. Explain.

1. **Vocabulary** How is the Triangle Inequality Theorem different from the Converse of the Pythagorean Theorem?

Three lengths are given. Use the inequality that follows to determine if it is possible to construct a triangle with the lengths. Explain.

2. 3 ft, 6 ft, 8 ft
$3 + 6 \overset{?}{>} 8$

3. 7 in., 8 in., 15 in.
$7 + 8 \overset{?}{>} 15$

4. 0.5 m, 2.5 m, 4 m
$0.5 + 2.5 \overset{?}{>} 4$

The lengths of the sides of a triangle are given. Use the equation that follows to determine whether the triangle is a right triangle. Explain.

5. 6 yd, 8 yd, 10 yd
$6^2 + 8^2 \overset{?}{=} 10^2$

6. 16 cm, 63 cm, 65 cm
$16^2 + 63^2 \overset{?}{=} 65^2$

7. 8 m, 24 m, 25 m
$8^2 + 24^2 \overset{?}{=} 25^2$

8. The sides of a triangular weather flag are 49.6 in., 49.6 in., and 25 in. in length. Is the flag in the shape of a right triangle? Explain.

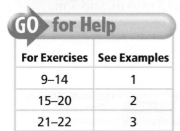

GO for Help

For Exercises	See Examples
9–14	1
15–20	2
21–22	3

Is it possible to construct a triangle with the given side lengths? Explain.

9. 2 ft, 4 ft, 7 ft

10. 1 in., 5 in., 6 in.

11. 15 m, 25 m, 35 m

12. 3.8 ft, 5.2 ft, 8.5 ft

13. $\frac{2}{3}$ in., $4\frac{2}{3}$ in., 5 in.

14. 22 m, 44 m, 66 m

Determine whether the given lengths can be side lengths of a right triangle. Explain.

15. 12 m, 16 m, 20 m

16. 8 in., 31.5 in., 32.5 in.

17. 10 yd, 12 yd, 16 yd

18. 5 cm, 13 cm, 14 cm

19. 8 ft, 15 ft, 17 ft

20. 7 mi, 24 mi, 26 mi

21. The three streets shown at the right intersect to form a triangle. Do the streets form a right triangle? Explain your reasoning.

22. The front view of an A-frame house is a triangle. The lengths of its sides are 39 ft, 39 ft, and 28 ft. Is the front view of the house in the shape of a right triangle? Explain.

23. Guided Problem Solving The lengths of two sides of a triangle are 5 in. and 7 in. What is the range of possible lengths of the third side x of the triangle?
- How can you use the Triangle Inequality Theorem to find the least possible length for the third side?
- How can you use the Triangle Inequality Theorem to find the greatest possible length for the third side?

GO Online
Homework Video Tutor
PearsonSuccessNet.com

24. <u>**Writing in Math**</u> Two sides of a right triangle measure 5 in. and 12 in. Why is this not enough information to find the length of the third side of the triangle?

25. Measurement Copy the triangle at the right. Use a ruler to test the Triangle Inequality Theorem.

26. Number Sense How do you know that a triangle with side lengths $\sqrt{1}$, $\sqrt{2}$, and $\sqrt{3}$ is a right triangle? Explain.

27. Challenge You can use the squares of the lengths of the sides of a triangle to find whether the triangle is acute or obtuse.

If $a^2 + b^2 < c^2$, then the triangle is obtuse.
If $a^2 + b^2 > c^2$, then the triangle is acute.

Vocabulary Tip

An *obtuse triangle* has one obtuse angle. An *acute triangle* has three acute angles.

In both cases, c represents the length of the longest side of the triangle. The lengths of the sides of a triangle are 5 m, 6 m, and 7 m. Is the triangle *acute*, *right*, or *obtuse*? Explain.

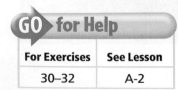
Test Prep and Mixed Review **Practice**

Multiple Choice

28. Which set of lengths could NOT represent the side lengths of a right triangle?
- Ⓐ 18 yd, 24 yd, 30 yd
- Ⓒ 7 yd, 24 yd, 25 yd
- Ⓑ 13 yd, 14 yd, 15 yd
- Ⓓ 15 yd, 36 yd, 39 yd

29. A 12-ft ladder leans against the side of a house. The ratio of the length of the ladder to the space between the bottom of the ladder and the house is 4 : 1. To the nearest tenth of a foot, what is the distance from the top of the ladder to the ground?
- Ⓕ 15.0 ft
- Ⓖ 12.4 ft
- Ⓗ 11.6 ft
- Ⓙ 9.0 ft

GO for Help

For Exercises	See Lesson
30–32	A-2

The lengths of two sides of a right triangle are given; a and b represent the lengths of the legs, and c represents the length of the hypotenuse. Find the missing side length.

30. $a = 20, b = 21$ **31.** $a = 13, c = 85$ **32.** $b = 14, c = 50$

Proving the Converse of the Pythagorean Theorem

You can write a proof of the Converse of the Pythagorean Theorem.

ACTIVITY

In $\triangle ABC$, $a^2 + b^2 = c^2$. Triangle DEF is a right triangle as shown.

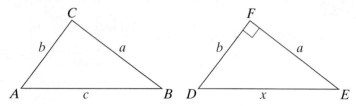

1. Write an equation relating the side lengths of $\triangle DEF$.

2. Use the equation for $\triangle ABC$ and your equation for $\triangle DEF$ to write an equation relating c and x.

3. If all three sides of a triangle are the same length as all three sides of another triangle, then the angles of the triangles are congruent. Use this fact to identify congruent angles in $\triangle ABC$ and $\triangle DEF$.

4. Classify $\triangle ABC$.

5. Summarize your findings to explain a proof of the Converse of the Pythagorean Theorem.

Exercises

1. Construct a triangle with side lengths of 3 cm, 4 cm, and 5 cm; another triangle with side lengths of 6 cm, 8 cm, and 10 cm; and a third triangle with side lengths of 5 cm, 12 cm, and 13 cm. Measure the angles of each triangle with a protractor. How are the side lengths and angle measures related?

2. Is it possible for a triangle that is *not* a right triangle to have side lengths that satisfy the Pythagorean equation? Why or why not?

3. How is the Pythagorean equation used in the proof of the Converse of the Pythagorean Theorem?

4. Some historians believe that the ancient Egyptians used a rope with knots tied at 12 equal intervals to help reconstruct boundaries that were washed out by the annual flooding of the Nile River. Explain how you could use this type of rope to form a right triangle.

Distance in the Coordinate Plane

Check Skills You'll Need

1. **Vocabulary Review** In the Pythagorean equation $a^2 + b^2 = c^2$, what do the variables a, b, and c represent?

Solve each equation for c by finding the positive square root of each side. If necessary, round to the nearest tenth.

2. $c^2 = 64$

3. $c^2 = 36$

4. $c^2 = 28$

5. $c^2 = 40$

 **for Help**
Lesson A-1

What You'll Learn

To graph points and to use the Pythagorean Theorem to find distances in the coordinate plane

New Vocabulary coordinate plane, y-axis, x-axis, quadrants, origin, ordered pair, x-coordinate, y-coordinate

Why Learn This?

Mapmakers use a coordinate grid system for maps. The coordinate plane is another type of grid system.

A **coordinate plane** is a grid formed by the intersection of two number lines. You can use a coordinate plane to locate and name points.

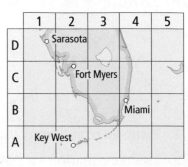

The **y-axis** is a vertical number line.

The **x-axis** is a horizontal number line.

The axes divide the plane into four **quadrants.**

O indicates the **origin,** where the axes intersect.

An **ordered pair** (x, y) gives the coordinates of the location of a point. In the graph above, point A has coordinates $(2, -4)$.

$$(2, -4)$$

The **x-coordinate** tells the number of horizontal units a point is from the origin.

The **y-coordinate** tells the number of vertical units a point is from the origin.

You can graph a point when you know its coordinates.

You can use the Pythagorean Theorem to find distances in the coordinate plane.

Finding Distance on a Coordinate Plane

① Find the distance between $C\,(2,2)$ and $D\,(6,5)$.

Graph C and D on a coordinate plane. Notice you can draw a right triangle by drawing a vertical segment down from D and a horizontal segment over from C. The point of intersection is $(6,2)$.

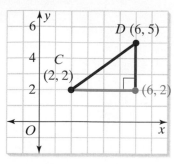

Subtract the x-coordinates to find the length of the horizontal leg. Subtract the y-coordinates to find the length of the vertical leg.

horizontal leg: $6 - 2 = 4$
vertical leg: $5 - 2 = 3$

Use the Pythagorean Theorem to find the distance between C and D.

$a^2 + b^2 = c^2$	**Pythagorean Theorem.**
$4^2 + 3^2 = c^2$	**Substitute.**
$16 + 9 = c^2$	**Simplify.**
$25 = c^2$	**Add.**
$\sqrt{25} = \sqrt{c^2}$	**Find the positive square root of each side.**
$5 = c$	

The distance between $C\,(2,2)$ and $D\,(6,5)$ is 5 units.

② **Multiple Choice** The library is 5 miles north of your house. The post office is 6 miles east of your house. To the nearest mile, how far is the library from the post office?

   Ⓐ 7 mi   Ⓑ 8 mi   Ⓒ 9 mi   Ⓓ 10 mi

Graph the three locations. Place your home at the origin. Draw a right triangle.

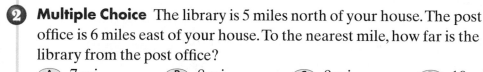

$a^2 + b^2 = c^2$	← **Pythagorean Theorem.**
$5^2 + 6^2 = c^2$	← **Substitute.**
$25 + 36 = c^2$	← **Simplify.**
$61 = c^2$	← **Add.**
$\sqrt{61} = \sqrt{c^2}$	← **Find the positive square root of each side.**
✓ 61 ▤ 7.8102496 76	← **Use a calculator.**
$c \approx 8$	

The answer is B.

✔ Quick Check

1. Find the distance between $(2,1)$ and $(7,9)$. Round to the nearest tenth.
2. Your school is 3 miles south of your house. The park is 5 miles east of your school. To the nearest mile, how far is your house from the park?

Vocabulary Match each ordered pair with the appropriate quadrant.

1. $(-4, 2)$

2. $(3, 5)$

3. $(12, -6)$

4. $(-7, -1)$

A. Quadrant I
B. Quadrant II
C. Quadrant III
D. Quadrant IV

Find the lengths of the horizontal and vertical legs of a right triangle that can be formed with the given segment as its hypotenuse.

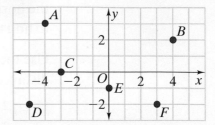

5. $\overline{AE}$ 6. $\overline{CF}$ 7. $\overline{ED}$

Homework Exercises

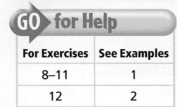

For Exercises	See Examples
8–11	1
12	2

Find the distance between each pair of points. If necessary, round to the nearest tenth.

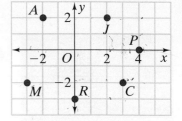

8. $(3, -2)$ and $(0, -3)$

9. $(-3, -2)$ and $(4, 0)$

10. $(4, 0)$ and $(-2, 2)$

11. $(3, -2)$ and $(-2, 2)$

12. **Softball** A softball diamond has the shape of a square. The distance from home plate to second base is about 85 ft. Find the distance a player would run going from first base to second base.

13. **Guided Problem Solving** Find the length of the hypotenuse to the nearest tenth.

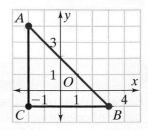

- The length of $\overline{AC}$ is ▮ units.
- The length of $\overline{BC}$ is ▮ units.
- Using the Pythagorean Theorem, the length of $\overline{AB}$ is the square root of ▮^{2} + ▮^{2}.

14. **a.** Graph each of these points on a coordinate plane:

$(-2, -2)$, $(-5, 3)$, $(-3, 3)$, $(-1, 0)$, $(1, 3)$, $(3, 3)$, $(0, -2)$, $(0, -7)$, $(-2, -7)$, $(-2, -2)$.

b. Connect the points in order and describe the figure formed.

15. On a graph, the points $(4, -2)$, $(7, -2)$, $(9, -5)$, and $(2, -5)$ are connected in order to form a trapezoid. To the nearest tenth, what is its perimeter?

16. Geography Degrees of longitude and latitude indicate locations on a map. The longitude of Chicago is about 88° W, and the latitude is about 42° N. Estimate the longitude and latitude of St. Paul and Lincoln.

In which quadrant is each point located?

17. (x, y) if $x > 0$ and $y < 0$

18. (x, y) if $x > 0$ and $y > 0$

19. Writing in Math Use coordinates to write directions that will get the mouse to the cheese in the maze at the right.

20. Challenge Graph and connect the points $(3, 2)$, $(-2, 2)$, $(-2, 7)$, $(3, 7)$, and $(3, 2)$ in order. Then graph and connect the points $(3, -2)$, $(-2, -2)$, $(-2, -7)$, $(3, -7)$, and $(3, -2)$ in order. How are these two figures related?

Test Prep and Mixed Review
Practice

Multiple Choice

21. The route of a cycling race is in the shape of a right triangle with vertices formed by the towns of Springfield, Jackson, and Troy. Springfield is 8 miles south of Jackson. Troy is 10 miles west of Springfield. To the nearest mile, what is the total length of the route?

  (A) 13 mi   (B) 18 mi   (C) 30 mi   (D) 31 mi

22. Which set of lengths could NOT be the side lengths of a right triangle?

  (F) 12 in., 16 in., 20 in.   (H) 30 m, 16 m, 34 m

  (G) 9 yd, 40 yd, 41 yd   (J) 10 mi, 24 mi, 25 mi

23. Sarah walks across a rectangular field as shown. Which is the closest to the distance she walks?

  (A) 100 ft   (C) 70 ft

  (B) 90 ft   (D) 50 ft

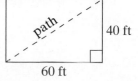

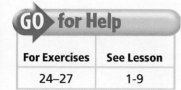

Find each square root. If necessary, round to the nearest tenth.

24. $\sqrt{50}$ **25.** $-\sqrt{\frac{1}{6}}$ **26.** $\sqrt{7}$ **27.** $\sqrt{0.18}$

Chapter Projects

HOME COURT ADVANTAGE

Chapter 1 Integers and Rational Numbers

In Malcolm's daydream, he floats in the air on his way to a slam dunk. In reality, he tosses pieces of paper into a wastebasket. He makes some shots, and he misses others.

Compare Basketball Statistics Your project will be to record and compare baskets attempted and baskets made by the players on your own imaginary basketball team. You can shoot baskets with a real basketball on a real court, or you can toss pieces of paper into a wastebasket. Write your results as rational numbers. How did you do? Compare results with a classmate.

Go Online

For information to help you complete your project
PearsonSuccessNet.com

One Small STEP

Chapter 2 Exponents

"That's one small step for man, one giant leap for mankind." In July of 1969, Neil Armstrong was the first man to touch the moon's surface. Today, many space mission advocates consider the moon to be the best launch pad for getting to Mars. Would you want to be stationed on the Mars colony? Or, would you prefer one of Jupiter's moons?

Can you even imagine what the space program will be like in 30 more years? How about in 100 years? Take a small step into the future. Pretend you are a travel agent— one who specializes in space travel!

Create a brochure For the chapter project, you will collect information about two planets, including travel between them, and calculate the approximate distance from Earth to each of them. Your final project will be to design a space-travel brochure that includes interesting and enticing information about travel between the two planets.

Go Online

For information to help you complete your project
PearsonSuccessNet.com

READ ALL ABOUT IT!

READ ALL ABOUT IT!

Flexible hours! Great pay! Work before or after school! Newspaper deliverers needed! Suppose to earn extra money you get a job delivering newspapers in your neighborhood. You plan to save the money you make so that you can buy yourself brand new snow skiing gear.

Chapter 3 Equations

Make a Savings Plan For this project, figure out how many hours you can commit to your job, how much money you can earn per week, and how much money you need to make per week in order to reach your savings goal. As part of your final project, you will write a letter to your boss at the newspaper office describing your level of commitment as a newspaper deliverer.

Go Online

For information to help you complete your project
PearsonSuccessNet.com

WORKING for a Cause

Have you ever participated in a fundraiser? Schools and sports clubs often use fundraisers as a way to pay for such things as equipment, trips, and camps. You have probably purchased candy bars, magazines, or wrapping paper to help a friend or group raise money.

Chapter 4 Inequalities

Plan a Fundraiser In this chapter project, you will plan a fundraiser. You will choose a cause or charity, decide how much money you would like to raise, and determine the type of event to hold or the type of product to sell. As part of your final project, you will present to your class a comparison of different fundraising plans, how they compare to your goals, and your final plan.

Go Online

For information to help you complete your project
PearsonSuccessNet.com

Weighty Matters

Have you ever loved a pet so much that you wanted a statue made of it? Imagine a statue of your pet on the front steps of your home. "Gee, what a wise way to spend hard-earned money," your admiring neighbors would say. Or maybe not. In addition to being expensive, these statues would also be heavy. For instance, a 35-lb dog cast in gold would weigh about 670 lb.

Chapter 5 *Ratios, Rates, and Proportions*

Using Specific Gravity For the chapter project, you will find the weight of different animals and the weight of different metals. Your final project will be a table of animals with their weights, the weight of their statues in different materials, and the cost of the statues.

Go Online

For information to help you complete your project
PearsonSuccessNet.com

chills and thrills

Your world is spinning. You are screaming. And you are loving every minute of it! Even though you are scared, you know that you will come to a safe stop at the end of the ride.

A successful amusement park attraction must be both fun and safe. Planners of amusement parks use a lot of math to create thrills but avoid any spills.

Chapter 6 *Percents*

Take a Survey For the chapter project, you will decide which rides are most likely to be most popular. Your final product will be a recommendation about which rides to include in a proposed amusement park for your town.

Go Online

For information to help you complete your project
PearsonSuccessNet.com

Larger Than Life

Mount Rushmore is an example of a scale model that is larger than the objects on which it is based—much larger! Other types of scale models, such as toy trains, dollhouses, and other toys, are smaller than the objects on which they are based.

Build a Scale Model For the chapter project, you will build your own scale model. First, you will choose an object to model. Use your imagination! Your model can be larger or smaller than the actual object—

you choose the scale. Then you will select building materials and assemble the model. Your final project will be to present the model to your class, explaining the scale and how you chose the item to model.

Go Online

For information to help you
complete your project
PearsonSuccessNet.com

Chances are there's at least one person in a large crowd who has the same birthday as you! How many people do you think have the same favorite food? How many like the same television show? What kinds of cars do the people in the crowd have? Pollsters consider questions like these all the time, and they take surveys to help answer them.

Estimate the Size of a Crowd and Take a Survey For the chapter project, you will use averages to estimate the size of a crowd. You will also take a survey and present your results in a graph.

Go Online

For information to help you
complete your project
PearsonSuccessNet.com

Everybody Wins

Remember the game "Rock, Paper, Scissors"? It is an unusual game because paper wins over rock, rock wins over scissors, and scissors win over paper. You can use mathematics to create and investigate a situation with similar characteristics.

Chapter 9 Probability

Make Three Number Cubes For this chapter project, you will design three number cubes A, B, and C, which have a surprising property: A usually beats B, B usually beats C, and C usually beats A. Your final step will be to construct your cubes.

Go Online

For information to help you complete your project
PearsonSuccessNet.com

Raisin' the Roof

Look around you. Triangles are everywhere in construction! You see them in bridges, in buildings, in scaffolding, even in bicycle frames! This project will give you a greater appreciation of the importance of triangles in construction. You might also develop a taste for raisins!

Chapter 10 Geometry and Area

Build a Tower For the chapter project, you will use toothpicks and raisins to build geometric shapes. Your final product will be a tower strong enough to support a baseball. Which shape or shapes made the strongest structure? Write a final report with your discoveries.

Go Online

For information to help you complete your project
PearsonSuccessNet.com

As the summer sun goes down on another hot day, you just have to get outside. Where do you go? To the park! For generations, people in towns and cities have used parks as places to escape. When properly planned, a park can be the perfect place to relax, meet friends, skate, and be surrounded by natural beauty.

Chapter 11 *Geometry Continued*

Design a Park For the chapter project, you will design a small park and be prepared to present your plan to the town council. Your final project will be a detailed plan of the park.

Go Online

For information to help you complete your project
PearsonSuccessNet.com

Have you ever spent time gazing into an aquarium full of fish? You can get lost in thought as you watch the fish through the glass. Many people enjoy having an aquarium because they feel peaceful while observing nature in this miniature environment.

Chapter 12 *Surface Area and Volume*

Design an Aquarium In this chapter project, you will design an aquarium for your classroom. Which 3-dimensional shape will have the greatest volume for the amount of space it will take in the classroom? You should consider how many fish you want in the aquarium. Also consider the size of each type of fish that you plan to place in the aquarium. As part of your final project, you will create a drawing of your proposed aquarium.

Go Online

For information to help you complete your project
PearsonSuccessNet.com

Mosaics

In Ancient Rome, the homes of the very wealthy often had floors and walls decorated with mosaics made from small tiles. Sometimes the tiles were black and white; sometimes they were many colors. Artists would travel with "pattern books" that allowed a team of workers anywhere to recreate a mosaic.

Create a Mosaic How many designs could you create with four simple polygons such as a rhombus, a trapezoid, an equilateral triangle and an isosceles triangle? What if you could dilate, translate, rotate, and reflect each figure?

Use only the four polygons mentioned. The shapes could be colorful tiles, stones, or pieces of glass. What sort of mosaic would you create? Use graph paper to draw your designs. Make sure that your designs can be reproduced anywhere by putting it in a pattern book.

Go  **nline**

For information to help you
complete your project
PearsonSuccessNet.com

Skills

● **Lesson 1-1** **Find the opposite of each number.**

1. 7   **2.** -18 **3.** -4 **4.** -100 **5.** 24

Compare using <, =, or >.

6. $2 \blacksquare 7$ **7.** $-13 \blacksquare 13$ **8.** $-5 \blacksquare -6$ **9.** $21 \blacksquare -12$

● **Lesson 1-2** **Find each sum or difference.**

10. $33 + (-17)$ **11.** $-12 + (-6)$ **12.** $82 + 10$ **13.** $-75 + 14$

● **Lesson 1-3** **Find each product or quotient.**

14. $-8 \times (-9)$ **15.** $30(-4)$ **16.** $-13 \cdot 4$ **17.** $(15)(-8)$

● **Lessons 1-4, 1-5** **Write each fraction as a decimal.**

18. $\dfrac{2}{3}$ **19.** $\dfrac{3}{25}$ **20.** $\dfrac{7}{4}$ **21.** $\dfrac{7}{12}$ **22.** $\dfrac{6}{15}$

Order from greatest to least.

23. $-1, 0.15, \dfrac{1}{5}$ **24.** $\dfrac{3}{11}, -\dfrac{1}{4}, -0.1$ **25.** $-0.3, \dfrac{3}{8}, \dfrac{7}{20}$

● **Lesson 1-6** **Simplify.**

26. $-\dfrac{7}{8} + \left(-\dfrac{5}{8}\right)$ **27.** $13.7 - 15$ **28.** $1\dfrac{1}{6} - \left(-\dfrac{2}{3}\right)$ **29.** $-4.59 + 5.49$

● **Lessons 1-7, 1-8** **Simplify.**

30. $\left(-\dfrac{7}{10}\right)\left(-\dfrac{5}{8}\right)$ **31.** $25.5 \div (-0.5)$ **32.** $-0.17 \cdot 1.8$ **33.** $\dfrac{5}{6} \div \left(-\dfrac{4}{9}\right)$

● **Lessons 1-9, 1-10** **Solve each equation.**

34. $x^2 = \dfrac{1}{4}$ **35.** $x^2 = \dfrac{25}{49}$ **36.** $x^2 = 0$ **37.** $x^2 = 81$

38. $x^3 = 1$ **39.** $x^3 = 1{,}728$ **40.** $x^3 = \dfrac{125}{1{,}000}$ **41.** $x^3 = -\dfrac{8}{27}$

Word Problems

● **Lessons 1-1, 1-2**

42. A football team was at the 38 yard line. In the next three plays, they lose 6 yards, gain 4 yards, and then lose 7 yards. Use integers to find the yard line are they on now.

43. The highest official recorded temperature for Chicago is 107°F in 1934. The lowest official recorded temperature is −27°F in 1985. What is the difference between these temperatures?

● **Lesson 1-3**

44. If a driver had 6 unpaid parking tickets and must pay $15 per ticket, what is the change in the driver's bank account after paying the fines?

45. You and seven of your friends share 2 large pizzas and bucket of wings. The bill is $56. What is the change in each person's available money if you share the cost equally?

● **Lessons 1-4, 1-5**

46. In a survey about music lessons, 0.05 of the students wanted violin lessons, $\frac{1}{2}$ wanted guitar lessons, $\frac{3}{20}$ preferred drum lessons and 0.3 chose piano lessons. Write the lesson in order of popularity from greatest to least.

● **Lessons 1-6 through 1-8**

47. The temperature was −3.7°C at 6:00 A.M. and 0.5°C at 8:00 A.M. What is the difference between the two temperatures?

48. Suppose the Beard family buys a large screen TV. They arrange to pay by making 48 equal payments of $99.50 but have not begun to pay yet. What is their total debt?

● **Lessons 1-9, 1-10**

49. A square has an area of 240.25 in.^{2}. What are the lengths of its sides?

50. A cube-shaped gift box has a volume of 8 cubic inches. What is the side length of the box?

Skills

● **Lesson 2-1** **Write each number in standard form.**

1. 7.2×10^5 **2.** 9×10^8 **3.** 4.9×10^{-3} **4.** 9.03×10^2
5. 4×10^{-5} **6.** 8.2×10^4 **7.** 1.7×10^6 **8.** 5.501×10^{-4}

Write each number in scientific notation.

9. 0.00002   **10.** 6,400   **11.** -503.4 **12.** 0.00997
13. 400,000,000   **14.** 0.000875   **15.** 38,000   **16.** -0.5002

● **Lesson 2-2** **Write each expression using a single exponent.**

17. $4^8 \cdot 4^{10}$ **18.** $(-9)^2 \cdot (-9)^4$ **19.** $3.2^8 \cdot 3.2^3$ **20.** $7^t \cdot 7^{3t}$
21. $8^{12} \cdot 8^{-12}$ **22.** $3^{-9} \cdot 3^{12}$ **23.** $(-5)^0 \cdot (-5)^{-2}$ **24.** $9^3 \cdot 9^{-8}$

Simplify each expression.

25. $(-142)^0$ **26.** $(4c)^{-1}$ **27.** 7^{-w} **28.** $(-3)^{-5}$
29. ab^0 **30.** 6^{-3} **31.** $k3^{-3}$ **32.** 5^{-4}

● **Lesson 2-3** **Write each product in scientific notation.**

33. $(3 \times 10^4)(2 \times 10^{12})$ **34.** $(5 \times 10^9)(7 \times 10^3)$ **35.** $8(9 \times 10^4)$
36. $(1 \times 10^3)(2.6 \times 10^8)$ **37.** $16(3 \times 10^2)$ **38.** $(7 \times 10^2)(8 \times 10^{10})$

Choose the most reasonable unit in parentheses to describe the quantity.

39. The mass of a baseball is about 145 _____. (grams, kilograms)
40. The length of a carpenter ant is about 18 _____. (meters, millimeters)

● **Lesson 2-4** **Write each expression using a single exponent.**

41. $\frac{4^7}{4^5}$ **42.** $\frac{8.1^{15}}{8.1^{12}}$ **43.** $\frac{(-654)^{20}}{(-654)^1}$ **44.** $\frac{2^{3x}}{2^x}$

● **Lesson 2-5** **Divide. Write each quotient in scientific notation.**

45. $(7 \times 10^3) \div (4 \times 10^8)$ **46.** $(6 \times 10^8) \div (2 \times 10^6)$ **47.** $(2.1 \times 10^3) \div (5.2 \times 10^1)$
48. $(8 \times 10^3) \div (2 \times 10^{-2})$ **49.** $(7.5 \times 10^4) \div 3.2$ **50.** $(8 \times 10^9) \div (8 \times 10^4)$

Estimate how many times greater the first number is than the second number. Round to the nearest multiple of ten.

51. 3.8×10^5 and 6.3×10^3 **52.** 6×10^8 and 2×10^7 **53.** 3.8×10^4 and 9.4×10^2
54. 4×10^7 and 8×10^5 **55.** 9.0×10^7 and 4.5×10^6 **56.** 2.7×10^7 and 3.8×10^5

Word Problems

● **Lesson 2-1**

57. **Physics** The wavelength of red light is about 0.0000076 meters. Write this number in scientific notation.

58. An electronic counter increases by 1 every second. If it starts at 0, what will the count be after 50 days? Express your answer in scientific notation.

● **Lesson 2-2**

59. **Probability** If you flip 5 coins, the odds that they will all land on heads is 2^{-5}. What is this number as a fraction?

● **Lesson 2-3**

60. **Biology** There are about 5×10^{10} white blood cells and about 500 times as many red blood cells in a human's bloodstream. Find the number of red blood cells. Write your answer in scientific notation.

61. **Sports** There are about 2.65×10^{32} possible ways a 30-player football team can form a line to run onto the field. When a thirty-first player is included, there will be about $31 \cdot (2.65 \times 10^{32})$ possible ways. Write this number in scientific notation.

● **Lesson 2-4**

62. **Chemistry** The mass concentration of a solution is 2^{-5} grams in one liter of water. What would the concentration be if the same mass were instead dissolved in 2^3 liters of water? Write your answer as a power of 2.

● **Lesson 2-5**

63. **Astronomy** The average distance from Earth to the Moon is 3.844×10^5 km. This distance is 2.57×10^{-3} times the average distance from Earth to the Sun. What is the average distance from Earth to the Sun?

Skills

● **Lesson 3-1** Evaluate each expression for $a = -2$, $b = 8$, and $c = 5$.

1. $c - b$ **2.** $2b + a$ **3.** $\frac{1}{2} + 2c$ **4.** $\frac{b}{a}$

Write an algebraic expression for each word phrase.

5. 50 meters longer than x meters

6. driving r miles per hour for 2.5 hours

● **Lesson 3-2** Simplify each expression.

7. $2r + 7 + r$ **8.** $14 - 2x - 5$ **9.** $4(1.5 - 3p)$ **10.** $\frac{1}{4}n + 1 + \frac{1}{2}n - 5$

● **Lesson 3-3** Use inverse operations to solve each equation. Check your answer.

11. $t - 13 = -29$ **12.** $17 + d = -7$ **13.** $d + 112 = 159$ **14.** $y - 68 = 94$

15. $\frac{m}{5} = -15$ **16.** $-7y = -42$ **17.** $0.4t = 16$ **18.** $\frac{x}{12} = -8$

● **Lessons 3-4 through 3-7** Solve each equation. Check the solution.

19. $2a = 3(a + 1)$ **20.** $-9 - 3y = 19 + y$ **21.** $k = 1.5(7 - k)$

22. $14 - 2w = 18w - 26$ **23.** $8(3a - 5) = 56a$ **24.** $\frac{3}{4}t + 1 = \frac{5}{8}t - 2$

● **Lesson 3-8** Tell whether each equation has one solution, infinitely many solutions, or no solution. Justify your answer.

25. $16d = 8(d + 4)$ **26.** $-1.8x + 5.4 = -1.8(x - 3)$

27. $2\left(\frac{7}{16}a + 5\right) = \frac{7}{8}a - 10$ **28.** $2g + 7 = -4g + 7 + 6g$

Word Problems

● **Lesson 3-1**

29. A dance club spends $20 on advertising to promote its fall show. Write an algebraic expression for the amount of money left in the budget if the club starts with *d* dollars.

● **Lesson 3-2**

30. You have $185 saved up. You received some money as a birthday gift. You still need twice the new total to buy a tablet computer that costs $500. Write and simplify an equation that shows the received as a gift.

● **Lesson 3-3**

31. Kobayashi set a world record for hot dog eating when he ate 50 hot dogs in 720 seconds. How many seconds it took him to eat one hot dog.

32. You mail a package at the post office. The postage costs $12.18. You pay with a $20 bill. How much change do you receive.

● **Lessons 3-4 through 3-7**   **Write and solve an equation for each situation.**

33. A peregrine falcon can fly as fast as 220 mi/h. This speed is 150 mi/h faster than the maximum running speed of a cheetah. What is the speed of a cheetah?

34. A snorkeler looks at coral 4.5 feet below sea level, or at −4.5 ft. A scuba diver looks at coral located at 10 times that depth. How far below sea level does the scuba diver descend?

35. An auto rental agency offers a rate of $38 per day plus $.30/mile. After a one-day rental, Misha's bill was $74. How many miles did Misha drive?

36. A pair of running shoes costs $37 less than twice the cost of a pair of basketball sneakers. The sneakers cost $48.50. How much do the running shoes cost?

● **Lesson 3-8**

37. Travel Bus fare for adults in one city is $1.50. The fare for students is $1.00. At one stop, twice as many students boarded the bus as adults. Is it possible that the total fares paid by students is the same as the total fares paid by adults? Justify your answer.

CHAPTER 4

Extra Practice

Skills

● **Lesson 4-1**

Which numbers of the given numbers are solutions of the inequality?

1. $x > -5; -10, 10, -1, -5$

2. $n \leq 7.3; 7, -7.3, -1\frac{1}{2}, 7\frac{3}{4}$

3. $g \leq -1; -4, 1, -\frac{1}{2}, -1$

4. $r < \frac{1}{4}; 0.25, 0, -\frac{3}{4}, 1$

Write an inequality for each statement.

5. The space shuttle can carry more than 38,000 pounds.

6. Today your break will be shorter than 15 minutes.

7. A song is less than 5 minutes long.

8. A shelf can hold at most 250 pounds.

● **Lesson 4-2** **Solve each inequality. Then graph the inequality.**

9. $y + 5 \geq 11$

10. $p + 7 < -3$

11. $a - 9 \leq 1$

12. $d - 3 > 13$

● **Lesson 4-3** **Solve each inequality. Then graph the inequality.**

13. $3y \geq 33$

14. $\dfrac{20 \text{ in.}}{6 \text{ ft}} < -2$

15. $\dfrac{a}{-8} \leq -7$

16. $4d > -36$

● **Lesson 4-4** **Solve each inequality. Then graph the inequality.**

17. $3p - 5 > 1$

18. $1.5 + 7y < 5$

19. $-\dfrac{1}{5} \geq x - \dfrac{4}{5}$

20. $r + 12 \geq -3$

21. $-1.9 < \dfrac{b}{4} + 0.1$

22. $\dfrac{5}{8}x < -5$

Word Problems

● **Lesson 4-1**

Write an inequality for each statement. Then graph the inequality.

23. You need to finish the test in less than 60 minutes.

24. For your party, you plan a game where each player needs three spoons. You buy a box of 50 spoons. At most, how many people can play the game?

● **Lesson 4-2**   **Write and solve an inequality for each problem.**

25. The farm workers need to plant at least 100 rows of seedlings. 78 rows are planted so far. At least how many more rows do they have to plant to reach their goal?

26. You spent $33.35 on a new baseball bat. You still have more than $42 left to spend on sports equipment. What is the amount money you could have started with?

● **Lesson 4-3**

27. The width of a new room that Johna is designing is 10 feet. If she wants the area to be at least 125 square feet, what dimensions can the length of the rectangular room be?

28. Carmen earns $8.50 an hour. What is the least number of full hours she will have to work to earn $175?

● **Lesson 4-4**

29. The local library is having a spring fair. Admission is $1 and snacks cost $1.50 each. What is the maximum number of snacks you can buy if you have $10 to spend?

Skills

● **Lesson 5-1**   **Write each fraction in simplest form.**

1. $\dfrac{20\text{ in.}}{6\text{ ft}}$

2. $15\text{ min} : 3\text{ h}$

3. $2\text{ kg to }500\text{ g}$

● **Lesson 5-2**   **Find each unit rate.**

4. 100 Calories in 5 crackers

5. 84 players on 7 teams

6. $\dfrac{1}{2}$ mi in $\dfrac{1}{5}$ h

7. $\dfrac{3}{8}$ lb in $\dfrac{2}{3}$ box

● **Lesson 5-3**   **By using cross products, tell whether the ratios can form a proportion.**

8. $\dfrac{4}{3}, \dfrac{12}{9}$

9. $\dfrac{8}{5}, \dfrac{11}{7}$

10. $\dfrac{21}{6}, \dfrac{7}{2}$

11. $\dfrac{6}{24}, \dfrac{2}{4}$

12. $\dfrac{50}{6}, \dfrac{3}{2}$

● **Lesson 5-4**   **Solve each proportion using cross products.**

13. $\dfrac{12}{a} = \dfrac{3}{5}$

14. $\dfrac{n}{12} = \dfrac{4}{16}$

15. $\dfrac{7}{8} = \dfrac{n}{4}$

16. $\dfrac{7}{10} = \dfrac{14}{a}$

17. $\dfrac{7}{n} = \dfrac{17.5}{5}$

● **Lesson 5-5**   **Each pair of figures is similar. Find the value of each variable.**

18.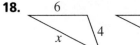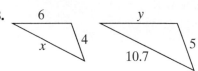

19.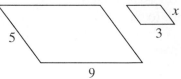

● **Lesson 5-6**   **The scale on a drawing is 0.5 in. : 15 ft. Find the actual length for each drawing length. Round to the nearest tenth, if necessary.**

20. 15 in.

21. 20 in.

22. 10 in.

23. 40 in.

24. 15.5 in.

25. 1.25 in.

● **Lesson 5-7**   **Find the constant of proportionality for each table of values.**

26. songs per hour

Hours (*h*)	3	5	7
Songs	54	90	126

27. price per pound

Walnuts (lb)	5	9	12
Price	$31.80	$57.24	$76.32

Word Problems

● **Lesson 5-1**

28. Nutrition The U.S. Department of Agriculture (USDA) recommends that no more than $\frac{3}{10}$ of your Calories come from fat. In a bowl of Tasty Crunch cereal, 15 out of 120 Calories are from fat. Is this within the USDA recommendation? Explain.

● **Lesson 5-2**

29. A bottle of 250 multivitamins costs $14.99. A bottle of 500 multivitamins costs $32.99. Which bottle is the better buy? Explain.

30. A 2-pint container of cider costs $2.49. A 6-pint container of cider costs $7.14. Which container is the better buy? Explain.

● **Lesson 5-3**

31. For a game, you need 3 yellow marbles for every 8 red marbles. If you have 42 yellow marbles and 112 red marbles, do you have the appropriate numbers of marbles for the game? Explain.

● **Lesson 5-4**

32. Business You sell packs of 12 pens for $3.48. At this rate, how much should you charge for a pack of 20 pens?

33. There are 144 tulips in 8 m^2 of a garden. Predict the number in 25 m^2.

34. A recipe for fruit salad serves 4 people. It calls for 2 oranges and 16 grapes. You want to serve 10 people. How many oranges and grapes will you need?

● **Lesson 5-5**

35. Geometry The ratio of the corresponding sides of two similar rectangles is 5 : 7. The smaller rectangle has a length of 3 cm and a width of 5 cm. Find the perimeter of the larger rectangle.

36. Indirect Measurement A student is 4 ft tall and his shadow is 3 ft long. A nearby building has a shadow 51 ft long. How tall is the building?

● **Lesson 5-6**

37. A map key shows that a distance of $\frac{1}{4}$ in. represents an actual distance of $\frac{7}{10}$ mi. What is the scale of this map?

● **Lesson 5-7**

38. A magazine subscription costs $32.64 for one year. Write an equation for the cost c of the magazine for m months.

CHAPTER 6

Extra Practice

Skills

● **Lesson 6-1**

Write each ratio as a percent.

1. $\frac{4}{5}$ **2.** $\frac{11}{5}$ **3.** $\frac{3}{25}$ **4.** $\frac{19}{20}$ **5.** $\frac{1}{10}$ **6.** $\frac{3}{2}$

Write each percent as a decimal.

7. 37.5%   **8.** 11.375%   **9.** 2.55%   **10.** 9%   **11.** 1.111%   **12.** 97.05%

Write each percent as a fraction in simplest form.

13. 225%   **14.** 0.1%   **15.** 0.07%   **16.** 398%   **17.** 156%   **18.** 0.2%

● **Lesson 6-2**   **Write a proportion and solve.**

19. 54 is what percent of 135?   **20.** What percent of 48 is 2.4?   **21.** What percent of 200 is 120?

22. 8 is what percent of 20?   **23.** 32.5 is what percent of 130?   **24.** What percent of 150 is 27?

● **Lesson 6-3**   **Write and solve an equation to find the part of a whole.**

25. 30% of 250 is what number?   **26.** What number is 90% of 70?   **27.** 45% of 200 is what number?

28. What number is 7% of 88?   **29.** 4% of 200 is what number?   **30.** What number is 22% of 1?

● **Lesson 6-4**   **Find each payment.**

31. $75 with a 5% sales tax   **32.** $219 with a 3.5% sales tax   **33.** $85.65 with a 3% sales tax

● **Lesson 6-5**   **Find the interest earned for each account.**

34. deposit $1,100; earns 5% simple interest; interest earned in 5 years

35. deposit $2,400; earns 4.5% simple interest; interest earned in 6 years

● **Lesson 6-6**   **Find each percent of change. Round to the nearest tenth. State whether the change is an increase or a decrease.**

36. 25 to 40   **37.** 95 to 45   **38.** 108 to 110   **39.** 50 to 95   **40.** 125 to 75

41. 8.5 to 10   **42.** 100 to 15   **43.** 63.5 to 20   **44.** 111 to 150   **45.** 25.9 to 30.2

Word Problems

● **Lesson 6-1   The table shows the percent of the Recommended Daily Allowance for some of the nutrients in a 6-oz baked potato.**

Potato Facts

Nutrient	RDA
Magnesium	14%
Iron	34%
Vitamin B6	35%

SOURCE: National Institutes of Health

46. Write each percent as a fraction and as a decimal.

47. Nutrition Suppose you eat a 6-oz baked potato. What percent of each nutrient do you still need to meet the Recommended Daily Allowance?

48. Environment A study has suggested that desert areas throughout the world could increase as much as 185% in the next 100 years due to global warming. Write the percent as a decimal and a fraction.

● **Lessons 6-2 and 6-3**

49. Four hundred students attended a school dance. If 35% of the students were boys, how many boys attended the dance?

50. The regular price of a backpack is $34. A store sells the backpack at 30% off. What is the sale price?

51. An awards banquet is attended by 120 people. Ribbons are awarded for first, second, and third place in each of 25 categories. No one gets more than one ribbon. What percent of the people attending the banquet receive a ribbon?

52. A frozen yogurt shop sold 45 strawberry cones on Friday. This is 30% of the number of strawberry cones they sold that week. How many strawberry cones did they sell that week?

● **Lessons 6-4 and 6-5**

53. You go to a stylist for a haircut. The cost of the haircut is $12.50. Find the amount of a 15% tip for the stylist.

54. A salesperson earns a salary of $2,500, plus 4% commission on sales of $1,500. What are the salesperson's total earnings?

55. You want to borrow $600. Loan A offers 8% simple interest for 30 months. Loan B offers 5% simple interest for 5 years. Which loan would result in paying the least interest?

● **Lesson 6-6**

56. If the cost of a dozen eggs rises from $.99 to $1.34, what is the percent of the increase?

57. A television is on sale for $449.95. This is $30 off the original price. Find the percent of the discount.

58. A bookstore pays $4.25 for paperback books and charges $9.95. What is the maximum percent of discount the store can offer, while making a profit of $2 on each book? Check your answer.

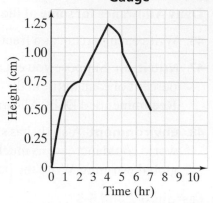

Level of Rain in Rain Gauge

CHAPTER 7 — Extra Practice

Skills

● **Lesson 7-1**   Use the graph at the right for Exercises 1–4.

1. When is the height increasing?

2. When is the height decreasing?

3. When is the change in height linear?

4. When is the change in height nonlinear?

● **Lesson 7-2**   Use the function rule $y = 2x - 1$. Find each output.

5. $x = 1$ **6.** $x = 0$ **7.** $x = -3$ **8.** $x = \dfrac{1}{2}$

● **Lesson 7-3**   Determine if each relationship is proportional.

9.

p	q
3	6
4	8
5	20
6	24

10.

s	t
−3	−15
−1	−5
1	5
3	15

11.

Ride Tickets

2 for $1
4 for $2
10 for $4
20 for $6

● **Lesson 7-4**   Determine whether the function represented by each table is linear or nonlinear.

12.

x	0	1	2	3	4
y	12	9	6	3	0

13.

x	−6	−2	2	6	10
y	0	2	4	2	0

14.

x	8	11	14	17	20
y	9	6	3	0	−3

● **Lesson 7-5** **Find the slope of each line.**

15.
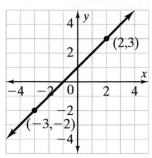

16.
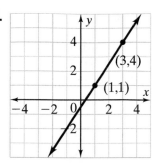

17.
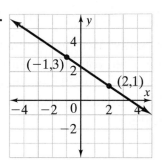

Use the table to find the slope. Then graph the data and each line.

18.

x	0	1	2	3	4
y	1	3	5	7	9

19.

x	−2	0	2	4	6
y	10	7	4	1	−2

20.

x	−4	−1	2	5	8
y	−5	0	5	10	15

● **Lesson 7-6** **Make a table of input-output pairs for each function. Then graph the function.**

21. $y = 3x$ **22.** $y = -2x + 3$ **23.** $y = \frac{3}{5}x + 1$ **24.** $y = 4$

For each function, find the slope and y-intercept.

25. $y = 2x - 5$ **26.** $y = x + 8$ **27.** $y = \frac{1}{4}x + 2$ **28.** $y = 9x$

● **Lesson 7-7** **Determine which function has the greater rate of change.**

29. $y = 4x + 3$

x	0	1	2	3	4
y	8	6	4	2	0

30. $y = \frac{1}{4}x - 2$

x	−3	−1	1	3	5
y	0	1	2	3	4

Word Problems

● **Lesson 7-1**

31. Your family drives for 30 min to get to a restaurant. You stay for 60 min. Then your family starts driving home. After 15 min, you stop at a store for 30 min. Then you drive the rest of the way home in 15 min. Sketch and label a graph showing your distance from home during your trip.

● **Lesson 7-2**

32. Potatoes cost $.99 per pound. The function rule $c = 0.99p$ gives the cost c in dollars for p pounds of potatoes. How much do 6 lb of potatoes cost?

33. A large cheese pizza costs $6.99 plus $1.50 for each topping. The function rule $c = 6.99 + 1.5t$ gives the cost c in dollars of a large cheese pizza with t toppings. How much does a large cheese pizza with 4 toppings cost?

● **Lesson 7-3**

34. Rico uses oil paints to create abstract artwork. Each month he buys one large canvas for $42. He also buys tubes of oil color for $8 each. He uses the function $s = 8t + 42$ to track his monthly expenses where s represents the total cost of supplies in dollars and t represents the number of tubes of oil color. Make an input-output table, graph your results, and determine if the function has a proportional relationship. Explain.

● **Lesson 7-4**

35. A cyclist has a goal of riding 300 mi each month. The function $m = 300 - 10d$ represents the number of miles the cyclist needs to ride to reach her goal after riding 10 mi on each of d days. Make a table and graph the function. Is it discrete or continuous?

● **Lesson 7-5**

36. Suppose a wheelchair ramp has a slope of $\frac{1}{15}$. If it reaches a doorway that is 2 ft above ground, how far from the doorway does the ramp begin?

37. A skateboard ramp has a slope of $\frac{1}{3}$. If the ramp is 12 feet long, what is its height at the tallest point?

● **Lesson 7-6**

38. Agriculture A bamboo plant is 23 cm high and grows 16 cm a day. The plant's height (output) depends on the number of days that have passed (input). Make a table and graph the function.

● **Lesson 7-7**

39. Canoe Cabin charges $15 per hour plus a $25 rental fee for canoes. Rental fees at Lake Riders are shown by the ordered pairs (3, 58) and (5, 78) in the form (number of hours, total cost in dollars). Both relationships are linear. Which company has the greatest initial cost?

40. Aaron charges a $50 setup fee for painting, plus $24 per hour of work. Shawn's charges are shown by the ordered pairs (2, 140) and (6, 220) in the form (number of hours, total charges). Both relationships are linear. Who charges the most initially?

Skills

● **Lesson 8-1**

1. A polling company wants to know which U.S. airline is rated highest by air travelers. Which sample is more likely to be random? Explain.
   a. The company surveys 50 randomly selected people on a flight from New York to Los Angeles.
   b. The company surveys every 20th person entering 5 different U.S. airports on one day.

2. Write a fair survey question and a biased survey question.

● **Lesson 8-2** **Use a proportion to estimate each animal population.**

3. total moose counted: 58
   marked moose counted: 7
   total marked moose: 52

4. total coyotes counted: 378
   marked coyotes counted: 68
   total marked coyotes: 204

5. Suppose 25 sea gulls were marked in a nesting area. Later, 500 sea gulls were counted, 19 of which were marked. Estimate the population

● **Lesson 8-3** **The table shows the heights of a random sample of 7-year-olds at a school. Use the sample to make an inference about each measure. Support your answer.**

6. the mean height of 7-year-olds at the school

7. the median height of 7-year-olds at the school

8. the percent of 7-year-olds at the school who are under 47 in. tall

9. the percent of 7-year-olds at the school who are at least 50 in. tall

Heights of 7-year-olds (in.)				
50	47	48	50	45
49	46	49	49	50
47	48	45	45	51
47	49	47	48	44

● **Lesson 8-4** **Compare each pair of measures for the data sets in the box-and-whisker plot, and use the comparison to make an inference.**

10. the medians of the data sets

11. the IQRs of the data sets

12. What number n multiplied by the IQR equals the difference between the medians of the data sets? What does this number tell you about the overlap of the data sets?

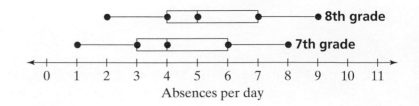

Word Problems

● **Lesson 8-1** **A car company wants to know how many miles per week owners of electric cars typically drive their cars.**

13. What question could the company ask someone to determine whether he or she is part of the population it wants to study?

14. Once a random sample has been selected, what is a fair question that the company could ask to determine what it wants to know?

15. An urban planner wants to know how road construction affects bus drivers. How can the planner survey a random sample of bus drivers?

● **Lesson 8-2**

16. **Ecology** Marine biologists are studying the otter population in a coastal region. There are 20 marked sea otters in the region. In a survey, the biologists count 42 sea otters, of which 12 are marked. About how many sea otters are in the area?

17. Biologists capture, tag, and release 32 foxes in a forest. A month later, the biologists capture 25 foxes in the forest, and all of them are already tagged. What does this indicate about the population of foxes in the forest?

● **Lesson 8-3** **A pollster selected 3 random samples of 15 users each on a social networking site. The pollster recorded the number of friends each user has on the site. The lists show the results.**
Sample 1: 96, 96, 116, 46, 46, 73, 114, 101, 137, 136, 66, 95, 148, 82, 112
Sample 2: 119, 120, 121, 77, 94, 77, 106, 85, 71, 97, 106, 81, 111, 106, 105
Sample 3: 111, 93, 78, 41, 85, 131, 113, 102, 92, 114, 137, 76, 115, 126, 108

18. For each sample, determine the median number of friends per user.

19. Describe the variation in the samples.

20. Make an inference about the median number of friends per user on the site.

● **Lesson 8-4** **The lists below show the prices in dollars of the e-readers at two different stores.**
Store A: 130, 80, 169, 199, 80, 249, 179, 95, 110, 179
Store B: 80, 99, 69, 189, 142, 229, 90, 100, 72, 180

21. Calculate the mean of each data set.

22. Determine the MAD for the price of the e-readers at store A.

23. Without making a data display, determine whether there is a large or small amount of overlap in the data sets. Support your answer.

Skills

● **Lesson 9-1   You roll a number cube. Find each probability.**

1. $P(2)$ **2.** $P(3 \text{ or } 5)$ **3.** $P(2, 4, \text{ or } 6)$

● **Lesson 9-2**

4. A quality control engineer at a factory inspected 300 glow sticks for quality.
The engineer found 15 defective glow sticks. What is the experimental
probability that a glow stick is defective?

Find the experimental probability for each basketball team.

5. Kingwood, Humble, Texas
Wins: 37, Losses: 4
Find $P(\text{Win})$.

6. Westchester, Los Angeles, Calif.
Wins: 25, Losses: 3
Find $P(\text{Loss})$.

● **Lesson 9-3   Make a table to show the sample space for each situation.
Then find the number of outcomes.**

7. You toss three coins.

8. You spin a number 1 to 6 and toss a coin.

9. You choose one letter from each of the two sets of letters E, F, G, H
and A, B, C.

10. You toss two coins and spin a spinner with three congruent sections
colored red, white, and blue. Draw a tree diagram to find the sample space.
Then find $P(2 \text{ heads, then blue})$.

● **Lesson 9-4   A bag contains 6 green marbles, 8 blue marbles, and 3 red
marbles. Find $P(B)$ after A has happened.**

11. A: Draw a green marble. Keep it.
B: Draw a red marble.

12. A: Draw a blue marble. Replace it.
B: Draw a red marble.

● **Lesson 9-5   What is an appropriate simulation tool for each situation? Explain.**

13. About $\frac{1}{2}$ of the members of a local service group are over the age of 50. You want to
estimate the probability that in a group of 8 members, at least 4 are over 50.

14. In a certain travel club, 28% of the residents have passports. You want to
estimate the probability that you will have to speak with at least 10
members of the travel club before finding one with a passport.

Word Problems

● **Lessons 9-1 and 9-2**

15. You write the letters M, I, S, S, I, S, S, I, P, P, and I on cards and mix them in a hat. You select one card without looking. Find the probability of selecting an I.

16. Suppose you have 3 red, 3 black, and 3 blue marbles in your pocket. Does the probability of randomly selecting a black marble equal the probability of randomly selecting a blue one? Explain.

17. A quality-control inspector finds flaws in 6 of 45 tools examined. If the trend continues, what is the best prediction of the number of defective tools in a batch of 540?

18. Crispy Cereal offers one free prize in every box: a baseball card, a keychain, or a bracelet. You buy 3 boxes. Find the experimental probability of *not* getting a baseball card. Simulate the problem.

● **Lessons 9-3 and 9-4**

19. Make a tree diagram for choosing one letter at random from each of two sets of letters: A, B, and C and W, X, Y, and Z. Then find the probability of choosing an A and a W.

20. A spinner has equal sections numbered 1 to 3. You spin the spinner 4 times. How many different outcomes are possible?

21. You drop a coin twice inside the rectangle. Estimate the probability that the coin lands in one of the circles both times. Use 3 for ⇔.

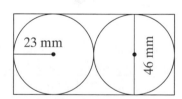

23 mm   46 mm

22. A volleyball team won 31 games and lost 4 games in one season. The coach has a summary sheet for each game. The coach selects two sheets at random to compare. Find P(win, then loss) without replacement.

● **Lesson 9-5**

23. A local restaurant puts instant win game stickers on its cups. Three out of every five stickers is a winner.

   a. Design a simulation that can be used to estimate the probability that a player will need to buy no more than 2 drinks to get a winning sticker.

   b. Perform 20 trials of the simulation. Then estimate the probability.

24. On average, 42% of a mini golf course's customers are children. Estimate the probability that the owner can speak with no more than five customers before speaking to a child.

Mini Golf				
13	32	48	79	61
08	84	60	55	15
59	47	53	90	72
26	03	19	44	94
63	58	49	77	72
80	19	04	33	62
31	11	86	40	92
94	37	51	58	73
42	53	21	06	13
70	66	47	69	55

Skills

● **Lesson 10-1** Write an equation relating the measures of the two angles and find the angle measures.

1.

2.

3.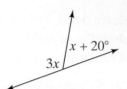

In the diagram at the right, $m\angle 1 = 63°$. Find the measure of each angle.

4. $\angle 2$

5. $\angle 3$

6. $\angle 4$

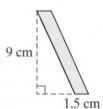

● **Lesson 10-2** Find the area of each parallelogram.

7.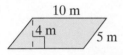
10 m, 4 m, 5 m

8.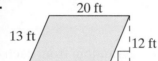
20 ft, 13 ft, 12 ft

9.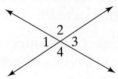
9 cm, 1.5 cm

● **Lesson 10-3** Find the area of each triangle.

10.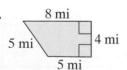
7 cm, 12 cm

11.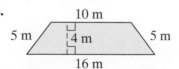
10 km, 25 km

12.
40 in., 60 in.

● **Lesson 10-4** Find the area of each trapezoid or irregular figure.

13.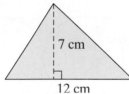
8 mi, 5 mi, 4 mi, 5 mi

14.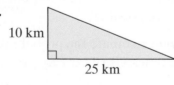
10 m, 5 m, 4 m, 5 m, 16 m

15.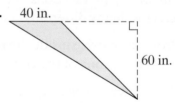
28 ft, 14 ft, 3 ft, 3 ft, 12 ft

● **Lesson 10-5** Find the circumference and area of each circle. Round to the nearest tenth of a unit.

16.
6 cm

17.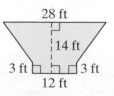
20 in.

18.
9 m

● **Lesson 10-1**

19. If $\angle P$ and $\angle Q$ are complementary and $m\angle P$ is 8 times $m\angle Q$, what are the measures of $\angle P$ and $\angle Q$?

20. $\angle S$ and $\angle T$ are supplementary. $m\angle S = 2x + 60°$ and $m\angle T = 4x$. What are the measures of $\angle S$ and $\angle T$?

● **Lesson 10-2**

21. A garden has the shape of a parallelogram. If the base is 16 feet, and the corresponding height is 10 feet, what is the area of the garden?

22. **Patterns** Copy and complete the table by finding the perimeter and area of each rectangle. What happens to the perimeter and area of a rectangle when you double, triple, or quadruple the dimensions?

ℓ	w	P	A
3 in.	1 in.	▨	▨
6 in.	2 in.	▨	▨
9 in.	3 in.	▨	▨
12 in.	4 in.	▨	▨

● **Lesson 10-3**

23. A triangular mirror is 12 in. wide and 37 in. tall. Find its area.

● **Lesson 10-4**

24. A park wall is designed to have the irregular shape shown. Use familiar figures to find the area of the park.

25. The stage in a theater is shaped like a trapezoid. The front edge is 60 feet long, and the back edge is 40 feet long. The distance from the front of the stage to the back is 20 feet. What is the area of the stage?

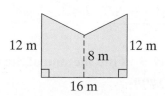

12 m   8 m   12 m

16 m

Skills

● **Lesson 11-1**   **In the diagram at the right, $\ell\|m$.**

  1. Identify a pair of alternate interior angles.

  2. If $m\angle 1 = 108°$, find the measure of each numbered angle.

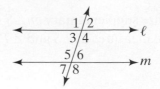

● **Lesson 11-2**   **Show that each pair of triangles is congruent.**

3. 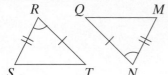   **4.** 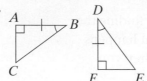   **5.**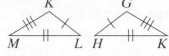

● **Lesson 11-3**   **Exercises 6–8 show pairs of similar polygons.**
Find the unknown lengths.

6.   **7.**   **8.**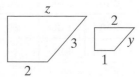

● **Lesson 11-4**   **Show that each pair of triangles is similar.**

9. 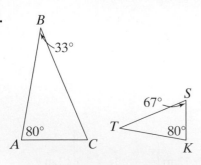   **10.**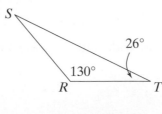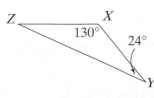

● **Lesson 11-5**   **Find the sum of the measures of the interior angles of**
each polygon.

  11. rhombus   **12.** hexagon   **13.** triangle   **14.** pentagon   **15.** trapezoid

● **Lesson 11-1** **Which pairs of lines, if any, are parallel? Explain.**

16.

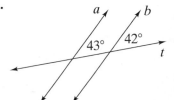

17.

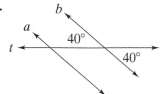

18.

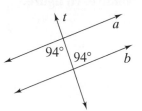

● **Lesson 11-2**

19. Sewing Eliana has many quilt pieces shaped like regular hexagons. If she cuts the pieces in half, does she make congruent figures? If so, show how the pieces are congruent.

● **Lessons 11-3 and 11-4**

20. Wallpaper Two walls on the top floor of Louis' house are trapezoidal in shape. One wall is 10 feet wide at the floor and 8.5 feet wide at the ceiling. The other wall is 8 feet wide at the floor and 6 feet wide at the ceiling. The walls are 8 feet high. Are the two walls similar figures? Explain.

21. Brian wants to reduce a panoramic photo that is 2 feet wide and 14.5 inches high. He wants the new photo to be 14.5 inches wide. How high will the new photo be? Round to the nearest hundredth.

An Antonov An-225 airplane model has a wingspan of 22.5 cm. The actual wingspan of an An-225 is 88.4 m.

22. If the actual length of an An-225 is 84 m, what is the length of the airplane model in decimal form?

23. Suppose another model of the An-225 has a scale of 1 cm to 36 m. What is the wingspan of this model in cm?

● **Lesson 11-5**

24. Find the measure of the interior angles of an octagonal stop sign.

Skills

● **Lesson 12-1** Name each figure.

1.

2.

3.

● **Lesson 12-2** Find the surface area of each solid. If necessary, round to the nearest tenth.

4.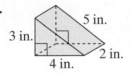
5 in.
3 in.
4 in.
2 in.

5.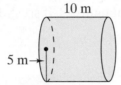
10 m
5 m

6.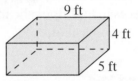
9 ft
4 ft
5 ft

● **Lesson 12-3** Find the volume of each figure. If necessary, round to the nearest tenth.

7.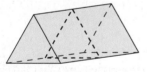
15 m
10 m
17.5 m

8.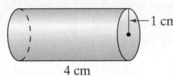
1 cm
4 cm

9.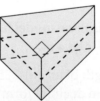
90 m
60 m
100 m
80 m

● **Lesson 12-4** Describe each cross-section.

10.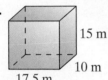

11.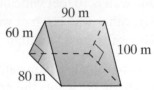

12.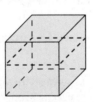

● **Lesson 12-5** Find the volume of the pyramid or cone to the nearest whole cubic unit.

13.
2.5 m
2 m
2 m

14.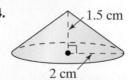
1.5 cm
2 cm

15.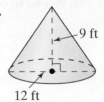
9 ft
12 ft

● **Lesson 12-6** Find each sphere's surface area and volume to the nearest whole number.

16.
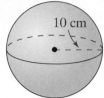
10 cm

17.
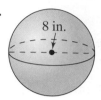
8 in.

18.
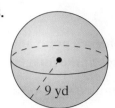
9 yd

Word Problems

● **Lesson 12-1** Use the square pyramid at the right.

19. Name four edges that intersect $\overline{AD}$.

20. Name any edges that are parallel to $\overline{CD}$.

21. Name two edges that are NOT parallel to $\overline{BC}$ and do NOT intersect $\overline{BC}$.

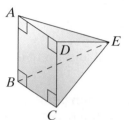

● **Lesson 12-3**

22. Some boxes are cut from a large sheet of cardboard. Find the amount of cardboard needed to make a box similar to the one at the right. Round to the nearest tenth.

23. Calculate the surface area of a cylinder with a height of 7 cm and a diameter of 3 cm. Use ⇔ = 3.14.

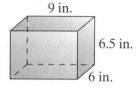
9 in.
6.5 in.
6 in.

● **Lesson 12-4**

24. Find the radius of the cylinder at the right. Use ⇔ = 3.14.

25. A jewelry box in the shape of a rectangular prism is 12 in. long, 7 in. wide, and 3 in. tall. Find the volume of the jewelry box.

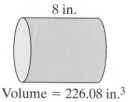
8 in.
Volume = 226.08 in.³

● **Lesson 12-5**

26. Timothy cut a cucumber shaped like a cylinder into small round slices. What shape is the cross section that he sees?

27. Tiffany cut a loaf of bread shaped like a rectangular prism into slices. What shape is the cross section she sees?

● **Lesson 12-6**

28. Jai's office has a water cooler that dispenses conical paper cups like the one at the right. How much water can each of the paper cups hold? Round to the nearest cubic inch.

29. Mercury has a radius of about 2,440 km. Find the volume and surface area to the nearest unit.

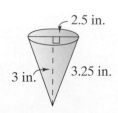
2.5 in.
3 in.
3.25 in.

Skills

● **Lesson 13-1** Graph each point and its image after the given translation. Name the coordinates of the image.

1. $D(3, 2)$, right 3 units   **2.** $E(-5, 4)$, down 4 units   **3.** $F(0, 6)$, up 1 unit, left 4 units

Copy the figure shown below for Exercises 4–6. Then graph its image after each translation.

4. translation 2 units left

5. translation 3 units up

6. translation 3 units right and 1 unit down

● **Lesson 13-2** Graph the given point and its image after each reflection over the given axis. Name the coordinates of the image.

7. $G(2, 5)$, x-axis   **8.** $H(-4, 3)$, y-axis   **9.** $J(0, -7)$, x-axis

$\triangle ABC$ has vertices $A(1, 2)$, $B(2, 7)$, and $C(5, 1)$. Graph $\triangle ABC$ and its image after a reflection over each line. Name the coordinates of the vertices of the image.

10. x-axis   **11.** y-axis   **12.** line through $(-1, 5)$ and $(-1, -2)$

● **Lesson 13-3** Determine whether each figure has rotational symmetry. If it does, find the angle of rotation. Write *no rotational symmetry* if applicable.

13.

14.

15.

Copy the figure shown at the right for Exercises 16–18. Then draw its image after a rotation of the given number of degrees about the origin.

16. $90°$ **17.** $180°$ **18.** $270°$

Lesson 13-4

19. The three triangles are congruent. Describe the sequence of transformations that maps $\triangle QRS$ onto $\triangle WXY$.

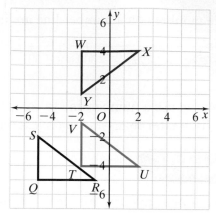

Lesson 13-5 Find the image of $\triangle ABC$ at the right after a dilation with the given center and scale factor.

20. center B, scale factor of 3

21. center A, scale factor of $\frac{1}{2}$

Lesson 13-6

22. The three triangles are similar. Describe the sequence of transformations that maps $\triangle ABC$ onto $\triangle DBF$.

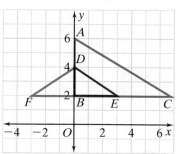

Word Problems

Lesson 13-1

23. Point Z is translated using the rule $(x, y) \rightarrow (x - 4, y + 11)$. The coordinates of Z' are $(4, -11)$. What are the coordinates of point Z?

Lesson 13-2

24. The vertices of $\triangle RST$ are $R(0, 4)$, $S(0, 0)$, and $T(-4, 0)$. Graph $\triangle RST$ on a coordinate plane. What are the coordinates of the vertices after the figure is reflected across the y-axis?

Lessons 13-3 and 13-4

25. Rotate the figure at the right 90° clockwise about the origin. What are the coordinates of point Q'?

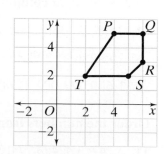

26. Geometry A regular polygon has all sides and all angles equal. All regular polygons have rotational symmetry. A certain regular polygon has an angle of rotation of 72°. How many sides does this polygon have?

Lessons 13-5 and 13-6

27. Photography Jorge is enlarging a digital photo that is 4 in. high by 6 in. wide. If the enlarged photo is $18\frac{1}{2}$ in. high, find its width.

Comparing and Ordering Whole Numbers

The numbers on a number line are in order from least to greatest.

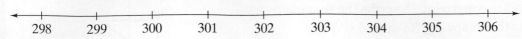

You can use a number line to compare whole numbers. Use the symbols
> (is greater than) and < (is less than).

EXAMPLE

1 Use > or < to compare the whole numbers.

a. 303 ▦ 299

303 is to the right of 299.

303 > 299

b. 301 ▦ 305

301 is to the left of 305.

301 < 305

The value of a digit depends on its place in a number. Compare digits
starting from the left.

EXAMPLE

2 Use > or < to compare the whole numbers.

a. 12,060,012,875 ▦ 12,060,012,675

8 hundreds > 6 hundreds, so
12,060,012,875 > 12,060,012,675

b. 465,320 ▦ 4,653,208

0 millions < 4 millions, so
465,320 < 4,653,208

Exercises

Use > or < to compare the whole numbers.

1. 3,660 ▦ 360

2. 74,328 ▦ 74,238

3. 88,010 ▦ 8,101

4. 87,524 ▦ 9,879

5. 295,286 ▦ 295,826

6. 829,631 ▦ 842,832

7. 932,401 ▦ 932,701

8. 60,000 ▦ 500,000

9. 1,609,372,002 ▦ 609,172,002

10. 45,248,315,150 ▦ 45,283,718,150

Order the numbers from least to greatest.

11. 3,747; 3,474; 3,774; 3,347; 3,734

12. 70,903; 70,309; 73,909; 73,090

13. 32,056,403; 302,056,403; 30,265,403; 30,256,403

14. 884,172; 881,472; 887,142; 881,872

Multiplying Whole Numbers

When you multiply by a two-digit number, first multiply by the ones and then multiply by the tens. Add the products.

EXAMPLE

1 Multiply 62×704.

Step 1	Step 2	Step 3
704	704	704
$\times\ 62$	$\times\ 62$	$\times\ 62$
1408	1408	1408
	42240	$+\ 42240$
		43,648

EXAMPLE

2 Find each product.

a. 93×6

$$\begin{array}{r} 93 \\ \times\ 6 \\ \hline 558 \end{array}$$

b. 25×48

$$\begin{array}{r} 48 \\ \times\ 25 \\ \hline 240 \\ +\ 960 \\ \hline 1{,}200 \end{array}$$

c. 80×921

$$\begin{array}{r} 921 \\ \times\ 80 \\ \hline 73{,}680 \end{array}$$

Exercises

Find each product.

1. 74 $\times\ 6$	**2.** 35 $\times\ 9$	**3.** 53 $\times\ 7$	**4.** 80 $\times\ 8$	**5.** 98 $\times\ 4$	**6.** 65 $\times\ 8$
7. 512 $\times\ 3$	**8.** 407 $\times\ 9$	**9.** 225 $\times\ 6$	**10.** 340 $\times\ 5$	**11.** 816 $\times\ 7$	**12.** 603 $\times\ 3$
13. 70 $\times\ 36$	**14.** 41 $\times\ 55$	**15.** 38 $\times\ 49$	**16.** 601 $\times\ 87$	**17.** 271 $\times\ 34$	**18.** 450 $\times\ 67$

19. 6×82 **20.** 405×5 **21.** 81×9 **22.** 3×274 **23.** 553×4

24. 60×84 **25.** 52×17 **26.** 31×90 **27.** 78×52 **28.** 43×66

Dividing Whole Numbers

First estimate the quotient by rounding the divisor, the dividend, or both. When you divide, after you bring down a digit, you must write a digit in the quotient.

EXAMPLE

Find each quotient.

a. $741 \div 8$

Estimate:
$720 \div 8 \approx 90$

$$
\begin{array}{r}
92 \text{ R5} \\
8\overline{)741} \\
-72 \\
\hline
21 \\
-16 \\
\hline
5
\end{array}
$$

b. $838 \div 43$

Estimate:
$800 \div 40 \approx 20$

$$
\begin{array}{r}
19 \text{ R21} \\
43\overline{)838} \\
-43 \\
\hline
408 \\
-387 \\
\hline
21
\end{array}
$$

c. $367 \div 9$

Estimate:
$360 \div 9 \approx 40$

$$
\begin{array}{r}
40 \text{ R7} \\
9\overline{)367} \\
-360 \\
\hline
7
\end{array}
$$

Exercises

Divide.

1. $4\overline{)61}$ **2.** $8\overline{)53}$ **3.** $7\overline{)90}$ **4.** $3\overline{)84}$ **5.** $6\overline{)81}$

6. $6\overline{)469}$ **7.** $3\overline{)653}$ **8.** $8\overline{)645}$ **9.** $9\overline{)231}$ **10.** $4\overline{)415}$

11. $60\overline{)461}$ **12.** $40\overline{)213}$ **13.** $70\overline{)517}$ **14.** $30\overline{)432}$ **15.** $80\overline{)276}$

16. $43\overline{)273}$ **17.** $52\overline{)281}$ **18.** $69\overline{)207}$ **19.** $38\overline{)121}$ **20.** $81\overline{)433}$

21. $94\overline{)1,368}$ **22.** $62\overline{)1,147}$ **23.** $55\overline{)2,047}$ **24.** $85\overline{)1,450}$ **25.** $46\overline{)996}$

26. $94 \div 4$ **27.** $66 \div 9$ **28.** $90 \div 5$ **29.** $69 \div 6$ **30.** $58 \div 8$

31. $323 \div 5$ **32.** $849 \div 7$ **33.** $404 \div 8$ **34.** $934 \div 3$ **35.** $619 \div 6$

36. $777 \div 50$ **37.** $528 \div 20$ **38.** $443 \div 40$ **39.** $312 \div 40$ **40.** $335 \div 60$

41. $382 \div 72$ **42.** $580 \div 68$ **43.** $279 \div 43$ **44.** $232 \div 27$ **45.** $331 \div 93$

46. $614 \div 35$ **47.** $423 \div 28$ **48.** $489 \div 15$ **49.** $1,134 \div 51$ **50.** $1,103 \div 26$

Place Value and Decimals

Each digit in a decimal has both a place and a value. The value of any place is one tenth the value of the place to its left. In the chart below, the digit 5 is in the hundredths place. So its value is 5 hundredths.

thousands	hundreds	tens	ones	.	tenths	hundredths	thousandths	ten-thousandths	hundred-thousandths
2	8	3	6	.	7	5	0	1	4

EXAMPLE

a. In what place is the digit 8?

   hundreds

b. What is the value of the digit 8?

   8 hundreds

Exercises

Use the chart above. Write the place of each digit.

1. 3   **2.** 4   **3.** 6   **4.** 7   **5.** 1   **6.** 0

Use the chart above. Write the value of each digit.

7. 3   **8.** 4   **9.** 6   **10.** 7   **11.** 1   **12.** 0

Write the value of the digit 6 in each number.

13. 0.162   **14.** 0.016   **15.** 13.672   **16.** 1,640.8   **17.** 62.135

18. 26.34   **19.** 6,025.9   **20.** 0.6003   **21.** 2,450.65   **22.** 615.28

23. 3.16125   **24.** 1.20641   **25.** 0.15361   **26.** 1.55736   **27.** 10.0563

Write the value of the underlined digit.

28. 2<u>4</u>.0026   **29.** 14.9<u>3</u>1   **30.** 5.78<u>9</u>4   **31.** 0.<u>8</u>7   **32.** 10.056<u>3</u>

Reading and Writing Decimals

A place value chart can help you read and write decimals. When there are no ones, write a zero before the decimal point.

billions	hundred millions	ten millions	millions	hundred thousands	ten thousands	thousands	hundreds	tens	ones	.	tenths	hundredths	thousandths	ten-thousandths	hundred-thousandths	millionths	Read
									0	.	0	7					7 hundredths
								2	3	.	0	1	4				23 and 14 thousandths
3	0	0	0	0	0	0	0	0	0	.	8						3 billion and 8 tenths
									5	.	0	0	0	1	0	2	5 and 102 millionths

EXAMPLE

a. Write thirteen ten-thousandths in numerals.

Ten-thousandths is 4 places after the decimal point. So the decimal will have 4 places after the decimal point. The number is 0.0013.

b. Write 1.025 in words.

The digit 5 is in the thousandths place. So 1.025 is one and twenty-five thousandths.

Exercises

Write a number for the given words.

1. three hundredths

2. twenty-one millions

3. six and two hundredths

4. two billion and six tenths

5. two and five hundredths

6. five thousand twelve

7. seven millionths

8. forty-one ten-thousandths

9. eleven thousandths

10. one and twenty-five millionths

11. three hundred four thousandths

Write each number in words.

12. 5,700.4

13. 3,000,000.09

14. 12.000069

15. 900.02

16. 25.00007

17. 0.00015

Rounding Whole Numbers and Decimals

You can use number lines to help you round whole numbers and decimals.

EXAMPLE

1 **a.** Round 7,510 to the nearest thousand.

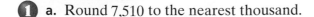
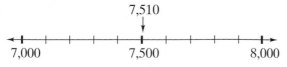

7,510 is between 7,000 and 8,000.

7,510 rounds to 8,000.

b. Round 0.248 to the nearest hundredth.

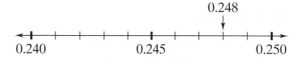

0.248 is between 0.24 and 0.25.

0.248 rounds to 0.25.

To round a number to a particular place, look at the digit to the right of that place. If the digit is less than 5, round down. If the digit is 5 or more, round up.

EXAMPLE

2 **a.** Round 2.4301 to the nearest whole number.

The digit to the right of 2 is 4, so 2.4301 rounds down to 2.

b. Round 0.0515 to the nearest thousandth.

The digit to the right of 1 is 5, so 0.0515 rounds up to 0.052.

Exercises

Round to the nearest ten.

1. 42	**2.** 89	**3.** 671	**4.** 3,482	**5.** 7,029	**6.** 661,423

Round to the nearest thousand.

7. 5,800	**8.** 3,100	**9.** 44,500	**10.** 9,936	**11.** 987	**12.** 313,591
13. 5,641	**14.** 37,896	**15.** 82,019	**16.** 808,155	**17.** 34,501	**18.** 650,828

Round to the nearest tenth.

19. 2.75	**20.** 3.816	**21.** 19.72	**22.** 401.1603	**23.** 499.491	**24.** 3.949
25. 4.67522	**26.** 20.397	**27.** 399.956	**28.** 129.98	**29.** 96.4045	**30.** 125.66047

Round to the nearest hundredth.

31. 31.723	**32.** 14.869	**33.** 1.78826	**34.** 0.1119	**35.** 736.941	**36.** 9.6057
37. 0.699	**38.** 4.231	**39.** 12.09531	**40.** 5.77125	**41.** 0.9195	**42.** 4.0033

Multiplying Decimals

When you multiply decimals, first multiply as if the factors were whole numbers. Then, count the decimal places in both factors to find how many places are needed in the product.

EXAMPLE

1 Multiply 2.5 × 1.8.

$$
\begin{array}{r}
1.8 \quad \leftarrow \text{one decimal place} \\
\times\ 2.5 \quad \leftarrow \text{one decimal place} \\
\hline
90 \\
+\ 360 \\
\hline
4.50 \quad \leftarrow \text{two decimal places}
\end{array}
$$

EXAMPLE

2 Find each product.

a. 0.7 × 1.02

$$
\begin{array}{r}
1.02 \\
\times\ 0.7 \\
\hline
0.714
\end{array}
$$

b. 0.03 × 407

$$
\begin{array}{r}
407 \\
\times\ 0.03 \\
\hline
12.21
\end{array}
$$

c. 0.62 × 2.45

$$
\begin{array}{r}
2.45 \\
\times\ 0.62 \\
\hline
490 \\
+\ 14700 \\
\hline
1.5190
\end{array}
$$

d. 75 × 3.06

$$
\begin{array}{r}
3.06 \\
\times\ 75 \\
\hline
1530 \\
+\ 21420 \\
\hline
229.50
\end{array}
$$

Exercises

Multiply.

1.
$$
\begin{array}{r}
0.3 \\
\times\ 8
\end{array}
$$

2.
$$
\begin{array}{r}
5 \\
\times\ 0.06
\end{array}
$$

3.
$$
\begin{array}{r}
0.04 \\
\times\ 7
\end{array}
$$

4.
$$
\begin{array}{r}
6 \\
\times\ 0.8
\end{array}
$$

5.
$$
\begin{array}{r}
3.1 \\
\times\ 0.05
\end{array}
$$

6.
$$
\begin{array}{r}
14 \\
\times\ 0.2
\end{array}
$$

7.
$$
\begin{array}{r}
3.1 \\
\times\ 6
\end{array}
$$

8.
$$
\begin{array}{r}
0.05 \\
\times\ 43
\end{array}
$$

9.
$$
\begin{array}{r}
0.27 \\
\times\ 5
\end{array}
$$

10.
$$
\begin{array}{r}
72 \\
\times\ 0.6
\end{array}
$$

11.
$$
\begin{array}{r}
0.8 \\
\times\ 312
\end{array}
$$

12.
$$
\begin{array}{r}
4.56 \\
\times\ 7
\end{array}
$$

13. 5 × 2.41

14. 704 × 0.3

15. 9 × 1.35

16. 1.2 × 0.3

17. 0.04 × 2.5

18. 6.6 × 0.3

19. 15.1 × 0.02

20. 0.8 × 31.3

21. 0.07 × 25.1

22. 42.2 × 0.9

23. 0.6 × 30.02

24. 0.05 × 11.8

25. 71.13 × 0.4

26. 48 × 2.1

27. 6.3 × 85

28. 0.42 × 98

Dividing a Decimal by a Whole Number

When you divide a decimal by a whole number, first divide as if the numbers were whole numbers. Then put a decimal point in the quotient directly above the decimal point in the dividend.

EXAMPLE

1 Divide $0.256 \div 8$.

Step 1

$$
\begin{array}{r}
32 \\
8\overline{)0.256} \\
-24 \\
\hline
16 \\
-16 \\
\hline
0
\end{array}
$$

Step 2

$$
\begin{array}{r}
0.032 \\
8\overline{)0.256} \\
-24 \\
\hline
16 \\
-16 \\
\hline
0
\end{array}
$$

← Put extra zeros to the left. Then place the decimal point.

EXAMPLE

2 Find each quotient.

a. $12.6 \div 6$

$$
\begin{array}{r}
2.1 \\
6\overline{)12.6} \\
-12 \\
\hline
06 \\
-6 \\
\hline
0
\end{array}
$$

b. $37.26 \div 81$

$$
\begin{array}{r}
0.46 \\
81\overline{)37.26} \\
-324 \\
\hline
486 \\
-486 \\
\hline
0
\end{array}
$$

c. $0.666 \div 9$

$$
\begin{array}{r}
0.074 \\
9\overline{)0.666} \\
-63 \\
\hline
36 \\
-36 \\
\hline
0
\end{array}
$$

Exercises

Divide.

1. $4\overline{)28.56}$ **2.** $5\overline{)16.5}$ **3.** $9\overline{)6.984}$ **4.** $6\overline{)91.44}$ **5.** $4\overline{)35.16}$

6. $81\overline{)33.291}$ **7.** $22\overline{)2.42}$ **8.** $26\overline{)1,723.8}$ **9.** $83\overline{)15.272}$ **10.** $39\overline{)26.91}$

11. $17.52 \div 2$ **12.** $10.53 \div 9$ **13.** $14.49 \div 7$ **14.** $37.14 \div 6$

15. $0.0324 \div 9$ **16.** $0.1352 \div 8$ **17.** $0.0882 \div 6$ **18.** $0.8682 \div 6$

19. $79.599 \div 13$ **20.** $45.918 \div 18$ **21.** $59.7 \div 15$ **22.** $74.664 \div 12$

23. $12.342 \div 22$ **24.** $29.792 \div 32$ **25.** $22.568 \div 26$ **26.** $11.340 \div 36$

Dividing Decimals by Decimals

To divide by a decimal divisor, multiply it by the smallest power of ten that will make the divisor a whole number. Then multiply the dividend by that same power of ten.

EXAMPLE

Find each quotient.

a. $3.348 \div 6.2$

Multiply by 10.

$$
\begin{array}{r}
0.54 \\
6.2)\overline{3.3.48} \\
-3\,1\,0 \\
\hline
2\,48 \\
-2\,48 \\
\hline
0
\end{array}
$$

b. $2.4885 \div 0.35$

Multiply by 100.

$$
\begin{array}{r}
7.11 \\
0.35)\overline{2.48.85} \\
-2\,45 \\
\hline
3\,8 \\
-3\,5 \\
\hline
35 \\
-35 \\
\hline
0
\end{array}
$$

c. $0.0576 \div 0.012$

Multiply by 1000.

$$
\begin{array}{r}
4.8 \\
0.012)\overline{0.057.6} \\
-48 \\
\hline
9\,6 \\
-9\,6 \\
\hline
0
\end{array}
$$

Exercises

Divide.

1. $268.8 \div 3.2$
2. $123.5 \div 1.9$
3. $135.6 \div 0.3$

4. $170.2 \div 2.3$
5. $252.8 \div 7.9$
6. $10.26 \div 5.7$

7. $71.53 \div 2.3$
8. $16.12 \div 3.1$
9. $24.18 \div 7.8$

10. $14.49 \div 6.3$
11. $134.42 \div 5.17$
12. $89.96 \div 3.46$

13. $160.58 \div 5.18$
14. $106.59 \div 6.27$
15. $62.4 \div 3.9$

16. $260.4 \div 8.4$
17. $316.8 \div 7.2$
18. $162.4 \div 2.9$

19. $1.512 \div 0.54$
20. $3.225 \div 0.43$
21. $2.484 \div 0.69$

22. $511.5 \div 5.5$
23. $0.992 \div 0.8$
24. $4.53 \div 0.05$

25. $3.498 \div 0.06$
26. $59.2 \div 0.8$
27. $2.198 \div 0.07$

28. $14.28 \div 0.7$
29. $1.98 \div 0.5$
30. $26.36 \div 0.04$

31. $3.922 \div 7.4$
32. $23.52 \div 0.98$
33. $71.25 \div 7.5$

34. $114.7 \div 3.7$
35. $0.832 \div 0.52$
36. $1.125 \div 0.09$

37. $9.666 \div 2.7$
38. $1.456 \div 9.1$
39. $0.4374 \div 1.8$

Powers of Ten

You can use shortcuts when multiplying and dividing by powers of ten.

When you multiply by…	move the decimal point…	When you divide by…	move the decimal point…
1,000	3 places to the right.	1,000	3 places to the left.
100	2 places to the right.	100	2 places to the left.
10	1 place to the right.	10	1 place to the left.
0.1	1 place to the left.	0.1	1 place to the right.
0.01	2 places to the left.	0.01	2 places to the right.

EXAMPLE

Multiply or divide.

a. 0.3×0.01

0.00.3 ← Move the decimal point 2 places to the left.

● $0.3 \times 0.01 = 0.003$

b. $0.18 \div 1,000$

0.000.18 ← Move the decimal point 3 places to the left.

$0.18 \div 1,000 = 0.00018$

Exercises

Multiply.

1. 3.2×0.01

2. $1,000 \times 0.12$

3. 0.7×0.1

4. 0.01×6.2

5. 0.09×100

6. 23.6×0.01

7. 5.2×10

8. $0.08 \times 1,000$

9. 100×0.05

10. 0.1×0.24

11. 18.03×0.1

12. 6.1×100

Divide.

13. $82.3 \div 0.1$

14. $0.4 \div 1,000$

15. $5.02 \div 0.01$

16. $16.5 \div 100$

17. $236.7 \div 0.1$

18. $45.28 \div 10$

19. $0.9 \div 1,000$

20. $1.03 \div 0.01$

21. $42.6 \div 0.1$

22. $203.05 \div 0.01$

23. $4.7 \div 10$

24. $0.07 \div 100$

Multiply or divide.

25. 0.32×0.1

26. $0.03 \div 100$

27. $2.6 \div 0.1$

28. $12.6 \times 1,000$

29. $0.8 \div 1,000$

30. 0.01×6.7

31. 100×0.15

32. $23.5 \div 10$

Adding and Subtracting Fractions With Like Denominators

When you add or subtract fractions with the same denominator, first add or subtract the numerators. Write the answer over the denominator.

EXAMPLE

1 Add or subtract. Write the answer in simplest form.

a. $\frac{5}{16} + \frac{3}{16}$

$$\begin{array}{r} \frac{5}{16} \\ + \frac{3}{16} \\ \hline \frac{8}{16} = \frac{1}{2} \end{array}$$

b. $\frac{7}{8} - \frac{1}{8}$

$$\begin{array}{r} \frac{7}{8} \\ - \frac{1}{8} \\ \hline \frac{6}{8} = \frac{3}{4} \end{array}$$

c. $\frac{3}{5} + \frac{2}{5}$

$$\frac{3}{5} + \frac{2}{5} = \frac{5}{5} = 1$$

To add or subtract mixed numbers, add or subtract the fractions first. Then add or subtract the whole numbers.

EXAMPLE

2 Add or subtract. Write the answer in simplest form.

a. $2\frac{5}{8} + 3\frac{1}{8}$

$$\begin{array}{r} 2\frac{5}{8} \\ + 3\frac{1}{8} \\ \hline 5\frac{6}{8} = 5\frac{3}{4} \end{array}$$

b. $4\frac{3}{4} - 1\frac{1}{4}$

$$\begin{array}{r} 4\frac{3}{4} \\ - 1\frac{1}{4} \\ \hline 3\frac{2}{4} = 3\frac{1}{2} \end{array}$$

c. $5\frac{5}{6} + 2\frac{5}{6}$

$$5\frac{5}{6} + 2\frac{5}{6} = 7\frac{10}{6}$$
$$= 7 + 1 + \frac{4}{6}$$
$$= 8\frac{2}{3}$$

Exercises

Add or subtract. Write the answers in simplest form.

1. $\begin{array}{r} \frac{2}{5} \\ + \frac{2}{5} \\ \hline \end{array}$

2. $\begin{array}{r} \frac{2}{6} \\ - \frac{1}{6} \\ \hline \end{array}$

3. $\begin{array}{r} \frac{2}{7} \\ + \frac{2}{7} \\ \hline \end{array}$

4. $\begin{array}{r} 9\frac{1}{3} \\ - 8\frac{1}{3} \\ \hline \end{array}$

5. $\begin{array}{r} 8\frac{6}{7} \\ - 4\frac{2}{7} \\ \hline \end{array}$

6. $\begin{array}{r} 3\frac{1}{10} \\ + 1\frac{3}{10} \\ \hline \end{array}$

7. $\frac{3}{8} + \frac{2}{8}$

8. $\frac{3}{6} - \frac{1}{6}$

9. $\frac{6}{8} - \frac{3}{8}$

10. $\frac{2}{9} + \frac{1}{9}$

11. $\frac{4}{5} - \frac{1}{5}$

12. $\frac{3}{4} + \frac{1}{4}$

13. $8\frac{7}{10} + 2\frac{3}{10}$

14. $1\frac{4}{5} + 3\frac{3}{5}$

15. $2\frac{2}{9} + 3\frac{4}{9}$

16. $8\frac{5}{8} - 3\frac{3}{8}$

17. $9\frac{7}{10} - 2\frac{3}{10}$

18. $9\frac{3}{4} + 1\frac{3}{4}$

Metric Units of Length

The basic unit of length in the metric system is the meter. All the other units are based on the meter. In the chart below, each unit is 10 times the value of the unit to its left.

Unit	Millimeter	Centimeter	Decimeter	Meter	Decameter	Hectometer	Kilometer
Symbol	mm	cm	dm	m	dam	hm	km
Value	0.001 m	0.01 m	0.1 m	1 m	10 m	100 m	1,000 m

To change a measure from one unit to another, start by using the chart to find the relationship between the two units.

EXAMPLE

Complete each equation.

a. $0.8 \text{ km} = \blacksquare \text{ m}$

$1 \text{ km} = 1,000 \text{ m}$

$0.8 \times 1,000 = 800$ ← To change km to m, multiply by 1,000.

$0.8 \text{ km} = 800 \text{ m}$

b. $17.2 \text{ mm} = \blacksquare \text{ cm}$

$1 \text{ mm} = 0.1 \text{ cm}$

$17.2 \times 0.1 = 1.72$ ← To change mm to multiply by 0.1.

$17.2 \text{ mm} = 1.72 \text{ cm}$

c. $\blacksquare \text{ cm} = 2.1 \text{ km}$

$1 \text{ km} = 100,000 \text{ cm}$

$2.1 \times 100,000 = 210,000$ ← To change km to cm, multiply by 100,000.

$210,000 \text{ cm} = 2.1 \text{ km}$

d. $\blacksquare \text{ m} = 5,200 \text{ cm}$

$1 \text{ cm} = 0.01 \text{ m}$

$5,200 \times 0.01 = 52$ ← To change cm to r multiply by 0.01.

$52 \text{ m} = 5,200 \text{ cm}$

Exercises

Complete each equation.

1. $1 \text{ mm} = \blacksquare \text{ cm}$

2. $1 \text{ m} = \blacksquare \text{ km}$

3. $1 \text{ mm} = \blacksquare \text{ m}$

4. $1 \text{ cm} = \blacksquare \text{ m}$

5. $1.2 \text{ cm} = \blacksquare \text{ km}$

6. $\blacksquare \text{ km} = 45,000 \text{ mm}$

7. $\blacksquare \text{ m} = 30 \text{ km}$

8. $6.2 \text{ cm} = \blacksquare \text{ mm}$

9. $3.3 \text{ km} = \blacksquare \text{ m}$

10. $0.6 \text{ mm} = \blacksquare \text{ cm}$

11. $72 \text{ cm} = \blacksquare \text{ m}$

12. $180 \text{ m} = \blacksquare \text{ mm}$

13. $\blacksquare \text{ cm} = 13 \text{ km}$

14. $\blacksquare \text{ m} = 530 \text{ cm}$

15. $4,900 \text{ mm} = \blacksquare \text{ m}$

16. $\blacksquare \text{ cm} = 24 \text{ m}$

17. $\blacksquare \text{ km} = 106,000 \text{ cm}$

18. $259,000 \text{ mm} = \blacksquare \text{ m}$

19. $1,200,000 \text{ mm} = \blacksquare \text{ km}$

Metric Units of Capacity

The basic unit of capacity in the metric system is the liter. All the other units are based on the liter. In the chart below, each unit is 10 times the value of the unit on the left. Note that we use a capital L as the abbreviation for *liter* to avoid confusion with the number 1.

Unit	Milliliter	Centiliter	Deciliter	Liter	Decaliter	Hectoliter	Kiloliter
Symbol	mL	cL	dL	L	daL	hL	kL
Value	0.001 L	0.01 L	0.1 L	1 L	10 L	100 L	1,000 L

To change a measure from one unit to another, start by using the chart to find the relationship between the two units.

EXAMPLE

Complete each equation.

a. 245 mL = ▓ L

   1 mL = 0.001 L

   245 × 0.001 = 0.245   ← To change mL to L, multiply by 0.001.

   245 mL = 0.245 L

b. ▓ mL = 4.5 kL

   1 kL = 1,000,000 mL

   4.5 × 1,000,000 = 4,500,000   ← To change kL to mL, multiply by 1,000,000.

   4,500,000 mL = 4.5 kL

Exercises

Complete each equation.

1. 1 L = ▓ mL

2. 1 mL = ▓ kL

3. 1 kL = ▓ L

4. 1 kL = ▓ mL

5. 200 L = ▓ kL

6. 1.3 kL = ▓ mL

7. ▓ kL = 240 L

8. 0.6 mL = ▓ L

9. ▓ kL = 106,000 L

10. 72 kL = ▓ mL

11. ▓ mL = 1.5 kL

12. ▓ kL = 450,000 mL

13. 4,900 L = ▓ kL

14. ▓ kL = 200,000 mL

15. ▓ L = 8 mL

16. 4.2 L = ▓ mL

17. 57,000,000 mL = ▓ L

18. 28,000 kL = ▓ L

19. ▓ mL = 9,000 L

20. 4,000 L = ▓ mL

21. 870 L = ▓ kL

Metric Units of Mass

The basic unit of mass in the metric system is the gram. All the other units are based on the gram. In the chart below, each unit is 10 times the value of the unit to its left.

Unit	Milligram	Centigram	Decigram	Gram	Decagram	Hectogram	Kilogram
Symbol	mg	cg	dg	g	dag	hg	kg
Value	0.001 g	0.01 g	0.1 g	1 g	10 g	100 g	1,000 g

To change a measure from one unit to another, start by using the chart to find the relationship between the two units.

EXAMPLE

Complete each equation.

a. $2.3 \text{ kg} = \blacksquare \text{ g}$

$1 \text{ kg} = 1,000 \text{ g}$

$2.3 \times 1,000 = 2,300$ ← **To change kg to g, multiply by 1,000.**

$2.3 \text{ kg} = 2,300 \text{ g}$

b.

$\blacksquare \text{ g} = 250 \text{ mg}$

$1 \text{ mg} = 0.001 \text{ g}$

$250 \times 0.001 = 0.25$ ←**To change mg to g, multiply by 0.001.**

$0.25 \text{ g} = 250 \text{ mg}$

Exercises

Complete each equation.

1. $1 \text{ mg} = \blacksquare \text{ g}$

2. $1 \text{ g} = \blacksquare \text{ kg}$

3. $1 \text{ mg} = \blacksquare \text{ kg}$

4. $1 \text{ g} = \blacksquare \text{ mg}$

5. $1 \text{ kg} = \blacksquare \text{ g}$

6. $1 \text{ kg} = \blacksquare \text{ mg}$

7. $\blacksquare \text{ g} = 8 \text{ mg}$

8. $1,500 \text{ mg} = \blacksquare \text{ kg}$

9. $\blacksquare \text{ kg} = 200,000 \text{ g}$

10. $\blacksquare \text{ mg} = 3.7 \text{ g}$

11. $0.6 \text{ mg} = \blacksquare \text{ g}$

12. $370 \text{ g} = \blacksquare \text{ kg}$

13. $\blacksquare \text{ kg} = 300,000 \text{ mg}$

14. $900 \text{ g} = \blacksquare \text{ mg}$

15. $\blacksquare \text{ kg} = 5.7 \text{ mg}$

16. $120 \text{ g} = \blacksquare \text{ kg}$

17. $\blacksquare \text{ kg} = 440 \text{ g}$

18. $\blacksquare \text{ kg} = 1,006,000 \text{ mg}$

19. $0.009 \text{ kg} = \blacksquare \text{ mg}$

20. $0.2 \text{ mg} = \blacksquare \text{ g}$

21. $8.6 \text{ kg} = \blacksquare \text{ g}$

Bar Graphs

Use bar graphs to compare amounts. The horizontal axis shows the categories and the vertical axis shows the amounts. A multiple bar graph includes a key.

EXAMPLE

Draw a bar graph for the data in the table at the right.

Place the categories (in the first column) on the horizontal scale. Place the amounts (in the second and third columns) on the vertical scale. Include a key to the two price categories.

List and Sale Prices

Item	List	Sale
Pocket PC	$450	$400
Digital Camera	$500	$350
Minidisc Player/Recorder	$230	$180

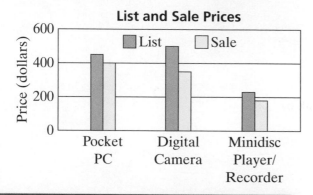

Exercises

Draw a bar graph for each set of data.

1. **Meat Consumption (pounds per person per year)**

Beef	Chicken	Pork	Turkey
62.9	53.9	46.7	13.7

SOURCE: U.S. Department of Agriculture. Go to **PHSchool.com** for a data update. Web Code: asg-9041

2. **Pets in Students' Homes**

Number of Pets	0	1	2	3	more than 3
Number of Students	11	16	9	11	6

Draw a multiple bar graph for the set of data.

3. **Weekly Leisure Time (hours)**

Activity	Sports	Reading	Working
Anna	12	8	12
Tobi	6	12	10

4. **Average SAT Math and Verbal Scores**

Year	1	2	3
Math	514	514	516
Verbal	505	506	504

SOURCE: U.S. Dept. of Education. Go to **PHSchool.com** for a data update. Web Code: asg-9041

Line Graphs

Use line graphs to show changes over time. A multiple line graph shows more than one category changing over time.

EXAMPLE

Display the data in the table below in a line graph.

Monthly Average Temperatures (°F)

Month	J	F	M	A	M	J	J	A	S	O	N	D
Houston, Texas	50	54	61	68	75	80	83	82	78	70	61	54
Chicago, Illinois	21	25	37	49	59	69	73	72	64	53	40	27

SOURCE: National Climatic Data Center. Go to **PHSchool.com** for a data update. Web Code: asg-9041

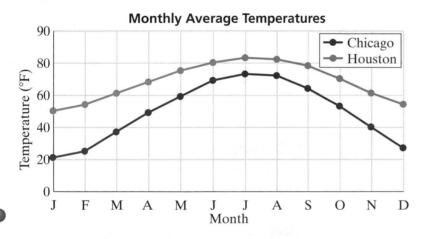

Exercises

Draw multiple line graphs for the data below.

1. **Average Baseball and Hockey Salaries (millions of dollars)**

Year	1998	1999	2000	2001
Baseball	1.4	1.6	1.9	2.1
Hockey	1.3	1.4	1.4	1.6

SOURCE: Major League Baseball Players Association and National Hockey League

2. **U.S. Newspaper Circulation (millions)**

Year	2000	2001	2002	2003
Morning	46.8	46.8	46.6	46.9
Evening	9.0	8.8	8.6	8.3

SOURCE: U.S. Census Bureau. Go to **PHSchool.com** for a data update. Web Code: asg-9041

3. **Movies Rented per Household**

Year	1	2	3	4	5
Videos	40.8	40.1	38.9	35.2	33.8
DVDs	3.1	8.5	10.9	25.4	29.9

4. **Space Launches**

Year	1	2	3	4	5
United States	38	36	33	31	24
Russia	29	25	28	36	23

Table 1 Measures

Metric	Customary
Length	**Length**
10 millimeters (mm) = 1 centimeter (cm) 100 cm = 1 meter (m) 1,000 mm = 1 m 1,000 m = 1 kilometer (km)	12 inches (in.) = 1 foot (ft) 36 in. = 1 yard (yd) 3 ft = 1 yd 5,280 ft = 1 mile (mi) 1,760 yd = 1 mi
Area	**Area**

100 square millimeters (mm^2) =
  1 square centimeter (cm^2)
10,000 cm^2 = 1 square meter (m^2)
	144 square inches ($in.^2$) =
	  1 square foot (ft^2)
	9 ft^2 = 1 square yard (yd^2)
	4,840 yd^2 = 1 acre

Volume	**Volume**

1,000 cubic millimeters (mm^3) =
  1 cubic centimeter (cm^3)
1,000,000 cm^3 = 1 cubic meter (m^3)
	1,728 cubic inches ($in.^3$) =
	  1 cubic foot (ft^3)
	27 ft^3 = 1 cubic yard (yd^3)

Mass	**Mass**
1,000 milligrams (mg) = 1 gram (g) 1,000 g = 1 kilogram (kg)	16 ounces (oz) = 1 pound (lb) 2,000 lb = 1 ton (t)
Liquid Capacity	**Liquid Capacity**
1,000 milliliters (mL) = 1 liter (L)	8 fluid ounces (fl oz) = 1 cup (c) 2 c = 1 pint (pt) 2 pt = 1 quart (qt) 4 qt = 1 gallon (gal)

Time

1 minute (min) = 60 seconds (s)
1 hour (h) = 60 min
1 day (d) = 24 h
1 year (yr) = 365 d

Table 2 Reading Math Symbols

$\approx$	is approximately equal to	p. 4
$-$	minus (subtraction)	p. 4
$=$	is equal to	p. 4
$+$	plus (addition)	p. 5
$\div$	divide (division)	p. 5
$(\ )$	parentheses for grouping	p. 9
$\times, \cdot$	times (multiplication)	p. 13
$\lvert a \rvert$	absolute value of a	p. 32
$-a$	opposite of a	p. 32
$>$	is greater than	p. 33
$<$	is less than	p. 33
$\circ$	degrees	p. 35
$[\ ]$	brackets for grouping	p. 49
$\sqrt{x}$	nonnegative square root of x	p. 50
a^n	nth power of a	p. 114
$\wedge$	raise to a power (calculator key)	p. 115
$\ldots$	and so on	p. 153
$\geq$	is greater than or equal to	p. 156
$\leq$	is less than or equal to	p. 156
$a : b$	ratio of a to b	p. 184
$\neq$	is not equal to	p. 192
$\frac{1}{a}$	reciprocal of a	p. 197
$\sim$	is similar to	p. 207
$\overset{?}{=}$	Is the statement true?	p. 230
$\%$	percent	p. 232
d	distance	p. 270
r	rate	p. 270
t	time	p. 270
(a, b)	ordered pair with x-coordinate a and y-coordinate b	p. 287
$\rightarrow$	arrow notation	p. 307
$P(\text{event})$	probability of the event	p. 342
$n!$	n factorial	p. 360
$\angle A$	angle with vertex A	p. 381
$\angle ABC$	angle with sides BA and BC	p. 381
$m\angle ABC$	measure of angle ABC	p. 381
AB	length of segment $\overline{AB}$	p. 389
$\overleftrightarrow{AB}$	line AB	p. 389
$\overrightarrow{AB}$	ray AB	p. 389
$\overline{AB}$	segment AB	p. 389
P	perimeter	p. 389
ℓ	length	p. 389
w	width	p. 389
A	area	p. 389
b	base length	p. 389
h	height	p. 389
$\triangle ABC$	triangle with vertices ABC	p. 394
b_1, b_2	base lengths of a trapezoid	p. 398
d	diameter	p. 404
r	radius	p. 404
C	circumference	p. 404
π	pi, an irrational number approximately equal to 3.14	p. 404
$\parallel$	is parallel to	p. 418
$\perp$	is perpendicular to	p. 418
$\cong$	is congruent to	p. 422
V	volume	p. 465
B	area of base	p. 465
$F \rightarrow F'$	F maps onto F'	p. 494
A'	image of A, A prime	p. 494

Table 3 Squares and Square Roots

Number	Square	Positive Square Root	Number	Square	Positive Square Root
n	n^2	$\sqrt{n}$	n	n^2	$\sqrt{n}$
1	1	1.000	51	2,601	7.141
2	4	1.414	52	2,704	7.211
3	9	1.732	53	2,809	7.280
4	16	2.000	54	2,916	7.348
5	25	2.236	55	3,025	7.416
6	36	2.449	56	3,136	7.483
7	49	2.646	57	3,249	7.550
8	64	2.828	58	3,364	7.616
9	81	3.000	59	3,481	7.681
10	100	3.162	60	3,600	7.746
11	121	3.317	61	3,721	7.810
12	144	3.464	62	3,844	7.874
13	169	3.606	63	3,969	7.937
14	196	3.742	64	4,096	8.000
15	225	3.873	65	4,225	8.062
16	256	4.000	66	4,356	8.124
17	289	4.123	67	4,489	8.185
18	324	4.243	68	4,624	8.246
19	361	4.359	69	4,761	8.307
20	400	4.472	70	4,900	8.367
21	441	4.583	71	5,041	8.426
22	484	4.690	72	5,184	8.485
23	529	4.796	73	5,329	8.544
24	576	4.899	74	5,476	8.602
25	625	5.000	75	5,625	8.660
26	676	5.099	76	5,776	8.718
27	729	5.196	77	5,929	8.775
28	784	5.292	78	6,084	8.832
29	841	5.385	79	6,241	8.888
30	900	5.477	80	6,400	8.944
31	961	5.568	81	6,561	9.000
32	1,024	5.657	82	6,724	9.055
33	1,089	5.745	83	6,889	9.110
34	1,156	5.831	84	7,056	9.165
35	1,225	5.916	85	7,225	9.220
36	1,296	6.000	86	7,396	9.274
37	1,369	6.083	87	7,569	9.327
38	1,444	6.164	88	7,744	9.381
39	1,521	6.245	89	7,921	9.434
40	1,600	6.325	90	8,100	9.487
41	1,681	6.403	91	8,281	9.539
42	1,764	6.481	92	8,464	9.592
43	1,849	6.557	93	8,649	9.644
44	1,936	6.633	94	8,836	9.695
45	2,025	6.708	95	9,025	9.747
46	2,116	6.782	96	9,216	9.798
47	2,209	6.856	97	9,409	9.849
48	2,304	6.928	98	9,604	9.899
49	2,401	7.000	99	9,801	9.950
50	2,500	7.071	100	10,000	10.000

Formulas and Properties

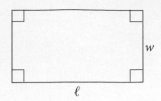

$P = 2\ell + 2w$
$A = \ell w$

Rectangle

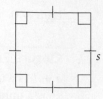

$P = 4s$
$A = s^2$

Square

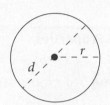

$A = \frac{1}{2}bh$

Triangle

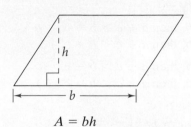

$A = bh$

Parallelogram

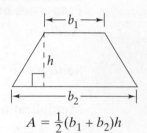

$A = \frac{1}{2}(b_1 + b_2)h$

Trapezoid

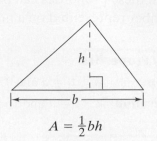

$C = 2\pi r$ or $C = \pi d$
$A = \pi r^2$

Circle

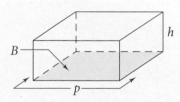

$V = Bh$
L.A. $= ph$
S.A. $=$ L.A. $+ 2B$

Rectangular Prism

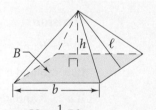

$V = \frac{1}{3}Bh$
L.A. $= 2b\ell$
S.A. $=$ L.A. $+ B$

Square Pyramid

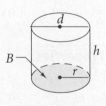

$V = Bh$
L.A. $= 2\pi rh$
S.A. $=$ L.A. $+ 2B$

Cylinder

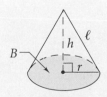

$V = \frac{1}{3}Bh$
L.A. $= \pi r\ell$
S.A. $=$ L.A. $+ B$

Cone

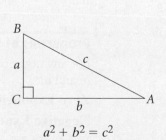

$a^2 + b^2 = c^2$

Pythagorean Theorem

Formulas and Properties

Properties of Real Numbers

Unless otherwise stated, the variables a, b, c, and d used in these properties can be replaced with any number represented on a number line.

Identity Properties

Addition	$a + 0 = a$ and $0 + a = a$
Multiplication	$a \cdot 1 = a$ and $1 \cdot a = a$

Commutative Properties

Addition	$a + b = b + a$
Multiplication	$a \cdot b = b \cdot a$

Associative Properties

Addition	$(a + b) + c = a + (b + c)$
Multiplication	$(a \cdot b) \cdot c = a \cdot (b \cdot c)$

Inverse Properties

Addition

$a + (-a) = 0$ and $-a + a = 0$

Multiplication

$a \cdot \frac{1}{a} = 1$ and $\frac{1}{a} \cdot a = 1 \ (a \neq 0)$

Distributive Properties

$a(b + c) = ab + ac \quad (b + c)a = ba + ca$
$a(b - c) = ab - ac \quad (b - c)a = ba - ca$

Properties of Equality

Addition	If $a = b$, then $a + c = b + c$.
Subtraction	If $a = b$, then $a - c = b - c$.
Multiplication	If $a = b$, then $a \cdot c = b \cdot c$.
Division	If $a = b$, and $c \neq 0$, then $\frac{a}{c} = \frac{b}{c}$.
Substitution	If $a = b$, then b can replace a in any expression.
Reflexive	$a = a$
Symmetric	If $a = b$, then $b = a$.
Transitive	If $a = b$ and $b = c$, then $a = c$.

Cross Products Property

$\frac{a}{c} = \frac{b}{d}$ is equivalent to $ad = bc$.

Zero-Product Property

If $ab = 0$, then $a = 0$ or $b = 0$.

Closure Property

$a + b$ is a unique real number.
ab is a unique real number.

Density Property

Between any two rational numbers, there is at least one other rational number.

Properties of Inequality

Addition	If $a > b$, then $a + c > b + c$.
	If $a < b$, then $a + c < b + c$.
Subtraction	If $a > b$, then $a - c > b - c$.
	If $a < b$, then $a - c < b - c$.

Multiplication

If $a > b$ and $c > 0$, then $ac > bc$.
If $a < b$ and $c > 0$, then $ac < bc$.
If $a > b$ and $c < 0$, then $ac < bc$.
If $a < b$ and $c < 0$, then $ac > bc$.

Division

If $a > b$ and $c > 0$, then $\frac{a}{c} > \frac{b}{c}$.

If $a < b$ and $c > 0$, then $\frac{a}{c} < \frac{b}{c}$.

If $a > b$ and $c < 0$, then $\frac{a}{c} < \frac{b}{c}$.

If $a < b$ and $c < 0$, then $\frac{a}{c} > \frac{b}{c}$.

Transitive

If $a > b$ and $b > c$, then $a > c$.

Comparative

If $a = b + c$ and $c > 0$, then $a > b$.

Properties of Exponents

For any nonzero number a and any integers m and n:

Zero Exponent	$a^0 = 1$
Negative Exponent	$a^{-n} = \frac{1}{a^n}$
Product of Powers	$a^m \cdot a^n = a^{m+n}$
Quotient of Powers	$\frac{a^m}{a^n} = a^{m-n}$

English/Spanish Illustrated Glossary

EXAMPLES

Acute angle (p. 381) An acute angle is an angle with a measure between 0° and 90°.

Ángulo agudo (p. 381) Un ángulo agudo es un ángulo que mide entre 0° y 90°.

$0° < m\angle 1 < 90°$

Addition Property of Equality (p. 114) The Addition Property of Equality states that if the same value is added to each side of an equation, the results are equal.

Propiedad aditiva de la igualdad (p. 114) La propiedad aditiva de la igualdad establece que si se suma el mismo valor a cada lado de una ecuación, los resultados son iguales.

Since $\frac{20}{2} = 10$, $\frac{20}{2} + 3 = 10 + 3$.
If $a = b$, then $a + c = b + c$.

Addition Property of Inequality (p. 160) The Addition Property of Inequality states that if you add the same value to each side of an inequality, the relationship between the two sides does not change.

Propiedad aditiva de la desigualdad (p. 160) La propiedad aditiva de la desigualdad establece que si sumas el mismo valor a cada lado de una desigualdad, la relación entre los dos lados no cambia.

If $a > b$, then $a + c > b + c$.
Since $4 > 2$, $4 + 11 > 2 + 11$.
If $a < b$, then $a + c < b + c$.
Since $4 < 9$, $4 + 11 < 9 + 11$.

Additive inverses (p. 10) Two numbers whose sum is 0 are additive inverses.

Inversos aditivo (p. 10) Dos números cuya suma es 0 son inversos aditivos.

$(-5) + 5 = 0$

Adjacent angles (p. 381) Adjacent angles share a vertex and a side but have no interior points in common.

Ángulos adyacentes (p. 381) Los ángulos adyacentes comparten un vértice y un lado, pero no tienen puntos interiores en común.

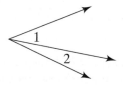

$\angle 1$ and $\angle 2$ are adjacent angles.

Algebraic expression (p. 103) An algebraic expression is a mathematical phrase that uses variables, numbers, and operation symbols.

Expresión algebraica (p. 103) Una expresión algebraica es un enunciado matemático que usa variables, números y símbolos de operaciones.

$2x - 5$ is an algebraic expression.

Alternate interior angles (p. 418) Alternate interior angles lie within a pair of lines and on opposite sides of a transversal.

Ángulos alternos internos (p. 418) Los ángulos alternos internos están ubicados entre un par de rectas y a lados opuestos de la secante.

$\angle 2$ and $\angle 3$ are alternate interior angles.

$\angle 1$ and $\angle 4$ are also alternate interior angles.

Angle (p. 381) An angle is formed by two rays with a common endpoint.

Ángulo (p. 381) Un ángulo está formado por dos rayos que tienen un punto final común llamado vértice.

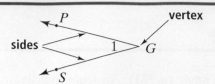

∠1 is made up of $\overrightarrow{GP}$ and $\overrightarrow{GS}$ with common endpoint G.

Angle of rotation (p. 507) The angle of rotation is the number of degrees that a figure rotates.

Ángulo de rotación (p. 507) El ángulo de rotación es el número de grados que se rota una figura.

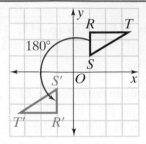

△RST has been rotated 180° to △R′S′T′.

Bases of three-dimensional figures (p. 454) See *Cone, Cylinder, Prism,* and *Pyramid.*

Bases de figuras tridimensionales (p. 454) Ver *Cone, Cylinder, Prism* y *Pyramid.*

Bases of two-dimensional figures (pp. 389, 394, 398) See *Parallelogram, Triangle,* and *Trapezoid.*

Bases de figuras bidimensionales (pp. 389, 394, 398) Ver *Parallelogram, Triangle* y *Trapezoid.*

Biased question (p. 317) A biased question is a question that makes an unjustified assumption or makes some answers appear better than others.

Pregunta tendenciosa (p. 317) Una pregunta tendenciosa es una pregunta que hace que una respuesta parezca mejor que otra.

"Do you prefer good food or junk food?"

Box plot (p. 331) A box plot uses 5 points on a number line to summerize a data set. The box shows the middle 50% of the data.

Gráfica de caja y bigotes (p. 331) En una gráfica de caja y bigotes se usan 5 puntos en una recta numérica para resumir un conjunto de datos. La caja muestra el 50% medio de los datos.

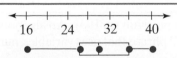

The box-and-whisker plot uses these data: 16 19 26 26 27 29 30 31 34 34 38 39 40.
The lower quartile is 26. The median is 30. The upper quartile is 36.

Center of rotation (p. 505) The center of rotation is a fixed point about which a figure is rotated.

Centro de rotación (p. 507) El centro de rotación es un punto fijo alrededor del cual se rota una figura.

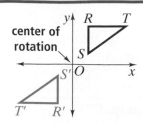

center of rotation

O is the center of rotation.

Circumference (p. 404) Circumference is the distance around a circle. You calculate the circumference of a circle by multiplying the diameter by π.

Circunferencia (p. 404) La circunferencia es la distancia alrededor de un círculo. La circunferencia de un círculo se calcula multiplicando el diámetro por π.

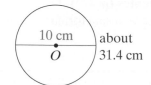

10 cm about 31.4 cm

The circumference of a circle with a diameter of 10 cm is 10π, or approximately 31.4 cm.

Coefficient (p. 108) A coefficient is a numerical factor of a term with a variable.

Coeficiente (p. 108) Un coeficiente es el factor numérico de un término que contiene una variable.

In the term $3a^2$, 3 is the coefficient.

Commission (p. 249) A commission is pay that is equal to a percent of sales.

Comisión (p. 249) Una comisión es un pago que es igual a un porcentaje de las ventas.

A salesperson receives a 6% commission on sales of \$200. Her commission is \$12.

Complement (p. 343) The complement of an event is the collection of outcomes not contained in the event.

Complemento (p. 343) El complemento de un suceso es la colección de resultados que el suceso no incluye.

The event *no rain* is the complement of the event *rain*.

Compound event (p. 360) A compound event is an event that consists of two or more events. The probability of a compound event can be found by multiplying the probability of one event by the probability of a second event.

Suceso compuesto (p. 360) Un suceso compuesto es un suceso que está formado por dos o más sucesos. La probabilidad de un suceso compuesto se puede hallar al multiplicar la probabilidad de un suceso por la probabilidad de un segundo suceso.

If $P(A) = \frac{1}{3}$ and $P(B) = \frac{1}{2}$, then $P(A, \text{then } B) = \frac{1}{6}$.

Cone (p. 455) A cone is a three-dimensional figure with one circular base and one vertex.

Cono (p. 455) Un cono es una figura tridimensional con una base circular y un vértice.

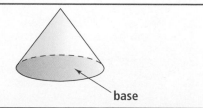

base

Congruent angles (p. 382) Congruent angles are angles that have the same measure.

Ángulos congruentes (p. 382) Los ángulos congruentes son ángulos que tienen la misma medida.

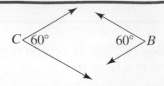

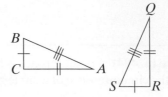

$\angle B \cong \angle C$

Congruent polygons (p. 422) Two polygons are congruent if they have exactly the same shape and size.

Polígonos congruentes (p. 422) Dos polígonos son congruentes si tienen exactamente la misma forma y tamaño.

$\triangle ABC \cong \triangle QSR$

Constant of proportionality (p. 222) The value of the ratio of quantities in a proportional relationship is called the constant of proportionality.

Constante de proporcionalidad (p. 222) El valor de la razón de las cantidades en una relación proporcional se llama constante de proporcionalidad.

Hours (h)	2	5	10
Earnings (e)	$12	$30	$60

The constant of proportionality is $c = \$6$.

Continuous data (p. 288) Continuous data are data where numbers between any two data values have meaning. Use a solid line to indicate continuous data.

Datos continuos (p. 288) Los datos continuos son datos donde los números entre dos valores de datos tienen significado. Entre los ejemplos se incluyen medidas de temperatura, longitud o peso. Se usa una recta sólida para indicar los datos continuos.

Data on the average daily temperature in Santa Barbara, California, are continuous data.

Corresponding angles (p. 418) Corresponding angles lie on the same side of the transversal and in corresponding positions.

Ángulos correspondientes (p. 418) Los ángulos correspondientes se ubican al mismo lado de una secante y en posiciones correspondientes.

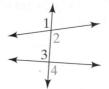

$\angle 1$ and $\angle 3$ are corresponding angles. $\angle 2$ and $\angle 4$ are also corresponding angles.

Cross products (p. 194) For two ratios, the cross products are found by multiplying the denominator of one ratio by the numerator of the other ratio.

In the proportion $\frac{2}{5} = \frac{10}{25}$, the cross products are $2 \cdot 25$ and $5 \cdot 10$.

Productos cruzados (p. 194) En dos razones, los productos cruzados se hallan al multiplicar el denominador de una razón por el numerador de la otra razón.

Cross section (p. 473) A cross section is the two-dimensional shape that can be seen after slicing through a three-dimensional object.

Sección transversal (p. 473) Una sección transversal es la figura bidimensional que se observa cuando se corta a través de un objeto tridimensional.

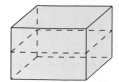

The cross section formed by this slice is a rectangle.

Cube (p. 454) A cube is a rectangular prism whose faces are all squares.

Cubo (p. 454) Un cubo es un prisma rectangular cuyas caras son todas cuadrados.

Cube root (p. 55) The cube root of a number is a number that, when used as a factor three times, is equal to the given number.

Since 2^3, or $2 \cdot 2 \cdot 2$, is 8, 2 is the cube root of 8.

Raíz cúbica (p. 55) La raíz cúbica de un número es un número que, cuando se usa tres veces como factor, es igual al número dado.

Cubic unit (p. 465) A cubic unit is a cube whose edges are one unit long.

Unidad cúbica (p. 465) Una unidad cúbica es un cubo cuyos lados tienen una unidad de longitud.

1 cm

Cylinder (p. 454) A cylinder is a three-dimensional figure with two congruent parallel bases that are circles.

Cilindro (p. 454) Un cilindro es una figura tridimensional con dos bases congruentes paralelas que son círculos.

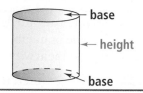

base
height
base

Dependent events (p. 361) Two events are dependent events if the occurrence of one event affects the probability of the occurrence of the other event.

Sucesos dependientes (p. 361) Dos sucesos son dependientes si el acontecimiento de uno afecta la probabilidad de que el otro ocurra.

Suppose you draw two marbles, one after the other, from a bag. If you do *not* replace the first marble before drawing the second marble, the events are dependent.

Diameter (p. 404) A diameter is a segment that passes through the center of a circle and has both endpoints on the circle.

Diámetro (p. 404) Un diámetro es un segmento que pasa por el centro de un círculo y que tiene ambos extremos sobre el círculo.

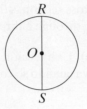

$\overline{RS}$ is a diameter of circle O.

Dilation (p. 517) A dilation is a transformation where the original figure and its image are similar. See also *Enlargement* and *Reduction*.

Dilatación (p. 517) Una dilatación es una transformación donde la figura original y su imagen son semejantes. Ver también *Enlargement* y *Reduction*.

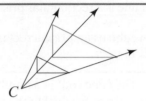

The blue triangle is an enlargement of the red triangle. The red triangle is a reduction of the blue triangle.

Discount (p. 259) The difference between the original price and the sale price of an item is called the discount.

Descuento (p. 259) Se llama descuento a la diferencia entre el precio de un artículo y su precio de venta.

A $20 book is discounted by $2.50 to sell for $17.50.

Discrete data (p. 288) Discrete data are data that involve a count of items, such as numbers of people or numbers of cars. For discrete data, plot the data points and connect them with a dashed line.

Datos discretos (p. 288) Los datos discretos son los datos que involucran un conteo de elementos, como número de personas o de carros. En los datos discretos cada elemento se indica con un punto, pero los puntos *no* se unen con una recta continua.

Data on the number of people different football stadiums can hold are discrete data.

Division Property of Equality (p. 115) The Division Property of Equality states that if both sides of an equation are divided by the same nonzero number, the sides remain equal.

Propiedad de división de la igualdad (p. 115) La propiedad de división de la igualdad establece que si ambos lados de una ecuación se dividen por el mismo número distinto de cero, los dos lados se mantienen iguales.

Since $3(2) = 6$, $3(2) \div 2 = 6 \div 2$. If $a = b$ and $c \neq 0$, then $\frac{a}{c} = \frac{b}{c}$.

Division Property of Inequality (p. 165) The Division Property of Inequality states that if you divide an inequality by a positive number, the direction of the inequality is unchanged. If you divide an inequality by a negative number, *reverse* the direction of the inequality sign.

Propiedad de división de la desigualdad (p. 165) La propiedad de división de la desigualdad establece que si se divide una desigualdad por un número positivo, la dirección de la desigualdad no cambia. Si se divide una desigualdad por un número negativo, se *invierte* la dirección del signo de desigualdad.

If $a > b$ and $c > 0$, then $\frac{a}{c} > \frac{b}{c}$.
Since $2 > 1$ and $3 > 0$, $\frac{2}{3} > \frac{1}{3}$.
If $a < b$ and $c > 0$, then $\frac{a}{c} < \frac{b}{c}$.
Since $2 < 4$ and $3 > 0$, $\frac{2}{3} < \frac{4}{3}$.
If $a > b$ and $c < 0$, then $\frac{a}{c} < \frac{b}{c}$.
Since $2 > 1$ and $-4 < 0$, $\frac{2}{-4} < \frac{1}{-4}$.
If $a < b$ and $c < 0$, then $\frac{a}{c} > \frac{b}{c}$.
Since $2 < 4$ and $-4 < 0$, $\frac{2}{-4} > \frac{4}{-4}$.

Edge (p. 454) An edge is a segment formed by the intersection of two faces of a three-dimensional figure.

Arista (p. 454) Una arista es un segmento formado por la intersección de dos caras de una figura tridimensional.

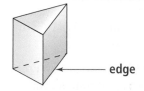
edge

Enlargement (p. 518) A dilation with a scale factor greater than 1 is an enlargement.

Aumento (p. 518) Una dilatación con un factor de escala mayor que 1 es un aumento.

See *Dilation*.

Equivalent ratios (p. 185) Two ratios that name the same number are equivalent ratios. Equivalent ratios written as fractions are equivalent fractions.

Razones equivalentes (p. 185) Las razones equivalentes indican el mismo número. Las razones equivalentes escritas como fracciones son fracciones equivalentes.

The ratios $\frac{4}{7}$ and $\frac{8}{14}$ are equivalent.

Event (p. 342) A collection of possible outcomes is an event.

Suceso (p. 342) Un suceso es un grupo de resultados posibles.

When you toss a coin, "heads" and "tails" are possible events.

Experimental probability (p. 347) Probability based on experimental data or observations is called experimental probability.
$P(\text{event}) = \frac{\text{number of times an event occurs}}{\text{total number of trials}}$

Probabilidad experimental (p. 347) En una serie de pruebas, la probabilidad experimental de un suceso es la razón del número de veces que ocurre un suceso al número total de pruebas.
$P(\text{suceso}) = \frac{\text{número de veces que ocurre un suceso}}{\text{número total de pruebas}}$

A basketball player makes 19 baskets in 28 attempts. The experimental probability that the player makes a basket is $\frac{19}{28} \approx 68\%$.

English/Spanish Glossary

Exterior angle of a polygon (p. 441) The exterior angle of a polygon is an angle formed by a side and an extension of an adjacent side.

Ángulo exterior de un polígono (p. 441) El ángulo exterior de un polígono es el ángulo formado por un lado y una extensión del lado adyacente.

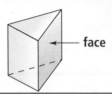

Angles 1, 2, 3, 4, and 5 are exterior angles of the polygon.

Face (p. 454) A face is a flat surface of a three-dimensional figure that is shaped like a polygon.

Cara (p. 454) Una cara es una superficie plana de una figura tridimensional que tiene la forma de un polígono.

Function (p. 275) A function is a rule that assigns to each input value exactly one output value.

Función (p. 275) Una función es una relación que asigna exactamente un valor resultante a cada valor inicial.

Earned income is a function of the number of hours worked w. If you earn $6/h, then your income can be expressed by the function $f(w) = 6w$.

Function rule (p. 275) A function rule is an equation that describes a function.

Fórmula de una función (p. 275) Una fórmula de una función es una ecuación que describe una función.

The function rule that describes the cost c of buying x movie tickets that cost $9 each is $c = 9x$.

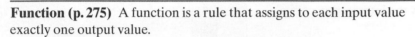

Height of three-dimensional figures (p. 454) See *Cylinder* and *Prism*.

Altura de figuras tridimensionales (p. 454) Ver *Cylinder* y *Prism*.

Height of two-dimensional figures (pp. 389, 394, 398) See *Parallelogram*, *Triangle*, and *Trapezoid*.

Altura de figuras bidimensionales (pp. 389, 394, 398) Ver *Parallelogram*, *Triangle* y *Trapezoid*.

Hypotenuse (p. 539) In a right triangle, the hypotenuse is the longest side, which is opposite the right angle.

Hipotenusa (p. 539) En un triángulo rectángulo, la hipotenusa es el lado más largo, que es el lado opuesto al ángulo recto.

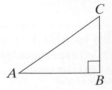

$\overline{AC}$ is the hypotenuse of $\triangle ABC$.

Image (p. 496) An image is the result of a transformation of a point, line, or figure.

Imagen (p. 496) Una imagen es el resultado de una transformación de un punto, una recta o una figura.

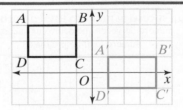

$A'B'C'D'$ is the image of $ABCD$.

Independent events (p. 360) Two events are independent events if the occurrence of one event does not affect the probability of the occurrence of the other.

Sucesos independientes (p. 360) Dos sucesos son independientes si el acontecimiento de uno no afecta la probabilidad de que el otro suceso ocurra.

Suppose you draw two marbles, one after the other, from a bag. If you replace the first marble before drawing the second marble, the events are independent.

Indirect measurement (p. 208) Indirect measurement uses proportions and similar figures to measure distances that would be difficult to measure directly.

Medición indirecta (p. 208) La medición indirecta usa proporciones y triángulos semejantes para medir las distancias que serían difíciles de medir directamente.

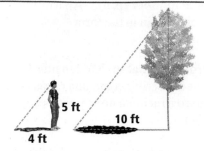

5 ft
10 ft
4 ft

A 5-ft-tall person standing near a tree has a shadow 4 ft long. The tree has a shadow 10 ft long. The height of the tree is 12.5 ft.

Inequality (p. 156) An inequality is a mathematical sentence that contains one of the signs $<$, $>$, $\leq$, $\geq$, or $\neq$.

Desigualdad (p. 156) Una desigualdad es una oración matemática que contiene uno de los signos $<$, $>$, $\leq$, $\geq$ o $\neq$.

$x < -5$, $x > 8$, $x \leq 1$, $x \geq -11$, $x \neq 7$

Inference (p. 326) An inference is a prediction or conclusion based on data or reasoning.

Inferencia (p. 326) Una inferencia es una prediccion o una conclusión basada en datos o razonamiento.

Random Sample of Ages				
8	12	2	41	39
47	16	20	26	25
16	35	14	57	9
25	23	12	30	20

Based on the sample, 70% of visitors are younger than 30.

Integers (p. 4) Integers are the set of positive whole numbers, their opposites, and 0.

Enteros (p. 4) Los enteros son el conjunto de números enteros positivos, sus opuestos y el 0.

$\ldots -3, -2, -1, 0, 1, 2, 3, \ldots$

Interior angle (p. 440) Two consecutive sides of a polygon form one interior angle.

Ángulo interior (p. 440) Los ángulos interiores son los ángulos que están en la parte interna de los vértices de un polígono.

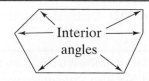

Interior angles

Interquartile range (p. 331) The interquartile range (IQR) of a data set is the difference between the upper and lower quartiles.

Rango entre cuartiles (p. 331) El rango entre cuartiles (IQR) de un conjunto de datos es la diferencia entre el cuartil superior y el cuartil inferior.

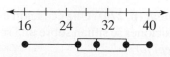

16   24   32   40

The lower quartile is 26. The upper quartile is 36.

The IQR is $36 - 26 = 10$.

Inverse operations (p. 114) Inverse operations are operations that undo each other.

Addition and subtraction are inverse operations.

Operaciones inversas (p. 114) Las operaciones inversas son las operaciones que se anulan entre ellas.

Irrational number (p. 52) An irrational number is a number that cannot be written in the form $\frac{a}{b}$, where a is any integer and b is any nonzero integer.

The numbers π and $2.41592653\ldots$ are irrational numbers.

Número irracional (p. 52) Un número irracional es un número que no se puede escribir como una razón de dos enteros. Como decimal, un número irracional no se puede escribir como decimal finito o periódico.

Legs of a right triangle (p. 540) The legs of a right triangle are the two shortest sides of the triangle.

Catetos de un triángulo rectángulo (p. 540) Los catetos de un triángulo rectángulo son los dos lados más cortos del triángulo.

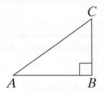

$\overline{AB}$ and $\overline{BC}$ are the legs of $\triangle ABC$.

Like terms (p. 108) Terms that have the same variable factors.

$2y$ and $7y$ are like terms.

Términos semejantes (p. 108) Términos que tienen los mismos factores variables.

Line of reflection (p. 501) A line of reflection is a line across which a figure is reflected.

Eje de reflexión (p. 501) Un eje de reflexión es una recta sobre la cual se refleja una figura.

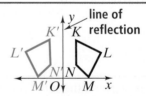

$KLMN$ is reflected over the y-axis.

Line of symmetry (p. 502) A line of symmetry divides a figure into mirror images.

Eje de simetría (p. 502) Un eje de simetría divide una figura en imágenes reflejas.

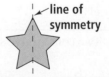

Linear (p. 270) An equation is a linear equation if it forms a straight line when graphed. See also *Slope-intercept form.*

Ecuación lineal (p. 270) Una ecuación es una ecuación lineal si todas sus soluciones se sitúan sobre una recta. Ver también *Slope-intercept form.*

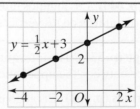

$y = \frac{1}{2}x + 3$ is a linear equation because the graph of its solutions is a line.

Linear function (pp. 287, 299) A linear function is a function whose points lie on a straight line when the function is graphed.

Función lineal (pp. 287, 299) Una función lineal es una función cuyos puntos están sobre una recta.

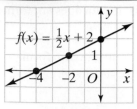

$f(x) = \frac{1}{2}x + 2$ is a linear function.

Markup (p. 259) The markup is the difference between the selling price and the original cost.

Sobrecosto (p. 259) El sobrecosto es la diferencia entre el precio de venta y el costo original.

A store buys a shirt for $15 and sells it for $25. The markup is $10.

Mean absolute deviation (p. 332) The mean absolute deviation (MAD) of a data set is the average distance between the mean and each data value.

Desviación absoluta media (p. 332) La desviación absoluta media (MAD) de un conjunto de datos es la distancia promedio entre la media y cada valor de dato.

18, 19, 21, 23, 26, 29, 31
The mean is 23.
The MAD is $\frac{28}{7} = 4$.

Multiplication Property of Equality (p. 114) The Multiplication Property of Equality states that if each side of an equation is multiplied by the same number, the results are equal.

Propiedad multiplicativa de la igualdad (p. 114) La propiedad multiplicativa de la igualdad establece que si cada lado de una ecuación se multiplica por el mismo número, los resultados son iguales.

Since $\frac{12}{2} = 6$, $\frac{12}{2} \cdot 2 = 6 \cdot 2$.
If $a = b$, then $a \cdot c = b \cdot c$.

Multiplication Property of Inequality (p. 167) The Multiplication Property of Inequality states that if you multiply an inequality by a positive number, the direction of the inequality is unchanged. If you multiply an inequality by a negative number, *reverse* the direction of the inequality sign.

Propiedad multiplicativa de la desigualdad (p. 167) La propiedad multiplicativa de la desigualdad establece que cuando se multiplica una desigualdad por un número positivo, la dirección de la desigualdad no cambia. Si se multiplica una desigualdad por un número negativo, se *invierte* la dirección del signo de la desigualdad.

If $a > b$ and $c > 0$, then $ac > bc$.
Since $3 > 2$ and $7 > 0$, $3 \cdot 7 > 2 \cdot 7$.
If $a < b$ and $c > 0$, then $ac < bc$.
Since $3 < 5$ and $7 > 0$, $3 \cdot 7 < 5 \cdot 7$.
If $a > b$ and $c < 0$, then $ac < bc$.
Since $3 > 2$ and $-6 < 0$,
$3 \cdot (-6) < 2 \cdot (-6)$.
If $a < b$ and $c < 0$, then $ac > bc$.
Since $3 < 5$ and $-6 < 0$,
$3 \cdot (-6) > 5 \cdot (-6)$.

Net (p. 458) A net is a two-dimensional pattern that can be folded to form a three-dimensional figure.

Plantilla (p. 458) Una plantilla es un patrón bidimensional que se puede doblar para formar una figura tridimensional.

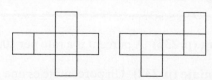

These are nets for a cube.

Nonlinear (p. 270) If data does *not* form a straight line when graphed, then its change is nonlinear.

No lineal (p. 270) Si lo datos *no* forman una recta en una gráfica, entonces su cambio es no lineal.

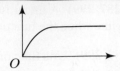

Obtuse angle (p. 381) An obtuse angle is an angle with a measure greater than 90° and less than 180°.

Ángulo obtuso (p. 381) Un ángulo obtuso es un ángulo que mide más de 90° y menos de 180°.

Opposites (p. 4) Opposites are two numbers that are the same distance from 0 on a number line, but in opposite directions.

Opuestos (p. 4) Opuestos son dos números que están a la misma distancia del 0 en una recta numérica, pero en direcciones opuestas.

17 and −17 are opposites.

Ordered pair (p. 554) An ordered pair gives the coordinates of the location of a point. The *x*-coordinate shows a point's position left or right from the origin. The *y*-coordinate shows a point's position up or down from the *x*-axis.

Par ordenado (p. 554) Un par ordenado identifica la ubicación de un punto. La coordenada *x* muestra la posición de un punto a la izquierda o derecha del origen. La coordenada *y* muestra la posición de un punto arriba o abajo del eje de *x*.

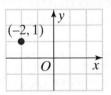

The *x*-coordinate of the point (−2, 1) is −2, and the *y*-coordinate is 1.

Origin (p. 554) The origin is the point of intersection of the *x*- and *y*-axes in a coordinate plane.

Origen (p. 554) El origen es el punto de intersección de los ejes de *x* y de *y* en un plano de coordenadas.

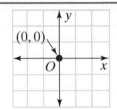

The ordered pair that describes the origin is (0, 0).

Outcome (p. 342) An outcome is the result of an action.

Resultado (p. 342) Un resultado es cualquiera de los posibles desenlaces que pueden ocurrir en un experimento.

The outcomes of rolling a standard number cube are 1, 2, 3, 4, 5, and 6.

Percent (p. 232) A percent is a rate per 100.

Porcentaje (p. 232) Un porcentaje es una razón que compara un número con 100.

$$\frac{25}{100} = 25\%$$

Percent Error (p. 250) Percent error uses the absolute value of the difference between the measured value and the actual or desired value.

Error porcentual (p. 250) El error porcentual usa el valor absoluto de la diferencia entre el valor medido y el valor real o deseado.

Measured value: 49.75 mm
Desired value: 50.0 mm

$$\text{Percent Error} = \frac{|50.0 - 49.75|}{50.0} \times 100$$
$$= 0.5$$

The percent error is 0.5%.

Percent of change (p. 258) The percent of change is the percent a quantity increases or decreases from its original amount.

Porcentaje de cambio (p. 258) El porcentaje de cambio es el porcentaje que aumenta o disminuye una cantidad a partir de su cantidad original.

The number of employees increases from 14 to 21. The percent of change is $\frac{21 - 14}{14} = 50\%$.

Perfect cube (p. 55) A perfect cube is a number that is the cube of a whole number.

Cubo perfecto (p. 55) Un cubo perfecto es un número que es el cubo de un número entero.

$2 \cdot 2 \cdot 2$, or 2^3, is 8. So 8 is a perfect cube.

Perfect square (p. 50) A perfect square is a number that is the square of a whole number.

Cuadrado perfecto (p. 50) Un cuadrado perfecto es un número que es el cuadrado de un entero.

Since $25 = 5^2$, 25 is a perfect square.

Pi (p. 404) Pi (π) is the ratio of the circumference C of any circle to its diameter d.

Pi (p. 404) Pi (π) es la razón de la circunferencia C de cualquier círculo a su diámetro d.

$$\pi = \frac{C}{d}$$

Polygon (p. 207) A polygon is a closed figure formed by three or more line segments that do not cross.

Polígono (p. 207) Un polígono es una figura cerrada que está formada por tres o más segmentos de recta que no se cruzan.

Population (p. 316) A population is a group of objects or people about which information is wanted.

Población (p. 316) Una población es un grupo de objetos o personas sobre el que se busca información.

A class of 25 students is a sample of the population of a school.

Principal (p. 254) Principal is the original amount deposited or borrowed.

Capital (p. 254) El capital es el monto original que se deposita o se toma prestado.

You deposit $500 in a savings account. Your principal is $500.

Prism (p. 454) A prism is a three-dimensional figure with two parallel and congruent polygonal faces, called bases. A prism is named for the shape of its base.

Prisma (p. 454) Un prisma es una figura tridimensional que tiene dos caras poligonales paralelas y congruentes llamadas bases. Un prisma recibe su nombre por la forma de su base.

Rectangular Prism   Triangular Prism

Proportion (p. 193) A proportion is an equation stating that two ratios are equal.

$\frac{3}{12} = \frac{9}{36}$ is a proportion.

Proporción (p. 193) Una proporción es una ecuación que establece que dos razones son iguales.

Proportional relationship (p. 280) A proportional relationship is a relationship between inputs and outputs in which the ratio of inputs and outputs is always the same.

Relación de proporción (p. 280) Una relación de porporción es una relación entre entradas y salidas en la que la razón de entradas y salidas siempre es la misma.

Input	Output
1	4
2	8
3	12

Ratio = $\frac{1}{4}$

$\frac{2}{8} = \frac{1}{4}$

$\frac{3}{12} = \frac{1}{4}$

Pyramid (p. 454) A pyramid is a three-dimensional figure with triangular faces that meet at a vertex and a base that is a polygon. A pyramid is named for the shape of its base.

Pirámide (p. 454) Una pirámide es una figura tridimensional que tiene caras triangulares que coinciden en un vértice y una base que es un polígono. Una pirámide recibe su nombre por la forma de su base.

Triangular Pyramid

Rectangular Pyramid

Pythagorean Theorem (p. 540) In any right triangle, the sum of the squares of the lengths of the legs (a and b) is equal to the square of the length of the hypotenuse (c): $a^2 + b^2 = c^2$.

Teorema de Pitágoras (p. 540) En cualquier triángulo rectángulo, la suma del cuadrado de la longitud de los catetos (a y b) es igual al cuadrado de la longitud de la hipotenusa (c): $a^2 + b^2 = c^2$.

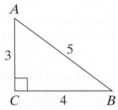

The right triangle has leg lengths 3 and 4 and hypotenuse length 5.
$3^2 + 4^2 = 5^2$

Quadrants (p. 554) The x- and y-axes divide the coordinate plane into four regions called quadrants.

Cuadrantes (p. 554) Los ejes de x y de y dividen el plano de coordenadas en cuatro regiones llamadas cuadrantes.

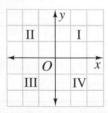

The quadrants are labeled I, II, III, and IV.

Radius (p. 404) A radius of a circle is a segment that connects the center of a circle to the circle.

Radio (p. 404) Un radio de un círculo es un segmento que conecta el centro del círculo con el círculo.

$\overline{OA}$ is a radius of circle O.

Random sample (p. 316) In a random sample, each member of the population has an equal chance of being selected.

For the population *customers at a mall*, a random sample would be every 20th customer entering in a 2-hour period.

Muestra aleatoria (p. 316) En una muestra aleatoria, cada miembro de la población tiene la misma posibilidad de ser elegido.

Rate (p. 188) A rate is a ratio that compares two quantities measured in different units.

You read 116 words in 1 min. Your reading rate is $\frac{116 \text{ words}}{1 \text{ min}}$.

Tasa (p. 188) Una tasa es una razón que compara dos cantidades medidas en diferentes unidades.

Rate of change (p. 292) A rate of change is a comparison between two quantities that are changing.

$$\text{rate of change} = \frac{\text{change in one quantity}}{\text{change in another quantity}}$$

Video rental for 1 day is $1.99. Video rental for 2 days is $2.99.

$$\text{rate of change} = \frac{2.99 - 1.99}{2 - 1}$$
$$= \frac{1.00}{1}$$
$$= 1$$

Tasa de cambio (p. 292) Una tasa de cambio es una comparación entre dos cantidades que cambian. La tasa de cambio se llama también pendiente.

$$\text{tasa de cambio} = \frac{\text{cambio en una cantidad}}{\text{cambio en otra cantidad}}$$

Rational number (p. 26) A rational number is a number that can be written as a quotient of two integers, where the divisor is not 0.

$\frac{1}{3}, -5, 6.4, 0.666\ldots, -2\frac{4}{5}, 0$, and $\frac{7}{3}$ are rational numbers.

Número racional (p. 26) Un número racional es un número que se puede escribir como cociente de dos enteros, donde el divisor es diferente de cero.

Real numbers (p. 52) Together, rational and irrational numbers form the set of real numbers.

$3, -5.25, 3.141592653\ldots$, and $\frac{7}{8}$ are real numbers.

Números reales (p. 52) Juntos, los números rationales e irracionales forman el conjunto de los números reales.

Reduction (p. 518) A dilation with a scale factor less than 1 is a reduction.

See *Dilation*.

Reducción (p. 518) Una dilatación con un factor de escala menor que 1 es una reducción.

Reflection (p. 499) A reflection is a transformation that flips a figure over a line of reflection.

Reflexión (p. 499) Una reflexión es una transformación que voltea una figura sobre un eje de reflexión.

$K'L'M'N'$ is a reflection of $KLMN$ over the *y*-axis.

English/Spanish Glossary

Reflectional symmetry (p. 500) If a figure can be reflected over a line so that its image matches the original figure, the figure has reflectional symmetry.

Simetría por reflexión (p. 500) Si una figura se puede reflejar sobre una recta de modo que su imagen coincida con la figura original, la figura tiene simetría por reflexión.

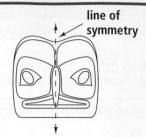

line of symmetry

Repeating decimal (p. 22) A repeating decimal is a decimal that repeats without end. The repeating block can be one or more digits.

Decimal periódico (p. 22) Un decimal periódico es un decimal que repite los mismos dígitos interminablemente. El bloque que se repite puede ser un dígito o más de un dígito.

$0.888\ldots = 0.\overline{8}$
$0.272727\ldots = 0.\overline{27}$

Right angle (p. 381) A right angle is an angle with a measure of 90°.

Ángulo recto (p. 381) Un ángulo recto es un ángulo que mide 90°.

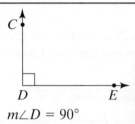

$m\angle D = 90°$

Rotation (p. 505) A rotation is a transformation that turns a figure about a fixed point, called the center of rotation.

Rotación (p. 505) Una rotación es una transformación que gira una figura sobre un punto fijo, llamado centro de rotación.

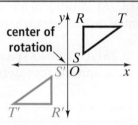

center of rotation

$\triangle RST$ has been rotated about the origin O to $\triangle R'S'T'$.

Rotational symmetry (p. 505) A figure has rotational symmetry if it can be rotated 180° or less and match the original figure.

Simetría rotacional (p. 505) Una figura tiene simetría rotacional si se puede rotar 180° o menos y calzar sobre la figura original.

This figure has 60° rotational symmetry.

S

Sample (p. 316) A sample is a part of the population.

Muestra (p. 316) Una muestra es una parte de la población.

A class of 25 students is a sample of a school population. The sample size is 25.

Sample space (p. 353) Sample space is the collection of all possible outcomes in a probability experiment.

Espacio muestral (p. 353) El espacio muestral es el total de todos los resultados posibles en un experimento de probabilidad.

The sample space for tossing two coins is HH, HT, TH, TT.

Scale (p. 213) A scale is the ratio that compares a length in a drawing to the corresponding length in the actual object.

Escala (p. 213) Una escala es la razón que compara la longitud en un dibujo con la longitud correspondiente en el objeto real.

A 25-mi road is 1 in. long on a map. The scale can be written three ways:
1 in. : 25 mi, $\frac{1 \text{ in.}}{25 \text{ mi}}$, 1 in. = 25 mi.

Scale drawing (p. 213) A scale drawing is an enlarged or reduced drawing of an object that is similar to the actual object.

Dibujo a escala (p. 213) Un dibujo a escala es un dibujo aumentado o reducido de un objeto que es semejante al objeto real.

Maps and floor plans are scale drawings.

Scale factor (p. 519) The ratio of the dimensions of the image to the dimensions of the original figure is called a scale factor.

Factor de escala (p. 519) La razón de las dimensiones de una imagen a las dimensiones de la figura original se llama el factor de escala.

This dilation has center C and scale factor 3.

Scientific notation (p. 66) A number is in scientific notation if the first factor is greater than or equal to 1 and less than 10, and the second factor is a power of 10.

Notatión científica (p. 66) Un número está en notación científica si el primer factor es mayor que o igual a 1 y menor que 10, y el segundo factor es una potencia de 10.

37,000,000 is written as 3.7×10^7 in scientific notation.

Similar figures (p. 428) Similar figures have the same shape, but not necessarily the same size.

Figuras semejantes (p. 428) Las figuras semejantes tienen la misma forma, pero no necesariamente el mismo tamaño.

$\triangle ABC \sim \triangle RTS$

Similar polygons (pp. 207, 428) Two polygons are similar if their corresponding angles have the same measure and the lengths of their corresponding sides are proportional.

Polígonos semejantes (pp. 207, 428) Dos polígonos son semejantes si sus ángulos correspondientes tienen la misma medida y las longitudes de sus lados correspondientes son proporcionales.

See *Similar figures.*

Simple interest (p. 254) Simple interest is interest calculated only on the principal. Use the formula $I = prt$ where I is the interest, p is the principal, r is the annual interest rate, and t is time in years.

Interés simple (p. 254) El interés simple se calcula sólo en relación al principal. Se usa la fórmula $I = prt$ donde I es el interés, p es el principal, r es la tasa de interés anual y t es el tiempo en años.

The simple interest earned on $200 invested at 5% annual interest for three years is $200 · 0.05 · 3, or $30.

English/Spanish Glossary

Simulation (p. 401) A model used to estimate the probability of an event.

The table shows the results of a simulation

Boxes Needed to Win Prize	Frequency
1	IIII
2	II
3 or more	IIII IIII IIII

Simulación (p. 401) Un modelo que se usa para estimar la probabilidad de que ocurra un suceso.

The probability to win the prizes is $\frac{7}{10}$ if a customer buys 3 or more boxes.

Slope (p. 293) Slope is a ratio that describes steepness.

$$\text{Slope} = \frac{\text{vertical change}}{\text{horizontal change}} = \frac{\text{rise}}{\text{run}}$$

Pendiente (p. 293) La pendiente es la razón que describe la inclinación.

$$\text{Pendiente} = \frac{\text{cambio vertical}}{\text{cambio horizontal}} = \frac{\text{elevación}}{\text{desplazamiento}}$$

Slope of a line (p. 293)

$$\text{Slope} = \frac{\text{change in } y \text{ coordinates}}{\text{change in } x \text{ coordinates}} = \frac{\text{rise}}{\text{run}}$$

Pendiente de una recta (p. 293)

$$\text{Pendiente} = \frac{\text{cambio en la coordenada } y}{\text{cambio en la coordenada } x} = \frac{\text{elevación}}{\text{desplazamiento}}$$

The slope of the given line is $\frac{2}{4} = \frac{1}{2}$.

Slope-intercept form (p. 299) An equation written in the form $y = mx + b$ is in slope-intercept form. The graph is a line with slope m and y-intercept b.

The equation $y = 2x + 1$ is written in slope-intercept form with $m = 2$ and $b = 1$.

Forma pendiente intercepto (p. 299) Una ecuación escrita en la forma $y = mx + b$ está en la forma pendiente intercepto. La gráfica es una recta en la que m es la pendiente y b es el intercepto y.

Solution of an inequality (p. 156) A solution of an inequality is any value that makes the inequality true.

7 is a solution of $x < 15$.

Solución (p. 156) Una solución es cualquier valor o valores que hacen que una ecuación o una desigualdad sea verdadera.

Sphere (p. 455, 482) A sphere is the set of all points in space that are the same distance from a center point.

Esfera (p. 455, 482) Una esfera es el conjunto de todos los puntos en el espacio que están a la misma distancia de un punto central.

Square root (p. 50) The square root of a number is another number that when multiplied by itself is equal to the given number.

$\sqrt{9} = 3$ because $3^2 = 9$.

Raíz cuadrada (p. 50) La raíz cuadrada de un número es un número que cuando se multiplica por sí mismo es igual al número dado.

Straight angle (p. 381) A straight angle is an angle with a measure of $180°$.

$m\angle TPL = 180°$

Ángulo llano (p. 381) Un ángulo llano es un ángulo que mide $180°$.

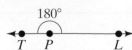

Subtraction Property of Equality (p. 114) The Subtraction Property of Equality states that if the same number is subtracted from each side of an equation, the results are equal.

Since $\frac{20}{2} = 10$, $\frac{20}{2} - 3 = 10 - 3$.
If $a = b$, then $a - c = b - c$.

Propiedad sustractiva de la igualdad (p. 114) La propiedad sustractiva de la igualdad establece que si se resta el mismo número a cada lado de una ecuación, los resultados son iguales.

Subtraction Property of Inequality (p. 161) When you subtract the same number from each side of an inequality, the relationship between the two sides does not change.

If $a > b$, then $a - c > b - c$.
Since $9 > 6$, $9 - 2 > 6 - 2$.
If $a < b$, then $a - c < b - c$.
Since $9 < 13$, $9 - 2 < 13 - 2$.

Propiedad sustractiva de la desigualdad (p. 161) Cuando se resta el mismo número a cada lado de una desigualdad, la relación entre los dos lados no cambia.

Surface area of a prism (p. 459) The surface area of a prism is the sum of the areas of its faces.

Each square = 1 in.^{2}

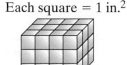

Área total de un prisma (p. 459) El área total de un prisma es la suma de las áreas de sus caras.

$4 \cdot 12$ in.^{2} $+ 2 \cdot 9$ in.^{2} $= 66$ in.^{2}

Terminating decimal (p. 21) A terminating decimal is a decimal that stops, or terminates.

Both 0.6 and 0.7265 are terminating decimals.

Decimal finito (p. 21) Un decimal finito es un decimal que termina.

Theoretical probability (p. 342) The formula used to compute the theoretical probability of an event is
$$P(\text{event}) = \frac{\text{number of favorable outcomes}}{\text{total number of possible outcomes}}.$$

Suppose you select a letter from the letters H, A, P, P, and Y. The theoretical probability of selecting a P is $\frac{2}{5}$.

Probabilidad teórica (p. 342) La fórmula que se usa para calcular la probabilidad teórica de un suceso es
$$P(\text{suceso}) = \frac{\text{número favorable de resultados}}{\text{número total de resultados posibles}}.$$

Three-dimensional figure (p. 454) Three-dimensional figures are figures that do not lie in a plane.

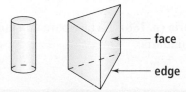

Figura tridimensional (p. 454) Las figuras tridimensionales son figuras que no están en un solo plano.

Transformation (p. 494) A transformation is a change in position, shape, or size of a figure. Three types of transformations that change position only are translations, reflections, and rotations.

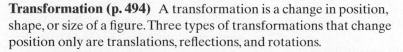

Transformación (p. 494) Una transformación es un cambio de posición, forma o tamaño de una figura. Los tres tipos de transformaciones que cambian la posición son las traslaciones, las reflexiones y las rotaciones.

$K'L'M'N'$ is a reflection, or flip, of $KLMN$ across the y-axis.

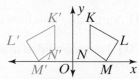

English/Spanish Glossary

Translation (p. 494) A translation is a transformation that moves each point of a figure the same distance and in the same direction.

Traslación (p. 494) Una traslación es una transformación que mueve cada punto de una figura la misma distancia y en la misma dirección.

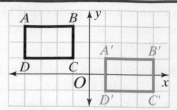

$A'B'C'D'$ is a translation image of $ABCD$.

Transversal (p. 418) A transversal is a line that intersects two or more lines at different points.

Secante (p. 418) Una secante es una recta que corta dos o más rectas en puntos diferentes.

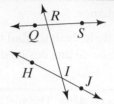

$\overleftrightarrow{RI}$ is a transversal of $\overleftrightarrow{QS}$ and $\overleftrightarrow{HJ}$.

Trial (p. 369) Each trial of a simulation results in an outcome.

Prueba (p. 369) Cada prueba de una simulación tiene un resultado.

In a simulation, a number cube is rolled 20 times and each outcome is recorded. The number of trials is 20.

Triangle Inequality Theorem (p. 549) The sum of the lengths of any two sides of a triangle is greater than the length of the third side.

Teorema de desigualdad del triángulo (p. 549) La suma de las longitudes de dos lados de un triángulo es mayor que la longitud del tercer lado.

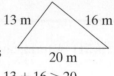

$13 + 16 > 20$
$16 + 20 > 13$
$20 + 13 > 16$

Unit cost (p. 189) A unit rate that gives the cost per unit is a unit cost.

Costo unitario (p. 189) Un costo unitario es una tasa unitaria que da el costo por unidad.

$\dfrac{\$5.98}{10.2\ \text{fl oz}} = \$.59/\text{fl oz}$

Unit rate (p. 188) The rate for one unit of a given quantity is called the unit rate.

Tasa unitaria (p. 188) La tasa para una unidad de una cantidad dada se llama tasa unitaria.

If you drive 130 mi in 2 h, your unit rate is $\dfrac{65\ \text{mi}}{1\ \text{h}}$, or 65 mi/h.

Variability (p. 331) Variability tells how much a data set is spread out.

Variabilidad (p. 331) La variabilidad indica la dispersión de un conjunto de datos.

The inter quartile range (IQR) and the mean absolute deviation (MAD) are measures of variability of data sets.

Variable (p. 103) A variable is a letter that stands for a number. The value of an algebraic expression varies, or changes, depending upon the value given to the variable.

x is a variable in the equation $9 + x = 7$.

Variable (p. 103) Una variable es una letra que representa un número. El valor de una expresión algebraica varía, o cambia, dependiendo del valor que se le dé a la variable.

Vertex of a polygon (p. 454) The vertex of a polygon is any point where two sides of a polygon meet.

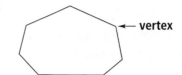
← vertex

Vértice de un polígono (p. 454) El vértice de un polígono es cualquier punto donde se encuentran dos lados de un polígono.

Vertical angles (p. 382) Vertical angles are formed by two intersecting lines. Vertical angles are opposite each other.

Ángulos verticales (p. 382) Los ángulos verticales están formados por dos rectas que se intersecan. Los ángulos verticales son opuestos entre sí.

$\angle 1$ and $\angle 2$ are vertical angles, as are $\angle 3$ and $\angle 4$.

Volume (p. 465) The volume of a three-dimensional figure is the number of cubic units needed to fill the space inside the figure.

Volumen (p. 465) El volumen de una figura tridimensional es el número de unidades cúbicas que se necesitan para llenar el espacio dentro de la figura.

The volume of the rectangular prism is 36 cubic units.

---

x-axis (p. 554) The x-axis is the horizontal number line that, together with the y-axis, forms the coordinate plane.

Eje de x (p. 554) El eje de x es la recta numérica horizontal que, junto con el eje de y, forma el plano de coordenadas.

---

x-coordinate (p. 554) The x-coordinate tells the number of horizontal units a point is from the origin.

The x-coordinate is -2 for the ordered pair $(-2, 1)$. The point is 2 units to the left of the origin.

Coordenada x (p. 554) La coordenada x es el primer número en un par ordenado. Indica el número de unidades horizontales a las que un punto está del origen.

---

y-axis (p. 554) The y-axis is the vertical number line that, together with the x-axis, forms the coordinate plane.

Eje de y (p. 554) El eje de y es la recta numérica vertical que, junto con el eje de x, forma el plano de coordenadas.

y-coordinate (p. 554) The y-coordinate tells the number of vertical units a point is from the origin.

The y-coordinate is 1 for the ordered pair (−2, 1). The point is 1 unit up from the x-axis.

Coordenada y (p. 554) La coordenada y es el segundo número en un par ordenado. Indica el número de unidades verticales a las que un punto está del origen.

y-intercept (p. 299) The y-intercept is the point where the graph of a function crosses the y-axis.

See x-intercept.

Intercepto y (p. 299) El intercepto y de una recta es la coordenada y del punto donde la recta cruza el eje de y.

Chapter 1

Check Your Readiness   p. 2

1. < 2. > 3. 37 4. 76 5. 216 6. 214 7. 3 tenths
8. 6 thousandths 9. 9 ones 10. 3 hundredths
11. 7 ten-thousandths 12. four hundred
twenty-one and five tenths 13. five thousand six
and twenty-five hundredths 14. fifteen and four
thousandths 15. three hundred twenty-nine
thousandths 16. seven hundred ten and four
hundred thirteen thousandths 17. 34.12
18. 278.79 19. 3.60 20. 81.80 21. 17.00

Lesson 1-1   pp. 4–5

Check Skills You'll Need 1. Absolute Value
2. 9, 19, 91, 109 3. 18, 78, 87, 807 4. 28, 82, 88, 208

Quick Check 1 a. 8 b. −13 c. 22 2. a. 0 b. 6 c. 0
3. −8 < −2 4. −4, −1, 2, 3

Lesson 1-2   pp. 10–11

Check Skills You'll Need 1. the same distance from
zero as the number 2. −73 3. 49 4. −22
5. −13 6. 424 7. 13

Quick Check 1 a. −7 b. −8 c. 0 2 a. −162 b. −18
c. 0 3. −7 4. 21 5 a. −137 − (−155) b. 18 ft

Lesson 1-3   pp. 16–20

Check Skills You'll Need 1. zero 2. 4 3. 5 4. −35 5. 0

Quick Check 1. 28 2. −524 ft/h

Checkpoint Quiz 1 1. −66 2. 44 3. −29 4. −4 5. −33
6. 3 7. > 8. < 9. = 10. 15°F; 18 + 5 · (−3)

Lesson 1-4   pp. 21–23

Check Skills You'll Need 1. quotient 2. 30 3. 11 4. 13
5. 13

Quick Check 1. 0.625 2. $0.\overline{5}$ 3 a. $1\frac{91}{250}$ b. $2\frac{12}{25}$
c. $3\frac{3}{5}$ 4. 1.862, $1\frac{7}{15}$, $1\frac{3}{8}$ 5. cats, dogs, fish, birds

Lesson 1-5   pp. 26–27

Check Skills You'll Need 1. Terminating decimal; the
decimal stops 2. 0.75 3. $-0.\overline{7}$ 4. $1.\overline{3}$ 5. 0.25

Quick Check 1. $-\frac{2}{3} < -\frac{1}{6}$ 2. −4.2 > −4.9
3. $-6\frac{1}{4}$, − 4, 6.55, $12\frac{1}{2}$

Lesson 1-6   pp. 33–37

Check Skills You'll Need 1. rational number 2. 0.5
3. $0.\overline{3}$ 4. 0.25 5. 0.2 6. $0.\overline{16}$ 7. 0.125

Quick Check 1 a. −14.80 b. $1\frac{1}{5}$ c. −4.10 2 a. $-\frac{3}{5}$
b. 12.62 c. −25.70 3. 3.5°F

Checkpoint Quiz 2 1. 0.8 2. $0.\overline{571428}$ 3. $0.\overline{4}$ 4. >
5. < 6. = 7. $-5\frac{1}{12}$ 8. 12.11 9. 0 10. 42.8°C

Lesson 1-7   pp. 38–40

Check Skills You'll Need 1. Commutative Property
of Multiplication 2. 2 3. −6 4. −12 5. 20
6. 30 7. −42

Quick Check 1 a. 10.45 b. $\frac{21}{4}$ or $5\frac{1}{4}$ c. 18.87 2 a. 6
b. 23.25 c. $\frac{16}{5}$ or $3\frac{1}{5}$ 3 a. $-\frac{5}{2}$ or $-2\frac{1}{2}$ b. −10.2
c. $-\frac{3}{2}$ or $-1\frac{1}{2}$ 4 a. $-8\frac{1}{4}°F$ b. −$149.70

Lesson 1–9   pp. 50–52

Check Skills You'll Need 1. A terminating decimal stops,
or terminates in 0s. A repeating decimal repeats
the same digit or group of digits forever.
2. terminating 3. repeating 4. repeating
5. terminating

Quick Check 1a. 6, −6 b. 1, −1 c. $\frac{1}{4}$, $-\frac{1}{4}$ 2. 6; 6.2
3. 4.7 4. 6.3 units 5. Rational; the decimal
repeats.

Lesson 1–10   pp. 55–56

Check Skills You'll Need 1. square root 2. 1, −1
3. $\frac{1}{5}$, $-\frac{1}{5}$ 4. 9, −9 5. $\frac{1}{12}$, $-\frac{1}{12}$

Quick Check 1a. 6 b. −1 c. $\frac{1}{3}$ 2. 5 feet 3. $\frac{3}{6}$, or $\frac{1}{2}$

Checkpoint Quiz 1 p. 18 1. 0.125 2. $0.\overline{5}$ 3. $0.\overline{51}$ 4. 40
5. $\frac{3}{7}$ 6. 9; 9.2 7. 2.8 units 8. −9 9. $\frac{2}{7}$ 10. 6 inches

Chapter 2

Check Your Readiness   p. 64

1. 7^5 2. $5^2 \cdot c^2$ 3. a^2b^3 4. x^3y^2 5. $(3x)^3$ 6. $c \cdot d^2 \cdot g^2$
7. 16 8. 16 9. −16 10. 32 11. 100 12. 1,000
13. 732 14. 0.752 15. 0.02048 16. 1030
17. 0.0007 18. 453 19. 2.8 20. 77.9 21. 4.7
22. 9.6 23. 2.6 24. 17.5

Instant Check System™ Answers

Lesson 2–1   pp. 66–67

Check Skills You'll Need   **1.** power **2.** 20 **3.** 451 **4.** 1,500 **5.** 18,030 **6.** 2,390,000

Quick Check   **1.** 7,660,000 km^2 **2.** 3.476×10^6 m **3.** 0.00025 in. **4.** 3.5×10^{-6}

Lesson 2–2   pp. 72–73

Check Skills You'll Need   **1.** x **2.** 1 **3.** 9 **4.** -9 **5.** -1

Quick Check   **1a.** 6^5 **1b.** $(-4)^8$ **1c.** 3^6 **2.** n^6 **3a.** $6a^3$ **3b.** x^{13} **3c.** $12y^8$

Lesson 2–3   pp. 76–77

Check Skills You'll Need   **1.** ten **2.** 2×10^4 **3.** 5×10^{-6} **4.** 9.3×10^6

Quick Check   **1a.** 8×10^9 **1b.** 6×10^{13} **1c.** 9.6×10^{21} **2.** about 1.08×10^9 km **3.** 7 cm; 7×10^{-2} m

Checkpoint Quiz 1   **1.** 600,000 **2.** 0.000802 **3.** 0.004 **4.** 9×10^4 **5.** 3.9×10^3 **6.** 3.01×10^{-3} **7.** 4.7^{21} **8.** $(-4a)^4$ **9.** x^4y^{12} **10.** 3.0×10^5 **11.** 1.5×10^{12} **12.** 3.6×10^7 **13.** $28f^8$ **14.** $15.5g^8$ **15.** $-17.6h^{18}$ **16.** 2.4 cm; 2.4×10^{-5} km

Lesson 2–4   pp. 82–84

Check Skills You'll Need   **1.** power **2.** 7^4 **3.** 4^3 **4.** 5^2 **5.** 1^5

Quick Check   **1.** w^3 **2a.** 1 **2b.** 1 **2c.** 2 **3a.** $\frac{1}{3}$ **3b.** $\frac{1}{w^4}$ **3c.** $-\frac{1}{8}$

Lesson 2–5   pp. 90–92

Check Skills You'll Need   **1.** 1, 10 **2.** 1.45×10^7 **3.** 3.4×10^{-2} **4.** 5.11×10^2 **5.** 4×10^{-4}

Quick Check   **1a.** 3.4×10^2 **1b.** 1.62×10^{-2} **1c.** 7.1×10^4 **2.** 8.5 min **3a.** 1.5×10^6 **3b.** -7.0×10^2 **3c.** 1.2×10^{-7} **4a.** 3×10^{-6}, 3.8×10^{-5}, 3.11×10^5, 3×10^6 **4b.** 1.8×10^{-2}, 1.7×10^{-2}, 1.5×10^3, 1.5×10^4 **5.** 6.9

Chapter 3

Check Your Readiness   p. 100

1. 4.414 **2.** -0.30 **3.** -3.40 **4.** $\frac{1}{4}$ **5.** 1.8 **6.** -3.9 **7.** -36 **8.** 1 **9.** 42 **10.** -6 **11.** $>$ **12.** $>$ **13.** $<$ **14.** $=$ **15.** $<$ **16.** $<$ **17.** 3.7, $2\frac{3}{4}$, 2.2, $\frac{13}{9}$, -2 **18.** 5, $0.\overline{5}$, $\frac{1}{5}$, 0, -0.5

Lesson 3-1   pp. 103–104

Check Skills You'll Need   **1.** order of operations **2.** 11 **3.** 10 **4.** -10 **5.** 3

Quick Check   **1.** $p - 16$ **2.** $9t$ **3.** Answers may vary. Sample: a number decreased by 50, 50 less than a number, 50 subtracted from a number **4.** 56

Lesson 3-2   pp. 108–112

Check Skills You'll Need   **1.** term **2.** $1\frac{1}{2}$ **3.** 6 **4.** 6.2 **5.** 11

Quick Check   **1 a.** $6x + 3$ **b.** $3y + 7$ **c.** $11r - 2$ **2 a.** $12x + 14$ **b.** $-4v + 6$ **c.** $-12z + 1$ **3 a.** $3(3x + 5)$ **b.** $12(3 + 2t)$ **c.** $4(2c - 5)$

Checkpoint Quiz 1 pp. 64   **1.** $x - 4$ **2.** $3x$ **3.** $\frac{4}{x}$ **4.** $x + 9$ **5.** $3k + 1$ **6.** $-n + 20$ **7.** $3x + 6$ **8.** $\frac{4}{5}t - 4$ **9.** $(y + 18)$ **10.** $5(5r - 2)$

Lesson 3-3   pp. 114–116

Check Skills You'll Need   **1.** equation **2.** about 9 **3.** about 18 **4.** about 25

Quick Check   **1.** 168 **2.** \$7.95 **3.** -390 **4 a.** -7.2 **b.** 9 **c.** 3

Lesson 3-4   pp. 120–122

Check Skills You'll Need   **1.** algebraic expression **2.** 1 **3.** 13 **4.** 24 **5.** -2

Quick Check   **1.** Let s = son's age; $3s - 2$ **2.** 37 **3 a.** 4 **b.** 5 **c.** 11 **4.** Let b = number of 3-point baskets; $8 + 3b = 23$; 5 baskets.

Lesson 3-5   pp. 126–127

Check Skills You'll Need   **1.** Multiplication Property of Equality **2.** 6 **3.** -5 **4.** -64 **5.** -18

Quick Check   **1.** 1 **2.** 200 **3.** Let m = number of markers; $0.79m + 1.25 = 7.57$; 8 markers

Checkpoint Quiz 2   **1.** -4.4 **2.** 1.8 **3.** -9.1 **4.** 48 **5.** 6 **6.** 10 **7.** 5 **8.** 40 **9.** 2 **10.** -9 **11.** -2 **12.** -5 **13.** 24 years 8 months **14.** Let c = the cost of a skirt; $12 + 2c = 38$; \$13.

Lesson 3–6   pp. 134–135

Check Skills You'll Need   **1.** $3x$, $2x$, $-x$ **2.** $12 - 26m$ **3.** $28 - 12r$ **4.** $8q + 5$

Quick Check   **1.** -11 **2.** 17 boys

Lesson 3-7 pp. 139–140

Check Skills You'll Need 1. inverse operations
2. $9t + 47$ **3.** $60 - 12r$ **4.** $-3x - 7$

Quick Check 1. 2 **2.** 61 text messages

Checkpoint Quiz 2 p. 70 1. -1 **2.** 2 **3.** 2.7 **4.** -2 **5.** 3
6. -5 **7.** 15 **8.** $\frac{1}{2}$ or 0.5 **9.** \$12 **10.** \$.42

Lesson 3-8 pp. 145–146

Check Skills You'll Need 1. solution **2.** $a = 3$
3. $w = -1$ **4.** $z = -3.5$

Quick Check 1a. no solution **b.** one solution
c. infinitely many solutions **d.** one solution
2. Let a = number of adults. $2a \cdot 8 = a \cdot 16$. This
results in the equation $1 = 1$. So, any number of
adults could have come to the museum.

Chapter 4

Check Your Readiness p. 154

1. -3.07 **2.** $1\frac{1}{2}$ **3.** 1.8 **4.** $-\frac{1}{8}$ **5.** $-10\frac{1}{2}$ **6.** 0.24 **7.** 7.2
8. -4 **9.** $-\frac{3}{4}$ **10.** 5.5 **11.** 5 **12.** 5.3 **13.** $\frac{1}{12}$ **14.** -2.4
15. $w = -20$ **16.** $-1\frac{1}{9}$ **17.** 5 **18.** 3 **19.** -1

Lesson 4-1 pp. 156–157

Check Skills You'll Need 1. opposites **2.** > **3.** > **4.** <
5. >

Quick Check 1. -2, 1.4 **2.**
3. $x < 4$ **4.** $t \le 62$ $-7\;-6\;-5\;-4\;-3\;-2$

Lesson 4-2 pp. 160–164

Check Skills You'll Need 1. because they "undo" each
other **2.** -6 **3.** 1 **4.** 9 **5.** 7

Quick Check 1. $y < 7$;
   4 5 6 7 8 9

2 a. $x > -4$;
   $-6\;-5\;-4\;-3\;-2\;-1$

b. $y < 1$;
   $-2\;-1\;\;0\;\;1\;\;2\;\;3$

c. $w \le -9$;
   -11 -9 -7

3. Let p = number of points;
$p + 109 > 200$; $p > 91$; you need more than
91 points.

Checkpoint Quiz 1 1. $x > -2$ **2.** $x \le 1$
3. **4.**
   $-11\;-10\;-9\;-8$ -4

---

5. **6.**
   -8 -2

7. Let m = minutes inside store; $8 + m \le 45$;
$m \le 37$; at most, 37 minutes. **8.** Let e = ears
of corn you buy; $e - 6 \ge 3$; $e \ge 9$; at least 9 ears
of corn.

Lesson 4-3 pp. 165–167

Check Skills You'll Need 1. You can add to each side of
an equation or inequality without changing the
relationship. **2.** $x \le 2$ **3.** $p > 7$ **4.** $3 \ge d$
5. $r < -6$

Quick Check 1 a. $p > -9$;
   $-11\;-10\;-9\;-8\;-7\;-6$

b. $m \le 3$;
   0 1 2 3 4 5

c. $n > -3$;   **2.** 416 min
   $-5\;-4\;-3\;-2\;-1\;\;0$

3. $k > 20$;
   18   20   22

4.
   -16

Lesson 4-4 pp. 172–173

Check Skills You'll Need 1. Two operations must be
used to isolate the variable instead of just one.
2. $d = 2$ **3.** $v = 8$ **4.** $c = -0.4$ **5.** $a = 3$

Quick Check 1.
   12

2. See margin.

3. $42.50 + 0.2m \le 50$; $m \le 37.5$; Lin can send at
least 0 messages and no more than 37 messages.

Chapter 5

Check Your Readiness p. 182

1. 14.4 **2.** $\frac{3}{40}$ **3.** $1\frac{5}{16}$ **4.** 10.52 **5.** $\frac{2}{3}$ **6.** 18 **7.** -8
8. 60 **9.** -2 **10.** 75 **11.** > **12.** < **13.** = **14.** >
15. $\frac{3}{4}$ **16.** $\frac{1}{2}$ **17.** $\frac{3}{8}$ **18.** $\frac{1}{3}$ **19.** $\frac{2}{7}$

Lesson 5-1 pp. 184–185

Check Skills You'll Need 1. A terminating decimal is a
decimal that stops or terminates. **2.** 0.5 **3.** 0.75
4. 0.375 **5.** $0.\overline{3}$

Quick Check 1 a. 7 to 12, 7 : 12, $\frac{7}{12}$, **b.** 7 to 5; 7 : 5; $\frac{7}{5}$
2. Answers may vary. Samples: $\frac{14}{18}, \frac{35}{45}$ **3.** $\frac{6}{5}$ **4 a.** not
equivalent **b.** not equivalent **c.** equivalent

Lesson 5-2   pp. 188–189

Check Skills You'll Need 1. division 2. $\frac{3}{5}$ 3. $\frac{3}{1}$ 4. $\frac{11}{8}$ 5. $\frac{1}{9}$

Quick Check 1. 70 heartbeats per min 2. $\frac{2}{5}$ mile per hour 3. \$.064/fl oz, \$.056/fl oz; the 64-fl-oz bottle is the better buy.

Lesson 5-3   pp. 193–197

Check Skills You'll Need 1. rational 2. > 3. = 4. < 5. <

Quick Check 1. no; $\frac{5}{6} \neq \frac{5}{7}$ 2 a. yes; 48 = 48 b. yes; 36 = 36 c. no; 36 ≠ 40

Checkpoint Quiz 1 1. $\frac{2}{3}$ 2. 12 to 7 3. 2 : 3 4. 42 words/min 5. $\frac{3}{4}$ cup per serving 6. \$.2633, \$.2475; the second item is the better buy. 7. \$7.80, \$6.57; the second item is the better buy. 8. no 9. yes 10. no

Lesson 5-4   pp. 199–200

Check Skills You'll Need 1. A ratio is a unit rate when you are finding the rate for one unit of something. 2. 8 km/d 3. 6.2 mph 4. 25 push-ups/min 5. \$1.25 per song

Quick Check 1 a. \$6.37 b. \$119.51 2 a. 9 b. 2 c. 10 3 a. 16.8 b. 27.2 c. 192.5

Lesson 5-5   pp. 207–208

Check Skills You'll Need 1. proportion 2. 6 3. 12 4. 42 5. 9.5

Quick Check 1. 20 2. 36 ft

Lesson 5-6   pp. 213–219

Check Skills You'll Need 1. For two ratios, the cross products are found by multiplying the denominator of each ratio by the numerator of the other ratio. 2. 8 3. 15 4. 1 5. 7

Quick Check 1. 10 m 2. 1 in. : 16 in. 3. 5 in. 4. 1 in. : $1\frac{3}{5}$ mi

Checkpoint Quiz 2 1. $h = 9$ 2. $z = 7$ 3. \$8.40 4. \$16.50 5. 120° 6. 26° 7. 9 8. 12 9. 1 in. : 12.5 ft 10. 1 cm : 20 km

Lesson 5-7   pp. 221–222

Check Skills You'll Need 1. Ratios form a proportion when they are equivalent. 2. yes 3. no 4. no 5. yes

Quick Check 1. No; all the ratios are not equivalent. 2. 20 pages per day 3 a. $c = 2$ b. $c = \$5.50$

Chapter 6

Check Your Readiness   p. 230

1. 0.6 2. 0.75 3. 0.375 4. 0.25 5. $\frac{17}{20}$ 6. $\frac{2}{5}$ 7. $\frac{17}{25}$ 8. $\frac{5}{4}$ 9. $\frac{1}{100}$ 10. 30 11. 800 12. 8.4 13. 3 14. 80 15. 2.16 16. 200

Lesson 6-1   pp. 232–234

Check Skills You'll Need 1. A repeating decimal is a decimal that repeats without end. 2. 0.3125 3. 0.275 4. $0.\overline{4}$ 5. $0.1\overline{3}$

Quick Check 1. 60.7%, 0.5%, 928.3% 2 a. 35 b. 0.125 c. 0.0078 3. 52.5% 4. $\frac{3}{50}$ 5 a. 29%, $\frac{3}{10}$, $\frac{11}{25}$, 0.74 b. 0.08, 15%, $\frac{7}{20}$, 500%

Lesson 6-2   pp. 237–238

Check Skills You'll Need 1. ratios 2. 8 3. 15 4. 87.5

Quick Check 1. 25% 2. 17 3. 15 problems

Lesson 6-3   pp. 241–245

Check Skills You'll Need 1. If both sides of an equation are divided by the same nonzero number, the results are equal. 2. 17 3. 48

Quick Check 1. 150 seats 2. 16.2 3. about 20.5%

Checkpoint Quiz 1 1. 0.45; $\frac{9}{20}$ 2. 1.35; $1\frac{7}{20}$ 3. 0.0098; $\frac{49}{5,000}$ 4. 56% 5. $\frac{1}{6}$, 20%, 0.245, $\frac{1}{4}$ 6. $58.\overline{3}$% 7. 16 8. 84% 9. 45% 10. 68.4 11. 222 12. about 0.6% 13. 35% 14. 75%

Lesson 6-4   pp. 248–250

Check Skills You'll Need 1. left 2. 0.065 3. 0.0425 4. 0.15 5. 0.2

Quick Check 1. \$195.18 2 a. about \$8.70 b. about \$9.30 c. about \$7.50 3. \$192 4. \$849 5. It is rejected, because its percent error is 0.96%. 6 a. \$0.44 b. \$6.33

Lesson 6-5   pp. 254–257

Check Skills You'll Need 1. A percent is a ratio that compares a number to 100. 2. 0.04 3. 0.09 4. 0.020 5. 0.065

Quick Check 1. \$44.00 2.

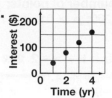

3. the 2-year loan

Checkpoint Quiz 2 **1.** $59.64 **2.** $37.79 **3.** $247.50
4. $6.91 **5.** $48.75 **6.** $180 **7.** $180 **8.** 0.38%

Lesson 6-6   pp. 258–259

Check Skills You'll Need **1.** 500 and $16n$ **2.** 10 **3.** 12.5
4. 50

Quick Check **1.** 8% **2.** 99.4% **3.** 40%

Chapter 7

Check Your Readiness   p. 268

1–3.

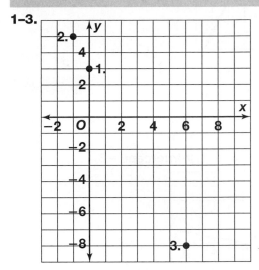

4. P **5.** $(-3, -2)$ **6.** $2(6) - 4 = 8$ **7.** $3(2) - 5 = 1$
8. $5(4) + 9 = 29$ **9.** $4(5) - 8 = 12$ **10.** $8(4) + 9 = 41$
11. $7(3) - 8 = 13$
12.

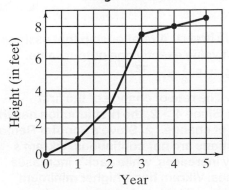

Height of Tree

13.

**Centerville Monthly Average
High Temperature**

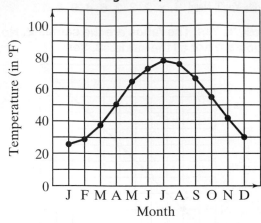

Lesson 7–1   pp. 270–271

Check Skills You'll Need **1.** Line graphs best display
changes over time. **2–3.** Answers may vary.
Samples are given. **2.** Line plots best display
frequency of data—for example, displaying the
number of siblings each class member has.
3. Bar graphs compare amounts in different
categories—for example, the number of students
in each grade.

Quick Check **1.** 0–5 mins
2.

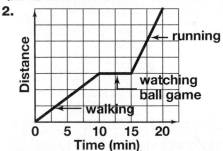

Lesson 7–2   pp. 275–279

Check Skills You'll Need **1.** a **2.** 8 **3.** 53 **4.** 9 **5.** −5

Quick Check **1.** $F = 68$

2.

Input n	Output m
−1	$\frac{2}{3}$
0	1
1	$1\frac{1}{3}$
2	$1\frac{2}{3}$

3.

c	d
5	$.50
10	$1.00
15	$1.50

Checkpoint Quiz 1 p. 91 **1.** 1 **2.** −17 **3.** −2 **4.** 28
5. 0.99p **6.** 20 mi/h **7.** 20 mi **8.** after 1 hour
9. 40 mi/h **10.** 65 mi/h

Lesson 7–3   pp. 280–281

Check Skills You'll Need   **1.** x **2.** 3   **3.** 6   **4.** 9   **5.** 12

Quick Check   **1.** Yes. The ratios are the same.   **2.** No. The ratios are not all the same.   **3.** Yes.

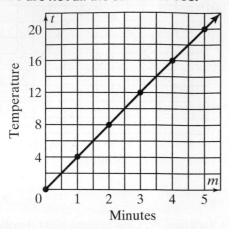

Lesson 7–4   pp. 287–291

Check Skills You'll Need   **1.** b **2.** 4   **3.** 8   **4.** 12   **5.** 16

Quick Check   **1.** Yes. The ratios between the changes in variables are the same.

2.

Tickets	0	1	2	3	4	5	6	7
Cost	0	15	30	45	60	75	90	105

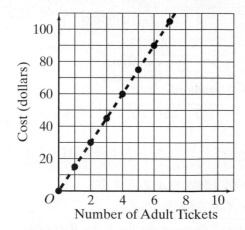

3.

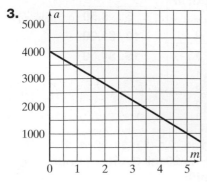

Checkpoint Quiz 2 p. 103   **1.** Yes   **2.** No   **3.** No   **4.** Yes   **5.** No   **6.** Yes

Lesson 7–5   pp. 293–295

Check Skills You'll Need   **1.** no   **2.** −4   **3.** 14   **4.** −6   **5.** −2

Quick Check   **1a.** $\frac{2}{5}$ **1b.** $-\frac{1}{2}$ **2.** undefined

3. −2

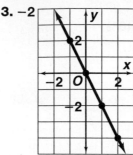

Lesson 7–6   pp. 299–301

Check Skills You'll Need   **1.** Divide the change in y by the change in x.   **2.** $-\frac{6}{7}$ **3.** 0   **4.** −1

Quick Check   **1.** slope: 1, y-intercept: −3

2.

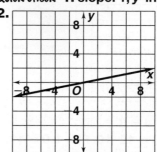

Lesson 7–7   pp. 304–306

Check Skills You'll Need   **1.** A relationship that assigns to each input value exactly one output value.   **2.** 2   **3.** −1   **4.** 3   **5.** $\frac{1}{2}$ **6.** $-\frac{12}{5}$

Quick Check   **1.** The rate of change of the first function is 4. Since 4 > 2, the first function has the greater rate of change.   **2.** Steve's Scooter Rentals   **3.** Both functions are not continuous. Vikram's account only increases, while Jack's increases and decreases. Vikram has a higher minimum balance ($150 vs. $100) and a higher maximum balance ($450 vs. $400).   **4.** Jala

Chapter 8

Check Your Readiness   p. 314

1. $x = 15$ 2. $n = 12.5$ 3. $c = 20$ 4. $s = 45$ 5. $a = 18$
6. $b = 14$ 7. $n = 68$ 8. $a = 108$ 9. $x = 35$ 10. $r = 4$
11. $m = 15$ 12. $t = 112$ 13. 40% 14. 30%
15. 24% 16. 12.5%

Lesson 8-1   pp. 316–317

Check Skills You'll Need 1. percent **2.** 80% **3.** 25%
4. 7%

Quick Check 1 a. Answers may vary. Sample: Less likely to be random; you may get only people shopping after work. **b.** More likely to be random; you won't just get people shopping after work.
2 a. Biased; the question implies that meat is greasy and vegetables are healthy. **b.** Fair; the question makes no assumptions about pizza toppings.

Lesson 8-2   pp. 320–323

Check Skills You'll Need 1. ratios **2.** 10 **3.** 44 **4.** 9

Quick Check 1. about 1,914 deer

Checkpoint Quiz 1 1. Sample answer: Only students on the basketball teams had a chance of being chosen for the survey. The students on the basketball teams may support a new gym more than students who do not use the gym as often.
2. This question is biased against highway projects. It implies that highway projects cost too much and are not a good use of city money.
3. This question is fair. It does not make any assumptions about the new highway project.
4. Check students' work. **5.** A; it is a more diverse sample. **6.** about 3,871 horses **7.** about 172 turtles

Lesson 8-3   pp. 326–327

Check Skills You'll Need 1. the products found by multiplying the numerator of each ratio in the proportion by the denominator of the other ratio **2.** $x = 60$ **3.** $n = 62$ **4.** $c = 49$

Quick Check 1. Sample answer: About 20% of customers in the sample spent more than $20, so the percent of all customers who spend more than $20 is likely close to 20%. **2 a.** Sample 1: 196; sample 2: 238; sample 3: 266 **b.** The predictions vary by 70 students. **c.** Sample answer: About 238 students spend at least 5 hours online per week.

Lesson 8-4   pp. 331–332

Check Skills You'll Need 1. The mean is the sum of the data values divided by the number of data values. The median is the middle value, or the mean of the two middle values, when the data are listed in numerical order. **2.** 99°F **3.** 8 minutes

Quick Check 1. The median weight for Boston terriers is 6 pounds greater than the median weight for Australian terriers. Sample: Boston terriers typically weigh more than Australian terriers. **2 a.** Station A: 36; Station B: 35 **b.** Station A: 1.2; Station B: 1.2 **c.** $n \approx 0.8$; The difference between the means is about 0.8 times the MAD. So, the distance between the centers is less than the variability of either data set. This indicates a large amount of overlap in the data sets.

Chapter 9

Check Your Readiness   p. 340

1. $\frac{3}{8}$ 2. $\frac{10}{27}$ 3. $\frac{3}{13}$ 4. $\frac{8}{11}$ 5. $\frac{1}{4}$ 6. $\frac{3}{7}$ 7. $x = 9$
8. $n = 43.75$ 9. $c = 5$ 10. $y = 43.75$ 11. $a = 64$
12. $f = 10.5$ 13. 46% 14. 26.5% 15. 7%
16. 25.6% 17. 82% 18. 80% 19. 45.5%
20. 57.1% 21. 40% 22. 46.9%

Lesson 9-1   pp. 342–343

Check Skills You'll Need 1. fraction, decimal, percent
2. 0.62; 62% **3.** 0.95; 95% **4.** 0.275; 27.5%
5. 1.1; 110%

Quick Check 1. $\frac{3}{5}$ **2.** $\frac{1}{3}$ **3.** $\frac{1}{2}$ **4.** 0

Lesson 9-2   pp. 347–352

Check Skills You'll Need 1. Answers may vary. Sample: An outcome is a single result, but an event can be a group of results. **2.** $\frac{1}{6}$ **3.** $\frac{1}{2}$ **4.** 0

Quick Check 1. $\frac{5}{12}$ **2.** 105 bikes **3.** $\frac{1}{20}$
Checkpoint Quiz 1 1. $\frac{2}{5}$; 0.4; 40% **2.** $\frac{2}{5}$; 0.4; 40%
3. $\frac{4}{5}$; 0.8; 80% **4.** $\frac{3}{5}$; 0.6; 60% **5.** unlikely **6.** neither unlikely nor likely **7.** $\frac{20}{119}$ **8.** 18,000
9. Check students' work. Sample: $\frac{6}{20}$

Lesson 9-3   pp. 353–355

Check Skills You'll Need 1. the ratio of the number of favorable outcomes to the total number of possible outcomes **2.** $\frac{1}{8}$ **3.** $\frac{7}{8}$ **4.** $\frac{1}{4}$ **5.** $\frac{1}{2}$

1.

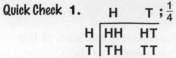

H   T ; $\frac{1}{4}$

	H	T
H	HH	HT
T	TH	TT

2 a.

Vessel	Stream	Outcome

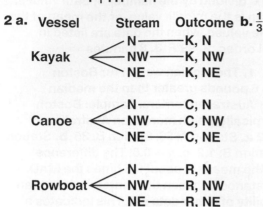

Kayak — N —— K, N
— NW —— K, NW
— NE —— K, NE

Canoe — N —— C, N
— NW —— C, NW
— NE —— C, NE

Rowboat — N —— R, N
— NW —— R, NW
— NE —— R, NE

b. $\frac{1}{3}$

3. 35 sandwiches

Lesson 9-4   pp. 360–365

Check Skills You'll Need **1.** Multiply the numerators of the rational numbers, and multiply the denominators. If the factors have the same sign, the product is positive. If the factors have different signs, the product is negative. **2.** $\frac{9}{16}$ **3.** $-\frac{6}{25}$ **4.** $\frac{1}{20}$ **5.** $\frac{6}{49}$

Quick Check **1.** $\frac{1}{4}$ **2.** $\frac{1}{10}$ **3.** $\frac{1}{1,326}$

Checkpoint Quiz 2

1.

First Spin

	P	B	R	G
P	P, P	B, P	R, P	G, P
B	P, B	B, B	R, B	G, B
R	P, R	B, R	R, R	G, R
G	P, G	B, G	R, G	G, G

Second Spin

2. $\frac{1}{16}$ **3.** $\frac{1}{16}$

4.

Number Card	Category Card	Outcome

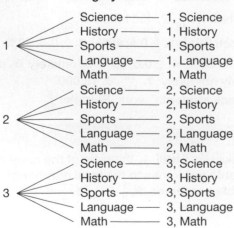

1 — Science —— 1, Science
— History —— 1, History
— Sports —— 1, Sports
— Language — 1, Language
— Math —— 1, Math

2 — Science —— 2, Science
— History —— 2, History
— Sports —— 2, Sports
— Language — 2, Language
— Math —— 2, Math

3 — Science —— 3, Science
— History —— 3, History
— Sports —— 3, Sports
— Language — 3, Language
— Math —— 3, Math

5. $\frac{6}{49}$ **6.** $\frac{4}{49}$ **7.** $\frac{2}{49}$ **8.** 0 **9.** $\frac{5}{49}$ **10.** $\frac{3}{56}$ **11.** $\frac{12}{56}$ or $\frac{3}{14}$ **12.** $\frac{4}{56}$ or $\frac{1}{14}$

Lesson 9-5   pp. 369–370

Check Skills You'll Need **1.** Answers will vary. Sample: Tossing two coins and getting heads on both coins **2.** $\frac{1}{6}$ **3.** $\frac{5}{18}$ **4.** $\frac{5}{18}$

Quick Check **1.** Answers will vary. Sample: Use a spinner divided into 4 equal sections numbered 1 to 4. Spinning a 1 represents a deer that carries the gene. For each trial, spin the spinner until you get a 1. The number of times you spin the spinner represents the number of deer the scientist must test before finding one that carries the gene.

2. Answers will vary.

Sample: $\frac{3}{5}$

Deer Tested to Find Disease	Frequency
3 or fewer	12
4 or more	8

3. Sample answer: $\frac{1}{10}$ (when the numbers 00 to 41 are used to represent a donor with type A blood)

Chapter 10

Check Your Readiness   p. 378

1. 4 **2.** 24 **3.** $6\frac{3}{4}$ **4.** $4\frac{2}{3}$ **5.** 3 **6.** 12 **7.** 5
8. $d = 2$ **9.** $m = 105$ **10.** $y = 94$ **11.** $s = 14$
12. $w = 224$ **13.** $a = 60$ **14.** $c = 10$
15. $z = 45$ **16.** $a = 16$ **17.** $h = 30$ **18.** $b = 24$
19. $d = 104$

Lesson 10-1   pp. 381–383

Check Skills You'll Need **1.** equation **2.** 9 **3.** 8 **4.** 4 **5.** 6

Quick Check **1.** 65°; 115° **2.** $m\angle A$ is 50°; $m\angle B$ is 40° **3.** 108°; 72°; 108°

Lesson 10-2   pp. 389–393

Check Skills You'll Need **1.** Changing the order of the factors does not change the product. **2.** 450 **3.** 28.08 **4.** 57.12 **5.** 2.04

Quick Check **1.** 90 cm² **2.** 22 cm

Checkpoint Quiz 1 **1.** 78°; 168° **2.** 43°; 133°
3. 25°; 115° **4.** $x + (x - 40°) = 90°$; 65°; 25°

---

5. $(4x + 30°) + x = 180°$; 150°; 30° 6. 115° 7. 65°
8. 65° 9. 240 in.^{2} 10. 18 cm^2

| Lesson 10-3 | pp. 394–395 |

Check Skills You'll Need 1. $\frac{1}{2}$ 2. 3 3. 2 4. 5 5. 4.5

Quick Check 1 a. 216 m^2 b. 48 cm^2 2. 9 cm

| Lesson 10-4 | pp. 398–403 |

Check Skills You'll Need 1. It is one of a pair of opposite sides. 2. 75 cm^2 3. 135 m^2

Quick Check 1 a. 34.1 m^2 b. 81 m^2 2. 8.75 in.^{2}

Checkpoint Quiz 2 1. 54 m^2 2. 160 in.^{2} 3. 90 m^2
4. 82 cm^2

| Lesson 10-5 | pp. 404–406 |

Check Skills You'll Need 1. Sample: You can simplify a fraction by using a common factor to divide both the numerator and denominator. 2. 9 3. $\frac{4}{15}$ 4. $\frac{2}{21}$
5. $\frac{1}{10}$

Quick Check 1. 28.3 m 2. 452 m^2

Chapter 11

Check Your Readiness   p. 416

1. 50°; acute 2. 120°; obtuse 3. 90°; right 4. 30°;
acute 5. $x = 3$ 6. $b = 18$ 7. $n = 2$ 8. $c = 3$
9. $p = 12$ 10. $s = 60$ 11. Yes; the ratio of each
y-value to each x-value is constant. The ratio is
always equal to 4. 12. No; the ratio of each
y-value to each x-value is not constant.

| Lesson 11–1 | pp. 418–419 |

Check Skills You'll Need 1. 120° and 60° 2. 132°
3. 61° 4. 113° 5. 49°

Quick Check 1a. alternate interior
1b. corresponding 1c. neither 2. $m\angle 6 =$
$m\angle 7 = 117°$ 3. The measure of each angle formed
by lines t and ℓ and lines t and m is 90°. Since pairs
of corresponding angles are congruent, the lines
are parallel.

| Lesson 11–2 | pp. 422–427 |

Check Skills You'll Need 1. equal 2. $m\angle 1 = 106°$,
$m\angle 2 = 74°$

Quick Check 1. $\triangle TRS \cong \triangle KJL$ 2a. $\triangle XYZ \cong \triangle RQP$
by SSS 2b. $\triangle KLM \cong \triangle JLM$ by SAS 3a. 40° 3b. 50°

Checkpoint Quiz 1 1. vertical 2. alternate interior
3. corresponding 4. 135° 5. 45° 6. 135°
7. Answers may vary. Sample: SAS, ASA, or SSS;
$\triangle JKD \cong \triangle WTB$. 8. 23°; 113° 9. 100° 10. 90°
11. 120° 12. 0.9 m 13. 1.6 m 14. 1.7 m

| Lesson 11–3 | pp. 428–429 |

Check Skills You'll Need 1. Sample answer: If the ratio
of the variable quantities in the relationship is
constant, the relationship is proportional. 2. Yes.
Each ratio of y to x is equal to 4. Because the
ratios are equal, the relationship is proportional.

Quick Check 1. Yes; the corresponding angles are
congruent and the corresponding side lengths are
proportional. 2. 11.2 in. 3. 21 ft

| Lesson 11–4 | pp. 432–438 |

Check Skills You'll Need 1. congruent; in proportion
2. Yes; the corresponding angles are congruent,
and the corresponding sides are in proportion.

Quick Check 1. 66° 2a. Sample answer: By the angle
sum of a triangle, $m\angle N = 75°$. $\angle L \cong \angle U$ because
both measure 75°. $\angle N \cong \angle T$ because both
measure 75°. So, $\triangle LMN \sim \triangle UST$ by AA similarity.
2b. Sample answer: By the angle sum of a triangle,
$m\angle B = 88°$. $\angle B \cong \angle ECD$ because both measure
88°. $\angle BDA \cong \angle CDE$ because both measure 28°.
So, $\triangle ABD \sim \triangle ECD$ by AA similarity.

Checkpoint Quiz 2 1. Yes, the corresponding angles
are congruent, and the corresponding sides are in
proportion. 2. 6 in. 3. $m\angle K = 71°$ 4. $m\angle T = 29°$
5. $m\angle B = 64°$ 6. $m\angle H = 35°$ 7. Sample answer:
By the angle sum of a triangle, $m\angle Y = 68°$. $\angle X \cong$
$\angle N$ because both measure 63°. $\angle Y \cong \angle L$ because
both measure 68°. So, $\triangle XYZ \sim \triangle NLM$ by AA
similarity. 8. Sample answer: By the angle sum of
a triangle, $m\angle PTQ = 52°$. $\angle QPT \cong \angle RPS$ because
both measure 33°. $\angle PTQ \cong \angle S$ because both
measure 52°. So, $\triangle PQT \sim \triangle PRS$ by AA similarity.

| Lesson 11–5 | pp. 440–441 |

Check Skills You'll Need 1. 180° 2. 126° 3. 90° 4. 72°
5. 162° 6. 104° 7. 30°

Quick Check 1. 900° 2. 151° 3. 147°

Chapter 12

Check Your Readiness   p. 452

1. 3.14 **2.** 82 **3.** 20 **4.** −12.04 **5.** 66 m² **6.** 15 yd²
7. 8 cm² **8.** 22.0 m **9.** 37.7 cm **10.** 15.7 mi

Lesson 12-2   pp. 458–464

Check Skills You'll Need 1. The height of a triangle is the length of the perpendicular segment from a vertex to the base opposite the vertex or to an extension of the base. **2.** 48 m² **3.** 6 ft²

Quick Check 1. Answers may vary. Sample:

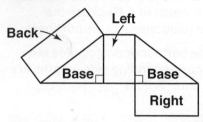

2. 328 ft² **3.** 3,455.8 m²

Checkpoint Quiz 1 1. sphere **2.** cone **3.** trapezoidal prism **4.** sphere

5. 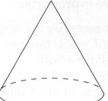   **6.**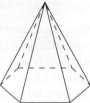

7.   **8.** 36 in.² **9.** 2,884 m² **10.** 504 in.²

Lesson 12-3   pp. 465–467

Check Skills You'll Need 1. $\Leftarrow = \frac{C}{d}$ **2.** 113 m² **3.** 177 in.²

Quick Check 1. 120 in.³ **2.** 72 cm³ **3 a.** about 6,000 cm³; 6,107 cm³ **b.** The estimate will be a little large.

Lesson 12-4   pp. 473–474

Check Skills You'll Need 1. face **2.** 2 triangular faces, 3 rectangular faces; triangular prism
3. 2 pentagonal faces, 5 rectangular faces; pentagonal prism

Quick Check 1 a. circle **b.** rectangle **2 a.** hexagon similar to the hexagon that is the base of the pyramid. **b.** triangle

Lesson 12–5   pp. 478–479

Check Skills You'll Need 1. The base of a pyramid is a polygon, whereas the base of a cone is a circle.
2a. square **2b.** circle

Quick Check 1. 92 m³ **2.** 129 m³ **3.** $r \approx 6.2$ cm

Lesson 12–6   pp. 482–486

Check Skills You'll Need 1. how many times the number, or base, is used as a factor **2.** 81 **3.** 36 **4.** 3,584
5. 4.41

Quick Check 1. 616 ft² **2.** 33,510 in.³

Checkpoint Quiz 2 1. 1,911 cm² **2.** 4,516 in.³ **3.** 32 cm³
4. 456 in.³ **5.** 452 cm³ **6.** 14,137 km³ **7.** 314 in.²
8. Check students' drawings.

Chapter 13

Check Your Readiness   p. 492

1–4.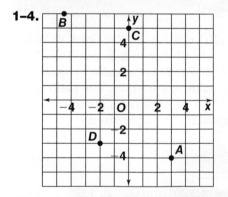

5. △~ABD ≅ △CBD **6.** EFJK ≅ GFIH
7. No, $\frac{7}{6} \neq \frac{5}{4}$. So the corresponding sides are not proportional. **8.** Yes, the corresponding sides are proportional. The triangles are similar by SSS~.

Lesson 13–1   pp. 494–495

Check Skills You'll Need 1. Quadrant II **2.** (4, 2)
3. (2, 1) **4.** (5, −2) **5.** (1, −1)

Quick Check 1.

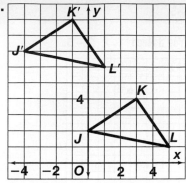

2. $(x, y) \rightarrow (x + 6, y + 2)$

Check Skills You'll Need 1. distance **2.**

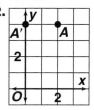

3.   **4.**

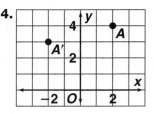

5.

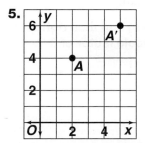

Quick Check 1. $D'(2, 1)$

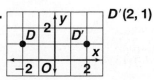

2. $E'(4,3), F'(3,1), G'(1,2)$

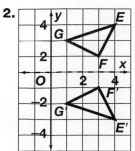

3.

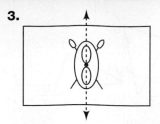

1. $M'(-3, 5)$ **2.** $N'(-4, -1)$ **3.** $P'(1, 0)$ **4.** $J'(-3, 6)$,
$K'(0, 8), L'(2, 5)$ **5.** $(x, y) \rightarrow (x - 3, y + 4)$
6.–10. Check students' graphs. **6.** $Q'(3, -4)$
7. $R'(-2, -5)$ **8.** $S'(9, 0)$ **9.** $D'(1, 0), E'(4.5, 1)$,
$F'(2.5, -2)$

Check Skills You'll Need 1. matches **2.** straight
3. obtuse **4.** obtuse **5.** acute **6.** acute **7.** right

Quick Check 1. $72°$

2a.

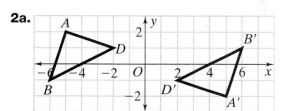

$A'(5, -2), B'(6, 1), D'(2, -1)$

2b.

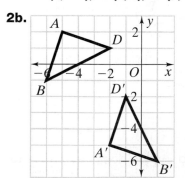

$A'(2, 5), B'(-1, 6), D'(1, 2)$

Check Skills You'll Need 1. angle of rotation **2.** $(-1, 2)$
3. $(0, -3)$ **4.** $(4, 1)$

Quick Check 1. translation 7 units up, followed by
reflection over the y-axis **2.** A reflection over the
x-axis, followed by a rotation of $180°$ about the
origin, followed by a translation 6 units down
maps $\triangle EFG$ onto $\triangle MNP$. So $\triangle EFG \cong \triangle MNP$.

Checkpoint Quiz 2 1.

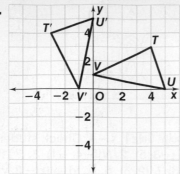

T' $(-3, 4)$, U' $(0, 5)$, V' $(-1, 0)$

2.

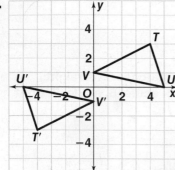

T' $(-4, -3)$, U' $(-5, 0)$, V' $(0, -1)$

3.

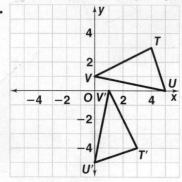

T' $(3, -4)$, U' $(0, -5)$, V' $(1, 0)$

4. JKLM ≅ STUV **5.** No. △UVW does not map onto △XYZ

Check Skills You'll Need 1. x **2.–5.**

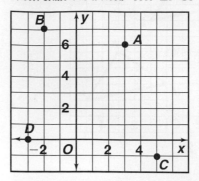

Quick Check 1.

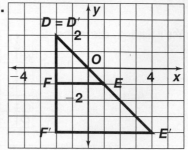

2. A'(0, 0), B'(0, 4), C'(4, 4), D'(4, 0)
3. 3; enlargement

Check Skills You'll Need 1. similar **2.** 6

Quick Check 1. A translation down and then right, followed by a dilation with a scale factor of 3

Selected Answers

Chapter 1

Lesson 1-1   pp. 6–7

EXERCISES **1.** Whole numbers do not include negative numbers. **3.** Yes, all numbers except zero have an opposite with a different sign. Zero is its own opposite. **5.** −4 **7.** 2 **9.** 5 **11.** −12 **13.** 8 **15.** −11 **23.** 22 **25.** 0 **33.** < **35.** < **41.** −5, −2, −1, 0, 7 **45 a.** Omaha, Nebr. **b.** Bismarck, N. Dak. **47.** −3551, −3515, −3155, −3151 **49.** No; there are no integers between the integers −3 and −4. **53.** 453

Lesson 1-2   pp. 13–14

EXERCISES **1.** A; always **3.** C; never **5.** 8 **7.** −1 **9.** 1 **13.** 38 **15.** 0 **19.** 13 **21.** 25 **29.** −1 + 4 = 3 **31.** −2 **33.** 8:00 A.M. **41.** >

Lesson 1-3   pp. 18–19

EXERCISES **1.** B **3.** 4 **5.** 80 **7.** −2 **9.** −5 **11.** 36 **13.** 21 **19.** 3 **21.** −14 **31.** −1 **37. a.** 278 − 5(15) **b.** $203 **41.** −42

Lesson 1-4   pp. 24–25

EXERCISES **1.** A terminating decimal stops, whereas a repeating decimal has a block of digits that repeat without end. **3.** $1\frac{3}{8}$ **5.** $3\frac{99}{100}$ **7.** 0.5, $1\frac{1}{3}$, 1.$\overline{9}$, 2 **9.** 0.8 **11.** 0.$\overline{6}$ **17.** $\frac{33}{50}$ **19.** $3\frac{3}{4}$ **25.** 3.84, $3\frac{41}{50}$, 3.789, 3 **31.** < **33.** > **35.** when the numerator is not a multiple of 3 **37.** N.Y.: $\frac{4,572}{19,227}$ Tex.: $\frac{6,267}{22,490}$ Calif.: $\frac{9,596}{33,893}$ Fla.: $\frac{4,003}{17,397}$ Ohio: $\frac{2,779}{11,459}$ **39.** Fla., N.Y., Ohio, Tex., Calif. **41.** The quotients are 0.5, 5, 50, 500, 5,000, and 50,000. As the divisor gets smaller, the quotient gets larger because divisor × quotient = dividend. **45.** 3

Lesson 1-5   pp. 28–29

EXERCISES **1.** Answers may vary. Sample: A rational number is a number that can be written as a quotient of two integers. **3.** > **5.** −236, −$7\frac{1}{7}$, −3.$\overline{3}$, 0, $\frac{41}{99}$ **7.** > **9.** < **19.** −1.0, −$\frac{3}{4}$, 0.25, $\frac{3}{2}$ **25.** > **27.** > **31.** $\frac{3}{4}$ **35.** 0.5.

Lesson 1-6   pp. 35–36

1. absolute value. **3.** −68.97 **7.** 24.8 **11.** 0.7 **14.** 8.3 **18.** 1.49 **20.** 15.3°F **23.** 72.1°F **25.** 33.6 m **29.** $\frac{3}{7}$

Lesson 1-7   pp. 41–42

1. C **3.** negative **5.** −0.24 **7.** 13.65 **9.** 3.9 **11.** 27.9 **14.** −1.44 **17.** −10.2 **23.** 10.35 **26.** −$1,055.53 **30.** −661.1m **32.** H **36.** 5.738

Lesson 1-8   pp. 46–47

1. B **3. a** negative **5.** −3 **8.** $3\frac{1}{4}$ **11.** 4.5 **14.** −1 **17.** −17 **20.** −6.8 **24.** −$9.00 **25.** 5 batches **33.** −$\frac{35}{9}$ or −$3\frac{8}{9}$

Lesson 1-9   pp. 53–54

EXERCISES **1.** irrational, real **3.** rational, real **5.** 2, −2 **7.** 10, −10 **9.** 7, −7 **11.** $\frac{1}{6}$, −$\frac{1}{6}$ **15.** 3 **17.** −11 **23.** 342 m/s **27.** Irrational; 40 is not a perfect square. **29.** Rational; 144 is a perfect square. **31.** 88ft **35.** 10 **47.** 0.3125

Lesson 1-10   pp. 57–58

EXERCISES **1.** 8 inches; Explanations may vary. Sample: The side length of a cube is the cube root of its volume; $\sqrt[3]{512}$. **3.** 0 **7.** 1 **13.** 5 **19.** $\frac{3}{8}$ foot **25.** 9 **29.**

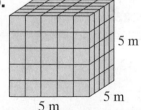

5 m
5 m
5 m

33. 5; Use the cube root of the nearest perfect cube. Since 100 is closer to 125 than to 64, $\sqrt[3]{100}$ must be closer to 5 than to 4. **37.** 4.2

Chapter Review   pp. 60–61

1. repeating decimal **2.** rational number **3.** terminating decimal **4.** opposites **5.** integers **6.** < **7.** = **8.** > **9.** > **10.** 6 **11.** 29 **12.** -30 **13.** -25 **14.** −$\frac{7}{8}$, 0.3, $\frac{3}{4}$ **15.** −$\frac{4}{11}$, -0.3, 2.7 **16.** −$\frac{5}{6}$, -0.5, 2.2 **17.** $\frac{1}{3}$ **18.** 3.8 **19.** −$\frac{2}{13}$ **20.** -7 **21.** 9 **22.** $\frac{10}{11}$ **23.** 5 **24.** $\frac{1}{2}$ **25.** $\frac{1}{3}$ **26.** $\frac{2}{5}$ **27.** −$\frac{2}{3}$ **28.** 0

Chapter 2

EXERCISES 1. 1 **3.** greater than 0, because the number remains positive even though the decimal point moves 5 places to the left **5.** 3,000 **9.** 260,000 lb **11.** 1.72×10^4 **15.** 0.0025 **19.** 0.00935 cm **21.** 1.05×10^{-3} **27.** 8 **31.** 3.92×10^8 **35a.** 2,750,000 calories **35b.** 2.75×10^6 calories **41.** 8

EXERCISES 1. 8 **3.** $-(6)^4$ **5.** 7^{10} **7.** Instead of just adding the exponents, the student multiplied the bases and then added the exponents. **9.** y^8 **11.** 3.4^{13} **17.** 2^{11} km **21.** 2^6 **23.** 3^{m+n} **27.** a^{10} **35.** $>$ **39.** 2 **43.** –170

EXERCISES 1. 17 **3.** 10 **5.** 1.86×10^5 mi/s **7.** 8×10^9 **11.** 4.5×10^{15} **13.** 1.75 mm; 1.75×10^{-1} cm **19.** 6.8×10^{12} **21.** 9.1×10^{-25} mg **23.** 2.5×10^{12} mg **27.** $\frac{4}{3}$

EXERCISES 1. Positive; any nonzero number to the power zero is equal to one. **3.** $\frac{2 \cdot 2 \cdot 2 \cdot 2 \cdot 2 \cdot 2}{2 \cdot 2 \cdot 2 \cdot 2 \cdot 2} = 2^1$ **7.** x^4 **9.** $(-1)^1$ **15.** 1 **17.** 1 **25.** 12 **29.** 1 **35.** False; $8^{-1} = \frac{1}{8}$ and $(-8)^1 = -8$. **37.** False; $(-2)^{-1} = \frac{1}{-2} = -\frac{1}{2}$ and $-\frac{1}{2} \neq 2$ **39.a** $2n^3 - 4$ **39.b** $2m^6 + 3m^3 + 1$ **43.** 11

EXERCISES 1. 3 **3.** 7 **5.** 6×10^8 **7.** Sample answer: The coefficient and the power of ten are multiplied. If you divide both by 3, you are actually dividing by 9. **9.** 8.4×10^3 **13.** 2×10^4 **17.** 500 **21.** 4.9×10^8 **23.** 51 **25.** 1.12×10^3 ft/s **29.** 3.13×10^8 **33.** $1\frac{1}{8}$

1. when computing with very large and very small numbers **2.** 2,500 **3.** 800,000 **4.** 0.0000061 **5.** 4×10^4 **6.** 3.205×10^{-4} **7.** 9.3×10^7 **8.** $\frac{1}{512}$

9. 8^{19} **10.** $(-3)^{13}$ **11.** 2.6^{24} **12.** x^3 **13.** c^3 **14.** $(-b)^{11}$ **15.** $7a^6$ **16.** $12x^8$ **17.** $25n^6$ **18.** $-8x^4$ **19.** r^6 **20.** $-5m^6$ **21.** $4x^5$ **22.** $\frac{1}{3}x^3$ **23.** $\frac{1}{16}$ in.; 0.0625 in. **24.** 6×10^{18} **25.** 7×10^6 **26.** 3×10^{14} **27.** 1.47×10^{20} **28.** 5.6×10^{-6} **29.** 3.4×10^4 **30.** 5×10^{-2} mm; 5×10^{-8} km **31.** 5^3 **32.** $(-8)^{10}$ **33.** 76^6 **34.** 1.8^1 or 18 **35.** 1 **36.** 1 **37.** g^5 **38.** 0 **39.** $\frac{1}{625}$ **40.** $\frac{1}{x^9}$ **41.** $\frac{1}{81}$ **42.** $\frac{1}{h^8}$ **43.** 2×10^3 **44.** 1.4×10^3 **45.** 4.4×10^{10} **46.** 8.5×10^7 **47.** 2.1×10^{-4} **48.** 1.5×10^6 **49.** 4.1×10^4, 4.0×10^3, 3.6×10^3, 3.7×10^{-4}

Chapter 3

EXERCISES 1. An algebraic expression differs from a numerical expression because it contains at least one variable, and the value changes. **3.** addition **5–7.** Answers may vary. Samples are given: **5.** the product of 5 and w **7.** the quotient of w and 4 **9.** 6 **11.** 6 **13.** $\frac{p}{5}$ **17–19.** Answers may vary. Samples are given. **17.** two more than a number **19.** nine and one tenth less than a number **25.** 42 **27.** 3 **33.** $10n$ **35.** Answers may vary. Sample: Multiply 24(60) to find the number of minutes in 24 h. Then multiply the answer by 1,260, the number of beats per minute. The heart beats 1,814,400 times in 24 h. **39.** Answers may vary. Sample: The second student charges $15 to start and $3/h. **43.** 45

EXERCISES 1. like terms **3.** $6n$ **5.** $3 - 3r$ **9.** 9 **13.** $16w - 6$ **15.** $2a - 1$ **22.** $4 - 5x$ **25.** $4(3x - 7)$ **31.** $5 + 12y$ **35.** $11.4y + 6.78$ **41.** $10x + 2.4$ **45.** 31 **49.** $0.\overline{3}$ **55.** $\frac{33}{100}$

EXERCISES 1. Inverse **3.** 12 **5.** B **7.** A **19.** 16 **25.** 15 yr **26.** about 198 plays **27.** $329 + 328 + n = 968$; 311 students **35.** 23

EXERCISES 1. A one-step expression uses only one operation, while a two-step expression uses two. **3.** B **5.** C **7.** 70 **9.** Let h = your height; $6h + 1$. **13.** 1.5 **15.** -0.9 **21.** 15.2 **23.** 7 **33.** 11.5 **35.** 45 **41.** Answers may vary. Sample: You need to keep the equation "balanced." **47.** $<$

Lesson 3-5   pp. 129–130

EXERCISES **1.** Let m = number of miles;
$2.00 + 0.50m = 5.00$; 6 mi **3.** 12 **5.** −3 **7.** 8
31. Let h = number of additional hours;
$3.95 + 1.25h = 7.70$; 3 h. **35.** 11 **39.** 15 credits

Lesson 3-6   pp. 137–138

EXERCISES **1.** like **3.** C **5.** B **7.** −20 **9.** 7
23. $n + n + 1 = -45$; −23 and −22
25. $n + (n + 1) + (n + 2) = -255$; −86, −85, −84
27. −1 **29.** 10 **31.** $4m + 5 = 21$; $m = 4$ ft **39.** 44

Lesson 3-7   p. 141

EXERCISES **1.** all of them **3.** 11 a and a, $-4.1a^2$
and a^2 **5.** The student added x to the left side but
subtracted x from the right side.
$$3x + 4 - x = 7 + x$$
$$2x + 4 = 7 + x$$
$$2x - x + 4 = 7 + x - x$$
$$x + 4 = 7$$
$$x + 4 - 4 = 7 - 4$$
$$x = 3$$
7. −2 **9.** 21 **17.** at about 9:57 A.M. **19.** 0.15 **23.** 3

Lesson 3-8   pp. 147–148

EXERCISES **1.** infinitely many **3.** A **5.** 3; $3 \cdot 2x =$
$6x$ and $3 \cdot 3 = 9$, so the equation can be simplified to
$9 = 9$. **7.** infinitely many solutions; result is $3 = 3$, of
form $a = a$ **15.** no solution; result is $-\frac{2}{27} = -\frac{5}{9}$, of
form $a = b$ **23.** Infinitely many; this equation
simplifies to $1.6 = 1.6$. **29.** $0.\overline{27}$

Chapter Review   pp. 150–151

1. variable **2.** Subtraction Property of Equality
3. algebraic expression **4.** like terms **5.** coefficient
6. 13 **7.** −6 **8.** −2.5 **9.** −25 **10.** $2x - 1$ **11.** $-4.6z + 12.3$
12. $\frac{11}{12n} = \frac{1}{2}$ **13.** $2r + 8$ **14.** $-9.3 - 7r$ **15.** $n + 2$
16. 24 **17.** 84 **18.** 99 **19.** −12 **20.** $1\frac{5}{8}$ **21.** 160
22. −1.05 **23.** 3 hours **24.** 2 **25.** −2.75 **26.** −4
27. 25 **28.** $3.25 **29.** none **30.** one **31.** Infinitely
many **32.** one

Chapter 4

Lesson 4-1   pp. 158–159

EXERCISES **1.** inequality **3.** C **5.** −1 **7.** −2
11.
13. **19.** $x \le 6$
25. $a \ge 17$; **31.** $w \le 3$
33. −3, −2, or −1 **41.** −9, −8, −6, 3, 12

Lesson 4-2   pp. 162–163

EXERCISES **1.** Addition Property of Inequality **3.** C
5. B **7.** $g \le -6$;
9. $y \ge 16$;
27. $109 + x \ge 212$; $x \ge 103$ **29.** $w > -\frac{1}{2}$
31. $j \ge -5$ **35.** No; the solution of $x + 5 \le -2$ is
$x \le -7$, and the solution of $-2 \le x + 5$ is $x \ge -7$.
39. no more than 1,220 Cal **43.** −54

Lesson 4-3   pp. 168–169

EXERCISES **1.** The inequality symbol is reversed.
3. > **5.** > **12.** at least 50 pages **23.** at least 278
times **26.** $4.4n \le -44$; $n \le 10$ **31.** at most 3 hot
dogs **33.** 4 bags of peanuts; $.50 **34.** The student
should not have reversed the inequality symbol.
39. $6\frac{1}{8}$

Lesson 4-4   pp. 175–176

1. Subtract 7 from each side **3.** Subtract $\frac{1}{5}$ from
each side
5. $a > 1\frac{1}{2}$ **8.** $r < -10$
11. $w < 6.5$ **16.** $t < -2$ **31.** $-5(n + 4) - 2 > -37$;
$n < 3$ **35.** $\frac{9}{20}$

Chapter Review   pp. 178–179

1. C **2.** B **3.** D **4.** A **5.** −3, −1 **6.** $\frac{1}{6}$
7. **8.**
9. **10.** $t \le 10$

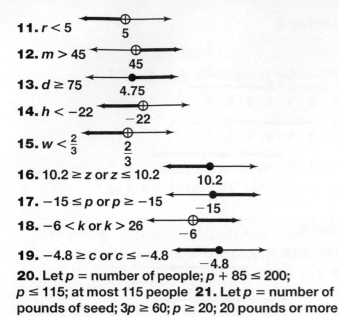

11. $r < 5$

12. $m > 45$

13. $d \geq 75$

14. $h < -22$

15. $w < \frac{2}{3}$

16. $10.2 \geq z$ or $z \leq 10.2$

17. $-15 \leq p$ or $p \geq -15$

18. $-6 < k$ or $k > 26$

19. $-4.8 \geq c$ or $c \leq -4.8$

20. Let p = number of people; $p + 85 \leq 200$; $p \leq 115$; at most 115 people **21.** Let p = number of pounds of seed; $3p \geq 60$; $p \geq 20$; 20 pounds or more

22. $q < 2$

23. $x \leq 2.52$

24. $r > -65$

25. $-3 \leq t$ or $t \geq -3$

26. $w > -\frac{1}{2}$

27. $2.04 < b$ or $b > 2.04$

28. at most, 4 **29.** 28 or greater

Chapter 5

Lesson 5-1 pp. 186–187

EXERCISES 1. Equivalent ratios name the same amount, as do equivalent fractions. **3.** 2 to 16 **5.** 20 to 18 **7.** $\frac{17}{24}$ **9.** equivalent **11.** equivalent **13.** 21 to 25, 21 : 25, $\frac{21}{25}$ **15.** 12 to 14 **17.** $\frac{1}{2}$ **23.** equivalent **25.** not equivalent **29.** Answers may vary. Sample: if the GCF of the numerator and denominator is 1 **31a.** 8 : 4, 7.5 : 3, 3.5 : 1 **31b.** 10 qt antifreeze, 5 qt water **37.** 45

Lesson 5-2 pp. 190–191

EXERCISES 1. Answers may vary. Sample: It gives the cost of one item or unit. **3.** 200 **5.** 5; 17.90 **7.** 16 points/game **9.** 34.82 students/classroom **11.** $3\frac{1}{5}$ chapters per hour **15.** \$.93/oz **17.** \$.06/fl oz, \$.05/fl oz; the 50-fl-oz detergent is the better buy. **21.** \$2.94 for 6 yd **23.** $\frac{1}{2}$ sandwich per minute

26. 5.54 m/s **29.** about 39,421,000 times; about 108,000 times; about 75 times

33. $m > 4$

Lesson 5-3 pp. 195–196

EXERCISES 1. ratios **3.** 8 **5.** 9 **7.** 12 **9.** No; you need to multiply the numerator of one by the denominator of the other.

$$\frac{3}{4} \stackrel{?}{=} \frac{12}{16}$$

$$3 \cdot 16 \stackrel{?}{=} 4 \cdot 12$$

$48 = 48$ They do form a proportion.

11. no **13.** yes **31.** yes **35.** no **37.** Yes; the weight ratios $\frac{174}{29}$ and $\frac{102}{17}$ are proportional because $174 \cdot 17 = 102 \cdot 29$. **45.** -407

Lesson 5-4 pp. 202–203

EXERCISES 1. Answers may vary. Sample: Finding a unit rate gives you a denominator of 1, so you only need to multiply to solve the proportion. $\frac{5}{1} = \frac{x}{8}$, $x = 40$ **3.** 4 **5.** 12 **7.** \$7.90 **9.** \$59.00 **11.** 6 **13.** 6 **17.** 20 **19.** 85.75 **27.** 17,100,000 votes **29.** Yes; when you simplify a ratio, it is still equivalent to the original ratio. **31.** 5 **35.** 240 should be the numerator. $\frac{2}{3} = \frac{240}{n}$ **43.** $-6, -3, -2, 1, 8$

Lesson 5-5 pp. 209–210

EXERCISES 1. Two polygons are similar if corresponding angles have the same measure and the lengths of the corresponding sides form equivalent ratios. **3.** $\overline{AB}$ **7.** 11.2 ft **9.** 53° **13.** 24 in. **15.** $\frac{7}{12}$ **17.** 2.88 km **19.** 99 cm **23.** 5 **25.** 6

Lesson 5-6 pp. 216–217

EXERCISES 1. ratio; length **3.** No; the scale should be written as model : actual, or 8 ft : 6 ft. **5.** 15 mi **7.** 231 ft **9.** 148.5 ft **11.** 15 in. **13.** 1 in. : 2 mi **17.** 1 cm : 0.71 mm **19.** about 47 mi **21.** about 47 mi **25.** $10\frac{1}{2}$ in. **29.** $x = 40, y = 32$

Lesson 5-7 pp. 223–224

EXERCISES 1. For a proportional relationship, both are the ratio when the second term is 1. **3.** Yes; all the ratios of bags to pounds of dog food are equivalent. **5.** $p = 2.5b$ **7.** Proportional; ratios for each pair are equivalent. **11.** $c = 1.99$ **13.** $h = \frac{1}{4}n$ **18.** $m = 300d$ **23.** $w > 2$

1. unit cost **2.** rate **3.** scale **4.** similar **5.** constant of proportionality **6.** $\frac{3}{10}$ **7.** $\frac{16}{5}$ **8.** 3 : 1 **9.** 15 : 4 **10.** $\frac{1}{4}$ **11.** 6 passengers/car **12.** 75 cal/serving **13.** \$.28/oz, \$.31/oz; the 10-oz size is the better buy. **14.** 12 **15.** 25 **16.** 3 **17.** 136 **18.** 7.5 ft **19.** 15 ft **20.** $x = 45$ **21.** $x = 45$, $y = 36$ **22.** 6,300 mi **23.** 0.75 in. **24.** no **25.** yes; $c = 40$ **26.** $d = 1.25s$

Chapter 6

Lesson 6-1   pp. 235–236

EXERCISES 1. 62%, $\frac{62}{100}$, 0.62 **3.** $\frac{1}{2}$, 0.54, 55% **5.** 57% **11.** 0.88 **15.** 90% **19.** 27.3% **21.** $\frac{3}{20}$ **25.** $\frac{17}{100}$ **27.** 0.25, $\frac{1}{2}$, 120% **31.** No, 0.4% is equal to 0.004 as a decimal. **34.** macaroni and cheese, 30%; spaghetti and meat sauce, 46% **39.** $-0.9 \leq x$

Lesson 6-2   pp. 239–240

EXERCISES 1. percent; 25% **3.** whole; 16 **5.** C **7.** B **9.** 10% **11.** 2% **15.** 5 **21.** 18.75 **23.** 80 **26.** 25% **31.** 37.5% **41.** 4

Lesson 6-3   pp. 243–244

EXERCISES 1. No; "20% of 40" asks for a part, "20 is what percent of 40" asks for a percent, and "20 is 40% of what number" asks for a whole. **3.** C **5.** $625p = 500$; 80% **7.** $0.96x = 24$; 25 **11.** 25 questions **13.** $x = 0.41 \cdot 800$; 328 **17.** $18 = 48x$; 37.5% **23.** 69% **29.** about 190 people **31.** 45 members **37.** yes

Lesson 6-4   pp. 251–252

EXERCISES 1. You earn 8% of the amount you sell. **3.** \$3.60 **5.** \$27 **7.** \$.71 **9.** \$77.12 **11.** about \$4.65 **15.** \$200 **19.** \$47.50 **21.** \$23 **25.** \$6,800 **33.** \$2.35/lb

Lesson 6-5   p. 256

EXERCISES 1. principal **3.** straight **5.** \$71.40
9.

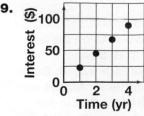

17. A **19.** 4.5% **23.** 36

Lesson 6-6   pp. 261–262

EXERCISES 1. Answers may vary. Sample: They both involve the difference between the original price and the selling price. Percent of markup is a percent of increase and percent of discount is a percent of decrease. **3.** $\frac{15}{35}$, 43% increase **5.** $\frac{374}{748}$, 50% decrease **7.** A **9.** 13% **17.** 50% **21.** 131% **23.** 56% **28.** about \$52,000 **31.** Find the difference in the number of students for last year and this year, divide that by last year's number, and express the result as a percent. If this year's number is greater than last year's number, the change is an increase. If this year's number is less, the change is a decrease. **33.** \$53.30 **41.** \$231.63

Chapter Review   pp. 264–265

1. C **2.** E **3.** D **4.** B **5.** A **6.** F **7.** 0.65 **8.** 0.02 **9.** 0.018 **10.** 0.625 **11.** 37.5% **12.** 16% **13.** 70% **14.** 47.5 **15.** 252 **16.** 12 **17.** 72 **18.** 20% **19.** \$57.60 **20.** \$0.60 **21.** \$119.60 **22.** 12.5% **23.** about \$10.52 **24.** \$268 **25.** \$63 **26.** \$216 **27.** \$275 **28.** \$225 **29.** \$450 **30.** 16.7% decrease **31.** 20% increase **32.** 15% increase **33.** 31% decrease

Chapter 7

Lesson 7-1   pp. 272–273

EXERCISES 1. Line graphs best display changes over time. **3.** when the bus stops **5.** Highway; the bus travels a greater distance over a shorter period of time on the highway. **7.** 12–24 min **9.** 0–8 min, 12–16 min **13.** Al **15.** Carlos

17.   **19.**

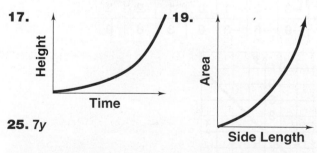

25. 7y

Lesson 7-2   pp. 277–278

EXERCISES 1. A function rule is an equation that describes a function. **3.** Always positive; the product of two negative numbers is always positive.

5. 3 **7.** 7 **11.**

n	t
44	4
132	12
165	15

18.

Input t	Output d
1	50
2	100
3	150
4	200

23. inifinite **25.** none

Lesson 7-3   pp. 282–283

EXERCISES 1. See if the ratio of each input to its corresponding output is the same. **3.** No. Ratios are not the same. **5.** yes **7.** no **11.** no **17.** Basketball. The graph shows it takes 2 hr to burn 1,500 calories which is 12.5 calories per minute.

Lesson 7-4   pp. 289–290

EXERCISES 1. If the ratios between the changes in variables are the same, then the function is linear. **5.** Yes; rates of change constant. **17.** $x = 10$ **19.** $x = -8$

Lesson 7-5   pp. 295–296

EXERCISES 1. run. **3.** $-\frac{1}{3}$ **5.** $\frac{3}{5}$ **9.**
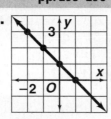
11. Your classmate found $\frac{run}{rise}$ instead of $\frac{rise}{run}$. **19.** $y > 8$

Lesson 7-6   pp. 302–303

EXERCISES 1. the point where the graph crosses the y-axis **3.** 4; −1
5.

x	−3	−2	−1	0	1	2	3
y	−9	−6	−3	0	3	6	9

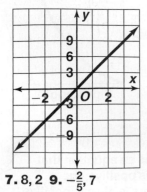

7. 8, 2 **9.** $-\frac{2}{5}$, 7

11.
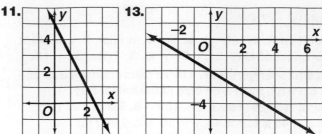

13.

23.
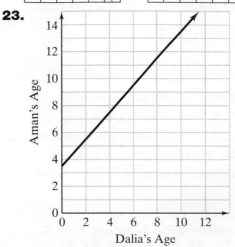
Dalia's Age / Aman's Age

25. **Cost to Fill Tank**
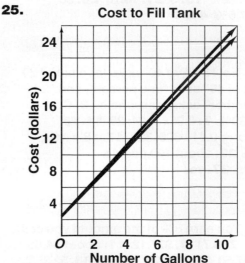
Number of Gallons / Cost (dollars)

29. No. A graph of the function does not pass through or touch the origin.

Lesson 7-7   pp. 307–308

EXERCISES 1. You can find two points on the line and use them to find the slope. **3.** B **5.** A **7.** the function given as a table (2.75 > 2.5) **9.** Both functions are continuous and neither increases or decreases at a constant rate. The function in the graph decreases until $x = 30$ and $y = 4$, then it increases. The other function always decreases, and gets closer and closer to zero. **11.** Reggie **13.** T, W, E, G **15.** The base fee for subcompact cars is $30 plus $25 per day. The base fee for compact cars is $40 plus $28 per day. The base fee for luxury cars is $40 plus $30 per day. The subcompact plan is always cheaper than the other two plans. **19.** $7.5x - 1.8y - 18$

Chapter Review pp. 310–311

1. function **2.** linear function **3.** 0–2 hr, 4–5 hr
4. 2–4 hr, 5–6 hr **5.** 2–4 hr **6.** $d = 5$ **7.** $d = 23$
8. d = –13 **9.** d = 59 **10.** d = –16 **11.** yes **12.** no
13. nonlinear **14.** linear **15.** nonlinear
16. Nonlinear

17. 18.

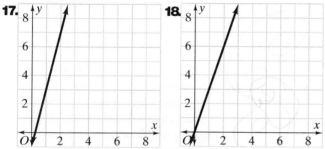

19. 3, 5 **20.** –1/2, –4 **21.** 1, 7 **22.** 2/3, 0
23. $y = 7x + 9$ **24.** function in table

Chapter 8

Lesson 8-1 pp. 318–319

EXERCISES 1. C **3.** B **5.** was not **7.** Part (b); the sample is more diverse. **11.** Fair; the question makes no assumptions. **21.** Yes; you will survey people in your population without any bias.
23. about 1,158 people **27.** $12n - 16$

Lesson 8-2 pp. 321–322

EXERCISES 1. Researchers capture, mark, and release animals, and then capture another group of animals. The number of marked animals in the second group indicates population size. **3.** about 13,661 bass **5.** about 305 bears **7.** about 2,010 deer **11.** about 2,535 deer **17.** 63 alligators

21. about 233 animals **25.** $x \le -\frac{1}{3}$

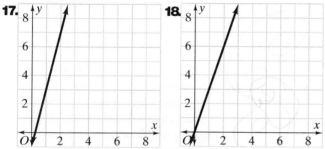

Lesson 8-3 pp. 328–329

EXERCISES 1. An inference is based on data or reasoning, but a guess may not be. **3.** about 106 **5.** about 22; The mean age of visitors in the sample is about 22, so the mean age of all visitors at the park is likely close to 22. **9.** sample 1: 3.7 letters; sample 2: 3.9 letters; sample 3: 3.4 letters **15.** about 51%; About 25% of all voters are males who will vote for the senator. About 26% of all voters are females who will vote for the senator. In all, about 25% + 26% = 51% of all the voters will vote to re-elect the senator.

Lesson 8-4 pp. 333–334

EXERCISES 1. Sample answer: A measure of center indicates the typical value in a data set, while a measure of variability indicates how spread out the values in a data set are. **3.** mean: 114 min; MAD: 10 min **5.** The IQR for store A is $6 more than the IQR for store B. Sample: The prices of shirts at store A tend to vary more than the prices of shirts at store B. **7.** bluegill: 8 in.; shoal bass: 15 in. **11.** Males: 6 lb; females: 6 lb **13.** Sample: The MADs of the data sets are very small, which means that the data sets are not spread out very far from the means. You also know that the means are very far apart. This information indicates that there is little or no overlap in the data sets. **17.** $0.\overline{1}$

Chapter Review pp. 336–337

1. biased question **2.** sample **3.** variability
4. mean absolute deviation **5.** population
6. Sample A is more likely to be random because each customer has a chance of being surveyed. In sample B, the only customers who have a chance of being surveyed are women trying on jeans.
7. Sample B is more likely to be random because each tree in the forest has a chance of being surveyed. In sample A, only trees at the edge of the road have a chance of being surveyed.
8. This question is fair. It does not make any assumptions about students' favorite activities.
9. This question is biased. The adjectives "calm" and "soothing" may influence responses.
10. about 450 **11.** about 81 **12.** about 368
13. sample 1: about 33; sample 2: about 135; sample 3: about 67 **14.** The greatest estimate is 135, and the least estimate is 33. So, the estimates vary by 102 batteries. **15.** The factory produced

about 78 defective batteries on Monday.
16. brand A: 37 raisins per package; brand B: 34 raisins per package **17.** brand A: 0.8; brand B: 0.8 **18.** $n = 3.75$; The difference between the means is 3.75 times the MAD. So, the distance between the centers is less than the variability of either data set. This indicates a large amount of overlap in the data sets.

Chapter 9

Lesson 9-1   pp. 344–345

EXERCISES 1. Answers may vary. Sample: the result or group of results of an action **3.** B **5.** A
7. $\frac{1}{12}$; $0.08\overline{3}$; about 8.3% **13.** 0 **15.** $\frac{3}{10}$ **21.** $\frac{108}{114}$, or $\frac{18}{19}$
23. Answers may vary. Sample: The probability that a female student will be chosen from an all-female school is 1. The complement is 0; it is impossible for a male student to be chosen. **25.** unlikely
29. 0.04 **31.** Any positive integer divisible by 4 can be the number of marbles, since $\frac{1}{4}$ of that number must be a positive integer. **35.** -4.08

Lesson 9-2   pp. 349–350

EXERCISES 1. Theoretical probability is computed by the formula
$$P(\text{event}) = \frac{\text{number of favorable outcomes}}{\text{total number of possible outcomes}}.$$
Experimental probability is based on experimental data or observation. **3.** 18 **5.** 5 coins; one for each baby **7.** $\frac{18}{25}$ **9.** Check students' work. **17.** $\frac{6}{25}$
23. $\frac{x}{252}$; 6 **27.** $\frac{3}{9}$ or $\frac{1}{3}$

Lesson 9-3   pp. 356–357

EXERCISES 1. the collection of all possible outcomes in an experiment **3.** 1 **5.** 7 **7.** 16
11. 1 2 3 4 5 6; $\frac{3}{6}$ or $\frac{1}{2}$

13. 1st Spin   2nd Spin; $\frac{1}{4}$ **15.** 12 recipes

```
        red
  red <
        blue

        red
  blue <
        blue
```

19. $\frac{2}{16}$ or $\frac{1}{8}$ **25.** small fruit punch, small lemonade, medium fruit punch, medium lemonade, large fruit punch, large lemonade, jumbo fruit punch, jumbo lemonade **33.** 5 goals

Lesson 9-4   pp. 363–364

EXERCISES 1. Two events are independent if the occurrence of one does not affect the probability of the other occurring; two events are dependent if the occurrence of one does affect the probability of the other occurring. **3.** independent **5.** $\frac{1}{36}$
7. $\frac{3}{36}$ or $\frac{1}{12}$ **11.** $\frac{1}{64}$ **15.** $\frac{2}{7}$ **21.** $\frac{10}{380}$ or $\frac{1}{38}$ **25.** $\frac{1}{25}$
27. $\frac{24}{729}$ or $\frac{8}{243}$ **31.** $\frac{5}{7}$ **36.**

	True-False	
	T	**F**
A	T, A	F, A
B	T, B	F, B
C	T, C	F, C
D	T, D	F, D

(Row label: Multiple-Choice)

Lesson 9-5   pp. 371–372

EXERCISES 1. The steps of the simulation that result in an outcome are repeated 25 times.
3. Answers will vary. Sample: Use random 2-digit numbers from 00 to 99. Because 5 out of 100 dogs have heartworms, you can use 5 of the possible 100 random numbers to represent a dog with heartworms. **5a.** Answers will vary. Sample: Toss 2 coins. Getting at least 1 head represents getting a number card. For each trial, toss the coins until you get at least 1 head. The number of times you toss the coins represents the number of cards a player must draw to get a number card.

5b. Answers will vary. Sample: $\frac{9}{10}$

Number of Cards	Frequency
2 or fewer	18
more than 2	2

7. Sample answer: $\frac{4}{10}$ (when the numbers 00 to 16 are used to represent a delayed flight)
11. There are 100 2-digits numbers, and the coach let 4 of them (00, 01, 02, and 03) represent hitting a home run. So, the coach let 4% of the possible random numbers represent a home run, when he should have let 3% of the numbers represent a home run. **15.** 120

Chapter Review   pp. 374–375

1. sample space **2.** event **3.** independent
4. complement **5.** Experimental **6.** $\frac{1}{7}$ **7.** $\frac{2}{7}$ **8.** $\frac{6}{7}$

9. $\frac{1}{50}$ **10.** 32 **11.** Appetizer Soup Main Dish

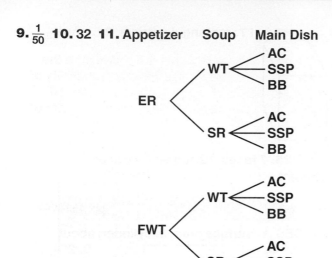

12. $\frac{1}{12}$ **13.** 12 dinners **14.** $\frac{30}{182}$ or $\frac{15}{91}$ **15.** $\frac{48}{182}$ or $\frac{24}{91}$
16. $\frac{56}{182}$ or $\frac{4}{13}$ **17.** $\frac{1}{16}$ **18.** Answers will vary. Sample:
Roll a number cube. Rolling a 1 or 2 represents
getting a card that causes a player to lose points.
For each trial, roll the number cube until you get a 1
or a 2. The number of times you roll the number cube
before getting a 1 or a 2 represents the number of
cards a player draws without losing any points.
19. Answers will vary. Sample: $\frac{1}{5}$

Cards Before Losing Points	Frequency
fewer than 4	16
at least 4	4

Chapter 10

Lesson 10-1   pp. 384–385

EXERCISES 1. Vertical angles lie opposite each
other, while adjacent angles lie next to each other.
3. acute, 45°, 135° **5.** acute, 15°, 105° **7.** $x + (2x +$
$30°) = 90°$; 70°, 20° **9.** $m\angle G = 144°$; $m\angle H = 36°$
11. 57° **15.** $\angle 3 = 25°$; $\angle 4 = 155°$ **19.** $\angle 9 = 145°$;
$\angle 10 = 70°$ **22.** 20.4 km

Lesson 10-2   pp. 391–392

EXERCISES 1. right **5.** 3 **7.** 25 m² **9.** 12 ft²
13. 625 mi² **19.** 9 m; 26.4 m **25.** area = 161 in.²;
perimeter = 62 in. **29.** 2; 2 **31.** 1 52; $1\frac{13}{25}$

Lesson 10-3   pp. 396–397

EXERCISES 1. right **3.** 8 **5.** 7 in.² **7.** 56 cm²
11. 187 in.² **13.** 36 ft² **15.** 50,000 yd² **19.** 10,000 km²
21. 27.68 km² **27.** 28

Lesson 10-4   pp. 401–402

EXERCISES 1. height **3.** $b_1 = 2.7$ in., $b_2 = 8$ in.,
$h = 10$ in. **5.** 144 m² **7.** 136 ft² **9.** 198 ft²
11. 500 km² **15.** $5\frac{3}{4}$ ft² **19.** 104 m²; 45.6 m
23. 38.5 **25.** $52.70

Lesson 10-5   pp. 406–408

EXERCISES 1. No; π is nonrepeating and
nonterminating. **3.** 2; 4; 4 π **5.** $\frac{1}{\pi}$; $\frac{2}{\pi}$; 2 **7.** 53.4 mm
13. 314 m² **18.** 177 ft² **21.** 88 m; 616 m² **25.** 42 in.;
21 in.; 1,386 in.² **31.** about 294.2 m **33.** 99 m²;
98.52 rounds to 99. **37.** $\frac{13}{20}$

Chapter Review   pp. 412–413

1. supplementary **2.** height **3.** base **4.** acute
5. circumference **6.** $3x + (2x + 40°) = 180°$; 84°; 96°
7. $(3x − 10°) + 2x = 90°$; 50°; 40° **8.** 36.3° **9.** 143.7°
10. 36.3° **11.** 112 in.² **12.** 14.4 m² **13.** 33 ft²
14. 30 cm² **15.** 54 in.² **16.** 7.2 m² **17.** 10.5 m²
18. 38 cm² **19.** 160 ft² **20.** 25.1 in.; 50.3 in.²
21. 44 mi; 153.9 mi² **22.** 22 km; 38.5 km²

Chapter 11

Lesson 11-1   pp. 420–421

EXERCISES 1. $\angle 2$ and $\angle 4$ **3.** UV **7.** corresponding
9. alternate interior **15.** 122° **21.** Alternate interior
angles are congruent. **25.** No parallel lines;
alternate interior angles are not congruent.
29. $m\angle 1 = 70°$; $m\angle 2 = 70°$; $m\angle 3 = 110°$; $m\angle 4 = 110°$
37. 10

Lesson 11-2   pp. 425–426

EXERCISES 1. size and shape **3.** SAS **5.** $\overline{EH} \cong$
$\overline{GF}$; $\angle EHF \cong \angle GFH$; $\overline{FH} \cong \overline{FH}$; $\angle FEH \cong \angle HGF$;
$\overline{EF} \cong \overline{GH}$; $\angle EFH \cong \angle GHF$ **7.** $PALK \cong PSNK$
9. SAS **11.** 104° **13.** 0.9 cm **21.** congruent; SAS
using vertical angles **33.** equation,
$m = 1$ (table, $m = \frac{1}{3}$)

Lesson 11-3
pp. 430–431

EXERCISES 1. No; similar figures must have the same shape. **3.** D **5.** Yes; the angles are all congruent and the sides are proportional. **7.** 5 **9.** 6 m **11.** 48 **13.** $x = 8, y = 14.4$ **17.** D **19.** They are the same. **23.** $n = -14$

Lesson 11-4
pp. 434–435

EXERCISES 1. 38° **3.** 53° **5.** Erika is incorrect. When she wrote the similarity statement for the triangles, she did not list the corresponding vertices in the same order in the name of each triangle. **7.** $m\angle K = 64°$ **9.** 32° **13.** Yes. $\angle NMP$ and $\angle PMQ$ are complementary, so $m\angle PMQ$ must be 30°. Apply the angle sum of a triangle to $\triangle MPQ$ to find that $m\angle Q = 105°$. **15.** $x = 70°$ **19.** $\angle A \cong \angle R$ because both measure 70°. AB and AC are in proportion to RS and RT because $AB/RS = 4/3$ and $AC/RT = 8/6 = 4/3$. So, $\triangle ABC \sim \triangle RST$ by SAS similarity. **23.** −11

Lesson 11-5
pp. 442–443

EXERCISES 1. Sample answer: An interior angle is formed by two adjacent sides of the polygon. An exterior angle is formed by a side of a polygon and an extension of an adjacent side. **3.** heptagon **5.** octagon **7.** 540° **11.** 180° **15.** 100° **17.** 119° **21.** $n = 135°$ **29.** 135° **35.** 63°

Chapter Review
pp. 448–449

1. transversal **2.** exterior **3.** Corresponding angles **4.** adjacent exterior angles **5.** similar polygons **6.** 35°; 55° **7.** 48°; 132° **8.** $\triangle CDE \cong \triangle HGF$; SAS **9.** $\triangle JLK \cong \triangle OMN$; SSS **10.** 10 cm **11.** 7.5 cm **12.** 4.5 cm **13.** Sample answer: By the angle sum of a triangle, $m\angle S = 66°$. $\angle R \cong \angle H$ because both measure 47°. $\angle S \cong \angle F$ because both measure 66°. So, $\triangle RST \sim \triangle HFG$ by AA similarity. **14.** Sample answer: By the angle sum of a triangle, $m\angle M = 65°$. $\angle M \cong \angle QNP$ because both measure 65°. $\angle MPL \cong \angle NPQ$ because both measure 25°. So, $\triangle LMP \sim \triangle QNP$ by AA similarity. **15.** 109° **16.** 105°

Chapter 12

Lesson 12-1
pp. 456–457

EXERCISES 1. cone **3.** rectangle; rectangular prism **5.** pentagon; pentagonal prism **7.** cone

13.

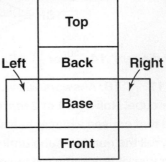

17. rectangular prism **21.** none

23. 7 m² **25.** 7 faces; 12 edges; 7 vertices **29.** straight

Lesson 12-2
pp. 461–462

EXERCISES 1. surface area **3.** cylinder; about 5,089.4 in.² **5.** **9.** 264 m²

	Top	
Left	Back	Right
	Base	
	Front	

14. 106.8 in.² **17.** 528 in.² **19.** 1,407 ft² **23.** 1960.4 in.² **27.** 990 ft² **31.** $23.04

Lesson 12-3
pp. 468–469

EXERCISES 1. volume **3.** 60 in.³ **5.** 166.375 in.³ **9.** 31.5 in.³ **11.** about 84 in.³; 88 in.³ **15.** 6.5 cm **19.** Since the volume of a cylinder is $V = \pi r^2 h$, you can substitute the values for V and h.

$$385 = 3.14 \cdot 10r^2$$
$$385 = 31.4r^2$$
$$12.26 \approx r^2$$
$$3.5 \approx r$$

The radius is about 3.5 in.
23. Yes; the height of the can is less than the height of the case. Since $3(2.5) < 7.6$, 3 cans will fit along the width of the case. Since $4(2.5) < 11$, 4 cans will fit along the length of the case. Then the case can hold 3×4, or 12, cans. **27.** 50°; 140°

Lesson 12-4
pp. 475–476

EXERCISES 1. cross section **3.** triangle with base the same length as the diameter of the circular base of the cone **5.** rectangle congruent to the base **9.** right triangle congruent to the triangular base of the prism **11.** square with diameter equal to that of the orange **13a.** a triangle **13b.** a triangle **13c.** Sample: the shape of the slice will always be a triangle; slices closer to a corner will be smaller than slices near a side. **21.** 150% increase

Lesson 12-5 pp. 480–481

EXERCISES 1. 15 m³ **3.** B **5.** 1,280 in.³ **7.** 2 m³
9. 13 ft³ **11.** 5 cm **15.** no; because the radius
is squared in the because the radius is squared in
the formula, and the height is not

Lesson 12-6 pp. 484–485

EXERCISES 1. C **3.** B **5.** 12.6 m² **7.** 1,810 cm²;
7,238 cm³ **13.** about 110 cm³ **15.** about 1.5 in.²
17. She forgot to divide by 3. **19.** 5,027 mm²;
33,510 mm³ **23.** 83 in.²; 64 in.³ **25.** about 3,397 km
29. 14 in.³

Chapter Review pp. 488–489

1. edge **2.** cube **3.** prism **4.** cross section
5. cone **6.** cylinder **7.** rectangular pyramid
8. pentagonal pyramid **9.** cube **10.** sphere
11. triangular prism **12.** 22 in.² **13.** 288 m²
14. 747.70 yd² **15.** 1,728 m³ **16.** 113.10 m³
17. 12.57 cm³ **18.** circle congruent to the base
19. circle with diameter equal to the diameter of
the sphere **20.** rectangle congruent to the vertical
face **21.** 48 m³ **22.** 268 cm³ **23.** 131 ft³ **24.** S.A. =
452 cm²; V = 905 cm³ **25.** S.A. = 172 in.²; V = 212 in.³
26. S.A = 7,854 m²; V = 65,450 m³

Chapter 13

Lesson 13-1 pp. 496–497

EXERCISES 1. transformation

3. 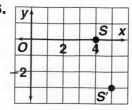 **5.**

9.

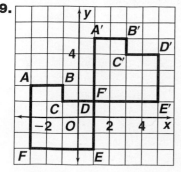

11. $(x, y) \rightarrow (x + 4, y + 3)$ **21.** Subtract 1 from the
x-coordinate and add 3 to the y-coordinate.
25.

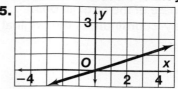

Lesson 13-2 pp. 501–502

EXERCISES 1. Line a is a line of symmetry if one
half of the figure matches the other half exactly
when the figure is reflected over line a. **3.** G **5.** G
7. F **15.**

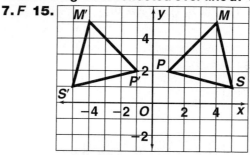

17.   **19.**

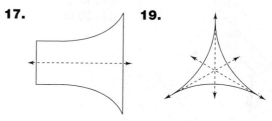

21. A, B, C, D, E, H, I, K, M, O, T, U, V, W, X, Y
27. An infinite number; any line passing through
the center of a circle is a line of symmetry. **33.** 13

Lesson 13-3 pp. 507–508

EXERCISES 1. 180 **3.** M'(−2, 4) **5.** yes; 45°
7. no rotational symmetry **13.** A complete rotation
has 360°. A square can be rotated 360° ÷ 4, or 90°.
15.   **17.** Answers may vary.
Sample: The repeating
figure is rotated 90°
and translated. It is
then rotated 270° and
translated.
25. M'(2, −4)

Lesson 13-4 pp. 511–513

EXERCISES 1. Translations, reflections, and
rotations can be used to prove two figures are
congruent because they all preserve the size and

shape of a figure. **3. F 5.** reflection over *y*-axis followed by translation 7 units down **13.** Find the opposite of the *x*-coordinate of the original point. Then subtract 5 from the *y*-coordinate of the original point. **19.** $8\frac{2}{3}$

Lesson 13-5   pp. 519–520

EXERCISES 1. Reduction; the dilation has a scale factor less than 1. **3.** 3 **5.**

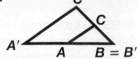

7. *A*'(1, 0), *B*'(1, 1), *C*'(2.5, 1), *C*'(2.5, 0)

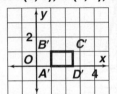

9. $\frac{1}{2}$; reduction

13.

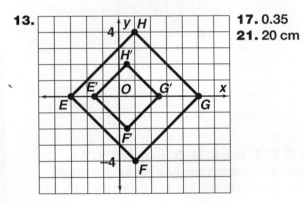

17. 0.35
21. 20 cm

Lesson 13-6   pp. 524–526

EXERCISES 1. A dilation with a scale factor < 1 reduces the size of a figure. A dilation with a scale factor > 1 enlarges the size of a figure.
3. reflection **5.** dilation **7.** a dilation with scale factor $\frac{1}{2}$, followed by a translation to the right
9. a rotation 90° about the origin followed by a dilation with scale factor 2 centered at (0, 0)
13. 4 units **21.** 16°, 106°

---

1. reduction **2.** translations; reflections; rotations **3.** angle of rotation; rotational symmetry **4.** line of symmetry; reflectional symmetry **5.** dilation

6.
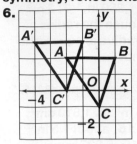

7.
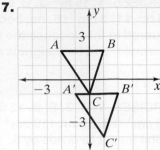

8.
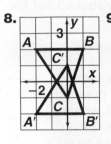

9.
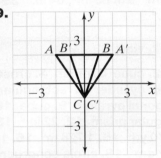

10.
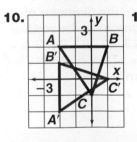

11.
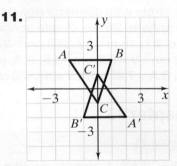

12. translation 6 units down, reflection over *y*-axis **13.** rotation 90° about the origin, reflection over *y*-axis **14.** 4; enlargement **15.** translation 5 units right and 4 units up, dilation with scale factor 2 centered at (0, 0) **16.** translation 4 units up, dilation with scale factor 3 centered at (0, 0)

Index

Index

Index

New Vocabulary, 4, 10, 21, 26, 50, 55, 66, 103, 108, 114, 156, 160, 165, 184, 188, 193, 207, 213, 221, 232, 248, 254, 258, 270, 275, 280, 287, 293, 299, 316, 326, 331, 342, 347, 353, 360, 369, 381, 389, 394, 398, 404, 422, 428, 440, 454, 458, 465, 473, 482, 494, 499, 505, 517

Nonagon, 440

Nonlinear change in data, 270

Nonlinear functions, 311
   comparing, 305

Notation
   arrow, 495
   prime, 494

Number(s)
   adding, 31–36, 61
   benchmark, 253
   comparing, 26–27
   dividing, 43–47, 61
   irrational, 50–54, 61
   mixed, 34, 38–40, 44, 45
   multiplying, 38–42, 61
   ordering, 27
   random, 351, 370, 371
   rational, 26–47, 61, 100, 154, 182, 234, 378, 452
   real, 52
   subtracting, 31–36, 61
   whole, 2, 188
   writing, in scientific notation, 66, 67, 96
   See also Decimals; Fractions

Number line
   adding and subtracting rational numbers on, 31
   adding integers on, 10–11
   box plots/box-and-whisker plots, 331, 333–335
   comparing and ordering integers on, 5
   comparing decimals on, 27
   comparing rational numbers on, 26
   decimals on, 23
   distance on, 33
   multiplying integers on, 16
   multiplying rational numbers on, 38
   ordering rational numbers on, 27, 234
   subtracting integers on, 11, 12

Number patterns, 463

Number Sense, 6, 18, 25, 35, 41, 48, 54, 58, 68, 111, 186, 195, 201, 223, 239, 243, 251, 255, 260, 277, 286, 406, 463
   solving equations using, 121–124, 128, 151
   solving inequalities using, 174

O

Obtuse angle, 381, 384

Octagon, 440

Online active math, 5, 12, 44, 51, 104, 167, 185, 208, 233, 237, 255, 270, 294, 320, 361, 441, 467, 518

Online Chapter Test, 61, 62, 152, 228, 266, 312, 338, 376, 414, 450, 489, 490, 532

Online Homework Video Tutor, 7, 14, 19, 25, 29, 34, 36, 42, 53, 69, 75, 79, 85, 93, 106, 111, 118, 124, 130, 137, 141, 148, 159, 169, 176, 196, 203, 209, 216, 224, 236, 240, 244, 251, 262, 272, 277, 289, 296, 303, 308, 318, 322, 329, 334, 344, 350, 356, 364, 372, 385, 392, 397, 402, 407, 420, 426, 431, 435, 443, 462, 469, 481, 484, 497, 502, 507, 520, 525

Online Lesson Quizzes, 7, 13, 19, 25, 29, 53, 58, 69, 75, 79, 85, 93, 94, 105, 117, 123, 129, 138, 141, 158, 169, 187, 191, 195, 203, 217, 235, 239, 243, 251, 256, 261, 273, 277, 319, 321, 357, 363, 385, 392, 397, 402, 408, 421, 425, 431, 435, 443, 457, 461, 469, 475, 484, 497, 501, 507, 513, 519, 525

Online Math at Work, 81, 131, 197, 323, 352, 393, 427, 486, 503, 515

Online Video Tutor Help, 77, 83, 114, 116, 184, 193, 241, 249, 254, 299, 343, 347, 382, 389, 465, 479

Online Vocabulary Quizzes, 60, 96, 150, 151, 178, 226, 264, 310, 311, 336, 374, 412, 448, 490, 530

Open-Ended, 19, 53, 62, 74, 79, 118, 123, 130, 147, 148, 152, 180, 191, 209, 211, 240, 312, 323, 346, 387, 462, 512, 525, 532

Operations
   choosing, 48–49
   inverse, 114–116

Opposites
   adding, 5
   defined, 4, 60
   finding, 4, 6

Ordering
   decimals, 23
   fractions, 23, 182
   integers, 4–9
   numbers in scientific notation, 92
   rational numbers, 27, 61, 100, 234
   whole numbers, 2

Origin
   equation of line passing through, 301

Outcome, 342, 343, 346

Output variable, 275

P

Parallel lines, 418–421, 448
   identifying, 419
   slopes of, 297
   transversal across, 419

Parallelograms
   area of, 388–394, 398, 413, 452
   base of, 389, 391, 413
   height of, 389, 391, 413

Parity, 63

Patterns
   describing, 102
   exercises using, 71, 439
   exponents, 71

for multiplying integers, 16
   number, 463
   ratios to describe, 184
   in solving inequalities, 165
   in three-dimensional figures, 463

Pentagon, 440

Pentagonal pyramid, 457

Percent(s), 230–380
   applications of, 248–252, 265
   benchmark numbers for, 253
   of change, 257–262, 265, 266
   commissions, 249, 251, 252, 265
   defined, 232, 264
   of discount, 259–262, 265
   equations, 253
   error, 250, 265
   estimation of, 242, 246
   expressing probability as, 342, 344, 352
   finding, using equations, 314
   finding, using proportions, 237–240, 264
   finding a part, 238, 239, 242, 243
   finding the whole, 238, 239, 241–243
   of increase, 258–259, 261, 265
   of markup, 259–262, 265
   modeling, 237–240, 242
   registration fee, 250
   sales tax, 248, 251, 252, 265, 266
   simple interest, 254–257, 265
   solving percent problems using equations, 241–247, 264
   tips, 248–249, 251, 252, 265
   writing as decimals, 233, 264
   writing as fractions, 234, 264
   writing decimals as, 232, 264, 340
   writing fractions as, 233, 264, 340

Perfect cube, 55, 61
   cube roots of, 55

Perfect square, 50, 61
   square roots of, 50

Perimeter
   of rectangle, 390
   relating area and, 390, 413

Perpendicular lines
   slopes of, 297

Pi (π), 404–407

Place value, decimals and, 2

Plane, 474
   See also Coordinate plane

Point, graphing reflections of, 499, 501

Poll, 324

Polygon(s), 422, 440–443, 449
   angle measures of, 439–443
   congruent, 422–427, 449
   defined, 207
   exterior angle of, 439, 441
   interior angle of, 439, 440
   list of common, 440
   modeling a circle using regular, 503
   similar, 207–211, 227, 428

Population
   comparing two, 331
   defined, 316, 336

Index

R

Radius
    of circle, 404–406
    defined, 404
    finding circumference and area of
        circle and, 405–406

Random numbers, 351, 370, 371

Random samples, 316–319
    comparing, 327
    defined, 316, 336
    drawing inferences about population
        using data from, 326–329, 337
    identifying, 316

Range
    of function, 278
    interquartile (IQR), 331, 333, 334
    of probability, 343

Rate(s)
    conversion factor as, 192
    defined, 188, 226
    unit, 188–191, 199, 226

Rate of change, 292, 304

Ratio(s), 184–187
    comparing, 185, 226
    defined, 184, 226
    equivalent, 185, 186, 220, 221, 226, 227
    golden, 88
    identifying unit rate using, 222
    proportional, 193–196
    scale, 213, 227
    writing, 184–185, 340
    writing in simplest form, 193, 226

Rational numbers, 26–47, 61
    adding, 31–36, 61, 100, 154
    comparing, 26–27, 61, 100
    defined, 26, 61
    dividing, 43–47, 61, 154, 182
    multiplication of, 38–42, 61, 154, 182,
        378, 452
    ordering, 27, 61, 100, 234
    repeating decimal in, 30
    subtracting, 31–36, 61, 100, 154

Reading Comprehension, 63, 229, 313,
    339, 534

Reading for Understanding, 177

Real numbers, 52

Real-world applications
    admission, 180
    air travel, 286
    altitude, 7, 16, 32, 102
    animals, 29
    aquariums, 469
    archaeology, 407
    architecture, 216, 227, 421, 455
    art, 252, 441, 450, 486, 502
    astronomy, 69, 77, 86, 91
    athletics, 305
    baking, 168
    ballooning, 228
    baseball, 349, 443, 484
    basketball, 122
    bicycle racing, 306
    bicycles, 407

biking, 190
biology, 24, 67, 98, 117, 334, 337, 372
birds, 18, 106
bowling, 152
boxing, 53
budgets, 238
business, 261, 262
chemistry, 79, 187, 273
class trips, 135
clothes/clothing, 261, 319, 343, 357, 431
college, 130
comparison shopping, 280
computers, 235, 520
construction, 414
consumer issues, 162
consumer math, 372
cooking, 186, 228, 356
crafts, 190, 261, 395, 460
decorating, 195
design, 385
diamonds, 265
distance-time relationships, 280
drilling wells, 43
earning money, 111
earth science, 74, 78, 85
ecology, 333
education, 356
energy, 277
engineering, 401, 435
entertainment, 117, 328, 333, 338
estimation, 106
event planning, 175
exercise, 312
Ferris wheels, 54
fitness, 271, 288
flying, 288
food, 122, 124, 137, 144, 244, 479
forestry, 352
freediving, 40
games, 371, 497
gemstones, 485
geography, 25, 61, 79, 191, 217, 392, 399
geometry, 75, 129, 148, 196, 209,
    273, 513
globes, 483
government, 258, 345
groceries, 152, 180, 288
health, 203
heart rate, 198
heat, 69
hiking, 18
history, 202
hobbies, 19
hockey, 277
insurance, 265
Internet, 303
jewelry, 281
jobs, 129, 137, 144, 266
journalism, 370
landscaping, 191, 282, 408
long-distance phone rate, 166
manufacturing, 337, 348, 349
maps, 426
masonry, 152
mass, 312
matching, 260

math in media, 236
meal planning, 44
measurement, 56
medicine, 370
melting points, 28, 36
meteorology, 96
models, 214
money, 29, 36, 41, 61, 111, 117, 123, 124,
    180, 286
mosaic, 409
movies, 430
muscles, 204
music, 24, 180, 240, 259, 317, 371, 402
music downloads, 173
nature, 201, 505
nutrition, 157, 233, 236, 302, 337
Olympics, 129
packaging, 468
painting, 467
parks, 319
patterns, 71, 439
paying bills, 45
percent error in manufacturing, 250
pets, 272
phone card cost, 149
physical science, 196
physics, 98
planning, 166
poll, 324
population, 25
probability, 96
public service, 104
quality control, 376
recreation, 242
recycling, 276
recycling math, 177
research, 218
rides, 168
river travel, 354
rock climbing, 17
running, 117
runway design, 383
sailboats, 62
sales, 252
sales tax, 248
sanitation, 286
savings, 180
science, 21, 66, 89, 112, 162, 228, 234,
    257, 272, 289, 344, 349
scuba diving, 289
sharks, 322
shipping, 180
shipwrecks, 4
shopping, 180, 189, 248, 265, 266, 333
social studies, 185, 209, 407
space, 196
space travel, 68, 94
special effects, 217
speed of sound, 94
sports, 7, 127, 129, 146, 152, 163, 261,
    332, 333, 371, 408, 495
student government, 327
surveying, 210
surveys, 23, 193
technology, 264
telephone, 124

Acknowledgments

Staff Credits

The people who make up the Prentice Hall Math team—representing design services, editorial, editorial services, educational technology, marketing, market research, photo research and art development, production services, publishing processes, and rights & permissions— are listed below. Bold type denotes core team members.

Dan Anderson, Carolyn Artin, Nick Blake, **Stephanie Bradley,** Kyla Brown, Patrick Culleton, Katherine J. Dempsey, **Frederick Fellows, Suzanne Finn,** Paul Frisoli, Ellen Granter, **Richard Heater,** Betsey Krieble, Lisa La Vallee, Christine Lee, Kendra Lee, Cheryl Mahan, **Carolyn McGuire,** Eve Melnechuk, Terri Mitchell, Jeffrey Paulhus, Mark Roop-Kharasch, Marcy Rose, Rashid Ross, Irene Rubin, Siri Schwartzman, Vicky Shen, **Dennis Slattery,** Elaine Soares, Dan Tanguay, Tiffany Taylor, Mark Tricca, Paula Vergith, Kristin Winters, Helen Young

Additional Credits

Paul Astwood, Sarah J. Aubry, Jonathan Ashford, Peter Chapman, Patty Fagan, Tom Greene, Kevin Keane, Mary Landry, Jon Kier, Dan Pritchard, Sara Shelton, Jewel Simmons, Ted Smykal, Steve Thomas, Michael Torocsik, Maria Torti

TE Design

Susan Gerould/Perspectives

Illustration

JB Woolsey: **189, 455**
John Edwards, Inc.: **216, 217, 350**
XNR Productions, Inc.: **216, 217, 218, 392, 396, 399, 401**
Brucie Roche: **459, 468, 344**
Wilkinson Studios: **467**
Kenneth Batelman: **342**
Das Grup: **355, 357**
John Schreiner: **359**
Joel Dubin: **363**

Additional Artwork

Rich McMahon; Ted Smykal

Title page: tl

Front Matter: xi, Navy Photo by Ensign John Gay; **xii,** © Ryan McVay/Thinkstock; **xiii,** © Ablestock.com/Thinkstock; **xiv,** © jbouzous/crestock; **xv,** © David De Lossy/Thinkstock; **xvi,** © Keith Garvelink; **xvii,** © Jupiter images/Thinkstock; **xviii,** © Comstock/Thinkstock; **xix,** © Robert Tyrell; **xx,** Superstock; **xxi,** © David Sacks/Thinkstock; **xxii,** © BernardBreton.

Chapter 1 Pages 3, © Terrence Lee/Fotolia; **4,** © Pinosub/Fotolia; **5,** © Alexander/Fotolia; **7,** EcoView/Fotolia; **9,** © Richard Haynes; **13,** © luchschen/Fotolia; **15,** © Richard Haynes; **16,** © Comstock/ Thinkstock; **17,** © Hemera Technologies/Thinkstock; **19,** ©Comstock Images/Thinkstock; **20,** © Richard Haynes; **21,** © Digital Vision/ Thinkstock; **23,** © Jupiterimages/Thinkstock; **25,** © Martin Schwan/ Fotolia; **26,** © Digital Vision/Thinkstock; **29,** © Sebastian Duda/ Fotolia; **31,** © Richard Haynes; **33,** ©Jaroslaw Grudzinski/Fotolia LLC.; **34,** © Richard Haynes; **36,** Ncjron Photo/Fotolia LLC.; **38,** Gemenacom/Fotolia LLC.; **42 cr,** Kovalenko Inna/Fotolia LLC.; **43,** Robert Kyllo/Shutterstock; **46,** Salajean/Fotolia LLC.

Chapter 2: Page 65, Adam Gault; **66,** NASA; **67,** Digital Vision; **68,** Alexander Kataytsev-Fotolia; **69,** Photodisc; **72,** Courtesy of michaeljung/Fotolia LLC.; **76,** Photos.com; **77,** Richard Haynes; **78,** © Stephan Baur; **81,** Getty Images/Comstock Images; **82,** © Andrea Danti; **83,** Richard Haynes; **84 mr,** Richard Haynes; **84 bl,** Richard Haynes; **89,** © Lijuan Guo; **90,** Courtesy of patrimonio designs limited/ Shutterstock; **91,** © Artshot; **94,** Navy Photo by Ensign John Gay.

Chapter 3: 101, Christophe Schmid/Fotolia; **102 tl,** © Comstock Images/Thinkstock; **102,** © Katrina Brown/Fotolia; **104,** © Steve Byland/Fotolia; **110,** © Prentice Hall; **111,** © Richard Haynes; **112,** © Richard Haynes; **113,** © Rémy MASSEGLIA/Fotolia; **114,** © Richard Haynes; **115,** Marek Kosmal/Fotolia; **118,** © Brand X Pictures; **121,** © stickmyhome/Fotolia; **123,** © Richard Haynes; **124,** © vekha/Fotolia; **125,** © John Foxx/Thinkstock; **126 tl & mr,** © Richard Haynes; **128,** © Patrick Clark/PhotoDisc/Getty Images; **132,** Richard Haynes; **135,** Jeffrey Hamilton; **136,** Richard Haynes; **137,** Silver Burdett Ginn; **139,** Comstock; **144,** Sidarta/Shutterstock; **145,** Andrii IURLOV/ Fotolia LLC.

Chapter 4: 155 tr, © Mog DDL/Fotolia; **155 tl,** © Jupiterimages/ Thinkstock; **156,** © Jim Mills/Fotolia; **157,** © Thinkstock; **159,** © Digital Vision/Thinkstock; **161,** © Jupiterimages/Thinkstock; **162,** © Thinkstock Images; **164,** © Stockbyte/Thinkstock; **168,** © John Giustina/Getty Images; **170 tl,** © William Wang/Fotolia LLC.; **170 ml,** © Iuliia Metkalova/Fotolia LLC.

Chapter 5: Page 183, © mccphoto/Fotolia; **184,** © Richard Haynes; **185,** © Jupiterimages/Thinkstock; **187,** © Jupiterimages/Brand X Pictures/Thinkstock; **188,** © Ryan McVay/Thinkstock; **192,** © Jupiterimages/Thinkstock; **193,** © Richard Haynes; **190,** © NASA; **197 mr,** © Grasko/Fotolia; **197 br,** © machista/Fotolia; **201 tl & mr,** © Richard Haynes; **202,** © Monkey Business/Fotolia; **203,** © Duncan Smith/Thinkstock; **206,** © Richard Haynes; **207,** © Alaska Stock LLC/Alamy; **210,** © Freefly/Fotolia; **212,** © Richard Haynes; **213,** © Wendy Kaveney/Fotolia; **218,** © Henryk Sadura/Fotolia; **219,** © Richard Haynes; **221,** Courtesy of geronimo/Shutterstock.

Chapter 6: Page 231, © Jupiterimages/Thinkstock; **233,** © ITStock Free/Thinkstock; **234,** © Oleg Znamenskiy/Fotolia; **236,** Hilary B. Price; **237,** © Jupiterimages/Thinkstock; **240,** © Susan Stevenson/ Fotolia; **241 tr,** © Alexander Rochau/Fotolia; **241 bl,** © Richard Haynes; **242,** © Jupiterimages/Brand X Pictures/Thinkstock; **244,** © Ross Anania/Superstock; **245,** © Richard Haynes; **248,** © Stockbyte/ Thinkstock; **249 tl,** © Steve Mason/Thinkstock; **249 bl,** © Richard Haynes; **250,** Courtesy of majeczka/Fotolia LLC.; **252,** © PureStock/

Superstock; **254 tr,** © BananaStock/Thinkstock; **254 bl,** © Richard Haynes; **256,** © Superstock/Alamy; **258,** © Natalia Bratslavsky/Fotolia; **260 tl & mr,** © Richard Haynes; **261,** © KaYann/Fotolia.

Chapter 7: Pages 269, Jupiterimages; **270,** Laima Druskis/Prentice Hall; **275,** Thinkstock; **278,** Creatas; **279,** Richard Haynes; **280,** Envision/Corbis Images; **287,** pf30/Fotolia LLC; **291,** Richard Haynes.

Chapter 8: Page 315, © John Foxx/Thinkstock; **316,** © Stockbyte/Thinkstock; **318,** © BananaStock/Thinkstock; **319,** © Jim Parkin/Fotolia; **320,** © Bruce MacQueen/Fotolia; **322,** © Ilan Ben Tov/Fotolia; **323,** © Rtimages/Fotolia; **326,** Courtesy of Monkey Business/Fotolia LLC; **329,** Courtesy of bmaynard/Fotolia LLC; **330,** © Richard Haynes; **331 tl,** Courtesy of Andreas Grandin/Fotolia LLC; **331 tr,** Courtesy of DenisDore/Fotolia LLC; **334,** Courtesy of OlegD/Fotolia LLC.

Chapter 9: Page 341, © Ryan McVay/Thinkstock; **342,** © Jupiterimages/Brand X Pictures/Thinkstock; **343,** © Richard Haynes; **345,** © Christopher Howey/Fotolia; **346,** © Richard Haynes; **347,** © peter Hires Images/Fotolia; **348,** © Jupiterimages/Thinkstock; **350,** © Jupiterimages/Thinkstock; **352,** Courtesy of Lisa F. Young/Fotolia LLC; **353,** © StarJumper/Fotolia; **354,** © Karl Weatherly/Thinkstock; **357,** © TRBPhoto/Getty Images; **358,** © katja kodba/Fotolia; **360,** © Stockbyte/Thinkstock; **362 tr & ml,** © Richard Haynes; **364,** © Cornstock/Alamy; **366,** © Richard Haynes; **369,** Courtesy of Image Source/Getty Images; **372,** Courtesy of Lori Labrecque/Shutterstock.

Chapter 10: Page 379, © Photodisc/Thinkstock; **381,** © r-o-x-o-r/Fotolia; **382 tl,** Courtesy of frenta/Fotolia LLC; **382 br,** © Richard Haynes; **383 mr & bl,** © Richard Haynes; **388,** © Richard Haynes; **389 tr,** © Ablestock.com/Thinkstock; **389 bl,** © Richard Haynes; **390,** © Digital Vision/Thinkstock; **393,** © nyul/Fotolia; **394,** Courtesy of yanlev; **397,** © scazza/Fotolia; **398,** © Jupiterimages/Thinkstock; **399,** © bonniemarie/Fotolia; **400 tl & br,** © Richard Haynes; **402,** © C Squared Studios/Getty Images; **403,** © Richard Haynes; **406,** © Pavel Losevsky/Fotolia; **407,** © Gooseman/Fotolia.

Chapter 11: Page 417, © steheap; **418,** David Sacks; **419,** Russ Lappa/Prentice Hall; **421,** Goodshoot; **422,** Comstock; **427,** Dorling Kindersley; **432,** Courtesy of Robert Naratham/Shutterstock; **443,** Jupiterimages.

Chapter 12: Page 453, © BlueOrange Studio/Fotolia ; **454,** © Risto Viita/Fotolia; **457 tl,** © Jupiterimages/Thinkstock; **457 tm,** © Thomas Northcut/Thinkstock; **457 tr,** © Spike Mafford/Getty Images; **460,** © Richard Haynes; **462,** © Brand X Pictures/Thinkstock; **464,** © Jupiterimages/Thinkstock; **465 tr,** © Jupiter Images/Thinkstock; **465 bl,** © Richard Haynes; **479,** Richard Haynes; **481,** Alexandra Rölleke; **482,** © Aurum; **483,** © Nando Azevedo; **485,** Jupiterimages; **486,** Jack Hollingsworth.

Chapter 13: Page 493, Courtesy of VRD/Fotolia LLC (Course 2 image); **494,** Galina Barskaya-Fotolia; **498 ml, m, &br,** Russ Lappa; **498 mr,** Richard Haynes; **499,** Jupiterimages/Getty Images; **500,** Russ Lappa; **503,** Stockbyte; **504,** Richard Haynes; **505,** Vasily Smirnov-Fotolia; **507 ml & m,** Nuncia-Fotolia; **507 mr,** Courtesy of qayyum125/Fotolia LLC; **508,** Russ Lappa; **509,** Courtesy of Carly Hennigan/Fotolia LLC; **514,** Richard Haynes; **515,** Jack Kurtz/ The Image Works; **517,** Getty Images/Pixland; **522 tr,** Courtesy of ecco/Fotolia; **522 ml & mr,** Richard Haynes.

Additional Credits:

Chapter 1: Lessons 1-8 taken from Chapter 1, Lessons 1-8, of *Prentice Hall Mathematics Course 2,* Common Core, 2013 Edition. Lessons 9 and 10 taken from Chapter 1, Lessons 2 and 3, of *Prentice Hall Mathematics Course 3*, Common Core, 2013 Edition.
Chapter 2: Whole chapter taken from Chapter 6 of *Prentice Hall Mathematics Course 3*, Common Core, 2013 Edition.
Chapter 3: Lessons 1-5 taken from Chapter 2, Lessons 1-5, of *Prentice Hall Mathematics Course 2*, Common Core, 2013 Edition. Lessons 6, 7, and 8 taken from Chapter 2, Lessons 3, 4, and 5, of *Prentice Hall Mathematics Course 3*, Common Core, 2013 Edition.
Chapter 4: Whole chapter taken from Chapter 3 of *Prentice Hall Mathematics Course 2*, Common Core, 2013 Edition.
Chapter 5: Whole chapter taken from Chapter 4 of *Prentice Hall Mathematics Course 2*, Common Core, 2013 Edition.
Chapter 6: Whole chapter taken from Chapter 5 of *Prentice Hall Mathematics Course 2*, Common Core, 2013 Edition.
Chapter 7: Lessons 1, 2, 3, and 4 taken from Chapter 3, Lessons 1-4, of *Prentice Hall Mathematics Course 3*, Common Core, 2013 Edition. Lessons 5, 6, and 7 taken from Chapter 4, Lessons 1, 2, and 4, or *Prentice Hall Mathematics Course 3*, Common Core, 2013 Edition.
Chapter 8: Whole chapter taken from Chapter 8 of *Prentice Hall Mathematics Course 2*, Common Core, 2013 Edition.
Chapter 9: Whole chapter taken from Chapter 9 of *Prentice Hall Mathematics Course 2*, Common Core, 2013 Edition.
Chapter 10: Whole chapter taken from Chapter 6 of *Prentice Hall Mathematics Course 2*, Common Core, 2013 Edition.
Chapter 11: Whole chapter taken from Chapter 7, Lessons 2-6, of *Prentice Hall Mathematics Course 3,* Common Core, 2013 Edition.
Chapter 12: Lessons 1, 2, 3, and 4 taken from Chapter 7, Lessons 1-4, of *Prentice Hall Mathematics Course 2,* Common Core, 2013 Edition. Lessons 5 and 6 taken from Chapter 9, Lessons 3 and 4, of *Prentice Hall Mathematics Course 3*, Common Core, 2013 Edition.
Chapter 13: Whole chapter taken from Chapter 8 of *Prentice Hall Mathematics Course 3*, Common Core, 2013 Edition.
Appendix: Appendix Lessons 1, 2, 3, and 4 taken from Chapter 1, Lessons 4, 5, 6, and 7, respectively, from *Prentice Hall Mathematics Course 3*, Common Core, 2013 Edition.